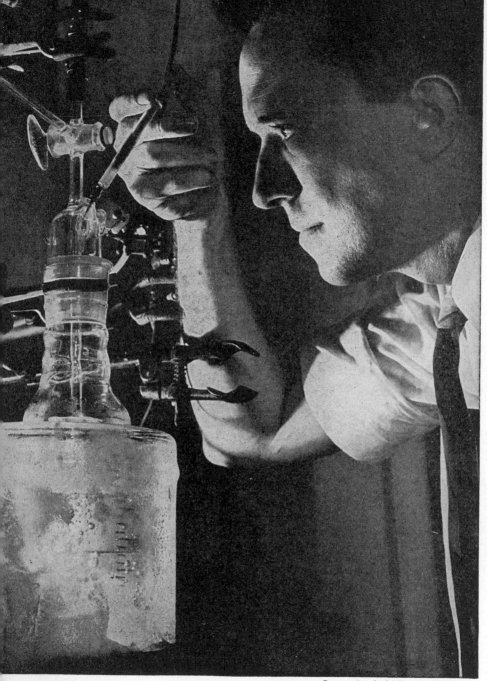

Research chemist injects controlled amount of impurity into a butyl rubber catalyst in order to study the effect of the impurity on butyl rubber.

THE FUNDAMENTALS OF

College Chemistry

SECOND EDITION

G. Brooks King

Professor of Chemistry
The State College of Washington
Pullman, Washington

William E. Caldwell

Professor of Chemistry and Chemical Engineering
Oregon State College
Corvallis, Oregon

AMERICAN BOOK COMPANY
New York

Table of Contents

Preface

The widespread acceptance of *Fundamentals of College Chemistry* has encouraged the authors to prepare a second edition. In the work of revision they have been guided, to a considerable extent, by suggestions from users of the first edition. The new edition, like the original, aims to present the fundamentals of chemistry in a concise and orderly treatment, which can readily be covered in a school year of nine months. Although the organizational structure and basic framework of the first edition have been retained, several changes have been made which the authors hope will enhance the usefulness of the book.

Attention has been called to the relationship between the size of atoms and their physical and chemical properties. The chapter on radioactivity and nuclear changes has been largely rewritten to incorporate recent knowledge in this rapidly expanding field. There has been substantial revision of the chapters dealing with periodic classification, valence, ionization, and electrochemistry. To simplify the presentation for the beginning student, the use of the hydronium ion in writing equations has been minimized. Care has been taken to emphasize the role of water in the ionization of acids, but once this is clearly understood by the student, it seems unnecessary to continue to complicate the writing and balancing of equations with this ion. Similarly, anhydrous forms of other ions are shown in equations, although it is recognized that most ions in aqueous solution are probably hydrated. As a further aid to the student, the use of ionic equations has been introduced early, along with molecular equations, before a detailed consideration of the theory of ionization.

The order of topics is that which the authors have found to be psychologically sound for beginning students. However, because few instructors agree completely on any given order of presentation, some chapters in this book may be taught in a different order without loss of coherence in treatment. For example, the organic chapters may follow immediately after carbon and its oxides, the chemistry of sulfur may precede that of nitrogen, or electrochemistry may follow oxidation-reduction. As an aid to the instructor, some sections dealing with topics of an advanced or special nature have been set in small type; if the instructor desires to omit them, he may do so without interrupting the continuity. In response to requests from teachers, the list of problems and references has been extended, with answers to many of the numerical exercises given.

The pedagogical approach of the book is in keeping with the scientific method of attaining new knowledge, namely, the acquisition of facts through observation and experimentation, the formulation of a theory for explaining the relationship between observed facts, and the application of organized facts or reasoned principles to human endeavor.

The authors have tried to strike an effective balance between theory and descriptive matter. They have made use of examples from daily life contacts or from industrial situations when these add to the chemical knowledge of a substance or the understanding of some chemical theory.

The authors are indebted to many users of the first edition for constructive criticisms. The suggestions coming from the chemistry department of the University of Wisconsin were especially helpful. Finally, the authors wish to acknowledge the generous assistance of their colleagues at the State College of Washington and at Oregon State College.

I

Introduction

Man has a lively curiosity concerning natural phenomena; he attempts to understand and explain the world in which he lives. Through the ages many facts about nature have been observed and much knowledge has been accumulated. The systematization of knowledge which includes the observation and classification of phenomena of a distinctive type and which by observation and experimentation formulates principles describing patterns of action is known as *science*. There are many subdivisions of science. Physics and chemistry are called the physical sciences, and have to do with inanimate things. The biological sciences have for their aim the study of living organisms and include bacteriology, zoology, and botany. Social sciences have as their aim the study of man in his group activities and include such fields as anthropology, sociology, and economics.

The scientific method. The ancients were prone to speculate regarding natural phenomena without recourse to experimentation. As a result many erroneous ideas were propounded which persisted for centuries. The early philosophers believed too much in the power of reason not substantiated by observed or experimentally determined facts. They believed that the earth was flat, that the stars revolved about the earth, and that the sun sank into the sea.

Only in the last century has man's progress in science been rapid. The scientist of today realizes that mere thinking about natural phenomena is inadequate; he must have facts upon which to base reason. The accumulation of facts is the first step in the *scientific method* of attaining knowledge.

Data or information about a given phenomenon may be obtained by careful observation of natural processes and by carrying out a series of well-planned experiments. The attainment of data is limited only by man's ingenuity in devising experiments and in the refinements of the instruments and apparatus at his disposal for obtaining experimental results. After facts have been obtained they must be organized and 'classified. The next step is to study these facts to discover relationships between them. Analysis of a group of closely related facts may point toward a general principle. A principle which describes a mode of behavior or a pattern of action is termed a *scientific law*.

The value of experiments cannot be overemphasized. Take, for example, Galileo's proof of the principle of falling bodies. Aristotle without benefit of experiments had said that bodies would fall with a speed proportional to their weight, *i.e.*, an object weighing 10 pounds would fall 10 times as fast as an object weighing one pound. This view was widely accepted until Galileo, before a multitude of spectators, demonstrated the falsity of the assertion by dropping simultaneously two cannon balls of different weights from the top of the Leaning Tower of Pisa. They saw the balls start together, fall at the same speed, and both strike the ground at the same time.

Imagination is brought into play in scientific procedure. The scientist speculates regarding particular phenomena and their behavior. Such a speculation is termed a *hypothesis*. The hypothesis then is tested by experimentation and more facts regarding a given phenomenon and its behavior are obtained, which lead to a verification of the hypothesis or to its modification and correction. As proof is obtained the hypothesis becomes a *theory*. A theory is not a permanent conclusion but is changed and modified as experimental results are obtained which are not readily explained by the theory. Theories are useful in that they allow one to anticipate the results of further experiments and aid in the discovery of new phenomena. As Shenstone has said, theories are "as searchlights which cast light into dark places and enable us to see, sometimes plainly, sometimes only in dim outline, much that would remain hidden if we were denied their aid."

What is chemistry? Chemistry is concerned with the *properties* of matter, *changes* in matter, and the *laws* or *principles* which describe these changes. Every substance has a set of properties or characteristics of its own; for example, cane sugar is a white crystalline solid with a sweet taste; iron is a grayish solid which has a certain density and which may be magnetized. By observing the properties of substances the chemist may classify them.

All of us daily observe many transformations or changes in matter taking place about us: water may be frozen to ice or converted into steam; coal is burned, leaving ashes; wood rots; tools and articles made of metal rust and corrode; plant material results from plant use of carbon dioxide, air, and soil minerals. The chemist is interested in these processes and in thousands more.

Man lives longer and in greater comfort today than he did a few generations ago because he knows more about changes in natural substances and has learned how to utilize these changes in producing thousands of modern-day conveniences and health aids. For example, coal, through chemical processes, may be converted into coke, coal gas, coal tar, and condensable liquids each having commercial value. Ammonia and fuel gas may be obtained from coal gas; coal tar may be converted through chemical processes into antiseptics, therapeutics, dyes, plastics, explosives, and numerous other useful things.

Both physics and chemistry deal with matter and energy. Physics is principally concerned with energy relationships, whereas chemistry is more concerned with matter and its changes.

Importance of chemistry. Aside from its cultural value as part of a general education, the application of chemical principles has done much to give man control over nature, to alleviate human suffering, and to enhance the comforts of modern living. The relatively recent discovery of the sulfa drugs for treatment of infection has resulted in lengthening the life of man and reducing untimely deaths. The production of synthetic textiles and fibers, synthetic rubber from petroleum, plastics in a large variety of forms from waste products are but a few of the achievements of chemistry.

Below in outline form are shown a few of the more important applications of chemistry to problems of human economic advancement and welfare:

Chemistry in agriculture. Constituents of soils and their relationship to soil fertility; synthesis of fertilizers and insecticides; conversion of by-products into useful substances.

Chemistry in medicine. New drugs to fight disease; local and general anesthetics.

Chemistry in biology. Studies of the complex changes taking place in life processes; plant and animal metabolism; transformations accompanying growth of plants and animals.

Chemistry in engineering. Manufacture of building materials such as cement, paint, glass, ceramics, alloys, steels; corrosion of metals.

Chemistry in geology. Composition of rocks and minerals; chemical changes accompanying weathering action.

Chemistry in foods. Composition of essential foods; manufacture and synthesis of vitamins; changes in food substances during digestion, etc.

Chemistry in industry. Manufacture of rayon, explosives, and sugars from cellulose; gasoline, kerosene, vaseline, and synthetic rubber from petroleum; extraction and purification of metals from their ores;

Fig. 1. The Alchemist.

manufacture of paints, varnishes, soaps, inks, drugs, perfumes, dyes, foods, clothing, etc.

The history of chemistry. Long before there were any theories about matter and its behavior, man had by chance become familiar with many substances and had developed useful products from them. He knew that certain rock mixtures could be heated to form a glass and that certain substances when properly treated yielded metals. The Greek philosophers were the first to formulate chemical theories regarding the nature of matter. Some philosophers of that day believed that everything was made up of different proportions of four elements: earth, air, fire, and water. Robert Boyle in his book, *The Skeptical Chemist*, published in 1661, suggests how they may have reasoned:

> For if you but consider a piece of green wood burning in a chimney, you will readily discern in the disbanded parts of it the four elements, of which we teach it and other mixt bodies to be composed. The fire discovers itself in the flame by its own light, the smoke by ascending to the top of the chimney, and there readily vanishes into air, like a river losing itself in the sea, sufficiently manifests to what element it belongs and gladly returns. The water in its own form boiling and hissing at the ends of the burning wood betrays itself to more than one of our senses; and the ashes by their weight, their firmness, and their dryness, put it past doubt they belong to the element of earth.

Democritus, about the year 400 B.C., conceived the idea that all matter is made up of minute, discrete particles, which he called atoms. On this assumption many facts about matter could be explained. This theory on the atomicity of matter is still tenable if we add to it the modern theory that the atoms are themselves made up of smaller units, namely, protons, electrons, and neutrons.

The *age of the philosophers*, just described, was followed by a period of about a dozen centuries, termed the *age of alchemy*, in which relatively little progress was made in the science of chemistry. Alchemy was a transition stage between a philosophical and scientific explanation of natural phenomena. The alchemists capitalized on superstition and public gullibility and yet did develop considerable skill in the extraction and purification of metals. Although much more experimentation was carried out in this period than in the preceding one, the alchemists failed to systematize their experimental work and did not reason logically from the facts at their disposal.

The time of the alchemists for the most part was occupied in seeking a means for the *transmutation of metals*, seeking a *universal solvent*, and trying to find an *elixir of life*. Transmutation refers to the changing of one metal to another. The alchemists were primarily interested in changing metals of lesser worth to gold. In their efforts to concoct a solvent which would dissolve anything they apparently overlooked the fact that if such a solvent were found there would be no container in which it might be kept. The alchemists made vain attempts to concoct an "elixir" which would restore youth or in general alleviate the ills of the human body.

> While among the alchemists there were some genuine enthusiasts, the annals of this queer practice are filled with accounts of charlatans and spurious adepts who, with a deluge of glib words but only a drop of truth, turned alchemy into one of the greatest popular frauds in history. The writings of these avaricious devils and honest fools are a meaningless jargon of cryptic terms and strange symbols. Their public demonstrations of transmutation were often clever enough to fool the most cautious. Many came to witness the making of gold from lead and iron, convinced that it could be done. For had they not seen iron vessels, plunged into certain natural springs containing copper salts, emerge covered with the red metal? It was a matter of common knowledge that a dark dirty ore could be heated until all its impurities were destroyed and a bright shiny metal was obtained. Traces of silver and gold had been found in many ores. Then why could not the further heating of these ores yield larger quantities of the precious metals? In fact, with sufficient treatment, it ought to be possible to change the ore entirely into lustrous gold. Simple enough questions in the light of their ignorance of chemical facts. Besides, nature was performing marvelous transmutations every minute of the day as food was changed into blood, and sugar into alcohol.[1]

The work of the alchemists has more than historical significance, not in that they attained their three main aims, but in that the compositions and properties of many substances became known and several chemical processes were discovered.

In 1662 Boyle discovered the quantitative relationship between the volume of a gas and its pressure, but the real advance of chemistry as a science had its beginning during the eighteenth century. The French chemist Lavoisier, with the aid of a quite accurate balance, made many studies of weight relations between substances entering into and products of chemical change; Priestley isolated oxygen and determined its properties; Scheele discovered chlorine and its method of preparation by oxidation of its compounds; and Dalton (in 1804) formulated the atomic theory of matter to explain chemical changes.

---

[1] Reprinted from *Crucibles* by permission of Simon and Schuster, Inc. Copyright, 1930, by Bernard Jaffe.

These men and others of this period laid the foundations for the modern scientific approach now employed in university and industrial laboratories in attaining the increasing volume of knowledge constituting the modern science of chemistry.

Chemistry applied to modern living. Today we live in an era in which multifold desires can be fulfilled only by the operation of complex industries, the basis of our modern industrial life. Industrial processes convert raw materials furnished by nature into products more valuable to the wants of man. Certain strategic mineral and plant substances serve as the starting materials for these industries and have become of such importance to maintaining the present mode of living that nations war over them. The United States happens to be endowed with an abundance of natural mineral and plant substances and has, by the energetic inventive exploitation of them, become a great world power.

Chemistry is second to none among the sciences which have seen the commercial exploitation of their principles. Numerous large industries today employ staffs of chemists for control of their processes and for research in finding the much advertised "better things for better living through chemistry." Large investments in chemical research have paid huge dividends to industry and contributed much to the comfort and efficiency of modern life.

To meet the huge demands of industry for research personnel, the colleges and universities are turning out increasing numbers of trained chemists. In a study of graduate training in 94 of 96 institutions in the United States granting the Ph.D. degree in various fields during the decade 1930–1940, Hollis[1] found that of 22,509 Ph.D. degrees granted, 3889, or about 17.3 per cent were in the field of chemistry. More than 60 per cent of these Ph.D.'s in chemistry were employed by non-academic agencies, mostly private industries — a fact which in itself shows the high regard held by commercial concerns for adequate chemical research programs.

The American Chemical Society with more than 60,000 members is the largest scientific organization in the world. Through its several monthly publications, the research findings of thousands of investigators are made known.

> "Science is a tree of many branches,
> bountiful are its fruits to man in
> more complete healthful living."

[1] E. V. Hollis, *Toward Improving Ph.D. Programs*, American Council on Education, Washington, D. C. (1945).

REFERENCES

Brooks Emeny, *The Strategy of Raw Materials*, Macmillan.
B. L. Clarke, *Marvels of Modern Chemistry*, Harpers.
Findlay, *Spirit of Chemistry*, Longmans.
H. N. Holmes, *Out of the Test Tube*, Emerson.
Bernard Jaffe, *Crucibles; The Lives and Achievements of the Great Chemists*, Simon and Schuster.
——, *Outposts of Science*, Simon and Schuster.
E. E. Slosson and H. E. Howe, *Creative Chemistry*, Appleton.
J. R. Partington, *A Short History of Chemistry*, Macmillan.
Lodder and Noble, *Films on Chemical Subjects*, Am. Chem. Soc., 1946.
H. D. Smyth, *Atomic Energy for Military Purposes*, Princeton, 1945.
Tenney L. Davis, "Primitive Science: the Background of Early Chemistry and Alchemy," *J. Chem. Ed.* **12**, 3 (1935).
Douglas G. Nicholson, "The Alchemist in Art — Relation to Current Science," *ibid.* **27**, 117 (1950).
O. N. Perti, "An Ancient Hindu Concept of a Chemical Laboratory," *ibid.* **28**, 485 (1951).
Desmond Reilly, "Robert Boyle and His Background," *ibid.* **28**, 178 (1951).
Lucy O. Lewton, "The Art of Searching the Literature," *ibid.* **28**, 487 (1951).

In general for references on various topics, consult the index of *Chemical Abstracts* or the yearly index of such magazines as *Journal of Chemical Education, Industrial and Engineering Journal, Chemical Engineering*.

II

Fundamental Principles

Matter and energy. *Chemistry is concerned with matter and the changes which it undergoes.* *Matter* may be considered as anything which possesses *weight* or *mass* [1] and occupies space. Rocks, soil, water, and the air we breathe are examples. Matter which is homogeneous (uniform throughout), such as sugar, table salt, iron, or baking soda, is called a *substance*.

Matter appears in any one of three physical states: *solid*, *liquid*, or *gas*. Solids are characterized by rigidity and a definite form; liquids flow; gases diffuse and fill any container in which they may be placed. Most substances can be made to appear in all three of these states; for example, water may exist as a solid (ice), a liquid, or a gas (steam). By adding heat, a liquid may be changed to a gas; by subtracting heat, a liquid may be changed to a solid.

Changes in matter are accompanied by changes in energy. *Energy is the power or ability to do work* and manifests itself in many forms. The more familiar forms of energy are *heat, mechanical, radiant, electrical,* and *chemical.* Energy may be neither created nor destroyed but may pass from one form to another. This law of nature is known as the Law of Conservation of Energy.

When coal is burned, heat is given up or evolved. This heat, termed heat energy, may be made to do useful work. For example, the heat

---

[1] The *mass* of a body is the quantity of matter it contains and is determined by its inertia, *i.e.*, the resistance offered to a change in its motion. *Weight*, on the other hand, is the attraction between the earth and the body. Since the attraction between two bodies is inversely proportional to the square of the distance between the centers of the bodies, the masses of two bodies will be proportional to their weights, as long as the weights are measured at the same distance from the earth's center. Consequently we may compare masses of objects by weighing them. The attraction of the earth for an object is counterbalanced against arbitrarily chosen units of weight. While the mass of an object is constant, its weight varies with its distance from the center of the earth. Since we mortals are bound to the earth's surface (plus or minus a few miles compared to the earth's 4000 mile radius), we shall use the terms "mass" and "weight" interchangeably.

from the burning coal might be used to generate steam, which in turn could operate a steam engine. The mechanical energy from the steam engine may be transformed into electrical energy by means of a dynamo. Electrical energy may be converted into light energy in a light bulb or into heat energy in an electric toaster.

Chemists are more interested in *chemical energy*, which is "stored energy" — the energy possessed by a substance that allows it to be changed into a new substance. When coal is burned, the chemical energy possessed by the coal is transformed into heat energy. Various forms of energy also may be transformed into chemical energy. This occurs, for example, when plants absorb radiant energy from the sun, which produces changes in the plants, resulting in the production of plant tissue.

UNITS OF MEASUREMENT

Metric system. The metric system of measurement is used in all scientific work. The standard unit of linear measurement is the *meter*, which is approximately one ten-millionth of the distance from the North Pole to the Equator and is equivalent to 39.37 inches. The standard meter bar composed of an alloy of iridium and platinum is kept in the International Bureau of Weights and Measures in Paris, France. The standard unit of weight is the *gram*, the weight of one milliliter of water at 4° centigrade, the temperature at which water has its maximum density. The standard unit of volume is the *liter*, which is equivalent to about 1.06 quarts. For the measurement of small quantities, the above standard units may be divided into smaller units. The commonly used units of the metric system as shown in Table 1:

TABLE 1

METRIC UNITS

Linear

1 millimeter[1] (mm.)	=	.001 meter (m.)
1 centimeter (cm.)	=	.01 m.
1 decimeter (dm.)	=	.1 m.
1 kilometer (km.)	=	1000. m.

Weight

1 milligram (mg.)	=	.001 gram (g.)
1 centigram (cg.)	=	.01 g.
1 decigram (dg.)	=	.1 g.
1 kilogram (kg.)	=	1000. g.

[1] The prefix *milli-* stands for one-thousandth; *centi-*, for one-hundredth; *deci-*, for one-tenth; and *kilo-*, for one thousand.

Volume

1 liter (l.) = 1000 milliliters (ml.) = 1000.027 cubic centimeters (cc.)

Weights are usually expressed decimally in terms of grams. For example, 10 grams and 150 milligrams is written as 10.150 g. The relationship between units of measurement used in the English system and those of the metric system is evident from Table 2 (see also the Appendix).

TABLE 2

ENGLISH–METRIC EQUIVALENTS

1 inch	=	2.54 centimeters
1 meter	=	39.37 inches
1 pound	=	453.6 grams
1 liter	=	1.06 quarts
1 kilogram	=	2.2 pounds

Measurement of temperature. *Centigrade* and *absolute* scales of temperature rather than the *Fahrenheit* scale are employed in scientific work. The student must understand the relationship between these three scales of temperature and be able to make conversions from one scale to another. The relationship between the three scales of temperature may be seen in Table 3. The horizontal lines *A* and *B* denote the boiling point and freezing point of water respectively.

TABLE 3

COMPARISON OF TEMPERATURE SCALES

	° F.	° C.	° A.
A Boiling temperature of water	212°	100°	373°
	} 180°	} 100°	} 100°
B Freezing temperature of water	32°	0°	273°
Lowest temperature of the universe	−459	−273	0°

Note that there are 100 degrees between the freezing and boiling points of water on *both* the centigrade and absolute scales of temperature. However, a reading on the absolute scale will always be 273 degrees higher than on the centigrade scale, since 273 on the absolute scale corresponds to 0 on the centigrade scale. To convert centigrade temperature to absolute temperature, we simply add 273 to the centigrade reading, thus

$$° \text{A.} = ° \text{C.} + 273.$$

The absolute scale of temperature is based on the fact that when a **gas** is cooled it contracts (decreases in volume) $\frac{1}{273}$ of its volume at 0° C. for every degree the temperature is lowered. Theoretically, then, a gas would possess no volume at a temperature of −273° C. Actually this condition has not been realized as all substances become solids before this temperature is reached. This theoretical temperature is termed absolute zero and is the lowest possible temperature of the universe.

Again referring to Table 3, we note that the freezing point of water on the Fahrenheit scale is 32° and the boiling point is 212°. Between the freezing and boiling points there are 180 (212 − 32) degrees or divisions; on the centigrade scale only 100 such divisions. One division on the centigrade scale, then, is equal to $\frac{180}{100} = 1.8$ or $\frac{9}{5}$ divisions on the Fahrenheit scale; or conversely one Fahrenheit degree is equal to $\frac{5}{9}$ of a centigrade degree.

Suppose we have a temperature of 20° C. — what temperature does this correspond to on the Fahrenheit scale?

$$20 \text{ divisions C} = \tfrac{9}{5} \times 20 = 36 \text{ divisions F}$$

But these 36 divisions are measured above the freezing point of water which is 32° F. To get the actual Fahrenheit temperature, then, we must add the 32 to the 36, which gives 68°. Therefore

$$20° \text{ C} = 68° \text{ F}$$

In converting the centigrade temperature to Fahrenheit temperature we multiplied the centigrade temperature by $\frac{9}{5}$, then added 32. Expressed mathematically,

$$F = \tfrac{9}{5} C + 32$$

To convert Fahrenheit degrees to centigrade degrees we may solve this expression for centigrade.

$$C = \tfrac{5}{9}(F - 32)$$

In other words to obtain the centigrade temperature from Fahrenheit temperature, first subtract 32 from the Fahrenheit temperature, then multiply the result by $\frac{5}{9}$.

Density. The density of a substance is its *weight in relation to its volume;* in other words, weight per unit volume. A piece of iron has a greater density than a piece of wood because the weight of a given volume of iron is greater than the weight of the same volume of wood. Expressed mathematically:

$$\text{Density} = \frac{\text{Mass}}{\text{Volume}} \quad \text{or} \quad D = \frac{M}{V}$$

In chemical work, the density of a substance is usually expressed in grams per milliliter, g. per ml.

MATTER AND ITS CHANGES

Changes in matter. We can hardly fail to notice the many changes in matter which are continually taking place about us. Nature plays an important role in bringing about many familiar changes. Ice melts to liquid water, which in turn may be converted into water vapor by the action of the sun's rays. Liquid water may be changed into ice, or steam may be condensed to a liquid by a lowering of the temperature. In these processes by which water is changed from one physical state to another, its composition remains the same. Similarly no change in composition occurs in the magnetization of iron, melting of solder, or stretching of rubber. Changes which take place without modifying the composition of matter are called *physical changes.*

In contrast to physical changes are processes which take place with a modification of composition. When a piece of iron rusts, a brittle reddish deposit is formed on the surface; the iron is converted into a new substance with a new set of properties. Such changes which occur with alteration of composition are called *chemical changes.* Decay of animal and vegetable matter, digestion of food, and action of acids on metals are further examples of chemical changes.

Chemical changes are always accompanied by the liberation or absorption of heat energy. If heat energy is liberated the change is said to be *exothermic;* if heat energy is absorbed the change is *endothermic.*

The unit of heat energy is the *calorie,* which is defined as the *quantity of heat necessary to raise the temperature of one gram of water from 15° to 16°.*[1]

---

[1] Unless otherwise designated all temperatures will hereafter be given in ° C.

Properties of matter. Every substance possesses qualities or characteristics by which we are able to identify it. Sugar is a white solid, dissolves in water, and tastes sweet; iron has a metallic luster, may be magnetized, melts at a certain temperature, and rusts with the formation of a reddish deposit. These qualities or characteristics are termed *properties.*

Properties which are associated with physical changes are termed *physical properties.* The melting point (temperature at which a substance changes from the solid state to the liquid state) of a substance is a physical property, since the change from solid to liquid is physical, the liquid having the same composition as the solid. Properties which may be perceived by the senses, such as color, odor, and taste, are physical properties. Other common physical properties are boiling point, density, and solubility in water and other solvents. Less common physical properties of a substance might include its thermal or electrical conductivity, heat of fusion or vaporization, coefficient of thermal expansion, hardness, malleability, ductility, and crystalline form.

Chemical properties are involved only when matter undergoes chemical change. The rusting of iron is a chemical property of iron, since a change in composition occurs and a new substance is formed. Similarly as coal burns it combines with oxygen, and new gaseous substances are formed. Water, soil minerals, and carbon dioxide are converted by growing plants to many chemical substances. The fact that acids will act on most metals is a general chemical property of acids. In chemical changes, the substance undergoing change is nearly always associated with at least one other substance, whereas in observing or measuring a physical property we are concerned with a single substance.

The classification of matter. On the basis of its chemical composition, matter may be conveniently classified as follows:

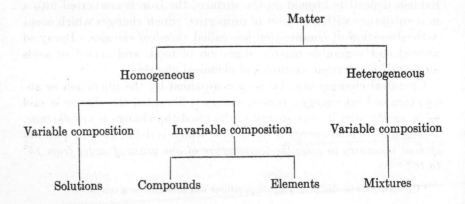

A *homogeneous* substance is one which is perfectly uniform in composition — every part is exactly like every other part. Every minute bit of sugar is exactly like every other minute bit of sugar. Substances which are homogeneous are sometimes termed *pure* substances. Salt, soda, aspirin, and saltpeter are further examples of pure or homogeneous substances.

Mixtures. Materials which are not uniform in composition are said to be *impure* or *heterogeneous* and are called *mixtures*.[1] Most of the materials which we encounter in everyday life are of this type. Food products, rocks, mineral matter, wood, and cement are examples. These materials are mixtures of pure substances.

The constituents of a mixture may be present in different proportions. For example, various cements contain variable proportions of calcium and aluminum silicates. Bread is a mixture of ingredients which may be present in different proportions.

The constituents of a mixture retain their identity, *e.g.*, a mixture of powdered iron and sulfur retains the properties of both iron and sulfur. Sulfur, which dissolves in carbon disulfide, may be separated from the iron by extraction with that solvent; or the iron, which is attracted to a magnet, may be separated from the sulfur in the mixture by magnetic attraction.

Compounds and elements. A *compound* is a pure substance which may be broken down or decomposed by chemical means into two or more simpler substances. Water, for example, is a compound substance, since it may be decomposed into hydrogen and oxygen by means of the electric current. Sugar may be decomposed by heat into carbon and water. Baking soda, alum, and table salt are further examples of compound substances.

There are a number of substances, however, which have not been decomposed into simpler substances by ordinary chemical means.[2] For example, such familiar substances as iron, copper, gold, sulfur, oxygen, hydrogen, and tin have not been decomposed. These substances are called *elements*. Ninety-eight elementary substances have been discovered up to the present time, a list of which will be found inside the front cover of this text. Several of these were known in ancient times, although they were not then considered as elementary substances. Compounds are made up of various combinations of

---

[1] The term "mixture" as used here refers to particles of matter which are at least of microscopic size (can be seen with a microscope). Solutions are sometimes referred to as mixtures, but the particles we shall find are very much smaller than can be observed with a microscope.

[2] Certain elements (termed "radioactive") are spontaneously decomposing into simpler elements. For a complete discussion of this see chapter XXXI.

two or more of these elements. Sugar, for example, is a combination of the elements carbon, hydrogen, and oxygen; water is composed of the elements hydrogen and oxygen.

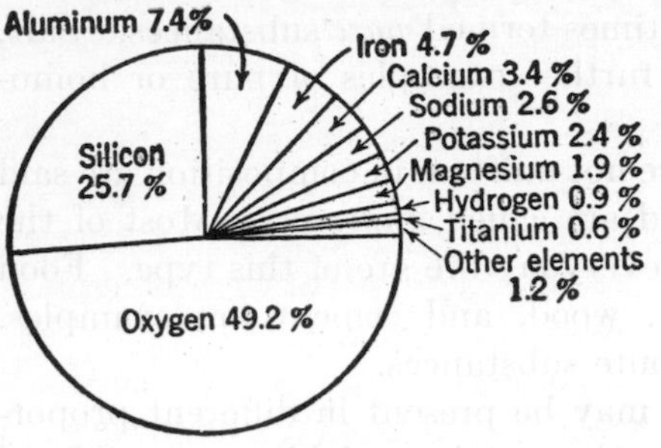

Fig. 2. Distribution of elements in the earth's crust.

The distribution of the elements in the earth's crust is shown in Figure 2. Note that nine elements comprise over 98 per cent of the earth's crust, which includes the atmosphere, oxygen alone making up nearly 50 per cent of all matter.

Compounds are characterized by their definite composition. All samples of a given compound contain the same elements in a fixed proportion. For example, the proportion of hydrogen to oxygen by weight in water is 1.008 : 8. Sodium chloride (table salt), no matter what the source of it may be, contains sodium and chlorine in the proportion of 23 parts by weight of sodium to 35.46 parts by weight of chlorine. This principle of the constancy of composition is termed the Law of Definite Composition. For further discussion of this law, see page 18.

Contrasting the properties of mixtures and compounds. The characteristics of mixtures and compounds are summarized below:

MIXTURES	COMPOUNDS
1. Heterogeneous — nonuniform.	1. Homogeneous — uniform.
2. Constituents retain original identity and properties.	2. Compounds have characteristic properties which are not those of the constituents.
3. Constituents may be present in any proportion by weight.	3. Constituent elements are present in fixed and invariable ratio by weight.
4. Constituents usually may be separated by mechanical means.	4. Not readily broken down into constituent elements.

Metals, nonmetals, and salts. Elements may be conveniently classified as metals and nonmetals. We are probably more familiar with the properties of metals than those of nonmetals. For example, we know that the elements iron, copper, tin, and other metals have, in general, properties of ductility (may be drawn into a wire), malleability (may be hammered into shape or rolled), and a metallic luster. In addition, metals usually have high melting points and a high density, and are good conductors of heat and electricity. Nonmetals, on the other hand, have, in general, low melting points, low densities, and are brittle, nonductile, and poor conductors of heat and electricity. Typical nonmetals are sulfur, phosphorus, and carbon. It should be pointed out at this time, however, that there is no sharp line of distinction between many metals and nonmetals.

The only metals that occur as the uncombined elements in naturally occurring rocks are gold, silver, copper, platinum, and rare platinum-like metals, plus unimportant small quantities of mercury, antimony, bismuth, and arsenic. The ancients consequently had very little metal to fashion into coins or trinkets. The bulk of the metals of modern use involve some chemical change in separating them from their natural occurrence of combination with some nonmetal. Practically all of our zinc, nickel, copper, lead, and arsenic are mined from deposits in which these elements are chemically combined with the nonmetal sulfur. The main ores of iron and of aluminum are oxygen compounds.

There are a number of metallic elements that are not in common use as metals but their compounds with nonmetals are of much use. For example, most people never see or use metallic sodium and yet the compound sodium chloride (common salt) is an essential food. The metal calcium has little use, but its compounds are important in bone structure, glass, cement, marble, and other innumerable industrial substances.

Since most metals will unite with most nonmetals to form compounds, one realizes the vast number of possible salts that occur naturally or can be made. A *salt* may be considered a compound of a metal with one or more nonmetals. Examples of salts are lead sulfide, magnesium bromide, zinc phosphide. Many salts consist of a metal combined with more than one nonmetal; for example, calcium carbonate is a compound of calcium, carbon, and oxygen.

Solutions. We have all observed that sugar dissolves in water to form a clear solution. The sugar distributes itself uniformly throughout the liquid so that every part of the solution is exactly like every other part. In other words, a solution is homogeneous. We know, too, that the amount of sugar which will dissolve in a given weight of water is variable; we may dissolve a teaspoonful or a cup of sugar in a pint of water. Solutions, then, are like compounds in that they are homogeneous, but unlike them in that the proportion of constituents is variable.

Although the solution of a solid in a liquid is the most common type of solution which we shall encounter, many other types may exist. We shall study this subject in more detail later (chap. XV).

LAWS OF CHEMICAL CHANGE

Law of conservation of mass. The French chemist, Lavoisier, in 1785, showed that *there is no detectable* [1] *gain or loss of mass in a chemical change;* in other words, the total weight of the substances entering into a chemical change is equal to the total weight of the substances produced as a result of the change. Since that time much evidence has accumulated in support of this statement, which is now known as the Law of Conservation of Mass. The law may be demonstrated, within the limits of experimental accuracy of our weighing devices, by measuring carefully the masses of the reactants and products of a chemical change.

In certain chemical reactions it might appear at first sight that the reactants weigh more or less than the products. For example, a piece of wood is burned, and ashes are the only visible evidence of any product of the reaction. However, in the burning process the wood combines with the oxygen of the air and forms the two invisible gases, carbon dioxide and water vapor, which pass into the atmosphere. If the carbon dioxide and water vapor are collected and weighed and added to the weight of the mineral matter (ashes) which remains, this total weight is found to be equal to the weight of the wood with which we started plus the weight of oxygen which has been taken from the atmosphere. Thus, if we take into account *all* of the reactants and products, we find no change in total mass during the reaction.

In certain cases the mass of the reactants seems to be less than that of the products. Iron rust, for example, weighs more than the iron from which it is formed. However, if we take into account the weight of the oxygen which combines with the iron during the rusting process, we then find that the weight of iron plus oxygen equals the weight of iron rust (iron oxide) produced in the chemical change.

Law of definite proportions. The law of definite composition which was stated on page 16 is sometimes referred to as the Law of Definite Proportions and may also be stated in the following form: *When elements combine to form a given compound, they do so in a fixed and invariable ratio by weight.* This law may be readily demonstrated in the laboratory by determining the ratio in which elements combine

---

[1] Einstein and others have demonstrated experimentally that mass and energy are interchangeable under certain conditions according to the Einstein equation $e = mc^2$ (where e = energy, m = mass, and c = velocity of light). A small mass change conceivably accompanies every chemical change, thus accounting for the energy change. However, in ordinary chemical changes the mass loss is so small that it is not detected by our most sensitive balances. Therefore the law of conservation of mass is a special case of the law of conservation of energy. See chapter XXXI for a more complete discussion of the equivalence of mass and energy.

with one another. For example, exactly 55.84 g. of iron, no more and no less, will combine with 32.06 g. of sulfur to form the compound ferrous sulfide. It makes no difference what ratio of weights of iron and sulfur we start with; we find that the above ratio (55.84 to 32.06) is always the exact ratio in which iron and sulfur combine to form ferrous sulfide. Naturally if a fixed ratio is maintained when these elements react, then the compound formed, ferrous sulfide, must have a fixed and definite composition.

Law of multiple proportions. Although elements always combine in a definite proportion to yield a given compound, we should point out that they may also combine in a different proportion to yield a different compound. For example, carbon and oxygen may combine to form two oxides of carbon, carbon monoxide and carbon dioxide. Chemical analysis of these compounds would show that in carbon monoxide, 6 g. of carbon combine with 8 g. of oxygen; in carbon dioxide, 3 g. of carbon combine with 8 g. of oxygen. Note that the ratio of the weights of carbon combining with 8 g. of oxygen in the two compounds (6 : 3) is in the ratio of small whole numbers, *i.e.*, 2 to 1.

Nitrogen forms a series of oxides in which the weights of oxygen combining with a fixed weight of nitrogen (14 g.) are shown in the following:

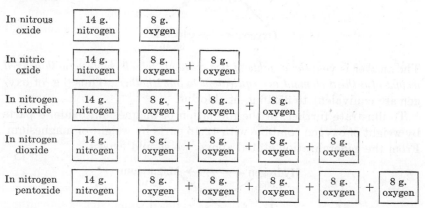

Again note that the ratio of the weights of one element (oxygen) 8 : 16 : 24 : 32 : 40 which combine with a fixed weight of the second element (nitrogen, 14 g.) stand as small whole numbers, 1, 2, 3, 4, 5. The relationship shown above is termed the Law of Multiple Proportions and might be stated: *The weights of an element which combine with a fixed weight of a second element in different compounds of the two elements are in the ratio of small whole numbers.*

In many other cases, elements combine in different proportions to form different compounds. We should keep in mind, however, that for a given compound the proportion is *fixed* and *invariable*.

Equivalent or combining weights. The law of definite proportions tells us that there is a definite relationship between the weights of elements in a given compound. A question is immediately suggested: Is there any simple relationship between the weights of the various elements which combine with one another in *different* compounds? To answer this question, let us study the combining proportions of elements in the two compounds, water and hydrogen chloride. Experiment shows that hydrogen combines with oxygen to form water in a ratio of 1.008 parts by weight of hydrogen to 8 parts by weight of oxygen.

$$\text{Hydrogen} \longleftrightarrow \text{Oxygen}$$
$$1.008 \qquad\qquad 8$$

In hydrogen chloride 1.008 parts by weight of hydrogen have combined with 35.46 parts by weight of chlorine.

$$\text{Hydrogen} \longleftrightarrow \text{Chlorine}$$
$$1.008 \qquad\qquad 35.46$$

Does it logically follow, then, that oxygen and chlorine will combine in a ratio of 8 to 35.46?

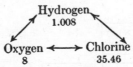

The answer is yes; *the weights of two elements which combine with a fixed weight of a third element are equivalent to one another.* Thus 8 g. of oxygen are equivalent to 35.46 g. of chlorine.

To illustrate further, in the formation of magnesium oxide, 8 parts by weight of oxygen combine with 12.16 parts by weight of magnesium. From the generalization stated above, we should expect

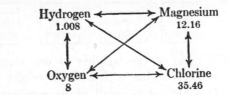

12.16 parts by weight of magnesium to combine with 35.46 parts by weight of chlorine. This is confirmed by experiment. Also we might expect magnesium and hydrogen to combine in a ratio of 12.16 to 1.008. Although magnesium does not combine with hydrogen, it does

displace hydrogen from an acid and experiment shows that 12.16 g. of magnesium displace exactly 1.008 g. of hydrogen.

In order to arrive at a system of related numbers to express equivalent or combining weights, it is necessary arbitrarily to choose some element as a standard for comparison. Because oxygen combines with most other elements, it has been chosen as a standard of comparison and has been assigned an equivalent weight of 8. The weight of an element which combines with 8 parts by weight of oxygen is termed its *equivalent* or *combining weight*. The equivalent weight expressed in grams is termed a *gram equivalent*. Thus 12.16 g. of magnesium and 35.46 g. of chlorine each represent a gram equivalent of these respective elements.

It was stated in the preceding section that carbon and oxygen may combine in two different proportions to form two different compounds. In carbon monoxide 6 parts by weight of carbon are combined with 8 parts by weight of oxygen, whereas in carbon dioxide 3 parts by weight of carbon are combined with 8 parts by weight of oxygen. While carbon exhibits two combining weights, 6 and 3, in these two compounds, these combining weights stand to each other as small whole numbers, 2 to 1. Chemists were led to conclude: *To each element may be assigned a number, its combining weight, which in itself, or when multiplied by a small whole number, expresses the weight of that element that combines with the combining weight of another element.* This generalization is known as the Law of Combining Weights.

It should be emphasized that though an element may exhibit more than one equivalent or combining weight, these weights are always related as small whole numbers. Thus the equivalent weight of carbon in carbon dioxide is 3, while its equivalent weight in carbon monoxide is 6 or 2 × 3.

Atoms and molecules. The fact that elements combine in fixed ratios by weight suggests that elements may be made up of particles or chunks of matter which act as units in chemical change. Much evidence has accumulated in recent years to indicate that such units of matter do exist, and the term *atom* is used to designate these units. An atom may be defined as *the smallest particle of an element which can enter into chemical change*.

Let us imagine subdividing a piece of iron into smaller and smaller particles. Eventually we would obtain a piece of iron which could no longer be divided or broken down into smaller pieces of iron. This ultimate particle would be an atom of iron.

The ultimate particle of a compound substance is termed a *molecule*. For example, in the subdivision of a compound substance such as sugar, which is composed of the elements hydrogen, oxygen, and carbon, the molecule is the smallest particle into which it may be divided without losing its identity. If divided further into atoms it would lose its properties so that the identity of the sugar would be destroyed. Atoms and molecules will be studied in more detail in the next chapter.

SYMBOLS AND FORMULAS

The chemist finds it convenient to use abbreviations or *symbols* for the chemical elements. Instead of writing out *hydrogen* the element is designated by the symbol H. *Oxygen* is designated by the symbol O; *sulfur*, by the symbol S; etc. The symbol of an element is usually derived from the first letter or letters of the English or Latin name of the element. In many cases only a single capitalized letter is used, as N for *nitrogen*, P for *phosphorus*, etc.; in other cases two letters from the name are used, only the first of which is capitalized; examples are He for *helium* and Ne for *neon*. The symbol for *sodium* is Na, which comes from the Latin, *natrium*. Many other symbols are derived from the Latin names of the elements; examples are *copper*, Cu; *iron*, Fe; *mercury*, Hg; and *silver*, Ag. A complete list of the chemical elements and their symbols will be found on the inside front cover of this book.

To the chemist the symbol is not only an abbreviation for an element; it also stands for one atom of the element in question. Thus S stands for one atom of sulfur; H, for one atom of hydrogen; and O, for one atom of oxygen. A number placed in front of the symbol indicates the number of atoms of that element, thus 3 H stands for three atoms of hydrogen, 10 N stands for ten atoms of nitrogen.

A chemical compound is expressed in abbreviated form as a *formula*, which consists of the proper combination of symbols, representing elements which are present in the compound. Thus iron sulfide, which is composed of the elements iron and sulfur, is represented as FeS, Fe being the symbol for iron, and S the symbol for sulfur; sodium chloride, a compound of sodium and chlorine, has the formula NaCl, Na being the symbol for sodium and Cl the symbol for chlorine.

A formula, like a symbol, is more than an abbreviation, as it tells at once the relative number of atoms of the constituent elements in the compound. FeS stands for ferrous sulfide which contains one atom of iron and one atom of sulfur. H_2O stands for two atoms of H (hydrogen) and one atom of O (oxygen) which compose water. A subscript 2 is placed after the hydrogen to indicate that two atoms of hydrogen are present in the molecule. A molecule of sulfuric acid, which contains two atoms of hydrogen, one atom of sulfur, and four atoms of oxygen, is represented as H_2SO_4; the subscript of the H is 2 to denote two atoms of hydrogen; the subscript of the O is 4 to indicate four atoms of oxygen present in each molecule of the compound. No subscript is necessary if only one atom of an element is present; thus in the above formula no subscript is placed after S, since only one atom of sulfur is present in the molecule.

The compound sugar contains the elements carbon, hydrogen, and oxygen. Its formula is $C_{12}H_{22}O_{11}$, which tells us that each molecule of sugar contains twelve atoms of carbon, twenty-two atoms of hydrogen, and eleven atoms of oxygen.

EXERCISES

1. Express 12 in. in centimeters; in millimeters; in decimeters; in meters.
2. Add: 5.25 g., 0.07 kg., 0.25 g., 550 mg., 3 dg., 50 cg.   Ans. 76.85 g.
3. Add: 0.30 m., 250 cm., 2.4 m., 800 mm., 2.5 cm., 5 dm., 50 mm.
4. Add: 2.5 l., 3500 ml., 0.25 l., 50 ml.   Ans. 6.3 l.
5. What is your weight in kilograms? What is your height in centimeters? What volume do you occupy?
6. This textbook page is approximately $5\frac{1}{2}$ in. by $8\frac{1}{2}$ in. What are the dimensions of the page in centimeters? What is its area?
7. A box is 5 in. wide, 10 in. long, and 3 in. deep. Calculate the volume in cubic centimeters; in liters.   Ans. 2460 cc.; 2.46 l.
8. Calculate the number of liters in a cubic meter.   Ans. 1000.
9. A container has the dimensions: 3 m. by 10 dm. by 50 mm. Calculate its volume in liters.   Ans. 150.
10. Convert to absolute temperature: $30°$ C.; $-40°$ C.
11. Calculate the density of a block of wood, 25 cm. $\times$ 100 mm. $\times$ 0.05 m., the weight of which is 0.9 kg.   Ans. .72 g./cc.
12. Calculate the volume of a tank which has the dimensions 300 mm. $\times$ 0.7 m. $\times$ 40 cm. What would be the weight of gasoline, density 0.8 g. per ml., which this tank could contain?
13. A piece of iron weighing 39.2 g. displaces 5 ml. of water when submerged. Compute the density of the iron.   Ans. 7.84 g./ml.
14. Calculate the quantity of heat required to raise the temperature of a quart of water (946 ml.) from $20°$ C. to $100°$ C.   Ans. 75,680 cal.
15. When a gram of coal is burned, 7600 cal. of heat are evolved. Calculate the quantity of coal necessary to supply the heat required in the previous problem.
16. Classify the following as physical or chemical changes: (a) rusting of iron; (b) molding of clay; (c) melting of iron; (d) digestion of food; (e) setting of mortar; (f) magnetization of iron; (g) souring of milk; (h) breaking of glass; (i) burning of coal.
17. When coal burns, do the ashes weigh more or less than the coal? Reconcile this with the law of conservation of mass.
18. List four characteristic differences between compounds and mixtures.

19. Classify the following as elements, mixtures, or compounds: soda; nitrogen; air; mayonnaise; soil; ink; baking powder; leather; alcohol; rubber; alum; lime; soap; chalk; platinum; helium; carbon dioxide; paint; aspirin.

20. Write the symbols and names of twenty of the more common chemical elements.

21. Differentiate between exothermic and endothermic reactions.

22. State the fundamental laws of chemical change.

23. Give some actual examples of the transformation of energy from one form to another.

24. Trees grow taller and larger. Is matter being created in the growing process? Explain.

25. Two elements A and B form three compounds which show on analysis the following weight relations:

Grams of A	Grams of B
15	15
30	45
15	45

Which of the laws of chemical change is illustrated here?

26. Analysis of compounds of A and B, A and C, B and C gives the following data:

	Grams of A	Grams of B	Grams of C
First compound	1	1.75	——
Second compound	2	——	4.30
Third compound	—	7.00	8.60

Which of the laws of chemical change is illustrated by this set of data?

27. A container having the dimensions: 2.5 m. × 10 cm. × 20 mm. is filled with water at a temperature of 32° F. How many calories will be necessary to heat the water to the boiling point?   Ans. 500,000.

28. The surface area of a piece of steel 10 mm. thick is 20 sq. cm. The piece weighs 0.160 kg. What is the density of the steel in grams per cubic centimeter?   Ans. 8.

29. It was observed on a certain morning that the Fahrenheit thermometer registered 8 deg. above the freezing point of water. What would have been the corresponding reading on a centigrade thermometer?

30. The gasoline tank on a car contains 40 l. of gasoline. Calculate the weight of gasoline if it has a density of 0.8 g./ml.   Ans. 32 kg.

31. Iron begins to glow red at 500° C. What is this temperature in degrees Fahrenheit?

32. A chemist analyzed two samples brought to him and found that one contained 0.636 g. of copper and 0.321 g. of sulfur, and the second contained 1.908 g. of copper and 0.963 g. of sulfur. What law is illustrated here?   Ans. Definite proportions.

33. It is found experimentally that every pure sample of zinc white, as zinc oxide is called, contains 4.08625 g. of zinc per gram of oxygen. What is the exact equivalent weight of zinc?

34. Show how the law of multiple proportions applies to the series of compounds: (a) Cl_2O, ClO_2, Cl_2O_7; (b) KCl, $KClO_2$, $KClO_3$, $KClO_4$.

35. A compound of iron and oxygen is analyzed and found to contain: 69.9 per cent iron and 30.1 per cent oxygen. What is the equivalent weight of iron in this compound? Ans. 18.6.

36. Three oxides of chromium on analysis gave the following data:

	CHROMIUM (per cent)	OXYGEN (per cent)
First compound	76.5	23.5
Second compound	68.4	31.6
Third compound	52.0	48.0

(a) What is the equivalent weight of chromium in each of the three compounds?

(b) Does the law of multiple proportions apply here? If so, explain.

Ans. (a) 26; 17.3; 8.7.

37. Make the following temperature conversions: 200° C. to F.; 104° F. to C.; −150° C. to A.; 302° F. to A.; 0° A. to F.

38. Determine the temperature at which both a Fahrenheit thermometer and a centigrade thermometer would (a) have the same reading, (b) have the same numerical reading but opposite in sign. Ans. (a) −40°.

REFERENCES

Briscoe, *General Chemistry for Colleges*, Houghton Mifflin.

Partington, *Textbook of Inorganic Chemistry*, Macmillan.

Moore, *A History of Chemistry*, rev. by W. T. Hall, McGraw-Hill.

Rudolf Winderlick, "Prevention of Accidents When Handling Chemicals," *J. Chem. Ed.* **27**, 670 (1950).

III

The Atom, Its Structure and Behavior

We learned from the laws of chemical change that (1) matter appears to be permanent, since no loss or gain of mass in chemical change has been detected (Law of Conservation of Mass), and (2) when elements combine to form a compound, they do so in a fixed and invariable ratio by weight (Law of Definite Proportions).

These facts in themselves suggest that matter is made up of discrete particles which function as units during chemical change. The idea that matter is discontinuous — that it is made up of finite particles and is not all in one piece — was first conceived by the Greek philosophers. Democritus reasoned that matter consists of very small particles, which he termed *atoms*. He did not distinguish between "atoms" of compounds and elementary substances, but believed that there were as many kinds of atoms as there were kinds of substances. It is rather surprising that the Greek philosophers were able so nearly to guess the truth of the structure of matter, since their conclusions were based on pure deduction without support of experimental data.

Dalton's atomic theory. It was not until 1804, however, that the atomic theory was developed more fully and accepted by chemists and physicists. In that year John Dalton, an English schoolmaster, made the following assumptions with regard to the structure of matter:

1. Substances are composed of tiny, indivisible particles called "atoms."
2. Atoms of any given substance are identical and have the same weight, size, form, etc.
3. The atom is the smallest part of an element which can enter into a chemical change.
4. Atoms of elements are permanent and cannot be decomposed.
5. Compounds are formed by the union of two or more atoms of elementary substances.

By means of the above assumptions, Dalton was able to explain the laws of chemical change. Since, according to the theory, atoms are permanent and not decomposable, there would be no change in mass during chemical reaction. When chemical compounds react with one another, there is simply a rearrangement of the atoms within the compounds. This rearrangement or regrouping produces new substances which have entirely new properties. Since all the atoms present are simply regrouped during a chemical change, and the atoms retain their weights, there is no gain or loss of weight (the Law of Conservation of Mass). Furthermore, if the atoms possess characteristic weights, the union of two or more atoms would require that combination take place in a fixed ratio by weight (Law of Definite Proportions).

Dalton did not recognize differences between units of elements and units of compounds. Avogadro, an Italian physicist, was the first to differentiate clearly between the two. He defined an atom as the smallest particle of an element which can enter into chemical change; the term *molecule* was used to denote the smallest unit of a substance (element or compound) which can exist and retain all the properties of the substance. A molecule may be a combination of two or more like or unlike atoms (Fig. 3).

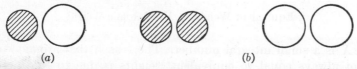

(a)   (b)

Fig. 3. (a) A combination of unlike atoms is a compound. (b) A combination of like atoms results in an element whose smallest unit contains more than one atom.

The differentiation between molecules of compounds and elements is a bit confusing. Many elements will exist in the free state as single atoms and as such the atom and molecule are the same; others may exist in the free state only in pairs or some other number of atoms.

Atomic weights. While atoms are much too small to be weighed individually, equal large numbers of atoms may be weighed and relative weights thus assigned to the elements by comparing their weights with some arbitrary standard. Because it is the most abundant of the chemical elements and because it combines chemically with most of the other elementary substances, oxygen has been chosen as the standard of atomic weights. Let us assign the number 16 to one atom of oxygen. An atom of sulfur weighs twice as much as an atom of oxygen, and on the basis chosen above has a relative weight of $2 \times 16 = 32$. An atom of iron weighs approximately $3\frac{1}{2}$ times as much as an atom of oxygen and therefore has a relative weight of $3\frac{1}{2} \times 16 = 56$. In a similar manner we may arrive at the relative weights of the atoms of other elements. These numbers are relative weights and not the actual weight or absolute weight of the atom of the element in question. When we say that the atomic weight of carbon is 12, we mean that one atom of carbon is $\frac{12}{16}$ or $\frac{3}{4}$ as heavy as one atom of oxygen which is our standard. One atom of lead, atomic weight 207, weighs $\frac{207}{16}$ times as much as one atom of oxygen. (See the inside front cover of this text for atomic weights of the elements.)

The number 16 has been assigned to oxygen, since on this basis the lightest known element, hydrogen, has a relative weight of about 1 (1.008). Of course a number larger than 16 might have been assigned to oxygen, but this would mean unnecessarily large numbers for the atomic weights of other elements. If, for example, the number 100 were assigned to oxygen, sulfur would have an atomic weight of 200, iron, an atomic weight of 350, etc.

Equivalent weights and atomic weights. Equivalent weights constitute fundamental information from which atomic weights are derived. A simple relationship exists between the equivalent weight of an element and its atomic weight as snown by the expression:

$$\text{Equivalent Weight} \times X = \text{Atomic Weight}$$

where X is a small integral number. The reason that atomic weights are not always equal to equivalent weights is due to the fact that atoms of the different elements do not always unite one atom to one atom. It was stated in the previous chapter that 1.008 parts by weight of hydrogen combine with 8 parts by weight of oxygen to form water, and it might appear at first sight that the atomic weight of oxygen should be 8 instead of 16. However, it may be shown experimentally that two atoms of hydrogen unite with one atom of oxygen in water, and therefore the combining capacity of the oxygen atom is twice that of the hydrogen atom. Some atoms, such as magnesium, have a combining capacity of 2; others, such as aluminum, have a capacity of 3; etc. This combining capacity of various elements, called *valence*, determines the magnitude of X. The determination of atomic weights will be studied in detail in chapter XIII.

The student must keep in mind that an atomic weight is just a *number* which expresses the relative weight of the atom in comparison to one atom of the arbitrarily selected standard (oxygen as 16).

The atomic weight of an element expressed in grams is termed a *gram atomic weight* or a *gram atom*. For example, a gram atomic weight or gram atom of oxygen is 16 grams, a gram atom of sulfur is 32 grams, etc.

Molecular weights. The smallest particle of a compound which can exist as such has been termed a *molecule*. A molecule of a compound is formed by the union of two or more atoms of the elements of which the compound is composed. The weight of a molecule will be the sum of the weights of the constituent atoms. For example, a molecule of water is composed of two atoms of hydrogen and one atom of oxygen, H_2O. The weight of a molecule of water or the *molecular weight* of water is then $(2 \times 1 = 2)$ plus $(1 \times 16 = 16) = 18$. Molecular weights, like atomic weights, are relative weights. The number 18 means that one molecule of water is $\frac{18}{16}$ as heavy as one atom of oxygen (our standard of comparison).

The molecular weight expressed in grams is termed a *gram molecular weight*. Thus a gram molecular weight of water is 18 grams. The term *gram molecular weight* is usually contracted to *gram mole*, or to just simply *mole*. These terms are synonymous.

Extensions of Dalton's theory. Dalton's atomic theory has undergone considerable change in recent years, and we may now point out several errors in the original assumptions. We now know that not all atoms of any given element are identical. For example, two kinds of chlorine atoms are known; one has an atomic weight of 35, while the other has an atomic weight of 37. Similarly, lead with atomic weights of 205, 206, and 207 has been shown to exist.

We know, too, that atoms may be disintegrated. Many elements, such as uranium, radium, etc. (radioactive elements), are spontaneously disintegrating, and their atoms are being transformed into atoms of simpler elements (see chap. XXXI).

Subatomic particles of matter. The idea that atoms are indivisible persisted for many years after the postulations of Dalton, and it has been only in the last fifty years or so that evidence has accumulated which indicates that atoms may actually be decomposed and resolved into subatomic particles much smaller than any known atom. Atoms of all of the elements are now regarded as being composed of three subatomic particles of matter:

1. *Electrons:* negative charges of electricity.
2. *Protons:* units of matter carrying a positive charge.
3. *Neutrons:* neutral units of matter of about the same mass as the proton.

The electron. The electron was the first of the subatomic particles to be discovered. The story of its discovery begins with a study of the discharge of electricity through gases at reduced pressures. For this study a so-called cathode ray tube (Fig. 4) may be used. It consists of a tube of glass in which are sealed two metal strips, and a glass side arm through which the tube may be evacuated by means of a pump. The metal strips act as electrodes between which a discharge of electricity will take place when the electrodes are connected to a source of high potential such as an induction coil. The nature of the discharge, then, is studied as the pressure is reduced. At atmospheric pressure an irregular violet colored discharge takes place.

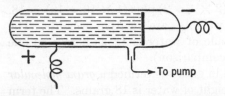

Fig. 4. Cathode ray tube. Electrons are emitted from the cathode in straight lines.

As the pressure is reduced, the discharge becomes pink and finally the whole tube glows. At very low pressures, streaks of white light appear to emerge at right angles from the negative pole or cathode, and to cause the appearance of a greenish fluorescence on the glass walls where the rays strike. These rays were at first referred to as *cathode rays*, and at first sight appeared to be light rays. An obstacle placed between the cathode and the glass wall casts a sharp shadow on the wall opposite the cathode, thus indicating that the rays travel in straight lines. A pinwheel placed in the path of the rays revolves, or if the rays are allowed to strike a piece of metal foil, the foil becomes hot. These observations suggested that the rays were material in nature. In 1879 Sir William Crookes showed that the rays were bent in an arc by an electromagnetic field. Subsequently, Sir J. J. Thomson showed that the rays were deflected toward a positively charged plate in an electric field and therefore must possess a negative charge. These negatively charged particles issuing from the cathode came to be called *electrons*. By observing the deflection of electrons in magnetic and electric fields, Thomson determined that the mass of a single electron is about $\frac{1}{1845}$ that of the hydrogen atom. Since electrons can be generated by using any cathode or any gas in the tube, it would seem that these particles are constituents of atoms of all elements.

The magnitude of the *charge* of an electron has been determined by R. A. Millikan. A container was constructed with electrically chargeable plates at top and bottom. Electrons and positively charged particles were produced in the container by a beam of X-rays. Fog droplets were introduced into the container and the rate of fall of a given fog droplet viewed as the plates were electrically charged or discharged. A fog particle could be accelerated in its fall, suspended in mid-air, or actually made to rise, dependent on the charge of the

Courtesy Central Scientific Company

Fig. 5. Precision instruments and relative sizes of natural objects.

plates. The explanation is that the fog droplet adsorbed electrons and thus becoming negatively charged would tend to move to the positively charged plate. The number of electrons adsorbed per droplet would influence the rate of movement to the positive plate, but all changes in velocity as electrons were adsorbed could be compensated by appropriate changes in charge between plates. It was noted that all changes in velocity of the rise or fall of the fog droplets were related to multiples of a certain unit charge between the plates. This unit charge between the plates must equal the electron charge and was found to be 1.59×10^{-20} electromagnetic units.

The actual *mass* of an electron has not been determined directly but may, as has already been mentioned, be calculated from data obtained by measuring the effect of magnetic and electrostatic fields upon a stream of cathode rays. From the deflection of the stream in a magnetic field and its counterbalancing by an electrostatic field, the ratio of charge to mass of the electron is obtained, and from this the mass has been calculated to be 9×10^{-28} g.

The proton. After electrons were found to be generated in a cathode ray tube, it was natural to ask whether or not positively charged particles were emanating from the region of the positive pole or anode of the tube at the same time electrons were being generated at the cathode. In 1886 Goldstein found that if the cathode is perforated with a cylindrical hole, a beam of rays passes through the cathode into a region behind the cathode and away from the anode. These rays were called *positive rays* or *canal rays*. By studying these rays in magnetic and electric fields in much the same manner that the cathode rays were investigated, it was shown that they possess a unit positive charge or an integral multiple of this charge, and are composed of particles of the residual gas used in the tube. Particles of lowest mass were found when hydrogen was the residual gas. The particles consist of hydrogen atoms with a unit positive charge; or, looking at it in another way, each particle is a hydrogen atom which has lost one electron. Since in no case is a smaller positively charged particle than this found, there is strong evidence that these particles are fundamental building units in the structure of atoms of all of the elements. These subatomic particles are termed *protons*.

The neutron. In 1932 Chadwick observed that neutral particles of a mass approximately that of the proton were produced when beryllium was exposed to the radiations from a radioactive substance (chap. XXXI). It was at first thought that each particle consisted of one proton and one electron. However, these neutral units of matter, which are called *neutrons*, are now regarded as a new and fundamentally distinct kind of particle.

X-rays. In 1895, Roentgen discovered a new kind of radiation of very short wave length emanating from a cathode ray tube in which a metallic element was made a target of the cathode rays (Fig. 6). For lack of a better name, the radiation was termed *X-rays*. The rays are capable of penetrating wood, paper, and flesh but are stopped by bones and metallic substances. Modern medical practice calls for the use of X-ray photographs in diagnosis of disease and fractured limbs. Also, X-rays have constituted a powerful tool in studies of the structure of matter.

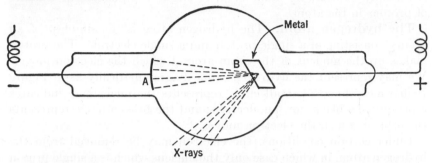

Fig. 6. X-ray tube. Electrons are emitted and brought to a focus by the concave cathode A. The cathode rays on striking a metal target, produce X-rays of a frequency characteristic of the metal.

The modern theory of atomic structure.

Although Dalton believed that atoms were solid, impenetrable particles, present-day knowledge shows that the atom is really of a porous nature. The modern picture of the atom consists of a comparatively compact center or nucleus, which is surrounded by an orbital structure. The atom might be likened to the solar system in which the sun acts as the nucleus and the planets which revolve about the sun as the outer structure. Except for the hydrogen atom, *the nucleus of an atom contains both protons and neutrons,* but no electrons, while *the outer structure of the atom consists of electrons only.* These electrons move in orbits or *energy levels* about the nucleus. Since only neutrons and protons are contained in the nucleus, the *nucleus of an atom must always bear a net positive charge.*

Protons and neutrons have approximately the same mass as the hydrogen atom, while the electron has only about $\frac{1}{1845}$ the mass of the hydrogen atom. Since the protons and neutrons are responsible for most of the mass of the atom and since the nucleus contains both protons and neutrons, it follows that most of the mass of the atom is concentrated in the nucleus.[1] The electrons, which are almost negligible

[1] The relative size of the nucleus and its density may be visualized from the following approximate figures. An average atom has a radius of about 1×10^{-8} cm., whereas the nucleus has a radius of about 1×10^{-12} cm.; in other words the radius of the nucleus is about $\frac{1}{10000}$ that of the atom. While the density of liquid or solid elements varies from less than 1 to 22.4 g./cc., the density of the nucleus is estimated at about 10^{14} g./cc., which would be 10^8 or 100 million tons per cubic centimeter.

in weight as compared to the protons and neutrons, are separated from the nucleus by relatively great distances, much the same as the planets in the solar system are situated at great distances from the sun. Just as planets move in orbits about the sun, so the electrons in the atom move in orbits about the nucleus. Since all atoms are electrically neutral, the number of electrons is equal to the number of protons in the atom.

The hydrogen atom. The hydrogen atom is the simplest of all atoms, consisting of a single proton and a single electron. The proton makes up the nucleus of the atom around which the electron moves. We may represent the hydrogen atom diagrammatically as in Figure 7, in which the solid small circle represents the nucleus; + indicates a proton; the black dot, an electron; and the broken circle represents the orbit in which the electron moves.

Under certain conditions, the electron may be removed from the hydrogen atom, in which case only the nucleus which is a single proton remains. This particle resulting as an electron leaves a H atom is positively charged and might be represented as H^+ (Fig. 8). An atom having an excess of either positive or negative charge is termed an *ion*.

Fig. 7. The hydro-   Fig. 8. A hydro-   Fig. 9. The helium
    gen atom.   gen ion.   atom.

Thus H^+ is a hydrogen ion. It becomes evident that a hydrogen ion and a proton are one and the same thing. The atomic weight of hydrogen is approximately 1 (actually 1.008), and since the mass of the atom is almost entirely contained in the nucleus, it follows that the mass of the proton is very nearly equal to one. Neutrons have practically the same mass as protons and so must have a weight also very close to unity.

The structure of other atoms. The element of simplest structure next to hydrogen is helium, atomic weight 4. The number 4 would indicate that 4 units of weight are necessary in the nucleus of the atom. These four units of weight must be due to protons or neutrons or both. As a matter of fact the helium nucleus is composed of two protons and two neutrons. Two electrons must be present in the atom to balance the charge of the two protons, and these two electrons revolve in an orbit about the nucleus (Fig. 9). The symbol n represents a neutron.

As we progress to the elements of higher atomic weight, the structures become more complex, and additional orbits must be added in which additional electrons may move (Figs. 10, 11, 12, 13).

   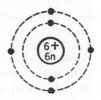

| Fig. 10. The lithium atom. | Fig. 11. The beryllium atom. | Fig. 12. The boron atom. | Fig. 13. The carbon atom. |

The capacity of the first orbit (called the *K* energy level) about the nucleus of an atom seems to be two electrons; in no case is this number exceeded. We may say that two electrons represent a stable or saturated condition for the first orbit of an atom. A total of eight electrons may be present in the second orbit of an atom (*L* energy level), eighteen electrons in the third orbit (*M* energy level), and thirty-two electrons in the fourth orbit[1] (*N* energy level) (Fig. 14).

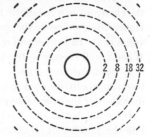

We shall learn, however, that the *number of electrons in the outermost orbit of an atom may never exceed eight.* The third orbit of an atom may have as many as eighteen electrons provided the third orbit is *not* the outer orbit, and likewise the fourth orbit may have as many as thirty-two electrons, provided it is *not* the outermost orbit. The arrangement

Fig. 14. The maximum number of electrons in the various orbits of atoms is: first orbit, 2; second orbit, 8; third orbit, 18; fourth orbit, 32.

of electrons in the various orbits about the nucleus for the elements is shown in Table 4 (p. 38).

Quantum numbers and subshells. While the orbital electrons in an atom group themselves into successive shells (or energy levels) in which there are 2 electrons in the first shell, 8 in the second, 18 in the third, 32 in the fourth, etc., spectral studies indicate that the electrons in a given shell do not move in exactly the same orbits or energy levels. The electrons in the different orbits are best described by sets of numbers known as *quantum numbers*, of which there are four:

---

[1] The maximum number of electrons that may appear in an orbit may be determined from the equation

$$\text{Max. No. of Electrons} = 2\,n^2$$

where *n* is the number of the orbit.

1. The *principal quantum number*, designated by n, which corresponds to the shell in which the electron moves. Instead of describing an electron by the numerical value of its principal quantum number, *e.g.*, 1, 2, 3, etc., it is sometimes the practice to employ the capital letters K, L, M, etc. Thus a K electron is an electron having a principal quantum number of unity; for an L electron the value of n is two, and so on.

2. The *azimuthal quantum number*, designated by l, gives a measure of the angular momentum of an electron in its orbital motion about the nucleus. The introduction of this term means that the main shells of electrons may be considered as being made up of one or more *subshells*. These subshells of electrons possess *nearly* the same energy as one another but not exactly so. The term l may have values of 0 to $(n-1)$. Hence for the first main shell where $n = 1$, l can have only a value of 0. For the first shell, then, the subshells and main shell would coincide. When $n = 2$, l can have values of 0 and 1. This would correspond to two subshells within the second main shell. When $n = 3$, l may have the values 0, 1, 2, corresponding to 3 subshells, etc.

3. *Magnetic quantum number*, designated by m to account for the behavior of the electrons in a magnetic field. m may have values from $-l$ to $+l$, including 0. Hence for the first main shell where $n = 1$, then $l = 0$, and m can have only a value of 0. In the second main shell where $n = 2$, l can have the values 0 and 1. When $l = 0$ then $m = 0$; and when $l = 1$, then m may be -1, 0, or $+1$.

4. *Spin quantum number*, designated by s, takes into account the spin of an electron about its own axis in a clockwise or counterclockwise direction. The direction of the spin is designated by $+$ or $-$.

If we follow the above set of rules for quantum numbers, we may easily calculate the number of electrons in the various subshells of the atoms, *e.g.*:

For the first shell where $n = 1$, $l = 0$, and $m = 0$, $s = +$ or $-$. Since according to Pauli no more than one electron can have given values for the four quantum numbers, the first shell can have only two electrons; i.e.

$$n = 1, l = 0, m = 0, s = +$$
$$n = 1, l = 0, m = 0, s = -$$

For the second main shell:

$$n = 2, l = 0, m = 0, \quad s = +$$
$$s = -$$
$$\overline{\quad \text{2 electrons}}$$

$$n = 2, l = 1, m = -1, s = +$$
$$s = -$$
$$m = 0, \quad s = +$$
$$s = -$$
$$m = +1, s = +$$
$$s = -$$
$$\overline{\quad \text{6 electrons}}$$

The second shell then consists of two subshells the first of which holds two electrons, and the second six electrons to make a total of eight. Following the same reasoning as above, it can be shown that the third main shell consists of three subshells, the first with 2 electrons, the second with 6 electrons, and the third with 10 electrons to make a total of 18. The fourth main shell by similar reasoning would have 4 subshells holding 2, 6, 10, 14 electrons respectively to make a total of 32.

The various subshells are frequently designated by letters, s for the 2 electron subshell, p for the 6, d for the 10, and f for the 14. Thus the maximum electrons in the various subshells could be described as

$$2 \ s \text{ electrons}$$
$$6 \ p \text{ electrons}$$
$$10 \ d \text{ electrons}$$
$$14 \ f \text{ electrons}$$

The maximum number of electrons in the various subshells of the main energy levels might be shown in diagrammatic fashion:

```
              s        s   p      s   p   d      s   p   d   f

Nucleus       2        2   6      2   6   10     2   6   10  14

              K          L            M               N
```

The above notations are convenient in describing the electronic configuration of an atom, for example neon with 10 electrons might be designated as $1 \ s^2; 2 \ s^2, 2 \ p^6$, which indicates 2 s electrons only in the first shell, 2 s electrons and 6 p electrons in the second shell. Iron with 26 electrons could be shown as (see Table 4)

$$1 \ s^2; \ 2 \ s^2, 2 \ p^6; \ 3 \ s^2, 3 \ p^6 \ 3 \ d^6; \ 4 \ s^2$$

Atomic numbers. It may be noted from Figures 10–13 (p. 35) that, as we proceed from one element to another, the number of electrons in the atom increases by one in each instance. Thus, the element lithium has three electrons, beryllium has four electrons, boron has five electrons, etc. If we arrange the elements according to their increasing atomic weights, we may assign numbers in order, starting with hydrogen as one, to the chemical elements. These numbers will represent the number of electrons present in the atom. The number for any given element is termed the *atomic number* of that element. It may be determined experimentally by X-ray studies of the element. Since the number of protons in an atom must equal the number of electrons, the atomic number is equal to the number of protons in the atom or the net positive charge on the nucleus.

TABLE 4
DISTRIBUTION OF ELECTRONS OF THE ELEMENTS

ELEMENT	SYM- BOL	ATOMIC NUMBER	NUMBER OF ELECTRONS IN VARIOUS ENERGY LEVELS						
			K	L	M	N	O	P	Q
Hydrogen	H	1	1						
Helium	He	2	2						
Lithium	Li	3	2	1					
Beryllium	Be	4	2	2					
Boron	B	5	2	3					
Carbon	C	6	2	4					
Nitrogen	N	7	2	5					
Oxygen	O	8	2	6					
Fluorine	F	9	2	7					
Neon	Ne	10	2	8					
Sodium	Na	11	2	8	1				
Magnesium	Mg	12	2	8	2				
Aluminum	Al	13	2	8	3				
Silicon	Si	14	2	8	4				
Phosphorus	P	15	2	8	5				
Sulfur	S	16	2	8	6				
Chlorine	Cl	17	2	8	7				
Argon	A	18	2	8	8				
Potassium	K	19	2	8	8	1			
Calcium	Ca	20	2	8	8	2			
Scandium	Sc	21	2	8	9	2			
Titanium	Ti	22	2	8	10	2			
Vanadium	V	23	2	8	11	2			
Chromium	Cr	24	2	8	13	1			
Manganese	Mn	25	2	8	13	2			
Iron	Fe	26	2	8	14	2			
Cobalt	Co	27	2	8	15	2			
Nickel	Ni	28	2	8	16	2			
Copper	Cu	29	2	8	18	1			
Zinc	Zn	30	2	8	18	2			
Gallium	Ga	31	2	8	18	3			
Germanium	Ge	32	2	8	18	4			
Arsenic	As	33	2	8	18	5			
Selenium	Se	34	2	8	18	6			
Bromine	Br	35	2	8	18	7			
Krypton	Kr	36	2	8	18	8			
Rubidium	Rb	37	2	8	18	8	1		
Strontium	Sr	38	2	8	18	8	2		
Yttrium	Y	39	2	8	18	9	2		
Zirconium	Zr	40	2	8	18	10	2		
Niobium	Nb	41	2	8	18	12	1		
Molybdenum	Mo	42	2	8	18	13	1		
Technetium	Tc	43	2	8	18	14	1		
Ruthenium	Ru	44	2	8	18	15	1		
Rhodium	Rh	45	2	8	18	16	1		
Palladium	Pd	46	2	8	18	18	0		
Silver	Ag	47	2	8	18	18	1		
Cadmium	Cd	48	2	8	18	18	2		
Indium	In	49	2	8	18	18	3		

Table 4 (*Continued*)

ELEMENT	SYM-BOL	ATOMIC NUMBER	NUMBER OF ELECTRONS IN VARIOUS ENERGY LEVELS						
			K	L	M	N	O	P	Q
Tin	Sn	50	2	8	18	18	4		
Antimony	Sb	51	2	8	18	18	5		
Tellurium	Te	52	2	8	18	18	6		
Iodine	I	53	2	8	18	18	7		
Xenon	Xe	54	2	8	18	18	8		
Cesium	Cs	55	2	8	18	18	8	1	
Barium	Ba	56	2	8	18	18	8	2	
Lanthanum	La	57	2	8	18	18	9	2	
Cerium	Ce	58	2	8	18	20	8	2	
Praseodymium	Pr	59	2	8	18	21	8	2	
Neodymium	Nd	60	2	8	18	22	8	2	
Promethium	Pm	61	2	8	18	23	8	2	
Samarium	Sm	62	2	8	18	24	8	2	
Europium	Eu	63	2	8	18	25	8	2	
Gadolinium	Gd	64	2	8	18	25	9	2	
Terbium	Tb	65	2	8	18	27	8	2	
Dysprosium	Dy	66	2	8	18	28	8	2	
Holmium	Ho	67	2	8	18	29	8	2	
Erbium	Er	68	2	8	18	30	8	2	
Thulium	Tm	69	2	8	18	31	8	2	
Ytterbium	Yb	70	2	8	18	32	8	2	
Lutetium	Lu	71	2	8	18	32	9	2	
Hafnium	Hf	72	2	8	18	32	10	2	
Tantalum	Ta	73	2	8	18	32	11	2	
Wolfram	W	74	2	8	18	32	12	2	
Rhenium	Re	75	2	8	18	32	13	2	
Osmium	Os	76	2	8	18	32	14	2	
Iridium	Ir	77	2	8	18	32	15	2	
Platinum	Pt	78	2	8	18	32	17	1	
Gold	Au	79	2	8	18	32	18	1	
Mercury	Hg	80	2	8	18	32	18	2	
Thallium	Tl	81	2	8	18	32	18	3	
Lead	Pb	82	2	8	18	32	18	4	
Bismuth	Bi	83	2	8	18	32	18	5	
Polonium	Po	84	2	8	18	32	18	6	
Astatine	At	85	2	8	18	32	18	7	
Radon	Rn	86	2	8	18	32	18	8	
Francium	Fr	87	2	8	18	32	18	8	1
Radium	Ra	88	2	8	18	32	18	8	2
Actinium	Ac	89	2	8	18	32	18	9	2
Thorium	Th	90	2	8	18	32	18	10	2
Protactinium	Pa	91	2	8	18	32	20	9	2
Uranium	U	92	2	8	18	32	21	9	2
Neptunium	Np	93	2	8	18	32	22	9	2
Plutonium	Pu	94	2	8	18	32	23	9	2
Americium	Am	95	2	8	18	32	24	9	2
Curium	Cm	96	2	8	18	32	25	9	2
Berkelium	Bk	97	2	8	18	32	26	9	2
Californium	Cf	98	2	8	18	32	27	9	2

From a knowledge of the atomic weight and the atomic number of an element we should be able to indicate its structure. The atomic weight is numerically equal to the number of protons plus the number of neutrons. The atomic number is equal to the number of protons or electrons in the atom. The difference between the atomic weight and the atomic number gives the number of neutrons present. All of the protons and neutrons appear in the nucleus, and all of the electrons are present in the orbits surrounding the nucleus.

X-rays and atomic numbers. Henry G. J. Moseley, a brilliant young British physicist who was killed in World War I, discovered that the wave length or frequency of X-rays produced when a substance was made a target in a cathode-ray tube (see p. 30) depended upon the elements of which the target was composed. After determining the frequency for nearly all of the elements, he arranged them in order of increasing frequencies and then assigned an *atomic number* to each element which corresponded to its position in the arrangement. Except for three pairs of elements (K, A; Co, Ni; Te, I) the order was identical with that of the elements arranged according to increasing atomic weights. Moseley reasoned that the frequency of radiation from the elements depended upon the number and arrangement of unit particles in their atoms, and therefore the atomic number was an important consideration in the structure of the atom. We now know that the atomic number of an element corresponds to the number of electrons in the atom, also to the number of protons.

Valence electrons. The electrons in the outermost ring or orbit of an atom largely determine the chemical properties of the element. The maximum number of electrons which can be present in the outer orbit is *eight*. Eight electrons in the outer orbit appear to represent a stable configuration. Atoms tend to approach this stable configuration by gaining or losing electrons. To illustrate, let us consider the sodium atom which has an atomic weight of 23 and an atomic number of 11. Since the atomic number is equal to the number of protons in the atom and also equal to the number of electrons, the sodium atom must contain 11 protons and 11 electrons. The difference between the atomic weight and the atomic number (23 − 11 = 12) gives the number of neutrons. Hence the nucleus will contain 11 protons and 12 neutrons. The first orbit will contain its capacity of two electrons, the second orbit likewise will have its capacity of eight electrons. This leaves one electron then to be put into the third orbit which in this case is the outermost orbit (Fig. 15). The sodium atom will tend toward a stable configuration (in which the outer orbit contains eight electrons) by gaining or losing electrons. In order to reach such a stable condition, the sodium atom could give up one elec-

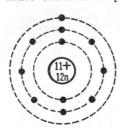

Fig. 15. The sodium atom.

tron, in which case the third orbit disappears, and the second orbit becomes the outermost orbit. As another possibility the sodium atom could take up seven electrons to complete the quota of eight in the orbit which already contains one. It seems logical to assume that the former process would take place more readily; that is, it would be easier for the atom to give up one electron than to take up seven electrons. As a matter of fact, the sodium atom does readily give up one electron, in which case it becomes a sodium ion, Na^+.

The electrons which are present in the outer shell of the atom are known as *valence* electrons and determine the manner in which atoms combine with one another. The valence of sodium is $+1$, since the atom tends to lose one electron and become a sodium ion, Na^+, with a net positive charge of one.

A wire of metallic sodium is a good conductor of electricity. Since an electron is a negative charge of electricity and since sodium has one outer electron which it tends to give up readily, a flow of electricity in a sodium wire is construed to be a movement of these outer electrons through the wire from one atom to the next. In general, a metal is a good electrical conductor, since the outer or valence electrons are comparatively lightly held by the atomic nucleus and are free to move successively from one atom to another.

Let us examine the structure of the chlorine atom, atomic weight 35, atomic number 17. The nucleus contains 17 protons (the atomic number) and 18 neutrons (atomic weight minus atomic number). Seven electrons appear in the outer ring (Fig. 16). From what has already been said, we conclude that the chlorine atom would tend to

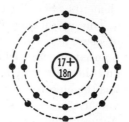

Fig. 16. The chlorine atom.

take on one electron to complete its quota of eight in the outer orbit. This would seem to be easier than giving up seven electrons. In either case the atom would then have eight electrons in its outermost orbit. If the chlorine atom gains one electron, it will have a net charge of -1 and may be represented as Cl^-, which is a chlorine ion. The valence of chlorine in such case is said to be -1.

As a general rule, we may say that atoms which have less than four electrons in the outer orbit tend to give up electrons, while those containing more than four electrons in the outer orbit tend to take up electrons to complete the quota of eight. The number of electrons given up or lost by an atom is its *positive valence;* the number of electrons taken up or gained by an atom is its *negative valence.*

In general we find that those elements which we classify as metals tend to give up electrons rather than take them up; consequently metals have a positive valence. On the other hand, those elements classified as nonmetals usually take up electrons, in which case they have a negative valence. We shall find that certain elements (metalloids) which may either give up or take up electrons have properties of both metals and nonmetals.

Incomplete orbits. Careful inspection of Table 4 (pp. 38–39) will reveal some interesting patterns in the manner in which the various orbits or shells accommodate electrons. First of all it may be noted that beyond the second orbit, it is not necessary for an orbit to complete its capacity of electrons before another orbit or shell is started. For example the third shell which has a capacity of 18 electrons is not completely filled between the elements potassium, atomic number 19, and copper, atomic number 29. Starting with scandium, atomic number 21, added electrons, instead of going into the outer orbit, start filling into the third orbit and this process continues until copper is reached which has a completed third orbit or shell. There are other such groups of elements in which an inner orbit is filling from 8 to 18 or from 18 to 32 electrons. Such elements are known as *transition* elements. See discussion on page 60.

The significance of these incompleted shells in determining properties of elements will be discussed in some detail later, but it should be pointed out now that electron movement between an incomplete orbit and the outer valence orbit is possible. For example, scandium which has the electron configuration 2, 8, 9, 2 might be expected to exhibit a valence of $+2$ since it contains two electrons in the outer orbit. Actually the common valence of this element is $+3$. Presumably, the 9th electron in the third orbit as well as the two electrons in the outer orbit may be lost to give scandium this valence.

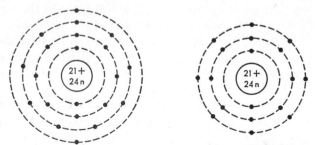

Fig. 16x. Scandium atom (left) and scandium ion. Note the stable configuration of the latter with eight electrons in the outer orbit. Although the scandium atom has but two electrons in its outermost orbit, the loss of a third electron from the third orbit accounts for scandium's common valence of three.

This movement of electrons between orbits also may give rise to *variable* valences. For example, iron with the configuration 2, 8, 14, 2 exhibits valences of $+2$ and $+3$. In the first case, two electrons from the fourth orbit are lost; in the second, an additional electron is lost from the third orbit. This matter of variable valences will be discussed in more detail in chapter IX.

Similarities of structure. Since the outermost orbit of an atom largely determines the chemical properties of the element, we might expect those atoms exhibiting the same outer structure (same number of electrons in outer shell) to be quite similar in chemical behavior. That this is true may be shown from a consideration of the structures of several of the chemical elements. Let us first consider the elements lithium, sodium, and potassium (Fig. 17).

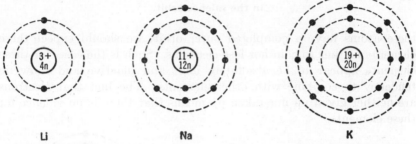

Li   Na   K

Fig. 17. The outer structure of atoms of lithium, sodium, and potassium is similar; each atom has one outer or valence electron.

While there is little similarity in the inner structure of these atoms, we note that the outer orbit in each case contains one electron. Each of these atoms would tend to lose one electron, in which case the valence of each would be $+1$. In a study of these elements later, we shall indeed find that they are very similar in chemical properties.

In a similar manner consider the elements fluorine, chlorine, and bromine (Fig. 18), and the elements helium, neon, and argon (Fig. 19). From the standpoint of their atomic structure we should expect fluorine, chlorine, and bromine to show similar chemical behavior, as the outer structure of each atom contains seven electrons. Each atom then would tend to take on one electron to complete the quota of eight, in which case the valence of each would be -1. Since electrons are gained by these elements, we should properly class them as non-metallic elements.

The elements helium, neon, and argon have similar outer structures in that each atom represents a stable configuration with regard to electrons in the outer orbit of the atom Helium has only two electrons in its outer orbit; however, we may recall that two electrons in the first orbit represent a stable configuration in the same way that eight electrons represent a stable configuration for the second orbit. Since

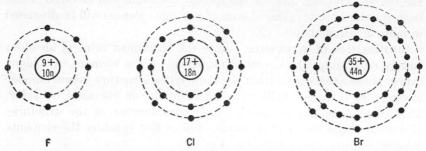

Fig. 18. Atoms of fluorine, chlorine, and bromine each have seven electrons in the valence orbit.

these atoms have a completed outer orbit, we should expect these elements neither to gain nor lose electrons. Such is the case, for these elements appear to be absolutely inert and inactive and show no tendency to combine with other elements. The fact that electrons are neither given up nor taken up means that there is no valence for these elements.

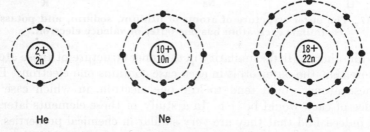

Fig. 19. Structures of the inert gases, helium, neon, and argon.

Isotopes. We have pointed out that the mass of an atom is due almost entirely to the protons and neutrons present in the nucleus. Electrons have a negligible weight as compared to protons and neutrons. Since protons and neutrons have unit mass, it follows that the weights of atoms (atomic weights) should be whole numbers if we neglect the very small mass due to the electrons. An examination of the table of atomic weights (front cover of the text) shows that many of the elements have atomic weights which deviate considerably from whole numbers. For example, chlorine has an atomic weight of 35.46; iron, an atomic weight of 55.84; etc.

Careful study has shown that most elements are really mixtures of two or more kinds of the element. Chlorine, for example, has been found to be made up of two kinds of chlorine, one of which has an atomic weight of 35 and the other of 37. In ordinary chlorine these two kinds are mixed in such a proportion as to give the average atomic weight of 35.46. The two kinds of chlorine have the same chemical properties, but the mass of their atoms is different (Fig. 20).

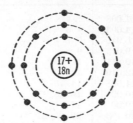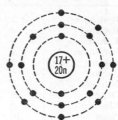

We note that the outer structure of the two atoms is exactly the same, seven electrons in the outer shell

Fig. 20. Isotopes of chlorine. Chlorine left has an atomic weight of 35; chlorine right has an atomic weight of 37.

of each, which accounts for the same chemical properties. The atomic number is the same for the two atoms; as a matter of fact, the only difference appears in the nucleus, which in the atom of atomic weight 35 has 18 neutrons and in the atom of atomic weight 37 has 20 neutrons. In reality we have the same element, chlorine, in both instances. Elements with the same atomic number but different atomic weights are termed *isotopes*. Thus ordinary chlorine is a mixture of two isotopes.

Isotopes of most of the chemical elements are known at the present time. Table 5 includes the stable isotopes of most of the elements. We may note that the number of isotopes of the elements is variable, from two isotopes in certain of the elements to ten isotopes in tin.

Measuring the mass of isotopes. Sir J. J. Thomson in studying the positive ray particles produced in a discharge tube between electrodes upon which a high potential was impressed, found that electrons emanating from the cathode hit molecules of gaseous substances and dislodged electrons, thus leaving positively charged gaseous particles. These positively charged particles formed in the rarefied gaseous region between the electrodes move with increasing velocity to the cathode. If the cathode is perforated, a beam of the positively charged particles passes through the cathode. This beam of positively charged particles will fog a photographic film. Because of its charged nature the beam may be deflected by magnetic and electrical fields. The magnitude of the deflection depends on various factors: strength of magnetic and electrical fields; the mass, charge, and velocity of the positive particles; and the dimensions of the apparatus. By keeping various factors constant, the mass of many positive particles may be determined.

When Thomson used neon in the discharge tube and evaluated the mass of the positive ray particles, he obtained two values for the mass of neon, 20 and 22,

TABLE 5

ISOTOPES OF ELEMENTS [1]

Element	Atomic Number	Atomic Weight	Mass of Isotopes
Hydrogen	1	1.008	1, 2
Helium	2	4.003	4, 3
Lithium	3	6.940	7, 6
Beryllium	4	9.013	9, 8
Boron	5	10.811	11, 10
Carbon	6	12.010	12, 13
Nitrogen	7	14.008	14, 15
Oxygen	8	16.0000	16, 18, 17
Fluorine	9	19.00	19
Neon	10	20.183	20, 22, 21
Sodium	11	22.997	23
Magnesium	12	24.32	24, 25, 26
Aluminum	13	26.97	27
Silicon	14	28.06	28, 29, 30
Phosphorus	15	30.98	31
Sulfur	16	32.066	32, 34, 33
Chlorine	17	35.457	35, 37
Argon	18	39.944	40, 36, 38
Potassium	19	39.096	39, 41, 40
Calcium	20	40.08	40, 44, 42, 43
Scandium	21	45.10	45
Titanium	22	47.90	48, 46, 47, 50, 49
Vanadium	23	50.95	51
Chromium	24	52.01	52, 53, 50, 54
Manganese	25	54.93	55
Iron	26	55.85	56, 54, 57, 58
Cobalt	27	58.94	59, 57
Nickel	28	58.69	58, 60, 62, 61, 64
Copper	29	63.54	63, 65
Zinc	30	65.38	64, 66, 68, 67, 70
Gallium	31	69.72	69, 71
Germanium	32	72.60	74, 72, 70, 73, 76
Arsenic	33	74.91	75
Selenium	34	78.96	80, 78, 76, 82, 77, 74
Bromine	35	79.916	79, 81
Krypton	36	83.7	84, 86, 82, 83, 80, 78
Rubidium	37	85.48	85, 87
Strontium	38	87.63	88, 86, 87, 84
Yttrium	39	88.92	89
Zirconium	40	91.22	90, 92, 94, 91, 96
Niobium	41	92.91	93
Molybdenum	42	95.95	98, 96, 95, 92, 94, 100, 97
Ruthenium	44	101.7	102, 101, 104, 100, 99, 96
Rhodium	45	102.91	103, 101
Palladium	46	106.7	106, 108, 105, 110, 104, 102
Silver	47	107.880	107, 109
Cadmium	48	112.41	114, 112, 110, 111, 113, 116, 106, 108
Indium	49	114.76	115, 113
Tin	50	118.70	120, 118, 116, 119, 117, 124, 122, 112, 114, 115

[1] Isotopes are listed according to decreasing abundance, the most abundant isotope is listed first. Their atomic masses are based on the most abundant oxygen isotope taken as 16. Atomic weights are based on the average oxygen atom taken as 16.

Table 5 (*Continued*)

Element	Atomic Number	Atomic Weight	Mass of Isotopes
Antimony	51	121.76	121, 123
Tellurium	52	127.61	130, 128, 126, 125, 124, 122, 123, 120
Iodine	53	126.92	127
Xenon	54	131.3	132, 129, 131, 134, 136, 130, 128, 124, 126
Cesium	55	132.91	133
Barium	56	137.36	138, 137, 136, 135, 134, 130, 132
Lanthanum	57	138.92	139
Cerium	58	140.13	140, 142, 138, 136
Praseodymium	59	140.92	141
Neodymium	60	144.27	142, 144, 146, 143, 145, 148, 150
Samarium	62	150.43	152, 154, 147, 149, 148, 150, 144
Europium	63	152.0	151, 153
Gadolinium	64	156.9	156, 158, 155, 157, 160
Terbium	65	158.2	159
Dysprosium	66	162.46	164, 163, 162, 161
Holmium	67	164.94	165
Erbium	68	167.2	166, 168, 167, 170
Thulium	69	169.4	169
Ytterbium	70	173.04	174, 172, 173, 176, 171
Lutetium	71	174.99	175
Hafnium	72	178.6	180, 178, 177, 179, 176
Tantalum	73	180.88	181
Wolfram	74	183.92	184, 186, 182, 183, 180
Rhenium	75	186.31	187, 185
Osmium	76	190.2	192, 190, 189, 188, 187, 186, 184
Iridium	77	192.1	193, 191
Platinum	78	195.23	195, 194, 196, 198, 192
Gold	79	197.2	197
Mercury	80	200.61	202, 200, 199, 201, 198, 204, 196
Thallium	81	204.39	205, 203
Lead	82	207.21	208, 206, 207, 204
Bismuth	83	209.00	209
Thorium	90	232.12	232
Uranium	92	238.07	238, 235

rather than 20.2, its atomic weight. The explanation is fairly obvious. There are two kinds of neon atoms and the two kinds are mixed together in ordinary samples of neon; moreover there is enough more of the lighter variety so that the gravimetrically determined atomic weight of naturally occurring neon is 20.2. These experimentally obtained data are good proof of the existence of isotopes.

The isotopic nature of most elements has been proved by F. W. Aston, who used a modified Thomson apparatus. It was comparatively easy to produce positive particle rays of gaseous elements by electron bombardment in a discharge tube, which rays could be evaluated as to mass by studying the magnitude of their deflection in a magnetic or electrical field. In the case of some elements, such as most metals of low vapor pressure, the anode was made of platinum with a small depression in it containing some salt of the difficultly volatile element. Electrons from the cathode migrated to the heated platinum anode and metal ions from the salt were given off as positive or anode rays, the deflection of which could be studied and mass determined, for particles having a constant mass-to-charge ratio are focused at the same point on a photographic plate. Aston's apparatus is known as the mass spectrograph. (See Fig. 21.)

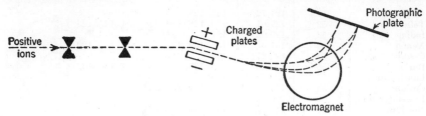

Fig. 21. Mass spectrograph.

The packing effect. As a result of investigation with the mass spectrograph, it was at first believed that the masses of isotopes were whole numbers compared to oxygen of atomic weight 16. Exacting determinations of isotopic weights have since shown however that they are not quite whole numbers; for example H = 1.00778, He = 4.002, N = 14.008, C = 12.0026. If these atoms are made up of neutrons, electrons, and protons, how can one account for the fact their masses are not multiples of 1.00778 which would be the mass of an electron-proton hydrogen atom? He = 4.002 in mass, but $4 \times 1.00778 =$ 4.03112. The mass loss, $4.03112 - 4.002 = .02912$, must mean that some mass is converted into energy as electrons, protons, neutrons pack themselves into He atoms. Likewise in the heavier atoms some mass-to-energy change must be concomitant with formation of the atoms from subatomic units. This mass loss over and above the summation of subatomic particle masses in the formation of atoms is known as the *packing effect.*

How atoms combine. The theory of atomic structure gives us an explanation for the manner in which atoms combine. The valence electrons in the atom, that is, those electrons present in the outermost orbit, seem to be the determining factors in chemical combination. We learned that some atoms tend to give up electrons, while others tend to take up electrons. It would seem that chemical combination would most likely take place between atoms in which electrons could be given up by one atom and taken up by another. We would hardly expect combination to take place between atoms both of which tend to take up electrons; neither should we expect reaction to take place between atoms which tend to give up electrons. These suppositions based on the theory of atomic structure are borne out by actual fact. Metals which tend to give up electrons show little tendency to combine with one another. On the other hand, metals do readily combine with elements (nonmetals) which will take up electrons. For example, since the sodium atom readily gives up an electron and a chlorine atom readily accepts an electron, we might expect sodium and chlorine to combine chemically. Such is the case with the formation of the compound sodium chloride. The change may be represented diagram-

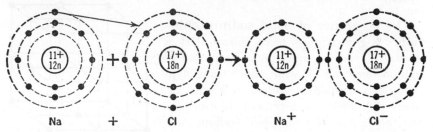

Na + Cl Na^+ Cl^-

Fig. 22. In the formation of the ionic compound, sodium chloride, an electron is transferred from the sodium atom to the chlorine atom.

matically as in Figure 22. One electron is transferred from the sodium atom to the outer orbit of the chlorine atom. In the compound sodium chloride thus formed, the two ions, Na^+ and Cl^-, are present. Such a compound in which ions exist is said to be *ionic* or *electrovalent*. The transfer of electrons from one atom to another which results in the formation of ions is termed *electrovalence*.

The combination of one atom of magnesium with two atoms of chlorine to form the compound magnesium chloride, $MgCl_2$, may be

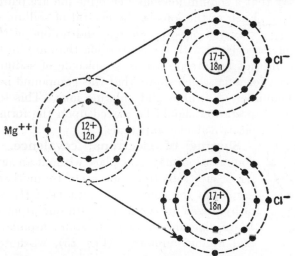

Fig. 23. Magnesium chloride is an electrovalent compound; two electrons are transferred from a magnesium atom to two atoms of chlorine, resulting in the formation of magnesium and chlorine ions.

represented diagrammatically as in Figure 23. Each of the chlorine atoms takes up one of the two electrons from the magnesium atom. The resulting compound is electrovalent or ionic and is composed of magnesium and chlorine ions in the ratio of one to two.

The structure of solid sodium chloride. X-ray studies have shown that a crystal of sodium chloride is composed of sodium ions and chlorine ions arranged in an orderly fashion as shown in Figure 24, where the black dots represent chlorine ions and the light circles represent sodium ions. These ions are definitely oriented in relation to one another. If a sodium ion occupies the center of a cube, then a chlorine ion appears in the center of each of the six faces

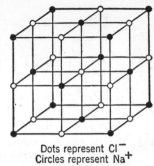

Dots represent Cl⁻
Circles represent Na⁺

Fig. 24. Structure of NaCl.

of the cube. All electrovalent compounds show a similar orientation of ions in the crystalline solid. When the solid is dissolved in water, the ions simply break away from the surface of the crystal and pass into the solution, where they are relatively widely separated and act as independent units.

It is incorrect to speak of a molecule of solid sodium chloride, since we cannot say that a sodium ion and a chlorine ion are paired to form a unit particle. Each of the ions in the crystal of sodium chloride is surrounded by six ions of opposite charge, and no one of the six ions is more closely associated with the central ion than any of the others. "NaCl" should not be interpreted as a molecule of sodium chloride but rather as a formula which shows that this compound is composed of an equal number of sodium and chlorine ions. This same interpretation should be placed upon the formulas of all electrovalent compounds.

Fig. 25. The carbon atom.

Sharing of electrons; covalence. Chemical combination may take place without an actual transfer of electrons from one atom to another. For example, in the compound methane, CH_4, four atoms of hydrogen are combined with one atom of carbon. If we diagram the carbon atom, atomic weight 12 and atomic number 6 (Fig. 25), we note that the outer orbit contains four electrons. We might assume that carbon would either take up or give up four electrons to reach a stable configuration. Actually the carbon atom does neither. Compounds of carbon are formed by a *sharing* of electrons. In the compound CH_4, each of the four hydrogen atoms shares its one electron with the carbon atom, while the carbon atom in turn shares its four electrons with the four hydrogen atoms (Fig. 26). No actual transfer of electrons takes place in this process, thus the compound is not ionic but molecular. Compounds formed by such a sharing process are termed *covalent* compounds.

We may simplify Figure 26 by representing the compound CH$_4$ as

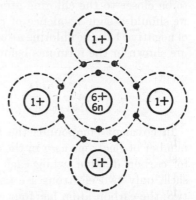

$$\begin{matrix} & H & \\ & \overset{\times}{\underset{\cdot}{\cdot}} & \\ H & \overset{\cdot}{\times} C \overset{\times}{\cdot} & H \\ & \overset{\cdot}{\underset{\times}{\cdot}} & \\ & H & \end{matrix}$$

Fig. 26. The methane, CH$_4$, molecule. Each of the four hydrogen atoms shares a pair of electrons with the carbon atom.

Only the outer structure of the atoms is shown; each of the dots represents one electron furnished by the carbon atom and each × represents an electron belonging to each of the four hydrogen atoms. A total of eight electrons surrounds the atom of carbon, which effectively fills its quota of eight electrons in the outer shell. Also each hydrogen atom now has two electrons, which is a stable configuration for the first orbit. In this compound four *pairs* of electrons have been shared between the carbon and hydrogen atoms. The valence of the carbon is said to be four, each pair of electrons representing one unit or bond of covalence.

Positive and negative valence loses much of its significance when applied to covalent compounds. In the compound CH$_4$, for example, can we assign a positive or negative character to the valence of four? If we do assign a positive value to the valence of carbon, +4, this would indicate that four electrons have been given up by the carbon atom. This is hardly true, since in the sharing process the carbon retains a share or interest in these four electrons. On the other hand, if we assign a negative valence to the carbon atom, −4, we would indicate that four electrons are taken up by the carbon atom and lost by the hydrogen atoms. This is hardly true either, as the sharing of electrons between the carbon atom and hydrogen atoms is a mutual sharing; each atom retains an interest in the electrons which it furnishes to the sharing process.

It does seem likely, however, that in such covalent compounds the pair of shared electrons lie closer to one atom than to the other. In the compound CH$_4$, it appears that the pairs of electrons are somewhat closer to the carbon atom than to the hydrogen atoms. On this basis, then, there appears to be some justification for saying that the valence of carbon is -4 rather than $+4$ and that the valence of hydrogen is $+1$. In the compound CCl_4, the pairs of electrons appear to be closer to the chlorine atoms than to the carbon atom, and thus we should assign a valence of positive 4 to the carbon and a valence of negative 1 to the chlorine atom. Other typical examples of covalence are shown in the formulas below:

$$O : \overset{..}{\underset{..}{\times}} C \overset{..}{\underset{..}{\times}} : O$$

carbon dioxide

$$: \overset{..}{\underset{..}{Cl}} : $$
$$: Cl \overset{\times \cdot}{\underset{\times \times}{P}} \overset{..}{\underset{..}{Cl}} :$$

phosphorus trichloride

In covalent compounds the valence of an element is taken as the number of electrons *used* in the sharing process. In the above diagram for carbon dioxide, while each oxygen has six electrons in its outer shell, only two electrons are used, therefore the valence of oxygen is two; the carbon atom has four electrons all of which are shared, therefore its valence is four. Likewise in the second diagram, while phosphorus has five electrons, only three are used; while each chlorine atom has seven electrons, only one is used. Therefore the valence of phosphorus and chlorine are respectively three and one.

In some instances electrons may be shared between two or more atoms of the same element. For example, two chlorine atoms combine to form a molecule of chlorine by a mutual sharing of electrons (Fig. 27). Other similar cases are O_2, H_2, Br_2, etc.

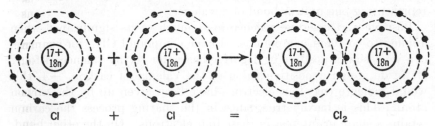

Fig. 27. Two chlorine atoms share a pair of electrons to form a molecule of chlorine.

Molecular weights and formula weights. The term *molecule* has a real significance when applied to covalent compounds, and we may properly refer to a molecular weight of the compound (weight of a molecule). However, the term *molecule* has no significance when applied to electrovalent compounds, since the parts of an ionic compound act as independent units. It follows that molecular weight would lose its meaning if applied to compounds composed of ions.

Hence we may adopt the term *formula weight* in referring to electrovalent compounds. Thus 2 NaCl would stand for two formula weights of sodium chloride; 6 $Al_2(SO_4)_3$ would stand for six formula weights of aluminum sulfate. The formula weight would be obtained by adding up the atomic weights of the atoms appearing in the formula. We may frequently refer also to formula weights of covalent compounds instead of molecular weights. We shall term the formula weight of a substance expressed in grams as a *gram formula weight*. Thus a gram formula weight of HCl would be 36.5 grams, a gram formula weight of NaCl would be 58.5 grams, etc.

EXERCISES

1. Explain the laws of chemical change by means of the assumptions of Dalton's atomic theory.
2. Distinguish clearly between an atom and a molecule of an element.
3. Define the terms; electron; proton; neutron; nucleus; valence; electrovalence; covalence; ion; ionic compound, isotope
4. Diagram the atoms of Be, Mg, and Ca. Would you expect these elements to exhibit similar chemical properties? Explain.
5. What determines whether an atom will tend to lose or gain electrons?
6. From our knowledge of modern atomic structure, would you expect the elements neon and argon to be active or inactive elements? Explain.
7. Show diagrammatically the formation of the ionic compound, $CaCl_2$.
8. Carbon disulfide (CS_2) is a covalent compound. Show diagrammatically its formation. How many pairs of electrons are shared?
9. Explain the deviation of the atomic weights of elements from whole numbers.
10. From a standpoint of atomic structure, how do metals differ from nonmetals?
11. How does an ion differ from an atom?
12. What is the relationship of the atomic weight of an element to the number of protons and neutrons in its atom?
13. Three isotopes of hydrogen are known. Diagram atoms of these three isotopes. How do they differ from one another?
14. Show by an electronic configuration (outer shell only) the arrangement of electrons in the following compounds, all of which are covalent: H_3PO_3; PCl_3; CH_2Cl_2; H_2S.
15. Draw diagrammatic representations of Li^+, K^+, Ca^{++}, Al^{+++}, F^-, S^{--}.

REFERENCES

K. T. Compton, "The Electron, Its Intellectual and Social Significance," *Science*, **85**, 27 (1937).

R. A. Millikan, *The Electron, Its Isolation and Measurement and the Determination of Some of Its Properties*, University of Chicago Press, 1928.

———, *Electrons (+ and —), Protons, Photons, Neutrons, and Cosmic Rays*, University of Chicago Press, 1935.

K. K. Darrow, "Nuclear Chemistry," *J. Chem. Ed.* **12**, 76 (1935).

A. H. Shadduck, "The Neutron," *ibid.* **13**, 303 (1936).

Wm. F. Kieffer, "The Use of Electronic Structure in Interpreting Chemical Reactions," *ibid.* **25**, 537 (1948).

IV

The Periodic Classification of the Elements

Soon after Dalton's atomic theory had received wide recognition, many attempts were made to find a relationship between atomic weights and the chemical properties of the elements. It was well known that some elements were very similar to others in chemical properties, for example, chlorine, bromine, and iodine were very much alike in their chemical conduct; sodium and potassium behaved similarly, etc. It appeared that possibly the elements could be grouped together in families and that this grouping might depend upon some property of the elements, common to all of them. Since the atomic weight is a characteristic property of all of the elements, attempts were made to correlate atomic weights with the grouping of elements.

Döbereiner, in 1829, arranged several of the elements which were similar in chemical properties in groups of three (triads) and showed that the atomic weight of one was approximately the mean of the other two. For example, chlorine (35), bromine (80), and iodine (127) constituted one such group. Br with an atomic weight of 80 is approximately the mean of the atomic weights of Cl and I, $i.e.$, $(35 + 127)/2 = 162/2 = 81$. Other "triads" of Döbereiner were:

Ca	40	S	32
Sr	87	Se	79
Ba	137	Te	127

Newlands, an English scientist, in 1863 pointed out that if the elements were arranged in order of increasing atomic weights, the eighth element was similar in chemical properties to the first, the ninth similar to the second, etc., much like the octaves in music. Newlands' "law of octaves" did not hold for elements of higher atomic weights where the interval between elements of similar properties seemed to be much greater than seven; also several elements when placed according to Newlands' arrangement showed great dissimilarities to those elements with which a close similarity would be expected. So many discrepancies in the arrangement raised grave doubts as to the validity of Newlands' proposal, so much so that his idea was received with much ridicule and it was many years before the significance of his discovery was appreciated.

In 1869, the Russian chemist, Mendeléeff, extended Newlands' ideas and was able to show a definite relationship between atomic weights and chemical properties. Most of the errors inherent in Newlands' arrangement were satisfactorily corrected. Mendeléeff arranged the elements in order of increasing atomic weights and pointed out a recurrence of properties at very definite intervals or periods. These intervals were not always of the same length, but in each interval a gradual change in properties of the elements from the beginning to the end of the interval was apparent. On the basis of this arrangement, Mendeléeff stated that *the properties of the elements are periodic functions of their atomic weights.* Since Mendeléeff's time the periodic classification has undergone some modification but the arrangement remains basically unchanged. It is now known that the atomic number is a more fundamental property of an element than its atomic weight; hence the modern periodic law is stated: *The properties of the elements are periodic functions of their atomic numbers.*

The periodic table. Let us arrange the elements as did Mendeléeff, except that we shall use atomic numbers instead of atomic weights and include the inert elements, which were unknown when Mendeléeff prepared his table. Omitting for the present the two lightest elements, hydrogen and helium, with atomic numbers of 1 and 2 respectively, we shall place in a horizontal row elements of atomic numbers 3 to 19 in order of increasing atomic numbers:

Element	Li	Be	B	C	N	O	F	Ne	Na	Mg	Al	Si	P	S	Cl	A	K
At. No.	3	4	5	6	7	8	9	10	11	12	13	14	15	16	17	18	19

As we progress from lithium to fluorine, the properties of the elements change gradually from the very active metal lithium to the very active nonmetal fluorine. Neon, atomic number 10, which follows fluorine, is very inert or inactive and does not seem to fit logically in the arrangement next to the very active fluorine; however, we shall soon explain this seeming irregularity on the basis of modern atomic structure. Sodium, which follows neon, is a very active metal and similar to lithium; hence we may start a second horizontal row by placing sodium directly under Li. Magnesium then comes next and is placed under beryllium. In chemical conduct, magnesium is very similar to beryllium. Continuing this arrangement, aluminum falls below boron, silicon below carbon, etc. When we reach potassium, we find an element very similar to lithium and sodium, hence we shall start a third horizontal row by placing K under Na. Our arrangement then assumes the form:

Li	Be	B	C	N	O	F	Ne
Na	Mg	Al	Si	P	S	Cl	A
K							

At definite intervals we are finding a recurrence of properties; the elements falling in the same vertical column have very similar properties.

Hydrogen and helium may now be fitted into the scheme. Since He is an inert gas like neon and argon it will be placed above these two elements. Hydrogen is more difficult to place as it has few similarities to other elements. Although it does not have the properties of an active metal, it does exhibit a valence of 1, and may therefore be placed above sodium which also exhibits a valence of 1. If we number the horizontal and vertical rows, our arrangement now becomes:

	I	II	III	IV	V	VI	VII	VIII
1.	H							He
2.	Li	Be	B	C	N	O	F	Ne
3.	Na	Mg	Al	Si	P	S	Cl	A
4.	K	..	..	..	.	.	..	..

The horizontal rows. In the fourth horizontal row complications begin to appear and it is necessary to modify our scheme somewhat. After potassium it is necessary to place eighteen elements in the arrangement before finding a recurrence of the properties of potassium. Some of the other elements following potassium show considerable differences in properties from the elements which appear just above them, and we are forced to observe dissimilarities as well as similarities in the vertical groups. Thus chromium differs considerably from sulfur and manganese is very unlike chlorine. Referring now to the complete periodic arrangement shown in Figure 28, these elements are placed to one side of the row to indicate the dissimilarity. After manganese come the elements iron, cobalt, and nickel. Since these latter three elements are very similar to one another in properties, but unlike argon, they are placed together but displaced to the right of argon in Group VIII. Copper follows nickel, and since it is metallic and exhibits a valence of one like sodium and potassium, it is placed in Group I with these metals. However, it is displaced to the right, since it does differ considerably in many properties from both sodium and potassium. Similarly, the elements which follow copper are dis-

Fig. 28. The periodic table, short form.

Period	I A	I B	II A	II B	III A	III B	IV A	IV B	V A	V B	VI A	VI B	VII A	VII B	VIII
1	1 H 1.0080														2 He 4.003
2	3 Li 6.940		4 Be 9.02		5 B 10.82		6 C 12.010		7 N 14.008		8 O 16.0000		9 F 19.00		10 Ne 20.183
3	11 Na 22.997		12 Mg 24.32		13 Al 26.97		14 Si 28.06		15 P 30.98		16 S 32.066		17 Cl 35.457		18 A 39.944
4a	19 K 39.096		20 Ca 40.08			21 Sc 45.10		22 Ti 47.90		23 V 50.95		24 Cr 52.01		25 Mn 54.93	26 Fe 55.85 · 27 Co 58.94 · 28 Ni 58.69
4b		29 Cu 63.54		30 Zn 65.38	31 Ga 69.72		32 Ge 72.60		33 As 74.91		34 Se 78.96		35 Br 79.916		36 Kr 83.7
5a	37 Rb 85.48		38 Sr 87.63			39 Y 88.92		40 Zr 91.22		41 Nb 92.91		42 Mo 95.95		43 Tc 99	44 Ru 101.7 · 45 Rh 102.91 · 46 Pd 106.7
5b		47 Ag 107.880		48 Cd 112.41	49 In 114.76		50 Sn 118.70		51 Sb 121.76		52 Te 127.61		53 I 126.92		54 Xe 131.3
6a	55 Cs 132.91		56 Ba 137.36			57 - 71 *		72 Hf 178.6		73 Ta 180.88		74 W 183.92		75 Re 186.31	76 Os 190.2 · 77 Ir 193.1 · 78 Pt 195.23
6b		79 Au 197.2		80 Hg 200.61	81 Tl 204.39		82 Pb 207.21		83 Bi 209.00		84 Po 210		85 At 211		86 Rn 222
7	87 Fr 223		88 Ra 226.05			89 - 98 **									

* Rare Earths

57 La 138.92	58 Ce 140.13	59 Pr 140.92	60 Nd 144.27	61 Pm 147	62 Sm 150.43	63 Eu 152.0	64 Gd 156.9	65 Tb 159.2	66 Dy 162.46	67 Ho 164.94	68 Er 167.2	69 Tm 169.4	70 Yb 173.04	71 Lu 174.99

** Radioactive Rare Earths

89 Ac 227	90 Th 232.12	91 Pa 231	92 U 238.07	93 Np 237	94 Pu 239	95 Am 243	96 Cm 245	97 Bk 245	98 Cf 246

placed in each of the vertical columns. Each vertical column is now resolved into two columns and while there are similarities between the two columns in any vertical row of elements, there are also pronounced dissimilarities.

The horizontal rows are called *periods* and are numbered 1, 2, 3, etc. The first three rows are termed *short periods,* since they contain only eight elements each (period 1 contains only the two elements hydrogen and helium). The fourth period is a *long period,* since it is made up of both the fourth and fifth horizontal rows which contain a total of eighteen elements. These two rows are considered as a single period, since eighteen elements must be placed in the arrangement before coming to the next element similar to lithium, sodium, and potassium, namely rubidium. After leaving the fourth period, eighteen more elements must be placed before coming to cesium, which is similar to lithium, sodium, potassium, and rubidium. These eighteen elements constitute another long period. This period is followed by still another long period of thirty-two elements.

The periodic table is a continuous arrangement and we should visualize it as being placed on a cylinder rather than on a plane. The elements then would assume positions as on a spiral, with elements of similar properties appearing in the same vertical line.

The vertical rows. The vertical rows are called groups and are numbered from I to VIII. Each group is divided into two subgroups or families, one of which is called the *A* series and the other the *B* series. Thus in Group I, lithium, sodium, potassium, rubidium, and cesium constitute the *A* series; copper, silver, and gold constitute the *B* series. Similarly in Group II, beryllium, magnesium, calcium, strontium, barium, and radium make up the *A* series; zinc, cadmium, and mercury make up the *B* series, etc. The elements present in either the *A* or *B* series of one of the groups are often spoken of as a family of elements. Thus in Group I, the *A* series is referred to as the alkali family of metals; in Group II, the *A* series is known as the alkaline earth family; in Group VII, fluorine, chlorine, bromine, and iodine are known as the halogen family, etc. The *A* series elements are referred to as *representative* or *main group* elements, and the *B* series as *transition* or *subgroup* elements.

The elements within either series of any one of the groups are very similar in chemical properties. Thus in series *A* of Group I, lithium, sodium, potassium, rubidium, and cesium exhibit marked similarities in properties. These elements are all very active metals, react vigorously with cold water, form strong bases, and have a characteristic valence of $+1$. The alkaline earth metals comprising magnesium, calcium, strontium, and barium likewise are similar chemically. The members of this group are distinctly metallic, are very active, and exhibit a valence of $+2$. The halogens are a family of very active nonmetals, with a characteristic valence of -1, etc.

The periodic table and modern atomic structure. It is probably evident by this time that the periodic classification of the elements is intimately related to their atomic structures. The significance of the number of elements appearing in the short periods, 2 and 8, and the number in the long periods, 18 and 32, is now apparent. These same numbers represented the maximum number of electrons in the various orbits of the atom.

The number of the group in the periodic table corresponds to the maximum number of electrons in the valence orbit of the atoms appearing in that group. Since eight is the maximum number of electrons in the valence orbit, eight is the maximum number of groups.

The rare gases Ne, A, etc., of Group VIII (except He with a stable configuration of two) have a maximum of eight electrons in their outer orbits and therefore would be expected to be inert elements. The great activity of the nonmetals, chlorine, bromine, etc. (Group VIIA) on one side of the inert gases and the equally great activity of the alkali metals, Na, K, etc. (Group IA) on the other side is readily explained by the tendency to take up or give up an electron. The seeming irregularity of inert elements appearing between two active groups thus disappears.

Other seeming irregularities in the periodic arrangement may likewise be explained with the aid of modern atomic theory although many of them are beyond the scope of this book. For example, the question might be asked: Why do the elements Fe, Co, Ni, which are much alike in properties, directly follow one another in the table? It will be recalled that elements of higher atomic weights may have incomplete inner shells of electrons (see Table 4). The inner shell of such an atom may add an electron while retaining the same number of electrons in the outer shell; this would mean another element with almost identical chemical properties. Thus the electronic configurations of Fe, Co, Ni are 2, 8, 14, 2; 2, 8, 15, 2; 2, 8, 16, 2, respectively. While the outer shell in each case is the same, thereby accounting for similar properties, the third orbit differs by one electron in each instance and would account for slight differences in properties. It is evident that the atomic numbers of Fe, Co, and Ni are respectively 26, 27, 28 and therefore these elements, although much alike chemically, should directly follow one another in the periodic arrangement. Many other examples could be cited in which incompleted inner orbits of atoms would account for what appears to be an irregularity.

Long form periodic table. Many modifications of the Mendeléeff periodic chart have been proposed — one of the most useful arrangements is shown in Figure 28x, in which each horizontal period begins with an alkali metal (except that the first period starts with hydrogen) and ends with an inert gas with a stable electronic structure, thus making a total of eighteen vertical groups instead of eight. This arrangement does away with subgroups and each family of similar elements occupies a separate vertical column. The two short periods of eight elements each contain the representative or main group elements and these groups are signified by the numbers I*A*, II*A*, etc. Elements which appeared as subgroups in the eight column chart of Mendeléeff appear in separate groups designated by I*B*, II*B*, etc. Three of the groups, headed by Fe, Co, Ni, are included as VIII*B* elements. This is justified because of the close similarity in properties of these triads.

The *B* groups elements, *i.e.*, those fitting into the chart between Groups II*A* and III*A*, are termed *transition* elements. These elements have essentially the same outer configuration or valence shell, *i.e.*, one or two electrons, but the next inner shell contains different numbers of electrons and this incomplete shell gives rise to differences in properties of the transition elements. For example, after calcium in Group II*A*, electrons start to fill in the incomplete third orbit (capacity 18) while the fourth or outer orbit remains essentially unchanged; Sc has 9 electrons in the third orbit, Ti has 10, V has 11, etc. Added electrons continue to fill in this orbit until a stable configuration of 18 is reached. After Zn, electrons add to the outer shell — Ga with 3, Ge with 4, etc.

After Ba in the arrangement, electrons start filling the 4th orbit from 18 to 32 electrons (capacity 32). These elements, atomic numbers 57–71, constitute a transition series within a transition series and are referred to as the *lanthanide* series or *rare earth* series. A second rare earth series, called the *actinide* series starts after Ra. These series are placed below the main table.

From the chart it may be noted that four different classes of elements may be listed as follows:

1. Those in which all orbits have stable configurations[1] of electrons. These include the rare gases, He, Ne, A, etc.
2. Those in which all orbits except the outermost have stable configurations. The main groups or *A* groups of elements. Electrons are filling outer orbit.

[1] A stable configuration means 8 or 18 electrons (except first orbit which has two electrons).

Fig. 28x. The periodic table, long form.

IA	IIA	IIIB	IVB	VB	VIB	VIIB	VIIIB			IB	IIB	IIIA	IVA	VA	VIA	VIIA	VIIIA
1 H 1.0080																	2 He 4.003
3 Li 6.940	4 Be 9.013											5 B 10.82	6 C 12.010	7 N 14.008	8 O 16.0000	9 F 19.00	10 Ne 20.183
11 Na 22.997	12 Mg 24.32											13 Al 26.98	14 Si 28.09	15 P 30.975	16 S 32.066	17 Cl 35.457	18 A 39.944
19 K 39.00	20 Ca 40.08	21 Sc ~4.96	22 Ti 47.90	23 V 50.95	24 Cr 52.01	25 Mn 54.93	26 Fe 55.85	27 Co 58.94	28 Ni 58.69	29 Cu 63.54	30 Zn 65.38	31 Ga 69.72	32 Ge 72.60	33 As 74.91	34 Se 78.96	35 Br 79.916	36 Kr 83.80
37 Rb 85.48	38 Sr 87.63	39 Y 88.92	40 Zr 91.22	41 Nb 92.91	42 Mo 95.95	43 Tc [99]	44 Ru 101.7	45 Rh 102.91	46 Pd 106.7	47 Ag 107.880	48 Cd 112.41	49 In 114.76	50 Sn 118.70	51 Sb 121.76	52 Te 127.61	53 I 126.91	54 Xe 131.3
55 Cs 132.91	56 Ba 137.36	57-71 Rare Earths	72 Hf 178.6	73 Ta 180.88	74 W 183.92	75 Re 186.31	76 Os 190.2	77 Ir 193.1	78 Pt 195.23	79 Au 197.2	80 Hg 200.61	81 Tl 204.39	82 Pb 207.21	83 Bi 209.00	84 Po 210	85 At [210]	86 Rn 222
87 Fr [223]	88 Ra 226.05	89-98 Radioactive Rare Earths	39-98														

Rare Earths:

57 La 138.92	58 Ce 140.13	59 Pr 140.92	60 Nd 144.27	61 Pm [145]	62 Sm 150.43	63 Eu 152.0	64 Gd 156.9	65 Tb 159.2	66 Dy 162.46	67 Ho 164.94	68 Er 167.2	69 Tm 169.4	70 Yb 173.04	71 Lu 174.99

Radioactive Rare Earths:

89 Ac [227]	90 Th 232.12	91 Pa 231	92 U 238.07	93 Np [237]	94 Pu 239	95 Am [243]	96 Cm [245]	97 Bk [245]	98 Cf [246]	99	100

3. Those in which all orbits except the two outermost have stable configurations. The subgroups or *B* groups of elements. Electrons are filling from 8 to 18, into next to outermost shell.

4. Those in which all orbits except the three outermost have stable configurations. The rare earth elements, lanthanide and actinide series. Electrons are filling from 18 to 32 into second from outermost shell.

Valence and the periodic table. Elements within any group exhibit a characteristic valence. For the *A* series of elements the number of the group corresponds to the number of electrons in the outermost orbit, and hence we may predict the valence of a particular element from its position in the table. The alkali metals of Group I*A* exhibit a valence of +1 since the atoms tend to lose the one electron in the outer orbit. The halogens of Group VII*A* exhibit a characteristic valence of −1, since one electron is readily taken up, which added to the seven already present in the outer orbit gives a stable configuration of eight. On the same basis, elements of Group III*A* would be expected to exhibit a characteristic valence of +3, those of Group VI*A* a valence of −2, etc.

The rare gases of Group VIII*A* consisting of He, Ne, A, etc., each of which has a stable outer configuration of electrons, would not be expected to give up or take up electrons and hence would have a zero valence. The inert or inactive characteristics of these elements is explained on this basis.

Although valences as measured by the loss or gain of electrons are quite clear cut for the *A* series of elements, they are much less well defined for the transition elements (*B* series). In the *A* series the outer orbit alone determines valence characteristics, while with the *B* series (in which there is at least one incomplete inner orbit) the incomplete orbit contributes also to valence characteristics. Most of the transition elements have one or two electrons in the outer shell. It appears that one or two electrons from an incomplete inner orbit may be lost in chemical change and these added to the one or two in the outer orbit gives rise to several possibilities of valence among the transition elements or even variable valences for some given elements. For example, the iron atom with the normal configuration 2, 8, 14, 2 may exhibit a valence of +2 by loss of the two outer electrons or a valence of +3 when an additional electron is lost from the incomplete third orbit.

Differences in properties of elements within families. Although the elements in a given group show marked similarities in chemical properties, a gradual change in properties takes place as we proceed from the elements of lower atomic weight to those of higher atomic weight. For example, the alkali group of metals except lithium gradually increases in activity with increasing atomic weight. Sodium is the least active of the group, followed by potassium, rubidium, and cesium, the latter of which is the most active of the metals. The members of the group are very much like one another, however, in that all are quite active.

The fact that the members of a given family do not possess exactly the same chemical properties, even though from the standpoint of atomic structure the outermost orbits contain the same number of electrons, is explained on the basis that the internal configuration will have some effect, though usually slight, on the properties of the atom.

The halogens in Group VIIA are very active nonmetals, but again we may observe a gradual change in activity from fluorine at the top of the group to iodine at the lower part. Fluorine is the most active and iodine is the least active; hence activity decreases as the atomic weights increase. This is exactly opposite to the observation with the metals of the alkali group.

In Group VA we may also observe a gradual change in properties from top to bottom. Nitrogen at the top is a typical nonmetal, while bismuth at the bottom is usually classed as a metallic element. The elements in between exhibit more marked metallic than nonmetallic properties as the atomic weight increases.

It is interesting that modern atomic theory will explain the slight differences in properties of elements within a given family as well as pronounced differences in properties of elements in different families. How this is done in part is explained in the next section.

Physical and chemical behavior of elements. Although as yet the student is not familiar with the properties of specific elements, it is appropriate to point out a few generalizations which can be made in relating chemical and physical behavior of atoms to certain fundamental properties.

One of the most important properties of an atom which influences its behavior is its *size*. We would expect that as shells are added in the structure of atoms, the size would increase, and this is true. In the periodic classification we may note that the elements in a given period (horizontal row) have the same number of shells, *i.e.*, one shell for period 1 elements H and He, two shells for period 2 elements, etc. As a new period is started a shell is added to the structure. It is apparent then that the vertical columns which represent families of elements will show a gradual increase in size in going from top to bottom as electron shells are added. Thus Fr would be the biggest atom of Group IA, Ra the largest of Group IIA, etc.

The change in size of atoms in a given period (horizontal row) is somewhat less obvious. In progressing from the left-hand side to the right-hand side in a given period, the atoms gradually decrease in size, *e.g.*, the sodium atom in Group I*A* is larger than the magnesium atom in Group II*A*, and the latter atom in turn is larger than the aluminum atom in Group III*A*. The explanation of this decrease in size is as follows: As the atomic number increases, the nuclear charge increases and this increased nuclear charge attracts the electrons in the shells more forcibly, pulling the shells in closer to the nucleus and thus shrinking the atom in size. Figure 28xx shows diagrammatically the relative sizes of atoms and ions.

On the basis of these considerations, atoms of Group I*A* elements, the alkali metals, are the largest. This would in part account for their lightness or low density. Group II*A* elements would possess a somewhat larger density because the atoms are somewhat smaller. In progressing from top to bottom in a given family the density increases since the atomic weight increases faster than atomic size. Hence the heavier elements would appear toward the bottom of the table.

Another important property in determining chemical behavior of an atom is the ease of removal of electrons from it (which can be measured as an *ionization potential*) or the *electron affinity* (its tendency to add electrons). Atoms of elements in Group I*A* readily give up an electron and are said to be very active because of this tendency. Likewise elements of Group VII*A* readily accept electrons and are very active. The former constitute a group of the most active metals, the latter a group of the most active nonmetals.

As the tendency to give up electrons becomes less in going from left to right in the table, the metals become less active; Group II*A* metals are less active than Group I*A*, and in turn Group III*A* metals are less active than those of Group II*A*. When we reach a point toward the middle of the table where electrons are more readily accepted than given up and the element is more nonmetallic in properties, the activity increases up to the halogen family, Group VII*A*. In a given period, the activity of metallic elements gradually decreases and the activity of nonmetallic elements gradually increases, *e.g.*, Mg is less active than Na but more active than Al; S is more active than P but less active than Cl. This is reasonable because we would expect Na with only one electron to lose it more easily than we would expect Mg to lose 2 electrons, since after one electron is taken away it would be more difficult to remove a second one because of the increased attraction of the nucleus for the remaining electrons. Mg in turn should be able to give up two electrons more readily than Al to give up three.

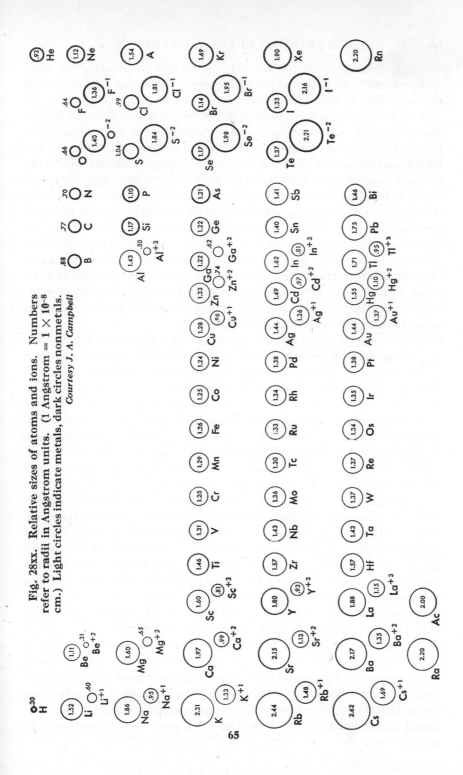

Fig. 28xx. Relative sizes of atoms and ions. Numbers refer to radii in Angstrom units. (1 Angstrom = 1 × 10⁻⁸ cm.) Light circles indicate metals, dark circles nonmetals.

Courtesy J. A. Campbell

65

Similarly it is reasonable to say that Cl can pick up one electron more readily than S can pick up two, or P three. As electrons are picked up the attraction of the nucleus for electrons lessens.

Now let us consider relative activity within a family of elements. These elements have the same outer configuration, *e.g.*, members of Group I*A* all have a single electron in the outer shell. As shells are added and the outer electron is moved farther from the positively charged nucleus, the attraction between the nucleus and the outer electron becomes less and the latter is more easily removed. Hence the activity increases in going from top to bottom in a given group of metals. K is more active than Na and less active than Rb, etc. In the case of nonmetals such as the halogen family, Group VII*A*, where the tendency is to acquire electrons, the smaller atoms will have a greater attraction for electrons since the distance between the nucleus and the outer shell is less. F is more active than Cl, which in turn is more active than Br, etc. In general, activity of nonmetals decreases in going from top to bottom in the table.

The change in chemical properties of the transitional elements, *i.e.*, those in the *B* groups of the table, is much less pronounced than in the *A* series. This is because the added electrons are filling incompleted inner shells rather than going into the outer shell which is much more sensitive to releasing or acquiring electrons.

Stability of compounds. We may think of a stable compound as being one which is difficult to decompose. Although undoubtedly many factors contribute to the stability of a substance, two of the most important are the ones discussed above, namely the size of the atoms or ions and the consequent closeness of approach to one another and the ease of electron removal or electron affinity. The latter is the more important criterion in predicting stability. The most stable compounds would be those from elements which most easily give up electrons and elements with a high electron affinity. Compounds of the alkali metals with the halogens are very stable since the former elements readily give up electrons and the latter readily acquire them. On the basis of position in the table we might expect KCl to be more stable than NaCl, KCl more than KI, KCl more than $CaCl_2$, HF more than H_2O, H_2O more than H_2S, BaF_2 more than MgI_2, etc.

In ionic compounds, *i.e.*, those formed by a transfer of electrons, the size of the ion is more important than size of atom. The closeness of its approach to a neighboring ion will determine the attractive forces between the ions and hence the tendency to remain in close association (stability). Obviously an ion formed by release of electrons would be smaller than the atom since the outer shell is destroyed or removed; furthermore on removal of an electron the nucleus exerts a stronger attraction for the fewer number of electrons remaining and tends to pull them closer to the nucleus. As we progress in a given period from left to right in the table, the ions become smaller as electrons are given up; Mg^{++} is smaller than Na^+, and Al^{+++} is smaller than Mg^{++}, etc. However when electrons are taken up to form negative ions the size increases since the attraction of the nucleus is distributed over a greater number of electrons than in the neutral atom and the ion tends to swell or expand. We would expect Cl^- to be smaller than S^{--} which in turn would be smaller than P^{---}.

Division into metals and nonmetals. While there is often no sharp line of division between metals and nonmetals, those elements which are classed as metallic always exhibit a positive valence. Nonmetals, on the other hand, usually show a negative valence, although positive valences of nonmetals are not uncommon.

In the short form Mendeléeff table, a diagonal line drawn from the upper left-hand corner to the lower right-hand corner divides the elements into two sections. Most of the elements falling below the line have metallic properties, while those above usually exhibit nonmetallic properties. Those elements falling on or near the diagonal usually exhibit properties of both metals and nonmetals and are termed *metalloids*.

In the long form periodic table, the nonmetals appear to the far right and toward the top. The metallic elements are in far greater number, including Groups I*A*, II*A*, all of the *B* series or transition elements and the heavier elements in Groups III*A* to V*A*. The transition elements (the *B* series) including the lanthanide and actinide series would be expected to exhibit a positive valence and therefore metallic characteristics since none of these elements possesses more than two electrons in the outer orbit. The position of an element in the table gives a good indication of its general physical properties, *e.g.*, the low melting metals, such as Cd, Ga, Hg, Pb, and Sn appear just to the left and below the nonmetallic elements; the metals in the middle of the table such as Fe, Co, Ni, Pd, Pt, Au, etc., are ductile and malleable; metals in Groups III*B* to VII*B* tend to be hard and brittle with high melting points; metals in Groups I*A* and II*A* are light and low melting.

Uses of the periodic table. The periodic table serves as a very useful classification of the elements to the chemist. Rather than learning the properties of each of the ninety-eight elements, one may master the properties of each of the groups. From a knowledge of the position of the element within the periodic table, the general properties of the element are known. If an element is known to be in a certain group, then by association with other members of the same group, the properties of which are known, its properties may be predicted. As a matter of fact, before the discovery of many of the chemical elements, the properties of the unknown elements were predicted with a high degree of accuracy. During the time the element was unknown, a blank space appeared in the table. Thus the periodic table has often stimulated research in the discovery of new elements.

Mendeléeff predicted the properties of eka-silicon, later named germanium, many years before it was discovered. How accurate were his predictions is evident from Table 6.

TABLE 6

COMPARISON OF PREDICTED PROPERTIES OF EKA–SILICON
WITH KNOWN PROPERTIES OF GERMANIUM

PROPERTY	EKA-SILICON	GERMANIUM
Atomic weight	72	72.6
Characteristic valence	4	4
Density	5.5	5.47
Color	Gray	Grayish-white
Reaction with water	Will decompose steam with difficulty	No reaction with steam
Action of acids	Slight	No reaction with HCl, oxidized by HNO_3
Action of bases	Slight	No reaction
Properties of the chloride . . .	Boiling point below 100° density 1.9	Boiling point 86°, density 1.9
Properties of the oxide	White, refractory, density 4.7	White, refractory, density 4.703

Imperfections of the classification. Despite its great usefulness, the periodic classification is not without its faults. A few of its weaknesses may be pointed out here.

Hydrogen perhaps does not fit into the table entirely satisfactorily. It is usually placed in Group IA since it does possess one valence electron (like the alkali metals) and combines with nonmetals such as the halogens, sulfur, etc. However the latter compounds are covalent in character and not like the electrovalent combination of alkali metals with the halogens. In some respects hydrogen resembles the members of Group VIIA, since it appears to be nonmetallic in character and furthermore, like the halogens, may combine with the alkali metals to form ionic compounds. For example, sodium hydride (NaH) is ionic in character like NaCl. ●

In the short form table where the A and B series fall within the same group, there is valid criticism that the two series are not similar in many respects. For example, Group I contains the most active metals, potassium, sodium, etc., and also the very inactive metals, silver, copper, and gold. This objection is removed in the long form table where each series of elements is in a separate group.

In either table a group of 15 elements collectively called the rare earths or lanthanide series with very similar chemical and physical properties must be fitted into a single space. Of course the long form table could be further elongated to take care of these elements but this would make the table unwieldy and would not add particularly to its usefulness. These elements should perhaps be considered separately anyway since they constitute a unique group as far as structural characteristics are concerned. In these elements as successive electrons are added, the latter enter a deep inner orbit (the 4th) until the orbit has its capacity of 32 electrons, while the two outer orbits remain unchanged. Consequently the chemical characteristics of these elements which are governed by the valence electrons in the two outer orbits are very nearly the same for this entire group of 15 elements. A second rare earth series called the actinide series, starts with element number 89 and the members like those of the lanthanide series are very similar in chemical behavior.

The advantages of the classification, however, greatly outweigh its disadvantages. It is indeed helpful to be able to study the properties of a group of elements as similar rather than more tediously studying each element.

EXERCISES

1. From the standpoint of modern atomic structure, why would you expect the elements calcium, strontium, and barium to fall in the same group in the periodic table?
2. Point out two or three irregularities which would appear in the table if the elements were arranged in order of increasing atomic weights rather than increasing atomic numbers.
3. Although we have not studied the element No. 85 in Group VII of the periodic table, predict some of its properties. What would be its physical state at ordinary conditions? Write the formulas for its sodium, calcium, and aluminum salts, assuming the symbol of the element to be At. Predict its approximate atomic weight.
4. What change has been made in recent years in the wording of Mendeléeff's periodic law?
5. List four defects in the periodic table of Mendeléeff.
6. On the basis of position in the periodic table how would you expect the following atoms and ions to compare in size? Explain your answer in each case: (a) Li and Be, (b) Li^+ and Be^{++}, (c) Ca^{++} and Sc^{+++}, (d) S^{--} and Br^-,

(e) Cu^{++} and Zn^{++}, (f) Cl$^-$ and A, (g) Ra^{++} and Ba^{++}, (h) Al and Ga, (i) Si and S, (j) Zn^{++}, Cd^{++}, and Hg^{++}, (k) O^{--} and F$^-$.

7. Which of the compounds in each of the following pairs would you expect to be most stable? Give reason for answer in each case: (a) LiBr and LiI, (b) CaS and CaCl$_2$, (c) H$_2$O and HCl, (d) CsBr and BaSe, (e) HBr and HF, (f) H$_3$P and H$_2$S, (g) H$_2$O and H$_2$S, (h) AlCl$_3$ and BF$_3$.

8. What is the fundamental difference in structure (electronic configuration) between the A and B divisions of elements in the periodic classification?

9. What changes in activity take place with increasing atomic weight of the
(a) metals in a given group?
(b) nonmetals in a given group?
(c) elements in a given horizontal series?

10. From the data recorded for the families of elements listed below, predict the properties of the last member of each family:

ELEMENT	DENSITY	MELTING POINT	BOILING POINT	COLOR
S	1.96	119	445	yellow
Se	4.5	217	680	gray
Te				
F		−223	−188	pale yellow
Cl		−102	− 35	greenish-yellow
Br	3.4	− 7	59	brown
I	4.93	113	183	black
At				

				SOL. OF SULFATE g./100g. H$_2$O
Mg	1.74	650	1107	27.
Ca	1.55	851	1487	.208
Sr	2.6	757	1384	.01
Ba	3.78	850	1640	.00024
Ra				

REFERENCES

Bernard Jaffe, *Crucibles; The Lives and Achievements of the Great Chemists,* Simon and Schuster, 1939.

"The Atom," *Life,* May 16 (1949).

G. N. Quam and M. B. Quam, "Types of Graphic Classifications of the Elements," *J. Chem. Ed.* **11**, 27 (1934).

W. H. Taylor, "Newlands, a Pioneer in Atomic Numbers," *ibid.* **26**, 491 (1949).

F. Y. Herron, "A Convertible Periodic Table," *ibid.* **26**, 540 (1949).

J. A. Campbell, "Atomic Size and the Periodic Table," *ibid.* **23**, 525 (1946).

Wm. F. Ehret, "The Role of Electrons in Interatomic Relations," *ibid.* **25**, 291 (1948).

I. H. Parsons, "Color and the Transition Elements," *ibid.* **25**, 207 (1948).

K. B. McCutchon, "A Simplified Periodic Classification of the Elements," *ibid.* **27**, 17 (1950).

J. A. Maxwell, "Periodicity," *ibid.* **27**, 510 (1950).

G. Glockler and A. I. Popov, "Valency and the Periodic Table," *ibid.* **28**, 212 (1951).

V

Formulas and Equations

The meaning of a formula. The chemist uses formulas to show the composition of compounds. Formulas are made up of the proper combination of symbols for the elements which are contained in the compound; at the same time the number of each kind of atom in the compound may be indicated in the formula by placing subscripts after the symbols. Thus the formula for sugar is written as $C_{12}H_{22}O_{11}$, since each molecule of sugar contains 12 atoms of carbon, 22 atoms of hydrogen, and 11 atoms of oxygen. If only one atom of an element is present in a molecule of a compound, no subscript is necessary. A molecule of water, which is made up of two atoms of hydrogen and one atom of oxygen, is written as H_2O. *A subscript applies only to the element or radical of which it is the subscript.* A chemical formula, then, is considerably more than abbreviation for a chemical compound, as it indicates not only the compound in question but its composition as well.

A formula also permits us to calculate the molecular weight or formula weight of the compound. Sulfuric acid has the formula H_2SO_4, which tells us that sulfuric acid is composed of 2 parts by weight of hydrogen (2×1, where 1 is the atomic weight of hydrogen), 32 parts by weight of sulfur (1×32, where 32 is the atomic weight of sulfur), and 64 parts by weight of oxygen (4×16, where 16 is the atomic weight of oxygen). Thus the weight of the molecule of sulfuric acid is the sum of the weights of the constituent atoms, $2 + 32 + 64 = 98$. Ninety-eight is the molecular weight or formula weight of the compound. Ninety-eight grams of sulfuric acid would be a gram molecular weight or mole of the compound; 98 grams of sulfuric acid contains 2 grams of hydrogen (2 gram atoms), 32 grams of sulfur (1 gram atom), and 64 grams of oxygen (4 gram atoms).

A coefficient placed before a formula multiplies every constituent of the formula which it precedes. For example, $3\,C_{12}H_{22}O_{11}$ denotes three molecules of sugar, which contain 36 atoms of carbon, 66 atoms of hydrogen, and 33 atoms of oxygen.

To illustrate further the information which may be derived from a formula, consider HNO_3, which represents one molecule of nitric acid. We derive the following from this formula:

1. One molecule of nitric acid contains 1 atom of hydrogen, 1 atom of nitrogen, and 3 atoms of oxygen.
2. Nitric acid is composed of 1 part by weight of hydrogen (see atomic weights), 14 parts by weight of nitrogen, and 48 parts by weight of oxygen.
3. The molecular weight of nitric acid $(1 + 14 + 48 = 63)$.
4. One gram-molecular or formula weight of nitric acid, 63 grams, contains 1 gram of hydrogen (1 gram atom); 14 grams of nitrogen (1 gram atom); and 48 grams of oxygen (3 gram atoms).

Chemical equations. When iron powder and sulfur powder are heated together, iron combines with sulfur to form the compound ferrous sulfide. This chemical change might be represented by the word statement:

Iron (Fe) plus sulfur (S) produces ferrous sulfide (FeS).

It is more convenient to represent the chemical change in the form of a *chemical equation* by using the symbols for the substances taking part in the chemical change, thus expressing the above relations as follows:
$$Fe + S = FeS$$

The symbols appearing to the left of the = sign are symbols for the *reactants*, that is, those things which are entering into the chemical change. The formulas to the right of the = sign represent the *products*, or those things which are produced as a result of the chemical change. For the term *chemical change* the chemist makes use of the word *reaction* as synonymous.

The above representation for the reaction between iron and sulfur is a true equation: the left side is equal to the right side in that one atom of iron and also one atom of sulfur appears on each side. The equation above is said to be balanced, since the same number of atoms of each kind appear on each side of the equation. The = sign is often replaced by an arrow which will indicate the direction in which the chemical change is taking place; thus

$$Fe + S \longrightarrow FeS$$

The chemical equation, like the chemical formula, has a great deal more significance to the chemist than does a word statement. The equation representing the reaction of iron and sulfur gives us the following information:

1. One atom of iron combines with one atom of sulfur to produce one formula weight of ferrous sulfide, or one gram atom of iron combines with one gram atom of sulfur to produce one gram formula weight of ferrous sulfide.

2. 55.85 (see atomic weights) parts by weight of iron combine with 32.06 parts by weight of sulfur to form 87.91 parts by weight of ferrous sulfide.

The formula must always express the true composition of the substance. When writing the equation for the reaction of hydrogen and oxygen to form water, the formula for hydrogen must be written as H_2 and not as H, since two hydrogen atoms are united to form a unit of free hydrogen; similarly the formula for oxygen is O_2, since two atoms always unite to form a unit particle (molecule) of free oxygen. Therefore the equation for the reaction of hydrogen and oxygen should be written as follows:

$$H_2 + O_2 \longrightarrow H_2O \quad \text{(not balanced)}$$

It is evident that the latter is not a *balanced* equation, since there are two atoms of oxygen on the left side of the equation and only one atom of oxygen on the right-hand side. Since the formula of a compound is fixed and definite, we cannot write H_2O_2, or in any other way change the formula for water. We may, however, balance the equation thus, since a number placed in front of a formula multiplies all the constituents in the formula which it precedes:

$$2\,H_2 + O_2 \longrightarrow 2\,H_2O$$

The coefficients (the numbers in front of the formulas) represent the number of molecules or formula weights undergoing chemical change. In case a single molecule enters into a change no number is placed in front of the formula. The above equation tells us that two molecules of hydrogen combine with one molecule of oxygen to form two molecules of water.

Ordinary sugar, when heated, decomposes into carbon and water, and the change may be represented by the equation:

$$C_{12}H_{22}O_{11} \longrightarrow C + H_2O \quad \text{(not balanced)}$$

To balance the equation, 12 atoms of carbon are necessary, and hence the number 12 is placed in front of the symbol for carbon; to balance the hydrogen and oxygen atoms, a coefficient of 11 is needed in front of the formula for water:

$$C_{12}H_{22}O_{11} \longrightarrow 12\,C + 11\,H_2O\,[1]$$

Balancing of equations is largely a matter of trial and error; small coefficients should be tried until a balance is obtained. A good general rule to follow is: Balance elements other than hydrogen and oxygen first; then balance hydrogen atoms, if present, and lastly balance oxygen atoms, if present. It will be found that the oxygen atoms are usually balanced when the others have been taken care of.

Radicals. In many chemical changes certain groups of atoms may function as a unit, in which case the same group or combination of atoms will appear on both sides of an equation; for example, in the reaction

$$Zn + H_2SO_4 \longrightarrow ZnSO_4 + H_2$$

one atom of sulfur and four atoms of oxygen make up the sulfate group, SO_4, which remains intact in the change. Such groups are termed "radicals" and may be treated as units in the chemical equation. Other such groups or radicals are hydroxide, OH; nitrate, NO_3; carbonate, CO_3; ammonium, NH_4; and phosphate, PO_4.

In writing a chemical formula of a compound, one formula weight of which contains more than one of the radicals, it is customary to enclose the group in parentheses and indicate the number of such groups in a formula weight by placing the proper subscript after the parentheses. For example, calcium hydroxide is written as $Ca(OH)_2$ rather than as CaO_2H_2 which equally well would express the true composition of the compound. Enclosing a group in parentheses has the advantage that we may recognize immediately that such a group functions as a unit. The subscript outside the parentheses applies to everything within the parentheses: the subscript 2 in $Ca(OH)_2$ indicates two atoms of oxygen as well as two atoms of hydrogen present in each formula weight. A formula weight of aluminum sulfate, $Al_2(SO_4)_3$, contains 2 atoms of aluminum, 3 atoms of sulfur, and 12 atoms of oxygen. A coefficient placed in front of the formula necessarily multiplies everything in the formula; thus $3\,Al_2(SO_4)_3$ would contain 6 atoms of aluminum, 9 atoms of sulfur, and 36 atoms of oxygen.

Some types of chemical change. We are not prepared to discuss at the present time the many types of chemical change which may occur. However, we can indicate here the more important types and study

---

[1] It would be incorrect to make the 12 a subscript of the carbon, thus C_{12}, since this would imply that twelve atoms of carbon remain together as a unit particle. This is not true, as a single atom of carbon may exist as such in the free state; hence the number 12 must be placed in front of the formula.

them in more detail later. Most chemical changes may be classified as one of the following four types:

(*a*) *Combination.* Many compounds are formed by direct *combination* of two or more elements or compounds. The following equations serve as examples:

$$Fe + S \longrightarrow FeS$$
$$CaO + CO_2 \longrightarrow CaCO_3$$
$$2\,Na + Cl_2 \longrightarrow 2\,NaCl$$

We note in the above that a *single* substance is formed by a combination of two substances. The combining substances may not in every case be elements, as is illustrated in the second equation above in which the two compounds, calcium oxide and carbon dioxide, are the reactants. A *combination* reaction then is one in which a *single* substance is produced by the union of two or more substances.

(*b*) *Decomposition.* Water may be broken down into hydrogen and oxygen by means of an electric current according to the equation

$$2\,H_2O \longrightarrow 2\,H_2 + O_2$$

Sugar, when heated, decomposes to form a charred mass, which is essentially carbon, and water in the form of steam. The equation for the change is represented:

$$C_{12}H_{22}O_{11} \longrightarrow 12\,C + 11\,H_2O$$

These are *decomposition* chemical changes; reactions in which two or more substances are produced from a *single* substance. This type of change is the reverse of combination. A compound may not always decompose into its constituent elements; this is illustrated in the above equation for the decomposition of sugar, where water, a compound substance, is one of the products.

(*c*) *Replacement or substitution.* In this type of chemical change one element replaces another from its compounds. For example,

$$Zn + 2\,HCl \longrightarrow ZnCl_2 + H_2$$
hydrochloric   zinc
acid   chloride

zinc replaces or substitutes for the hydrogen in the compound, hydrochloric acid.

If chlorine is passed into a solution of sodium bromide, the chlorine replaces the bromine, thus

$$2\,NaBr + Cl_2 \longrightarrow 2\,NaCl + Br_2$$
sodium   chlo-   sodium   bro-
bromide   rine   chloride   mine

(d) *Double decomposition.* A solution of silver nitrate reacts with a solution of sodium chloride according to the equation

$$\underset{\substack{\text{silver}\\\text{nitrate}}}{AgNO_3} + \underset{\substack{\text{sodium}\\\text{chloride}}}{NaCl} \longrightarrow \underset{\substack{\text{silver}\\\text{chloride}}}{AgCl\downarrow} + \underset{\substack{\text{sodium}\\\text{nitrate}}}{NaNO_3}$$

There has been a double exchange, since silver and sodium have both exchanged position. Such a chemical change is termed *double decomposition.*

In the above reaction the silver chloride is insoluble and *precipitates* from the solution, or, in other words, separates from the solution as a solid. The sodium nitrate, being soluble, remains in solution and may be separated from the insoluble AgCl by filtration (Fig. 29).

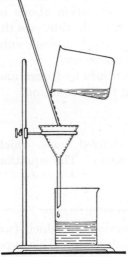

Calculation of percentage composition from a formula. Since the formula of a compound is fixed, we may calculate the per cent of each element present from a consideration of the parts by weight of each element in one formula weight of the compound. Consider the formula of water, H_2O. The atomic weights of hydrogen and oxygen are 1 and 16 respectively; hence the formula weight of H_2O is 18. One formula weight of water is made up of 18 parts by weight, 2 parts of which are hydrogen and 16 parts of which are oxygen. The fraction of hydrogen is $\frac{2}{18}$ and the fraction of oxygen is $\frac{16}{18}$. These fractions may be converted to percentage by multiplying by 100.

Fig. 29. Filtration.

Thus the per cent of hydrogen in water is $\frac{2}{18} \times 100 = 11.1$ per cent. The per cent of oxygen would then be $\frac{16}{18} \times 100 = 88.9$ per cent.

The calculation of percentage composition is further illustrated in the examples below:

PROBLEM 1: Calculate the percentage composition of aluminum sulfate, $Al_2(SO_4)_3$.

$$
\begin{array}{lrr}
\text{2 atoms of aluminum weigh} & 2 \times 27 = & 54 \\
\text{3 atoms of sulfur weigh} & 3 \times 32 = & 96 \\
\text{12 atoms of oxygen weigh} & 12 \times 16 = & \underline{192} \\
& \text{Formula weight} & 342
\end{array}
$$

$$
\begin{array}{lll}
\text{Per cent aluminum} & = \frac{54}{342} \times 100 = & 15.8 \\
\text{Per cent sulfur} & = \frac{96}{342} \times 100 = & 28.1 \\
\text{Per cent oxygen} & = \frac{192}{342} \times 100 = & \underline{56.1} \\
& & 100.00
\end{array}
$$

PROBLEM 2. Calculate the weight of iron in 350 pounds of Fe_2O_3. First, calculate the per cent of iron in the compound:

$$2 \text{ atoms of Fe weigh} \quad 2 \times 55.8 = 111.6$$
$$3 \text{ atoms of oxygen weigh } 3 \times 16 \quad = \underline{\ \ 48\ }$$
$$\text{Formula weight} \quad 159.6$$

Per cent iron $= 111/159.6 \times 100 = 69.9$
Weight of iron in 350 lb. of $Fe_2O_3 = 350 \times .699$
$$= 244.5 \text{ lb.}$$

EXERCISES

1. List all the information derivable from the formulas: H_2SO_4; $C_{12}H_{22}O_{11}$.
2. Balance the equations:
   (a) $Ca + HCl \longrightarrow CaCl_2 + H_2$
   (b) $KClO_3 \longrightarrow KCl + O_2$
   (c) $NaOH + H_2SO_4 \longrightarrow Na_2SO_4 + H_2O$
   (d) $Al + HCl \longrightarrow AlCl_3 + H_2$
   (e) $Na + H_2O \longrightarrow NaOH + H_2$

3. Define the terms: symbol; formula; chemical equation; radical; percentage composition; formula weight; filtrate.

4. Balance the equations:
   (a) $Ca(OH)_2 + HCl \longrightarrow CaCl_2 + H_2O$
   (b) $Al_2(SO_4)_3 + BaCl_2 \longrightarrow BaSO_4 + AlCl_3$
   (c) $Cu(NO_3)_2 + H_3PO_4 \longrightarrow Cu_3(PO_4)_2 + HNO_3$
   (d) $Bi_2(CO_3)_3 + HC_2H_3O_2 \longrightarrow Bi(C_2H_3O_2)_3 + H_2CO_3$
   (e) $(NH_4)_3PO_4 + KOH \longrightarrow K_3PO_4 + NH_4OH$

5. Classify the following reactions as one of the four types given on pages 75–76.
   (a) $Zn + 2 AuCl \longrightarrow ZnCl_2 + 2 Au$
   (b) $2 NaCl + H_2SO_4 \longrightarrow Na_2SO_4 + 2 HCl$
   (c) $2 Na + 2 HCl \longrightarrow 2 NaCl + H_2$
   (d) $2 BaO_2 \longrightarrow 2 BaO + O_2$
   (e) $S + O_2 \longrightarrow SO_2$
   (f) $Na_2O + CO_2 \longrightarrow Na_2CO_3$
   (g) $Pb(NO_3)_2 + Na_2SO_4 \longrightarrow PbSO_4 + 2 NaNO_3$
   (h) $Cl_2 + Hg \longrightarrow HgCl_2$

6. Calculate the percentage of each element in the compounds:
   (a) $NaCl$; (b) $CaCO_3$; (c) $K_2Cr_2O_7$.

7. Calculate the weight of zinc obtainable from one ton of the mineral ZnS.

8. A solution is 5 per cent $Cr_2(SO_4)_3$. From a ton of this solution one could obtain how many pounds of Cr?

9. What is the per cent lead in the insecticide material lead arsenite, $Pb_3(AsO_3)_2$?

10. Calculate the percentage of aluminum in the clay mineral, $H_2Al_2(SiO_3)_4$.

11. What is the per cent of calcium in calcium chloride? What is the weight of calcium that might be obtained from 250 pounds of calcium chloride?

Ans. 90 lb.

REFERENCES

J. R. Partington, "The Origin of Modern Chemical Symbols and Formulae," *Journal Society Chemical Industry*, **55**, 759 (1936).

VI

Oxygen

$$_8\mathbf{O}^{16}\ {}^{1\ 1}_{2\ 6}\ {}_{1\ 1}$$

Occurrence. In beginning our study of the chemical elements, we shall select oxygen, the most abundant of all the elements and one which plays a very important role in our everyday life. From Figure 2, page 16, we may note that oxygen makes up about one-half of the earth's crust, which includes the atmosphere. The weight of all oxygen in the world is approximately equal to the combined weights of all the other elements.

Oxygen occurs in both the free (uncombined) and combined states. In the free state it comprises approximately 20 per cent by volume of the air we breathe. Water is a compound of two elements, oxygen and hydrogen, both of which are colorless gases at ordinary temperatures. Eight-ninths of the weight of water is due to the oxygen present. We might list several other familiar oxygen-containing materials, such as sugars, starches, fats, proteins, limestone, sand, clay, nearly all food products, cotton, and wool. Approximately 60 per cent by weight of the human body is oxygen.

The importance of oxygen. Oxygen is the vitally essential substance in the air we breathe. Air is taken into the lungs, where the oxygen is taken up by the blood stream which carries this vital substance to body tissues. The food we consume combines with oxygen, and this chemical change produces energy which maintains our body temperature and gives us strength for physical activity.

But this is only one of the many functions of oxygen. Coal and wood must have oxygen to burn and produce heat. Oxygen in the air causes

NOTE: In showing the atomic number and atomic weight of an element in conjunction with its symbol, the system above has been adopted in which the atomic number of the element is made a subscript just preceding the symbol while the atomic weight is placed as a superscript of the symbol. The numbers to the right of the symbol indicate the electronic configuration of the atom — in the above, 2 electrons in the first energy level and 6 electrons in the second and outermost energy level.

metals to corrode, wood to rot, paints to harden, gasoline to burn, iron to rust, and many other chemical processes with which we are not yet familiar to take place. Not only is oxygen the most abundant element, but also it is perhaps the most important element.

The discovery of oxygen. Although oxygen is very abundant, it was not discovered until after many of the less common elements were well known. Joseph Priestley, an English clergyman, is credited with its discovery in 1774. This makes it a relatively recent discovery.[1] Priestley was experimenting with many kinds of gases or "airs," which he obtained by heating various substances, when he discovered that mercuric oxide yielded an "air" of unusual properties when heated. He found that substances burned much more vigorously in this gas than in ordinary air. The gases which Priestley prepared by heating various substances were not regarded by him as essentially different substances, but he thought of them as different kinds of air. In heating substances, Priestley made use of heat energy from the sun by focusing rays of light upon the object to be heated by means of a lens. Although he found that combustion proceeded much more rapidly in this new "air," he did not associate it with the component of ordinary air in which combustion of many substances was known to take place. Following are portions of Priestley's own account of his experiments on oxygen:

On the 1st of August, 1774, I endeavoured to extract air from mercurious calcinatus per se (mercuric oxide); and I presently found that, by means of the lens, air was expelled from it very rapidly. Having got about three or four times as much as the bulk of my materials, I admitted water to it, and found that it was not imbibed by it. But what surprised me more than I can well express, was, that a candle burned in this air with a remarkably vigorous flame. . . .

On the 8th of this month I procured a mouse, and put it into a glass vessel, containing two ounce-measures of the air from mercurious calcinatus. Had it been common air, a full-grown mouse, as this was, would have lived in it about a quarter of an hour. In this air, however, my mouse lived a full half hour; and though it was taken out seemingly dead, it appeared to have been only exceedingly chilled; for, upon being held to the fire, it presently revived, and appeared not to have received any harm from the experiment. . . .

From the greater strength and vivacity of the flame of a candle, in this pure air, it may be conjectured, that it might be peculiarly salutary to the lungs in certain morbid cases, when the common air

[1] It is probable that oxygen was first discovered by the Swedish chemist Scheele in about 1771. His results were not made public until 1775, and Priestley's work had received considerable attention by this time.

would not be sufficient to carry off the phlogistic putrid effluvium
fast enough. But perhaps, we may also infer from these experiments,
that though pure dephlogisticated air might be very useful as a medicine, it might not be so proper for us in the usual healthy state of the
body; for, as a candle burns out much faster in dephlogisticated air
than in common air, so we might, as may be said, live out too fast,
and the animal powers be too soon exhausted in this pure kind of air.
A moralist, at least, may say, that the air which nature has provided
for us is as good as we deserve.

My reader will not wonder, that, after having ascertained the
superior goodness of dephlogisticated air by mice living in it, and
the other tests above mentioned, I should have the curiosity to
taste it myself. I have gratified that curiosity, by breathing it,
drawing it through a glass syphon, and by this means, I reduced a
large jar of it to the standard of common air. The feeling to my
lungs was not sensibly different from that of common air; but I
fancied that my breast felt peculiarly light and easy for some time
afterwards. Who can tell but that, in time this pure air may become
a fashionable article in luxury. Hitherto only two mice and myself
have had the privilege of breathing it. . . .[1]

The phlogiston theory. The phenomenon of combustion was not very well
understood until the nineteenth century. Combustion, or the production of
fire, usually was associated with destruction of the material being burned.
It was commonly known that most substances burned with a resulting loss in
weight, since only a fraction of the original weight was left in the form of ash.
It seemed natural to the alchemists that the combustible substance must contain something responsible for the burning which escaped during the process of
combustion. This hypothetical something supposedly present in combustible
materials was called "phlogiston." However, it was known that when some
substances burned, the residue after combustion weighed more than the original
substance. This fact must have caused grave doubts to arise in the minds of
the chemists of that period as to the correctness of the phlogiston theory. The
phlogiston concept, however, was so firmly implanted in the minds of many of
the alchemists that it was not soon discarded. Phlogiston with a negative weight
was postulated; accordingly as something burned with loss of negative phlogiston,
the residue would possess a greater weight than the initial substance. It is difficult for us today to conceive of something with a negative weight.

It remained for Lavoisier, a French chemist, to show that Priestley's "air"
was the constituent in the air which caused substances to burn. Lavoisier
recognized that since substances burned more vigorously in Priestley's "air"
than in ordinary air, Priestley's "air" must be responsible for combustion in
ordinary air, where it seemed to be less concentrated. Lavoisier proved this
theory by heating mercury with air (see Fig. 30). He found that a "red pre-

cipitate" (mercuric oxide) was formed on the surface of the mercury and the volume of air decreased by about one-fifth. On heating the "red precipitate" at a higher temperature, he found that a volume of gas was released exactly equal to the decrease in volume of the original air used. He concluded that air must be composed of two gases, one of which in a concentration of approximately 20 per cent by volume is responsible for combustion processes. Lavoisier said that burning was the combination of the burning substance with oxygen. The weight of the product then would be greater than the weight of the original sub-

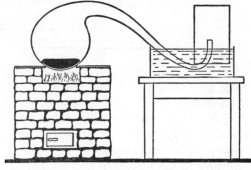

Fig. 30. Lavoisier's apparatus for preparing mercuric oxide.

stance by an amount equal to the weight of the substance in the air which united with the burning body. He called the inactive substance in the air "azote," a French word meaning lazy. We now know this substance as the element nitrogen. Lavoisier called the active ingredient "oxygen" which signifies acid former. He believed that all acids contain oxygen. This latter view was erroneous, for we shall presently study several acids which contain no oxygen.

Lavoisier's contribution to this phase of chemistry lay in the fact that he had overthrown the phlogiston theory and gave us our modern concept of combustion.

Laboratory preparation. (*a*) *By heating certain oxides.* Oxygen is conveniently prepared in the laboratory by repeating Priestley's experiment of heating certain substances. Mercuric oxide, a reddish powder, readily gives up its oxygen when heated, leaving metallic mercury as a residue (Fig. 31):

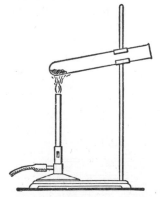

Fig. 31. Heating mercuric oxide yields mercury and oxygen.

$$2\,HgO \longrightarrow 2\,Hg + O_2$$
mercuric   mercury oxygen
oxide

Silver oxide, gold oxide, and platinum oxide react similarly, yielding the metal and liberating oxygen when heated. These four metals, mercury, silver, gold, and platinum are called the *noble* metals.

Certain dioxides are unstable toward heat, breaking down to give an oxide of the metal and free oxygen, *e.g.*

$$2\,PbO_2 \longrightarrow 2\,PbO + O_2$$
lead   lead
dioxide   oxide

$$2\,BaO_2 \longrightarrow 2\,BaO + O_2$$
barium   barium
dioxide   oxide

We must not assume from the above reactions that all metallic oxides give up oxygen when heated. As a matter of fact, most of the oxides of metals are stable and undergo no change when heated.

(*b*) *By heating certain salts.* Potassium chlorate, a white crystalline substance composed of the elements potassium, chlorine, and oxygen, gives up all of its oxygen when heated above its melting point, 368° C., according to the equation

$$2\,KClO_3 \longrightarrow 2\,KCl + 3\,O_2$$
potassium   potassium
chlorate   chloride

If we wish to collect some of the oxygen gas, in order to study some of its properties, we may use the apparatus shown in Figure 32. As

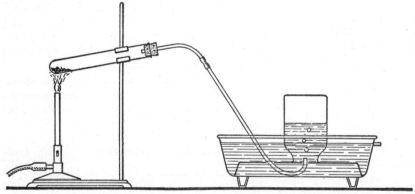

Fig. 32. Collection of oxygen gas by displacement of water.

oxygen gas is not very soluble in water, we may collect it by displacement of water as shown. As the gas is evolved, it displaces the water in the bottle, and we may collect the bottle full of the gas.

Potassium nitrate when heated yields oxygen, but the reaction differs from the decomposition of potassium chlorate in that only one-third of the oxygen in the former compound is released. This is evident from the equation
$$2\,KNO_3 \longrightarrow 2\,KNO_2 + O_2$$
potassium   potassium
nitrate   nitrite

Again it should be pointed out that not all oxygen-containing compounds give up their oxygen when heated; e.g., K_2SO_4 and SiO_2 are stable toward heat.

(c) *The reaction of sodium peroxide with water.* Sodium peroxide, a white noncrystalline powder, reacts vigorously with water to give oxygen and sodium hydroxide:

$$2\,Na_2O_2 + 2\,H_2O \longrightarrow 4\,NaOH + O_2$$
sodium   sodium
peroxide   hydroxide

Catalysts. The speed of many chemical reactions may be increased or decreased by the addition of certain foreign substances. These substances do not appear to enter into the reaction; at least they are not permanently altered chemically. Such substances are called "catalysts" or "catalytic agents." When potassium chlorate is heated it melts to a clear liquid, and tiny bubbles of gas may be noticed escaping from the liquid. As indicated above, the gas is oxygen but its evolution is slow. The addition of a small amount of manganese dioxide to the potassium chlorate greatly increases the speed at which the oxygen is evolved; furthermore, the oxygen gas is evolved at a much lower temperature. This added substance does not give up oxygen and remains unchanged in composition in the reaction. That the latter is true may be shown by analysis of the reaction products. All of the catalyst added to the reaction mixture may be recovered and used over and over again. Since a catalyst does not appear actually to enter into the reaction, its formula is usually placed over the arrow in the equation; thus the above catalytic decomposition of potassium chlorate would be represented:

$$2\,KClO_3 \xrightarrow{\;MnO_2\;} 2\,KCl + 3\,O_2$$

In some reactions the speed of reaction may be decreased by the presence of a catalyst. However, in most cases, catalysts are used to speed up chemical processes. A catalyst may be defined as *a substance which alters the speed of a chemical reaction but itself remains unchanged chemically.* Catalysts have important industrial applications because in many reactions speed is a decisive factor.

Commercial preparation of oxygen. It would not be practical to make large quantities of oxygen by the methods employed in the laboratory, as the cost would be prohibitive. We might naturally expect to obtain large quantities of oxygen from those sources where it occurs most extensively. Since approximately 20 per cent of the atmosphere is composed of oxygen, air should be a potential source. Water is nearly 90 per cent oxygen. Since water is so readily available, we might expect to use it in preparing oxygen on an industrial scale. As a matter of fact, most of the oxygen for commercial purposes is obtained from air. It is stored in heavy steel cylinders under high pressure.

(*a*) *From the air.* Since air is essentially a mixture of oxygen and nitrogen gases, the problem is to separate these gases. When air is cooled to a temperature of approximately −200°, it becomes liquid. Air is actually liquefied by a combination of low temperature and high pressure. If compressed air is allowed to expand rapidly through a valve, heat is absorbed and the gas is cooled. (For explanation of this see chap. VIII.) The cooled gas may be compressed and again allowed to expand to further cool itself. By alternate compression, cooling, and expansion of air, the temperature is continuously lowered until the air becomes a liquid. During the cooling, water vapor and carbon dioxide in the air condense to liquids and are removed.

When a mixture of liquids is heated to the boiling point, the component with the lowest boiling point boils or distils off first; thus if an alcohol-water mixture is boiled, the first portion of the vapor will be richer (have a higher percentage) in alcohol than the mixture from which it was distilled. (See chap. XV for a further discussion of this.)

Liquid air behaves similarly to the alcohol-water mixture when distilled. Liquid oxygen boils at −183°, liquid nitrogen at −195.8°.

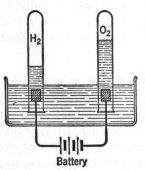

Fig. 32x. Electrolysis of water.

Hence the nitrogen with the lower boiling point will distil first, leaving behind practically pure oxygen as a liquid. The liquid oxygen is then allowed to evaporate and is stored in steel cylinders.

(*b*) *From water.* When an electric current is passed through water containing a small amount of sulfuric acid or sodium hydroxide, the water is broken down into its constituent elements, hydrogen and oxygen, which are evolved as gases:

$$2 H_2O \longrightarrow 2 H_2 + O_2$$

This process is called *electrolysis*. Oxygen is liberated at the positive pole (anode), and hydrogen gas is liberated at the negative pole (cathode). Sulfuric acid or sodium hydroxide is used to make the solution a good conductor of electricity. Industrial oxygen is prepared by electrolysis of water containing sodium hydroxide in iron tanks. As a commercial method, the foregoing has the disadvantage of requiring large quantities of electricity, which is expensive. However, it has the advantage of producing hydrogen as a by-product, which also has industrial importance.

Properties of oxygen. (a) *Physical.* Oxygen is a colorless and tasteless gas which may be changed to a liquid at a temperature of $-183°$ and the liquid changed to a solid at $-225°$. The gas may be liquefied at a temperature of $-118°$, if the pressure is 50 atmospheres. Above this temperature the gas cannot be liquefied regardless of the pressure applied.

Gaseous oxygen is slightly heavier than air. It is but slightly soluble in water, about 2 per cent by volume dissolving at room temperature. Since oxygen gas is a little more soluble in water than nitrogen gas, dissolved air contains a slightly higher percentage of oxygen than ordinary air. Marine life and fish depend upon the dissolved oxygen for respiration.

(b) *Chemical.* Many substances combine vigorously with oxygen particularly at high temperatures. A glowing wood splint thrust into an atmosphere of oxygen bursts into flame and burns brilliantly. The latter is used as a test for oxygen gas in the laboratory. Oxygen combines slowly with most of the metals and nonmetals at ordinary temperatures. When iron rusts, the iron combines with oxygen present in the atmosphere to form a reddish-brown powder, commonly known as iron rust. The principal chemical change is shown by the equation:

$$4\,Fe + 3\,O_2 \longrightarrow 2\,Fe_2O_3$$
$$\text{iron} \qquad\qquad \text{ferric oxide}$$

In pure oxygen the foregoing reaction takes place much more rapidly than in air.[1] Only about one-fifth of the air is made up of oxygen; thus in pure oxygen, the oxygen is about five times as concentrated. In air only one-fifth of the surface of the iron is covered with oxygen molecules, the other four-fifths of the total surface being covered with nitrogen molecules. Nitrogen, a very inactive substance, takes no part in the above reaction. Substances burn better in oxygen than in the air because (1) the concentration of oxygen is greater, and (2) an inactive substance such as nitrogen is not present to absorb heat and slow down the rate of reaction.

---

[1] The effect of the concentration of oxygen on the rate of combination of iron and oxygen may be demonstrated very convincingly by the following experiment: Steel wool heated in a flame in air burns only slowly. If the burning steel wool is then placed in an atmosphere of pure oxygen, it sends off sparks of a dazzling brilliance. The reaction produces magnetic oxide of iron:

$$3\,Fe + 2\,O_2 \longrightarrow Fe_3O_4$$
$$\text{magnetic}$$
$$\text{oxide of iron}$$

Nonmetals such as sulfur, phosphorus, and carbon burn very rapidly in pure oxygen, forming *oxides* of the elements:

$$S + O_2 \longrightarrow SO_2$$

sulfur   sulfur dioxide

$$C + O_2 \longrightarrow CO_2$$

carbon   carbon dioxide

$$4 P + 5 O_2 \longrightarrow 2 P_2O_5$$

phosphorus   phosphorus pentoxide

Sulfur dioxide and carbon dioxide are gases at ordinary temperatures, while phosphorus pentoxide is a white solid.

In addition to the elementary substances, many compounds react with oxygen. Gasoline requires oxygen for its combustion. In the automobile carburetor, gasoline and air are mixed thoroughly and ignited in the cylinder by means of a spark from a spark plug. This reaction produces carbon dioxide (the same gas as formed in the combustion of coal or carbon) and water. The oil in paints absorbs oxygen slowly to form a tough, hard film which is resistant to wind and rain.

These combinations of oxygen with elements and compounds are examples of *oxidation*[1] reactions. The substance which combines with the oxygen is said to be *oxidized*. Oxidation may take place at varying speeds. The formation of iron rust is a slow oxidation. When iron is burned in pure oxygen, the reaction takes place much more rapidly, and heat and light are produced. An oxidation process in which heat and light are produced is called *combustion*. When most substances are oxidized, heat is evolved in the process. Thus when coal, gasoline, or wood are burned, the reactions produce heat. It makes no difference whether the reaction takes place rapidly or slowly, the same quantity of heat is evolved, although in the former case a much higher temperature is reached because of the heat being generated during a brief period of time.

The amount of heat liberated per unit quantity of substance burned is called *heat of combustion*. One gram of sulfur on burning to sulfur dioxide liberates 2200 calories, one gram of carbon burning to carbon dioxide yields 7900 calories. Heats of combustion of mixtures such as coal, fuel oil, or foods are called *calorific values*.

Reaction of oxides with water. The oxides of the nonmetals, sulfur, carbon, and phosphorus, dissolve in water to form *acids*. Acids constitute a class of chemical compounds which have a sour taste and

---

[1] Oxidation reactions, however, are not confined to combinations with oxygen. The term "oxidation" has a much broader significance and will be discussed in more detail in chapter XX.

turn blue litmus paper red. (Litmus is a vegetable dye which is pink or red in acid solution.)

$$SO_2 + H_2O \longrightarrow H_2SO_3$$
sulfur   sulfurous
dioxide   acid

$$CO_2 + H_2O \longrightarrow H_2CO_3$$
carbon   carbonic
dioxide   acid

$$P_2O_5 + 3 H_2O \longrightarrow 2 H_3PO_4$$
phosphorus   phosphoric
pentoxide   acid

We may formulate the general rule: *The oxide of a nonmetal reacts with water to form an acid*.

The oxides of metals, if dissolved in water, form *bases*, another class of chemical compounds. Bases are bitter in taste, have a soapy feeling, turn red litmus paper blue, and in water solution contain the hydroxide, OH, radical:

$$CaO + H_2O \longrightarrow Ca(OH)_2$$
calcium   calcium
oxide   hydroxide

The oxide of iron is insoluble in water, as are most of the metallic oxides. These insoluble oxides and water give no basic reaction to litmus.

Kindling temperature. Chemical processes take place more rapidly when the temperature is raised. At ordinary temperatures iron rusts slowly, but at an elevated temperature the combination with oxygen takes place rapidly. If the temperature of a combustible substance is raised to a certain point in the presence of air or oxygen, the substance will burst into flame. The temperature at which this occurs is called the *kindling temperature* of the substance. The kindling temperature varies with the nature of the substance. This fact may be demonstrated by the following experiment. If small pieces of phosphorus, sulfur, and wood are placed in a shallow pan and the pan heated by means of a burner, it will be observed that the phosphorus takes fire when the pan is barely warm, the sulfur takes fire at a much higher temperature, and at a still higher temperature the wood bursts into flame

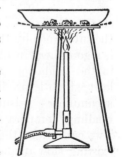

Fig. 33. Demonstration of kindling temperature.

(Fig. 33). The kindling temperature of phosphorus is lower than that of sulfur, which in turn is lower than that of wood.

Spontaneous combustion. We frequently hear of fires starting spontaneously. Spontaneous combustion will occur when the temperature of a substance has been raised to its kindling temperature because at this point oxidation is occurring so rapidly the substance will burst into flame. A pile of oily rags or a pile of coal may take fire spontaneously. Spontaneous combustion is the result of a cumulative process which takes place rather slowly at first. (During the early

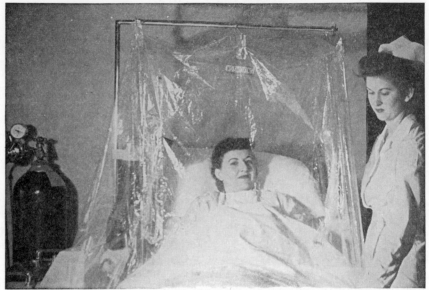

Courtesy of B. S. Pollak Hospital for Chest Diseases, Jersey City, N. J.

Fig. 34. Hospital patient in oxygen tent.

stages the process is really not combustion, but a slow oxidation of the substance by the oxygen of the air.) If the combustible substance is a good heat insulator, that is, if it retains most of the heat given off in the oxidation process, the combustion stage may develop. The heat which is produced as a result of the oxidation process gradually accumulates, raising the temperature of the substance finally to the kindling temperature, at which point self-combustion takes place. Two conditions then are essential for spontaneous combustion: (1) an existing slow oxidation with the evolution of heat and (2) good heat insulation, or the ability of the substance to retain a large part of the heat generated in the oxidation process.

Uses of oxygen. Oxygen has a number of important uses. Industry uses annually about 2500 tons of the gas compressed in steel cylinders. In modern medical practice its uses are increasing. In certain diseases, such as pneumonia, tuberculosis, gas poisoning, and other respiratory impairments, pure oxygen may be administered in an "oxygen tent."

In the use of anesthetics, oxygen may be mixed with ethylene, nitrous oxide, etc.

The largest amount of commercial oxygen is used in oxyacetylene torches and the hydrogen-oxygen blowpipe for welding purposes. Since oxidation occurs so rapidly in an atmosphere of pure oxygen, high temperatures may be reached, sufficient for melting and cutting metals.

Airplanes carry tanks of oxygen which may be used when flying at high altitudes. Flights into the stratosphere where the concentration of oxygen is low make necessary the use of oxygen for the respiratory needs of the passengers. Other uses of oxygen include pulmotors, basal metabolism machines, submarines, diving bells, etc.

Ozone. If a high electrical discharge is allowed to pass through oxygen gas at low temperatures, a gas is formed with a peculiar, generator-room odor. The composition of the substance has been proved to be that represented by the formula O_3. It has been given the name ozone, from the Greek "to smell." Since its boiling point is $-112°$ C., which is markedly higher than for oxygen ($-183°$ C.), ozone may be condensed as a liquid from oxygen gas containing small percentages of ozone.

Ozone is quite unstable, breaking down to form oxygen

$$2\ O_3 \longrightarrow 3\ O_2 + \text{energy}$$

with the liberation of a large amount of energy. Ozone is much more active than ordinary oxygen and reacts vigorously with most of the elements and many compounds. Organic matter is rapidly oxidized. Ozone is sometimes used to purify water by destruction of bacteria and micro-organisms, and to purify air which has become polluted. It finds limited use also as a bleaching agent.

An example of its chemical activity is the liberation of free iodine from iodides, such as potassium iodide; this property is the basis for testing for the substance.

EXERCISES

1. How does oxygen occur in nature?
2. Why do substances burn better in pure oxygen than in ordinary air?
3. How may oxygen be collected during its laboratory preparation?
4. List four metals whose oxides are unstable toward heat.
5. Do all compounds containing oxygen give up oxygen when heated?
6. Name two metals which oxidize in air; two which do not.
7. Define: density, combustion, oxidation, kindling temperature, oxide, catalyst, exothermic.
8. What two conditions are necessary for spontaneous combustion?

9. Give three important uses of oxygen.
10. What is the function of the carburetor in your car?
11. Why have dampers on heating stoves and furnaces?
12. Compare the quantities of heat evolved during the rapid and slow oxidation of iron.
13. Can you suggest a method for demonstrating that MnO_2 is not changed chemically when it is employed as a catalyst in the decomposition of $KClO_3$?
14. Theoretically, what quantity of potassium chlorate could be catalytically decomposed with one gram of MnO_2?　　　　　　　　Ans. Any amount
15. Remembering that lead dioxide gives up one-half of its oxygen on being heated; potassium chlorate all of its oxygen and potassium nitrate only one-third of its oxygen, which of these compounds would be the cheapest source of oxygen in the laboratory assuming the following costs per pound: lead dioxide $0.40; potassium chlorate $1.25; potassium nitrate $0.90.
16. If all of the oxygen from the decomposition of 2.45 g. of potassium chlorate is used to burn carbon to carbon dioxide, what weight of carbon dioxide would be produced?　　　　　　　　Ans. 1.32 g.
17. Diagram the three isotopes of oxygen, atomic weights 16, 17, 18.

REFERENCES

R. Boyle, *The Skeptical Chemist*, Dutton.

H. P. Cady, "Liquid Air," *J. Chem. Ed.* **8,** 1027 (1931).

R. A. Worstell, "Ozone," *ibid.* **7,** 1120 (1930); **9,** 291 (1932).

J. E. Ransford, "Demonstration of Ozone from Bottled Oxygen," *ibid.* **28,** 477 (1951).

J. Priestley, "Discovery of Oxygen," *Alembic Club Reprints*, No. 7.

C. W. Scheele, "Discovery of Oxygen," *Alembic Club Reprints*, No. 8.

VII

Hydrogen

H

Early history. Hydrogen was prepared many times before it was identified as an elementary substance. Early investigators noted that acids acted with certain metals to produce a "colorless, odorless gas." Paracelsus (1493–1541) stated that when sulfuric acid is allowed to act on iron, "an air arises which bursts forth like the wind." Since the only named gas at this time was air, it was believed that this gas, which later was called hydrogen, was just another kind of "air." Henry Cavendish (1731–1810), who was given credit for its discovery in 1776, noted that "air" produced from the action of metals with acids was inflammable and that it burned in the air to produce water. Lavoisier gave this new "air" the name hydrogen, which signified "water former."

Occurrence. Hydrogen is one of the more abundant of the chemical elements. By weight it makes up approximately 1 per cent of the earth's crust. Unlike oxygen, it is seldom found in the free state (uncombined with other elements). It is found in the atmosphere in very small amounts (about .01 per cent) and in slightly larger amounts in gases issuing from volcanoes. Spectroscopic studies indicate that large amounts of free hydrogen are present in gases surrounding the sun and many stars.

In combination with other elements, hydrogen is widely distributed. Water is about one-ninth hydrogen by weight, the other eight-ninths being oxygen. Compounds of organic origin (those compounds associated with living organisms or their products) such as sugar, food products, fats, proteins, and oils contain hydrogen. Combined with carbon, hydrogen is found in natural gas, kerosene, gasoline, and other petroleum products. It is also a constituent of all acids and hydroxides (bases), two classes of compounds which we shall presently discuss.

If we could count the atoms of the various elements present in the earth's crust, we would undoubtedly find that hydrogen atoms are exceeded in number only by atoms of oxygen. However, since hydrogen is the lightest of the elements, with an atomic weight of 1, the proportion of hydrogen by weight in the earth's crust is relatively small.

Action of hydrochloric acid on metals. Certain metals have the property of displacing hydrogen from acids. When hydrochloric acid, HCl, is added to granulated zinc, hydrogen gas is evolved at a rapid rate:

$$Zn + 2\,HCl \longrightarrow ZnCl_2 + H_2 \uparrow$$
$$\text{hydrochloric} \qquad \text{zinc}$$
$$\text{acid} \qquad \text{chloride}$$

In this chemical change the metal zinc has displaced or replaced the hydrogen in the acid. The hydrogen is set free, and the zinc combines with the chlorine to form zinc chloride. A compound formed by the replacement of the hydrogen of an acid with a metal is termed a *salt*. Thus zinc chloride is a salt; furthermore, it is said to be a salt of hydrochloric acid, since it is derived from that acid by replacement of hydrogen. It may be noted that zinc chloride is composed of the metal zinc and the nonmetal chlorine. A compound of a metal and a nonmetal may be called a salt (see p. 17).

Aluminum reacts similarly with hydrochloric acid to form aluminum chloride and hydrogen:

$$2\,Al + 6\,HCl \longrightarrow 2\,AlCl_3 + 3\,H_2$$
$$\text{aluminum}$$
$$\text{chloride}$$

The action, once started, is more rapid than with zinc. Aluminum chloride is a salt of hydrochloric acid, since it is derived from the acid by replacement. All salts of hydrochloric acid are chlorides.

Iron and tin will replace hydrogen from hydrochloric acid, but less vigorously than zinc and aluminum:

$$Fe + 2\,HCl \longrightarrow FeCl_2 + H_2$$
$$\text{ferrous}$$
$$\text{chloride}$$

$$Sn + 2\,HCl \longrightarrow SnCl_2 + H_2$$
$$\text{stannous}$$
$$\text{chloride}$$

The activity series. The rate at which metals displace hydrogen from hydrochloric acid varies with the metal used. Certain metals displace hydrogen rapidly, while others react slowly or not at all. On the basis of the rate of displacement of hydrogen from hydrochloric acid, metals may be arranged in an activity series. Of the common metals, potassium and sodium are found to be the most active, while lead and tin are the least active in displacing hydrogen from an acid. The relative activity of copper, gold, platinum and other metals which do not displace hydrogen from acids of course cannot be determined by this method. However, other reactions of these metals serve to show their relative activity.

If we place the most active metal at the top followed by metals of gradually decreasing activity, we obtain the *activity series* of the metals as indicated on the right of this page. Hydrogen is placed in the list to divide those metals which displace hydrogen from acids from those metals which do not. Those metals appearing above hydrogen in this series will displace hydrogen from an acid, those below hydrogen will not react with an acid to produce free hydrogen. This activity series is sometimes referred to as the "electromotive series of metals," since the position of the metals in the list can be determined from electromotive force measurements. (See chap. XXXII.)

K
Na
Ba
Ca
Mg
Al
Mn
Zn
Cr
Cd
Fe
Co
Ni
Sn
Pb
Hydrogen
Sb
Bi
As
Cu
Hg
Ag
Pt
Au

Action of other acids with metals. The action of other acids on metals in most cases is similar to that of hydrochloric acid. For example, metals above hydrogen in the activity series displace the hydrogen from sulfuric acid to form a *sulfate* salt and free hydrogen:

$$Zn + H_2SO_4 \longrightarrow ZnSO_4 + H_2$$
$$\text{sulfuric} \quad\quad \text{zinc}$$
$$\text{acid} \quad\quad\quad \text{sulfate}$$

$$Fe + H_2SO_4 \longrightarrow FeSO_4 + H_2$$
$$\text{ferrous}$$
$$\text{sulfate}$$

Salts of sulfuric acid are called *sulfates;* thus $ZnSO_4$ is zinc sulfate and $FeSO_4$ is ferrous sulfate.

Phosphoric acid, H_3PO_4, acts similarly with metals above hydrogen to produce hydrogen and *phosphates:*

$$3\, Zn + 2\, H_3PO_4 \longrightarrow Zn_3(PO_4)_2 + 3\, H_2$$
$$\text{zinc}$$
$$\text{phosphate}$$

$$2\, Al + 2\, H_3PO_4 \longrightarrow 2\, AlPO_4 + 3\, H_2$$
$$\text{aluminum}$$
$$\text{phosphate}$$

The action of nitric acid, HNO_3, on metals is somewhat different from that of most of the other acids. This is due to the fact that nitric acid possesses oxidizing properties in addition to acid properties (see chap. XX). Nitric acid dissolves many of the metals appearing below hydrogen in the activity series, and its action on metals above hydrogen in the series produces substances other than free hydrogen. These reactions will be discussed at a later time.

In general, if the acid exhibits only acid characteristics, it will act on metals appearing above hydrogen in the activity series to liberate free hydrogen. We may formulate the general rule:

Metal (above hydrogen) + Acid $\longrightarrow$ Salt + Hydrogen

Further examples of displacement. The activity series has a further significance. Any metal will displace a metal lying below it in the activity series (a less active metal) from its salt in water solution. Thus iron which appears above copper in the series will displace the copper from a copper salt solution. An iron nail placed in a solution of copper sulfate is rapidly coated by metallic copper. The more active metal, iron, has displaced the less active metal, copper:

$$Fe + CuSO_4 \longrightarrow Cu + FeSO_4$$
copper
sulfate

Similarly a strip of copper placed in a solution of a mercury salt soon becomes coated with metallic mercury:

$$Cu + HgSO_4 \longrightarrow CuSO_4 + Hg$$
mercuric
sulfate

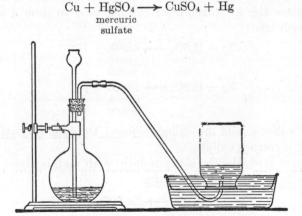

Fig. 35. Apparatus for generating hydrogen.

Laboratory preparation of hydrogen. For the preparation of hydrogen in laboratory quantities, the action of sulfuric acid on zinc is frequently employed. The apparatus shown in Figure 35 may be used. Acid is added through the thistle tube and reacts with the zinc placed in the flask. The hydrogen gas is collected by displacement of water in which it is relatively insoluble:

$$Zn + H_2SO_4 \longrightarrow ZnSO_4 + H_2$$

This reaction may be catalyzed by the addition of a few drops of copper sulfate solution. The zinc, being more active than copper, displaces the latter:

$$Zn + CuSO_4 \longrightarrow ZnSO_4 + Cu$$

The finely divided copper deposits on the zinc and acts as a catalyst for the reaction.

Action of water on metals. Those metals near the top of the activity series are sufficiently active to displace hydrogen from water. If a small piece of sodium metal is dropped into water, a very vigorous reaction ensues with the liberation of hydrogen gas. The experiment must be carried out with a great deal of caution, as the action takes place with almost explosive violence.

Sodium displaces only one hydrogen atom in the water molecule, forming sodium hydroxide and hydrogen. Sodium hydroxide is a base and turns red litmus blue:

$$2\,Na + 2\,H_2O \longrightarrow \underset{\substack{sodium \\ hydroxide}}{2\,NaOH} + H_2$$

Potassium, barium, and calcium displace hydrogen from water in a similar manner; in each case the metal hydroxide (base) and hydrogen are produced. These first metals in the activity series are sufficiently active to displace hydrogen from ice water:

$$Metal\ (K,\ Na,\ Ba,\ Ca) + H_2O \longrightarrow Metal\ Hydroxide + H_2$$

The next nine metals in the activity series, magnesium, aluminum, manganese, zinc, chromium, cadmium, iron, cobalt, and nickel, while not active enough to displace hydrogen from cold water, will act with water in the form of steam. These metals displace all of the hydrogen in the water molecule and yield the oxide of the metal used and free hydrogen:

$$Metal + H_2O\ (steam) \longrightarrow Oxide\ of\ Metal + H_2$$

Lead and tin, which follow in the series, are too inactive to act with water at any temperature to any noticeable degree.

Preparation of hydrogen from bases. Certain metals will displace hydrogen from certain bases (metallic hydroxides) to yield hydrogen. For example, zinc or aluminum will act with either sodium or potassium hydroxide to liberate hydrogen:

$$Zn + 2 \, KOH \longrightarrow K_2ZnO_2 + H_2$$
potassium
zincate

$$2 \, Al + 6 \, NaOH \longrightarrow 2 \, Na_3AlO_3 + 3 \, H_2$$
sodium
aluminate

Commercial preparation of hydrogen. (a) Electrolysis of water. Described on page 84. (b) When steam is passed over carbon which has been heated to a high temperature, carbon monoxide and hydrogen gases are produced:

$$C + H_2O \longrightarrow CO + H_2$$
carbon
monoxide

Since both carbon monoxide and hydrogen are combustible, the mixture has fuel value and in many cases no attempt is made to separate the products. The mixture has been given the trade name "water gas."

Hydrogen may be separated from the mixture by cooling to a low temperature (about $-200°$) and liquefying the carbon monoxide. The hydrogen is left in the gaseous condition. The mixture of the two gases may be treated with steam in the presence of a catalyst to oxidize the carbon monoxide to carbon dioxide, and yield more hydrogen:

$$CO + H_2O \longrightarrow CO_2 + H_2$$
carbon
dioxide

The carbon dioxide may be separated from the hydrogen by absorption in water or alkaline solution, leaving relatively pure hydrogen.

A reversible reaction. If steam is passed over red hot iron filings in a tube (Fig. 36, a), hydrogen gas is produced and may be removed from the opposite end of this tube:

$$3 \, Fe + 4 \, H_2O \text{ (steam)} \longrightarrow Fe_3O_4 + 4 \, H_2 \qquad (1)$$
iron
oxide

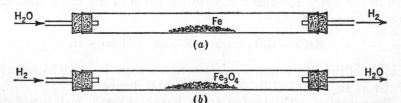

Fig. 36. A reversible reaction.

This reaction, however, is *reversible* since it may be made to proceed in the opposite direction. For example, if hydrogen gas is passed over heated iron oxide (Fig. 36, *b*), metallic iron and steam are produced:

$$Fe_3O_4 + 4 H_2 \longrightarrow 3 Fe + 4 H_2O \tag{2}$$

The latter is exactly the reverse of reaction (1). We shall find that many chemical reactions are reversible under certain conditions; that is, they may be made to proceed in *either* direction.

Properties of hydrogen. (*a*) *Physical.* Hydrogen is a colorless, odorless gas and is relatively insoluble in water; 100 ml. of water dissolves about 2 ml. of hydrogen gas under ordinary conditions of temperature and pressure. It is the lightest known substance, therefore has the smallest density. Hydrogen gas can be liquefied and solidified only with considerable difficulty — the gas liquefies at temperatures below −253°, and solidifies at −259°.

Certain metals, such as platinum and palladium, have the property of adsorbing large volumes of hydrogen, often adsorbing many hundred times their own volume of the gas. If the metal is finely divided, thus increasing its surface area, more gas will be adsorbed. This hydrogen appears to be more active than ordinary hydrogen in many reactions and is referred to as "activated hydrogen gas." This is the basis for the use of platinum as a catalyst for many reactions in which hydrogen is one of the reacting substances.

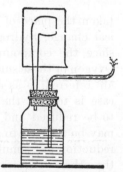

Fig. 37. Apparatus to show relative rates of diffusion of air and hydrogen.

Hydrogen gas *diffuses* more rapidly than any other gas — by diffusion we mean that it mixes rapidly with other gases. All gases will diffuse or mix with one another, and the speed of diffusion is a function of the density of the gases; the lower the density the more rapid the rate of diffusion. This property may be demonstrated by the following experiment. A beaker of hydrogen gas is placed over a porous clay pipe arranged as shown in Figure 37. The hydrogen gas passes into the pipe faster than the air can diffuse out (since hydrogen is the lighter gas and therefore diffuses more rapidly). As a result, the increased pressure inside of the pipe and bottle forces liquid up through the jet.

(*b*) *Chemical.* A mixture of hydrogen and oxygen gases may be heated moderately without any apparent action taking place; however, if the mixture is ignited by a spark even at ordinary temperatures, combination takes place with explosive violence to form water:

$$2\,H_2 + O_2 \longrightarrow 2\,H_2O$$

This action may be used as a basis for testing the purity of a sample of hydrogen. A small amount of the gas is ignited in a test tube; if a slight explosion occurs, the gas contains air or oxygen and is therefore impure. Pure hydrogen burns quietly with an almost colorless flame. It does not support combustion.

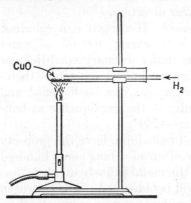

When hydrogen gas is passed over heated copper oxide in a test tube, the latter gradually changes from black to a copper-colored powder (Fig. 38). Small drops of liquid condense on the sides of the test tube. The reddish deposit remaining in the test tube is metallic copper, and the liquid formed on the side of the tube is water:

$$CuO + H_2 \longrightarrow Cu + H_2O$$

Fig. 38. Reduction of cupric oxide by hydrogen gas.

The above is another example of displacement, since the hydrogen has taken the place of the copper in the copper oxide. In such a chemical change, hydrogen is sometimes referred to as a *reducing* agent, since the compound has been reduced or changed to an element. Oxygen or those substances which give up oxygen in a chemical change are referred to as *oxidizing* agents; hence copper oxide in the above case is termed the oxidizing agent. The copper oxide may be said to be reduced and the hydrogen to be oxidized. The entire process may be referred to as an oxidation-reduction reaction. Oxidation and reduction are simultaneous processes; one never takes place without the other. The terms oxidation and reduction have a much broader significance than indicated above, and the subject will be treated in more detail in chapter XX.

Certain other metallic oxides may be reduced with hydrogen to form the free metal. Advantage is taken of this fact in the preparation of some of the less common metals in a very pure condition. Tungsten and molybdenum may be obtained in this manner. In general, the cost of production with hydrogen as a reducing agent is relatively high, and cheaper reducing agents are employed in the commercial preparation of most of the common metals.

Hydrogen combines directly with many of the nonmetals:

$$H_2 + S \longrightarrow H_2S$$
hydrogen
sulfide

$$H_2 + Cl_2 \longrightarrow 2\,HCl$$
hydrogen
chloride

$$3\,H_2 + N_2 \longrightarrow 2\,NH_3$$
ammonia

Atomic hydrogen. If hydrogen gas is bubbled into indigo-blue solution, no color change occurs. However, if the hydrogen is generated in contact with the indigo blue by placing a piece of zinc and a few drops of sulfuric acid in the solution, decolorization takes place. This would indicate a greater degree of activity for freshly generated hydrogen. Such hydrogen is termed "active" or "nascent" hydrogen.

The explanation for the activity of nascent hydrogen over and above that of common gaseous hydrogen, H_2, is that the former is composed of single atoms which have not yet combined to form molecular hydrogen, e.g.

$$Zn + 2\,HCl \longrightarrow ZnCl_2 + 2\,H$$

Atomic hydrogen also results from the electrolysis of dilute acids when certain metals are made the negative pole (cathode) of the cell. Very little active hydrogen is produced with platinum as a cathode; this would indicate that platinum is a particularly effective catalyst for the reaction

$$H + H \longrightarrow H_2 + energy$$

Metals such as zinc and lead are said to be poor catalysts for this reaction since hydrogen gas generated on their surfaces is of the active kind.

Further evidence for the existence of atomic hydrogen is afforded in the development by I. Langmuir of an "atomic hydrogen" flame. When hydrogen gas, H_2, is passed through an electric arc, the molecules are apparently decomposed to atoms. As the atoms of hydrogen are catalyzed to molecules again, a flame of about 4000° C. results from the highly exothermic nature of this union. This very high temperature flame with a reducing atmosphere is useful in welding high melting metals.

Uses of hydrogen. Since hydrogen is a very light gas, it has considerable lifting power in the air, and advantage is taken of this property in its use in lighter-than-air craft.[1] At one time, hydrogen

[1] The lifting power of a substance in air is the difference in weight of a unit volume of air and a unit volume of the substance under the same conditions of temperature and pressure.

Fig. 39. Cans being filled with hydrogenated cooking fat.

gas was used exclusively in filling balloons and dirigibles. However, the gas is inflammable and therefore dangerous for this purpose. At the present time a mixture of hydrogen and noninflammable helium gases is used; the gases are mixed in such a proportion that the mixture is not inflammable.

Since 1925, large amounts of motor fuel and gasoline have been synthesized from coal. Coal contains carbon and compounds of carbon, hydrogen, and nitrogen. Gasoline is a mixture of several hydrocarbons (compounds of carbon and hydrogen), of which octane, C_8H_{18}, is an example. When finely powdered coal and hydrogen together are subjected to high temperatures and pressures, gasoline, lubricating oils, and other products are obtained. The process is particularly important in Germany where it was first developed by Bergius.

Certain liquid fats at high temperatures in the presence of a nickel catalyst combine with hydrogen, and in so doing, change from the liquid state to a solid or semisolid condition. Cottonseed and coconut oils are liquid fats which may be "hydrogenated" and used as substitutes for butter and lard, and for the production of soap.

Other uses include the catalytic preparation of ammonia and methyl alcohol.

EXERCISES

1. Point out several similarities and differences of hydrogen and oxygen.
2. What action, if any, takes place when iron (heated if necessary) is treated with (a) steam; (b) phosphoric acid; (c) oxygen; (d) hydrogen; (e) hydrochloric acid?
3. What are the advantages and disadvantages of using hydrogen in balloons?
4. Describe two procedures for the preparation of hydrogen from water.
5. What is the "activity series" and why is it of value to the chemist?
6. Balance the equations:

(a) $Fe + H_2O \longrightarrow Fe_3O_4 + H_2$ (c) $CH_4 + H_2O \longrightarrow CO + H_2$
(b) $Ca + H_2O \longrightarrow Ca(OH)_2 + H_2$ (d) $C + H_2O \longrightarrow CO_2 + H_2$

7. List five important uses of hydrogen.
8. In the electrolysis of water to which a small amount of sulfuric acid is added, how could you prove that the hydrogen and oxygen come from the water and not the acid?
9. Compare the relative efficiencies of hydrogen and methane (CH_4) for lifting a balloon.
10. With the aid of the activity series predict which of the following reactions would take place:

(a) $Fe + Ag_2SO_4 \longrightarrow FeSO_4 + 2 Ag$
(b) $SnCl_2 + Mg \longrightarrow MgCl_2 + Sn$
(c) $CaSO_4 + Cu \longrightarrow CuSO_4 + Ca$
(d) $ZnCl_2 + 2 Ag \longrightarrow 2 AgCl + Zn$
(e) $Hg_2SO_4 + 2 Ag \longrightarrow 2 Hg + Ag_2SO_4$
(f) $Sn + 2 HCl \longrightarrow SnCl_2 + H_2$
(g) $Cu + H_2SO_4 \longrightarrow CuSO_4 + H_2$

11. Which of the following metals would displace Cu from a solution of copper sulfate: Al, Sn, Ag, Au, Fe, Hg?

12. In terms of electrons, what change takes place when Zn displaces Cu from $CuSO_4$?

13. 9.8 grams of H_2SO_4 is treated with an excess of Zn. The hydrogen gas is collected and allowed to react with CuO. What weight of water will be formed?

Ans. 1.8 g.

REFERENCES

C. F. Armstrong, "Hydrogen in Industry," *Chemical Age,* **26,** 249 (1932).

H. Cavendish, "Experiments on Air," *Alembic Club Reprints,* No. 3.

A. Farkas, *Orthohydrogen, Parahydrogen, and Heavy Hydrogen,* Cambridge University Press, England, 1935.

I. Langmuir, "Flames of Atomic Hydrogen," *Ind. Eng. Chem.* **19,** 667 (1927).

J. B. Phillips, "Industrial Hydrogenation," *J. Soc. Chem. Ind.* **52,** 51 (1933).

H. C. Urey, F. G. Brickwedde, and G. M. Murphy, "A Hydrogen Isotope of Mass 2," *Physical Review,* **39,** 164 (1932); **40,** 1 (1932).

—— and G. K. Teal, "The Hydrogen Isotope of Atomic Weight 2," *Reviews Modern Physics,* **7,** 34 (1935).

Wm. F. Kieffer, "The Activity Series of the Metals," *J. Chem. Ed.* **27,** 659 (1950).

VIII

The Gaseous State of Matter

Familiar properties of gases. Matter in the gaseous state is characterized by its lack of any definite volume or shape. If a gas is placed in a closed container, it rapidly expands and very quickly becomes uniformly distributed throughout the entire space in the container. When a gas is cooled sufficiently, it becomes a liquid. Although all gases may be liquefied, some are changed to the liquid state only with a great deal of difficulty. Hydrogen and helium gases are the most difficult to liquefy, since temperatures near 0° absolute are necessary. On the other hand, such gases as chlorine and ammonia are liquefied quite easily.

If two gases are placed in a container, each gas acts independently of the other and diffuses uniformly throughout the volume of the container.

Gases may undergo expansion and compression. Air forced into an automobile tire is compressed; when the air is allowed to escape, it expands. Gases also exert pressure, and this pressure is exerted uniformly on all sides and top and bottom of the containing vessel. We shall presently find an explanation for the diffusion and pressure of gases.

The measurement of air pressure. The pressure of the atmosphere is measured with an instrument called a *barometer*. A simple barometer (Fig. 40), can be prepared by inverting a piece of glass tubing about three feet long and closed at one end, filled with mercury, over a shallow pan containing mercury. The open end of the tube lies beneath the surface of the mercury in the pan. The mercury will sink in the tube to a level such that the weight of the column of mercury is just equal to the weight of the column of air of equal cross section above the surface of the mercury in the outside container. This column of air extends many miles high. The air exerts a pres-

sure on the surface of the mercury in the container and supports the
column of mercury in the tube. The exact pressure is determined by
reading the difference between two mercury levels, the one in the tube
and the other in the pan. The height of the mercury column is usually
expressed in terms of millimeters. The average
air pressure at sea level will support a column of
mercury 760 mm. in height. This pressure is termed
1 atmosphere of pressure or *standard pressure*. A
pressure of 50 atmospheres would be a pressure
50 times as great as that exerted by the atmosphere at sea level. In scientific work, pressures
are usually referred to in terms of millimeters of
mercury. A pressure of 700 mm. would be a pressure equal to that exerted by a column of mercury
700 mm. high, etc. A column of water approximately 34 feet high would be supported by the
atmosphere at sea level.

Fig. 40. A mercury barometer.

**The effect of pressure on the volume of a
gas.** When the pressure on a gas is increased, the
gas is compressed; an increase in pressure brings about a diminution
of volume of the gas. Let us imagine a gas, such as air, enclosed in a
cylinder fitted with a piston (Fig. 41). We shall assume that the piston
is weightless and frictionless. The pressure exerted on the gas will
be adjusted by means of weights placed on the top side of the piston.
Suppose we have 100 ml. of gas in the cylinder with a certain weight
on the piston; if the weight on the piston is doubled, assuming that
the temperature remains constant, the piston will move downward

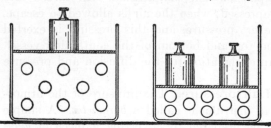

until the volume of gas
is 50 ml. By doubling
the pressure, the vol-
ume is halved. If the
pressure is increased
threefold, the volume
becomes one-third of
the original volume,
etc. The relationship
between the volume of
a gas and the pressure

**Fig. 41. If the pressure upon a gas is doubled
(at a constant temperature), the volume is
halved (Boyle's Law).**

was first stated by Robert Boyle in 1662 as follows: *The volume of a
given mass of gas at constant temperature varies inversely as the pressure.*
This relationship, which is virtually independent of the nature of the
gas, is known as Boyle's Law.

By means of the law, we may calculate the volume of a gas at any pressure, provided we know the volume at a given pressure.

EXAMPLE 1. 100 ml. of gas are enclosed in the cylinder (Fig. 41) under a pressure of 760 mm. What would the volume be at a pressure of 1520 mm., *i.e.*, 2 × 760 mm.?

It is immediately evident that the corrected volume will be less than 100 ml., since the pressure has been increased from 760 to 1520 mm., and an increase in pressure results in a smaller volume. The volume will decrease in the same ratio that the pressure increases. The new volume then must be

$$100 \times \tfrac{760}{1520} = 50 \text{ ml.}$$

In the above calculation we have multiplied the volume by a fraction less than one, that is, $\tfrac{760}{1520}$. It is evident that had we multiplied by the larger ratio, the answer would have been greater than 100, which we know must be incorrect.

EXAMPLE 2. 100 ml. of gas at a pressure of 1000 mm. will occupy what volume at standard pressure (760 mm.)?

Again we reason that since the pressure is decreased (from 1000 mm. to 760 mm.), the volume must *increase*. Consequently the new volume will be greater than 100 ml., and we must multiply the original volume by a fraction greater than one. We have two possible ratios of pressures, $\tfrac{760}{1000}$ or $\tfrac{1000}{760}$. Since the ratio to be used must, in this case, be greater than one, we use the latter ratio, thus

$$\text{New Volume} = 100 \text{ ml.} \times \tfrac{1000}{760} = 131.6 \text{ ml.}$$

In computing a new volume, first reason whether or not this new volume will be greater or less than the original volume. If the pressure is increased, the volume must be less; if the pressure decreases, the volume must be greater. Then multiply the original volume by a fraction (which is a ratio of the two pressures involved) so that the required condition will be satisfied. If the volume is to increase, the fraction (ratio of pressures) must be greater than unity. If the volume is to decrease, this fraction must be less than one. In accordance with the above we may write the general equation

$$v_2 = v_1 \times p_1/p_2 \quad \text{or} \quad p_1 v_1 = p_2 v_2$$

where v_1 is the volume at pressure p_1, and v_2 the volume at p_2.

The effect of temperature on the volume of a gas. We are all familiar with the fact that a gas expands as the temperature rises. If the gas is placed in a closed container, expansion cannot take place, and the rise in temperature brings about an increase in pressure. If a gas is allowed to expand at a constant pressure, we may note a definite relationship between the volume change and temperature change.

Let us again make use of the cylinder and movable piston shown in Figure 41. Suppose the volume of a given mass of gas in the cylinder is 273 ml. at a given pressure and a temperature of 0° C. Now, keeping the pressure constant (this is accomplished by using a constant weight on the piston), let us heat the cylinder of gas. The piston will move upward and for every centigrade degree rise in temperature, the volume will increase 1 ml. At a temperature of 1°, then, the volume would be 274 ml.; at a temperature of 10°, the volume would be 283 ml. If the temperature is decreased to 1° below 0°, that is, −1°, the volume decreases to 272 ml. A gas, then, at 0° contracts $\frac{1}{273}$ of its volume for every degree decrease in temperature, or it expands $\frac{1}{273}$ of its volume for every degree increase in temperature. Theoretically the volume of a gas would decrease to zero at −273°. This temperature is called absolute zero and is the basis of the absolute scale of temperature which was explained in chapter II. Actually this condition of zero temperature is never realized because all substances liquefy or solidify before the absolute zero temperature is reached. If the temperature is expressed as absolute temperature, it is evident that *the volume of a gas at constant pressure is directly proportional to the absolute temperature.* This is a statement of Charles' Law.

By means of Charles' law, we can calculate the volume of a gas at any temperature if we know its volume at any given temperature, assuming that the pressure remains constant.

EXAMPLE 1. A certain gas occupies a volume of 100 ml. at a temperature of 20°; what will its volume be at 10° if the pressure remains constant?

First we must change these centigrade temperatures to absolute temperatures, since Charles' law states that the volume is directly proportional to the *absolute* temperature. We learned in chapter II that centigrade temperature may be changed to absolute temperature by adding 273. Then

$$20° \text{ C.} = 20 + 273 = 293° \text{ A.}$$
and
$$10° \text{ C.} = 10 + 273 = 283° \text{ A.}$$

The temperature is being decreased (from 293 to 283), and since decrease in temperature brings about a decrease in volume, the corrected volume will be less than 100 ml., and the correction factor must be less than unity. The two possible ratios of temperature are $\frac{293}{283}$ and $\frac{283}{293}$. We must use the latter ratio, as this is the one which will give us a volume of less than 100 ml., thus

$$\text{New Volume} = 100 \times \tfrac{283}{293} = 96.6 \text{ ml.}$$

EXAMPLE 2. The volume of a gas at 20° is 100 ml. What is the volume at 100°?

Again we first convert centigrade temperatures to absolute temperatures:

$$20° \text{ C.} = 20 + 273 = 293° \text{ A.}$$
$$100° \text{ C.} = 100 + 273 = 373° \text{ A.}$$

Since the temperature is increasing, the volume must increase. If the volume is to increase, we must multiply the original volume by a fraction greater than unity, that is, $\frac{373}{293}$; hence

$$\text{New Volume} = 100 \times \tfrac{373}{293} = 127.3 \text{ ml.}$$

In solving these problems, we always multiply the original volume by a fraction (greater or less than unity). This fraction is a ratio of the absolute temperatures involved. We reason that if the temperature is decreased, the volume likewise must decrease; consequently we must use the ratio less than one. If the temperature is increased, the volume must increase, so we use the fraction greater than unity.

In accordance with the above, we may write the general formula,

$$v_2 = v_1 \times T_2/T_1 \quad \text{or} \quad \frac{v_2}{v_1} = \frac{T_2}{T_1}$$

where v_2 is the volume at absolute temperature T_2, and v_1 is the volume at absolute temperature T_1.

The combined gas laws. We have learned from Boyle's law that the volume of a gas at constant temperature is inversely proportional to the pressure, and from Charles' law that the volume at constant pressure is directly proportional to the absolute temperature. The two laws may be combined and stated as follows: *The volume of a given mass of a gas is inversely proportional to the pressure and directly proportional to the absolute temperature.*

PROBLEM 1. A gas occupies a volume of 1 liter at a temperature of 27° and 500 mm. pressure. Calculate the volume of the gas if the temperature is changed to 60° and the pressure changed to 700 mm.

In solving this problem, first consider the volume change with change of pressure. The pressure is increased from 500 mm. to 700 mm. An increase in pressure decreases the volume, so we must multiply the original volume by a ratio less than one, *i.e.*, $\frac{500}{700}$. Now consider the change in volume with change in temperature. The temperature is increased from 27° (300° A.) to 60° (333° A.). Since increase in temperature causes an increase in volume, the corrected volume must be greater than one liter. The original volume must then be multiplied by a ratio greater than unity, i.e., $\frac{333}{300}$. Correcting for changes in both temperature and pressure, we have

$$\text{New volume} = 1 \times \tfrac{500}{700} \times \tfrac{333}{300} = .79 \text{ liter}$$

The general formula for the combined gas laws may be written,

$$v_2 = v_1 \times \frac{p_1}{p_2} \times \frac{T_2}{T_1}, \quad \text{or} \quad \frac{p_1 v_1}{T_1} = \frac{p_2 v_2}{T_2}$$

where p_1 and T_1 are pressure and absolute temperature respectively of the gas at volume v_1, and p_2 and T_2 are pressure and absolute temperature respectively at volume v_2.

It is obvious that if five of the six variables in the formulation $\frac{p_1 v_1}{T_1} = \frac{p_2 v_2}{T_2}$ are fixed, then the sixth can be calculated.

PROBLEM 2. Calculate the pressure required to compress 2 liters of a gas at 700 mm. pressure and 20° C. into a container of 100 ml. capacity at a temperature of $-150°$ C.

We may reason this way: the final pressure must be the original pressure corrected for the volume change and the temperature change. Since a decrease in volume means an increase in pressure, the original pressure must be multiplied by the ratio of volumes greater than one, i.e., 2 liters/.1 liter. The temperature is decreasing from 293° A. (20° C.) to 123° A. ($-150°$ C.) and since pressure decreases with decreasing temperature, the original pressure must be multiplied by a ratio of less than one, i.e., 123/293. Hence,

$$\text{New pressure} = 700 \text{ mm.} \times \frac{2}{.1} \times \frac{123}{293} = 5877 \text{ mm.}$$

Of course we might substitute directly into the formula developed above to arrive at the same result:

$$\frac{p_1 v_1}{T_1} = \frac{p_2 v_2}{T_2}$$

ORIGINAL CONDITIONS	FINAL CONDITIONS
$p_1 = 700$ mm.	$p_2 = ?$
$v_1 = 2$ liters	$v_2 = .1$ liter
$T_1 = 20° + 273° = 293°$	$T_2 = -150 + 273° = 123°$

Substituting:

$$\frac{(700 \text{ mm.})(2 \text{ liters})}{293°} = \frac{(p_2)(.1 \text{ liter})}{123°}$$

$$p_2 = \frac{(700 \text{ mm.})(2 \text{ liters})(123°)}{(.1 \text{ liter})(293°)} = 5877 \text{ mm.}$$

PROBLEM 3. 750 ml. of gas at 300 mm. pressure and 50° C. is heated until the volume of gas is 2000 ml. at a pressure of 700 mm. What was the final temperature of the gas?

In this case, since volume is directly proportional to absolute temperature, the original temperature must be multiplied by the larger ratio, *i.e.*, 2000/750. Pressure is directly proportional to absolute temperature so the original temperature must be multiplied by the ratio 700/300. Hence

$$\text{New temperature} = 323° \text{ A} \times \tfrac{2000}{750} \times \tfrac{700}{300} = 2010° \text{ A}$$
$$\text{Centigrade temperature} = 2010° - 273° = 1737°$$

Or, substituting directly into the formula:

$$\frac{p_1 v_1}{T_1} = \frac{p_2 v_2}{T_2}$$

ORIGINAL CONDITIONS	FINAL CONDITIONS
$p_1 = 300$ mm.	$p_2 = 700$ mm.
$v_1 = 750$ ml.	$v_2 = 2000$ ml.
$T_1 = 50° + 273° = 323°$ A.	$T_2 = ?$

Substituting:

$$\frac{(300 \text{ mm.})(750 \text{ ml.})}{323°} = \frac{(700 \text{ mm.})(2000 \text{ ml.})}{T_2}$$
$$T_2 = \frac{(700 \text{ mm.})(2000 \text{ ml.})(323°)}{(300 \text{ mm.})(750 \text{ ml.})} = 2010°$$
$$\text{Centigrade temperature} = 2010° - 273° = 1737°$$

Sometimes it is convenient to use the general gas law formula

$$\frac{p_1 v_1}{T_1} = \frac{p_2 v_2}{T_2}$$

even though only two variables are involved. Suppose, for example, that one wishes to determine the change in volume of a gas caused by a given change of pressure, the temperature remaining constant. Instead of using the formula for Boyle's law (p. 104), he could substitute directly in the general gas law formula, canceling out the two T terms, which are obviously identical. Or, if he wished, he could by algebraic manipulation derive the formula for Boyle's law from the general gas law formula. Not the least of the advantages of the general formula is that it makes it unnecessary to memorize the three special formulas. Let us now turn to the solution of an actual problem.

PROBLEM 4. A steel cylinder containing 10 liters of gas at a pressure of 4 atmospheres and a temperature of 40° C. is heated to 70° C. What is the pressure of the gas at the higher temperature?

<table>
<tr><td colspan="2" align="center">ORIGINAL CONDITIONS</td><td colspan="2" align="center">FINAL CONDITIONS</td></tr>
</table>

ORIGINAL CONDITIONS	FINAL CONDITIONS
$p_1 = 4$ atm.	$p_2 = ?$
$v_2 = 10$ l.	$v_2 = 10$ l.
$T_1 = 40° + 273° = 313°$	$T_2 = 70° + 273° = 343°$

Since the volume is constant, the general formulation becomes

$$\frac{p_1}{T_1} = \frac{p_2}{T_2}$$

Substituting:

$$\frac{4 \text{ atm.}}{313°} = \frac{p_2}{343°}$$

$$p_2 = \frac{(4 \text{ atm.})(343°)}{313°} = 4.383 \text{ atm.}$$

Standard pressure and temperature. Since the volume of a gas changes with temperature and pressure, the volume is not defined unless the temperature and pressure of the gas are given. In order to get a comparison of the weights of equal volumes of gases, chemists have decided to refer all gas volumes to a standard set of conditions of temperature and pressure. We have already indicated (p. 104) that the standard of pressure is the average pressure of the atmosphere at sea level, namely 760 mm. The standard temperature has been selected as the melting point of ice, namely, 0° C. or 273° A. Unless otherwise specified, when referring to gas volumes, we shall assume standard conditions of pressure and temperature.

Dalton's law of partial pressures. *Each of the gases in a gaseous mixture behaves independently of the other gases and exerts its own pressure, the total pressure of the mixture being the sum of the partial pressures exerted by each gas present.* Since the atmosphere is composed of approximately 20 per cent oxygen and 80 per cent nitrogen, the oxygen exerts a partial pressure of about $\frac{1}{5} \times 760$ mm. = 152 mm., and the nitrogen a partial pressure of $\frac{4}{5} \times 760$ mm. = 608 mm.

Frequently gases in the laboratory are collected by displacement of water, as shown in Figure 42. The pressure of the gas inside the bottle is most conveniently measured by making it equal to the pressure of the atmosphere which can be determined with a barometer.

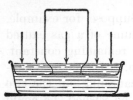

Fig. 42. Collection of a gas over water.

If the level of water inside the bottle is adjusted to the same level as the water in the container outside the bottle, then the pressure inside the bottle must be equal to the pressure outside the bottle; that is, the pressure inside must be equal to the barometer reading. The pressure inside the bottle is equal to the sum of the pressures of *two* gases, the gas collected and *water vapor*. Above the liquid in the bottle, some of the water is in the form of vapor, the amount present being dependent upon the temperature and the space above the liquid. At any given temperature, however, the pressure exerted by the water vapor is a constant.

Since the pressure of the air as measured by the barometer is equal to the total pressure of the two gases inside the bottle, we may write:

$$P_{air} = P_{gas} + P_{water\ vapor}$$

Since we are interested in the actual pressure exerted by the gas, we may transpose the above equation:

$$P_{gas} = P_{air} - P_{water\ vapor}$$

The pressure exerted by the water vapor at the temperature of the experiment may be obtained from a standard table of vapor pressure.

EXAMPLE. Suppose 100 ml. of oxygen were collected over water in the laboratory at a pressure of 700 mm. and a temperature of 20°. What would the volume of the dry oxygen gas be at standard conditions?

The vapor pressure of water at 20° (see table 10, p. 148) is 17.5 mm. The actual pressure of the oxygen gas is then 700 − 17.5 = 682.5 mm. Applying the combined gas laws, we obtain:

$$\text{New Volume} = 100 \times \frac{682.5}{760} \times \frac{273}{293} = 83.67 \text{ ml.}$$

Graham's law of diffusion. If a piece of sulfur is burned at one end of a closed room, the odor of the sulfur dioxide formed is soon noticed throughout the room. The sulfur dioxide gas has intermingled with the air. It is a property of gases that all gases will completely admix with each other. The movement of a gas as it proceeds to mix with another gas is called *diffusion*. The question arises, do all gases diffuse at the same speed? It is not difficult to determine experimentally that lighter gases diffuse faster than heavier ones. If equal volumes of O_2 gas and H_2 gas are mixed and enclosed in a porous clay pot, it can be shown that the hydrogen gas will diffuse through the pores of the pot and into the surrounding air four times as fast as the oxygen gas.

Typifying the scientific method of attaining new generalizations or laws of natural behavior is the work of Thomas Graham in 1832.

After experimentation to acquire facts as to the comparative rates of movement of different gases as they diffuse into another gas, Graham was able to state: *The comparative speeds of diffusion of gases are inversely proportional to the square roots of their densities.*

EXAMPLES: Oxygen gas is approximately 16 times as heavy as hydrogen.

$$\frac{\text{Speed of Diffusion } H_2}{\text{Speed of Diffusion } O_2} = \sqrt{\frac{16}{1}} = \frac{4}{1}$$

The lighter gas, hydrogen, at a given temperature moves four times as fast as oxygen.

Since the molecular weight of a gas is directly proportional to its density, we may use molecular weights directly in the calculations. Consider the gases SO_2, molecular weight 64, and HBr, molecular weight 81.

$$\frac{\text{Speed of Diffusion } SO_2}{\text{Speed of Diffusion HBr}} = \sqrt{\frac{81}{64}} = \frac{9}{8}$$

The lighter gas, SO_2, at a given temperature moves $1\frac{1}{8}$ times as fast as HBr.

The kinetic theory of gases. We have learned in the preceding sections that all gases behave alike under the same set of conditions. Gases expand and may be compressed; the volume of any gas is affected in the same way by changes of temperature and pressure, regardless of the nature of the gas. All gases diffuse and mix with one another in all proportions. A mixture of gases exerts a total pressure which is the sum of the partial pressures of the constituent gases, regardless of their nature. The like behavior of gases finds an explanation in the kinetic theory of gases.

Assumptions of the kinetic theory:

1. All gases are made up of tiny particles, called molecules.
2. The molecules are small in relation to the distances between them.
3. Gas molecules are in a constant state of motion and move in straight lines in all directions until they collide with one another or with the walls of the container.
4. The molecules are perfectly elastic. When they collide, they rebound with perfect elasticity and without loss of energy.
5. The velocity of the molecules changes with the temperature, increasing with increasing temperature and decreasing at lower temperatures.
6. The average energy possessed by the particles is the same, regardless of the mass. The kinetic energy (energy of motion)

of the particles is proportional to the product of their mass and the square of their velocity. The particles of high mass have a lower velocity than those of lower mass.

How the theory explains the facts. Since gases are supposedly made up of particles relatively far apart, they may readily be compressed; the molecules are simply crowded closer together. We know that solids and liquids can hardly be compressed at all, and we attribute this fact to the close proximity of the molecules in the solid and liquid states.

The diffusion of gases may be explained by the motion of the particles and the relatively large distances between the particles. The particles of each gas are free to move about between the particles of one another. Each gas then is free to act independently of other gases present in a mixture.

Pressure is due to the bombardment of the walls of the containing vessel with particles of the gas. Since the particles are moving in all directions, and since, on the average, equal numbers of molecules are traveling in all directions, equal pressures are exerted on the bottom, top, and sides of the containing vessel. The combined effect of all these collisions on a unit area gives the total pressure.

If the particles be enclosed in a smaller space (decrease in volume), the collisions with the walls become more frequent, and the pressure is increased. Conversely, if the gas is expanded, fewer collisions take place, and the pressure is decreased. In other words, the volume of gas is inversely proportional to the pressure at constant temperature (Boyle's law).

If the temperature of a gas be increased, the energy of the particles is increased and they move faster. If the volume is maintained constant, the pressure must increase, since the number of collisions on the walls in a given time will now be increased. This explains the increase in pressure of a gas with increase in temperature at constant volume. Now if pressure is to be maintained constant when the temperature is raised, the gas must be allowed to expand so that the number of collisions of the particles per unit area of the walls (pressure) will remain constant. An increase in volume with increase of temperature at constant pressure (Charles' law) is thus explained.

Since the particles in a gaseous mixture are free to move about in an independent fashion and each exerts a pressure of its own, then we would expect the total pressure of the gaseous mixture to be the sum of the pressures of all the molecular species present (Dalton's law of partial pressures).

The question might be asked, how can a light gas such as hydrogen exert as much pressure on the walls of a container as heavier oxygen gas? Since pressure is due to the summation of the magnitudes of blows of molecules on the confining walls, we are concerned with the kinetic energy of moving molecules. Energy of a moving particle is dependent upon both the mass and velocity as given by the formula

$$\text{Kinetic Energy} = \tfrac{1}{2} MV^2$$

where M is the mass of the particle and V its velocity. Recall from consideration of Graham's law of diffusion that hydrogen gas diffuses 4 times as fast as oxygen, whereas their comparative masses are 2 to 32.

$$\text{K. E. of Hydrogen} = \tfrac{1}{2} \cdot 2 \cdot 4^2 = 16$$
$$\text{K. E. of Oxygen} = \tfrac{1}{2} \cdot 32 \cdot 1^2 = 16$$

The kinetic energies of hydrogen and oxygen molecules are equal. It can likewise be further shown that at a given temperature the kinetic energy of all gas molecules is the same; the heavier gas molecules move slower than the lighter ones; and thus, insofar as pressure on the wall of a container is concerned, all gas molecules behave alike and hit with equal force.

Liquefaction of gases. The kinetic molecular theory also explains the fact that all gases may be liquefied. By slowing down molecular movement by decreased temperature, and forcing molecules nearer together by increased pressure, a state is reached where intermolecular attraction somewhat offsets the kinetic energy of particles and the conditions of the liquid state are obtained. At still lower temperatures the kinetic energy of molecules further decreases and the liquid changes to solid.

Both temperature and pressure, then, are factors in determining the condensation of a gas to liquid or conversely the vaporization of liquid to gas. Gaseous water at 100° C. and 760 mm. pressure will condense to liquid water as heat is removed. It similarly will condense to liquid if the pressure is increased. It should be emphasized that both temperature and pressure must be defined to determine the condensation or boiling point. At a pressure of 3580 mm. in a pressure chamber, water will boil at 150° C. when heat is applied, or gaseous water will condense at 20° C. under 17.4 mm. pressure. This discussion will be expanded in chapter XI.

Oxygen and hydrogen gases may be condensed to liquids at −183° C. and −252.5° C. respectively at 760 mm. pressure. At higher pressures they will condense at higher temperatures; *viz.*, at 50 atmospheres pressure, O_2 will condense to liquid at −118° C.

Above a definite temperature for each gas the kinetic energy of the molecules is of such magnitude that no increase in pressure however large can liquefy it. This temperature for each gas is its *critical temperature* and the concomitant pressure is the *critical pressure*. Oxygen cannot exist as a liquid above $-118°$ C. even at much higher than 50 atmospheres. Water cannot exist as a liquid above $374°$ C. no matter how high the pressure.

Gay-Lussac's law of combining volumes. When water is electrolyzed (Fig. 32x, p. 84), the compound is decomposed into its constituent elements, hydrogen and oxygen. Quantitative measurements show that the volume of hydrogen produced from a given weight of water is exactly *twice* the volume of oxygen produced. When water is synthesized from its elements, this same relationship between the volume of oxygen and hydrogen holds; that is, exactly twice as much hydrogen as oxygen *by volume* is required. The equation for the reaction is

$$2 H_2 + O_2 \longrightarrow 2 H_2O$$

We may note in the equation that the coefficients of the formulas are in exactly the ratio in which hydrogen and oxygen combine by volume, that is, 2 to 1. These experiments illustrate an important law of chemistry, first stated by Gay-Lussac: *Whenever gases appear or disappear in a chemical reaction they do so in the ratio of small whole numbers by volume.* It is assumed that all gases involved in such a reaction are at the same conditions of temperature and pressure. Ordinarily in the change above, the water which is formed as a product is allowed to condense to liquid water. However, if the water is allowed to remain in the form of gas (steam) and the volume measured, it is found that the volume of steam produced has the same volume as the hydrogen used, and twice the volume of the oxygen used, all gases being measured under the same conditions of temperature and pressure. We note again that the ratio by volume of the gases in the reaction is the same as shown by the coefficients of the equation, that is 2 to 1 to 2. The equation may be read as follows: two volumes of hydrogen react with one volume of oxygen to produce two volumes of water vapor (gases at same conditions). Of course, any unit of volume might be used, for example, we may say that two liters of hydrogen react with one liter of oxygen to produce two liters of steam.

Gay-Lussac's law applies to all substances in the gaseous state. The equation

$$N_2 + 3 H_2 \longrightarrow 2 NH_3$$

tells us that one volume of nitrogen combines with three volumes of hydrogen to form two volumes of ammonia. The numbers in front of the formulas (coefficients) always give us the relationship between the gases by volume.

The ratio in which substances combine by volume must not be confused with the ratio in which they combine by weight. Two parts by weight of hydrogen combine with 16 parts by weight of oxygen to form water. Substances do not combine in the ratio of small whole numbers by weight.

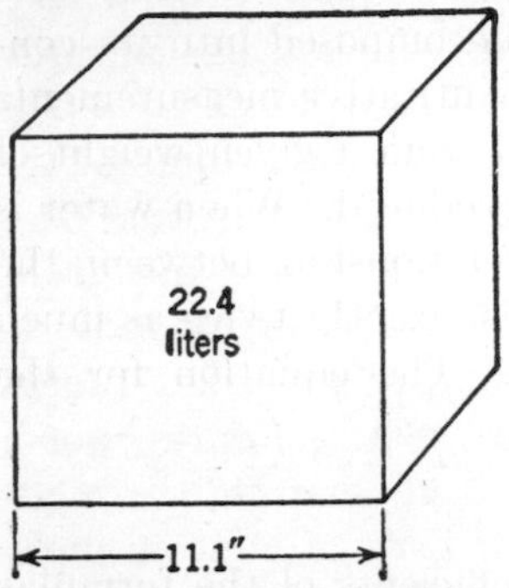

Gram molecular volume. Let us study further the equation for the electrolysis of water:

$$2\,H_2O \longrightarrow 2\,H_2 \; + \; O_2$$
$$\text{36 g.} \qquad \text{4 g.} \qquad \text{32 g.}$$
$$\text{44.8 l.} \quad \text{22.4 l.}$$

22.4
liters

|←———11.1″———→|

Fig. 44. A gram molecular weight of any gas at standard conditions occupies a volume of 22.4 liters. This volume is contained in a cube 11.1 inches on an edge.

According to the equation 2 × 18 or 36 g. of water yield 2 × 2 or 4 g. of hydrogen and 2 × 16 or 32 g. of oxygen. Experiment shows that 36 grams of water on being decomposed by the electric current produces 44.8 liters of hydrogen and 22.4 liters of oxygen, the gases being measured at standard conditions. Then, 44.8 liters of hydrogen at standard conditions must weigh 4 grams, and 22.4 liters of oxygen must have a weight of 32 grams. Four grams of hydrogen represent 2 gram molecular weights, or 2 moles of hydrogen. If the volume of 2 moles is 44.8 liters, the volume of 1 mole of hydrogen must be 22.4 liters. Similarly 32 grams of oxygen represent 1 gram molecular weight of oxygen or 1 mole of oxygen, and the volume of 1 mole of oxygen is also 22.4 liters at standard conditions. If we should study the relationship between volume and weight of other gases, we should find that *one gram molecular weight (one mole) of any gas occupies a volume of 22.4 liters at standard conditions.* This volume, 22.4 liters, is called the *gram molecular volume* of a gas.

This relationship between volume and weight of a gas is used as a basis for the determination of molecular weights of substances in the gaseous state; it is simply a matter of determining the weight of 22.4 liters of the gas measured at standard conditions. This weight is the molecular weight. The method is not applicable to those substances which are not readily converted into the gaseous condition.

Avogadro's hypothesis. In the study of gases it was found that all gases behave alike under the same conditions. All gases expand and contract according to very definite physical laws. We now find that when gases combine, there is a simple ratio in which they react by volume. These facts suggest that the same physical structure is possessed by all gases. Avogadro, an Italian physicist, was the first to suggest that *equal volumes of all gases under the same conditions of temperature and pressure contain the same number of molecules.* While this view was first held as a speculation, evidence has accumulated until at present Avogadro's statement is regarded as a law. The number of molecules in one gram molecular weight (22.4 liters of the substance in the gaseous form at standard conditions) has been determined by several independent methods and been found to be 602,000,000,000,000,000,000,000 or 6.02×10^{23}. This number is inconceivably large. The following illustration may give the student some appreciation of its magnitude. Assume that the entire population of the world, about 2 billion, is engaged in counting the molecules in one gram molecular weight of a substance. Counting molecules at the rate of 2 per second and working 24 hours a day and 365 days in a year, it would require about 5 million years to complete the job.

EXERCISES

1. Explain in terms of the kinetic molecular theory:
   (a) the compressibility of gases
   (b) diffusion of gases
   (c) why gases do not settle
   (d) Boyle's law
   (e) Charles' law
   (f) Dalton's law of partial pressures

2. A certain gas occupies a volume of 100 ml. at a temperature of 50° and a pressure of 700 mm. Calculate the volume of the gas if the temperature is raised to 100°, the pressure remaining constant. Ans. 115 ml.

3. Two liters of a gas at a pressure of 500 mm. will occupy what volume if the pressure is doubled, the temperature remaining constant?

4. Ten liters of a gas are collected at a temperature of 30° and a pressure of 700 mm. Calculate the volume of gas at standard conditions. Ans. 8.3 l.

5. 500 ml. of gas at 20° and a pressure of 780 mm. will occupy what volume if the temperature is reduced to -150° and the pressure increased to 1560 mm. ? Ans. 105 ml.

6. Diagram and explain the use of the barometer.

7. 453 ml. of oxygen gas are collected by displacement of water in the laboratory at 20° and a pressure of 700 mm. What volume of gas would have been collected if the temperature had been 40° and the pressure 780 mm.? Vapor pressure of water at 20° = 17.4 mm., at 40° = 55 mm. Ans. 457 ml.

8. 0.27 gram of dry gas occupies a volume of 354 ml. at a temperature of 18° and a pressure of 696 mm. Calculate the weight of 1 liter of the gas at standard conditions.   Ans. 0.89 g.

9. When J. F. Piccard made a stratosphere flight in a balloon, the balloon seemed to be but half filled as it left the ground near Detroit; the gas temperature was about 27° C. and the pressure 700 mm. The volume of gas in the balloon was 80,000 cubic feet. What was the gas volume at high altitude (assuming no leakage) where the temperature was −3° C., and the pressure 400 mm.?
                                                        Ans. 126,000 cu. ft.

10. If an industrial plant had a mixture of equal volumes of HCl and HBr gases in a porous container, what would be the comparative rates of diffusion of these gases through the porous walls? The molecular weights of HCl and HBr are respectively about 36 and 81. Compare the kinetic energies of these two gases.

11. Given 600 ml. of a gas at standard conditions. If the pressure is trebled and the temperature be raised to 546° C., what volume will the gas then occupy?   Ans. 600 ml.

12. 60 liters of a gas were collected over water when the barometer read 741 mm. and the temperature 23° C. The vapor pressure of water at 23° C. = 21.1 mm. What volume would the dry gas occupy at standard conditions?
                                                            Ans. 52.4 l.

13. Two gases, HCl (mol. wt. 36) and SO_2 (mol. wt. 64) are allowed to diffuse through a small opening. Which gas diffuses fastest? How many times as fast?

14. 600 ml. of a gas at 27° C. and 1 atmosphere pressure is heated to 177° C. What pressure must be applied to the gas in order to maintain the same volume?   Ans. 1.5 atm.

15. On a hot day the pressure in an automobile tire increases. If the air in a tire at 59° F. is under a pressure of 30 lb. per square inch and the pressure increases to 32 lb. per square inch on driving, (a) what is the temperature of the air in the tire, assuming no change in volume? (b) what would be the pressure in the tire if the temperature rises to 104° F.?
                                        Ans. (a) 93° F.   (b) 32.6 lb./in.².

16. What is the molecular weight of a gas which diffuses one third as fast as methane gas, CH_4 (mol. wt. 16)?   Ans. 144.

17. A very small amount of oxygen and hydrogen gases is admitted into an evacuated tube 100 ft. long. How far have the oxygen molecules traveled when the hydrogen molecules have reached the other end of the tube?
                                                            Ans. 25 ft.

18. 50 ml. of gas at 27° C. is heated at constant pressure to a temperature of 327° C. What will the new volume be?   Ans. 100 ml.

19. SO_2 and CH_4 are gases with molecular weights of 64 and 16 respectively. If SO_2 diffuses through a certain opening at a rate of 3 ml. per second, at what rate will CH_4 diffuse through the same opening?   Ans. 6 ml./sec.

20. The magnitude of absolute zero may be evaluated by plotting to scale the following experimental data: One cubic foot of a gas at 0° C. expands to 1.366 cu. ft. at 100° C. An ideal gas would contract theoretically to zero volume at absolute zero. On graph paper lay off on the horizontal axis the temperatures 100, 0, −100, −200, −300. On the vertical axis, lay off the values 0, 1.0, and 2.0. Plot the points (0,1) and (100,1.366). Extend a line

through these points to the horizontal axis. Record the magnitude of absolute zero.

21. 5.6 liters of phosgene gas, $COCl_2$, at standard conditions will weigh how many grams? Ans. 24.8.

22. 11.2 liters of a gas at 0° C. and at 76 mm. pressure, contains how many molecules? Ans. 3×10^{22}.

REFERENCES

H. S. Booth, "Experimental Manipulation of Gases from Cylinders," *J. Chem. Ed.* **7**, 1249 (1930).

R. W. Bridgman, "Compressibility of Five Gases to High Pressures," American Academy of Arts and Sciences, *Proceedings*, **59**, 173 (1924).

"Liquefaction of Gases," *Alembic Club Reprints*, No. 12.

IX

Valence

Valence is a most useful concept to the chemist, since it enables one to write formulas for the numerous compounds of the elementary substances. It would be almost an endless task to memorize the formulas of all the compounds we are to study. We shall see how formulas may be derived from consideration of valence.

Valence and atomic structure. In the study of atomic structure, we learned that the outer orbit of an atom contains electrons, which are called valence electrons. These valence electrons determine the way in which the atoms combine with one another. It was pointed out that all elements tend to complete the outer orbit of their atoms with electrons to form a stable configuration, that is, one in which the outer orbit holds its capacity of electrons. The sodium atom has a single electron in its outer orbit and tends to give up this electron to other atoms. By giving up this single electron the atom reverts to a stable configuration.

Sodium is said to have a valence of one, since one electron is given up by the atom. Since the release of an electron leaves the sodium atom with an excess of one positive charge, we may say the valence is a positive one. The charged atom which remains after the release of an electron is a sodium ion, Na^+. The charge on the ion is the valence. Calcium which gives up the two electrons in its outer orbit and becomes calcium ion, Ca^{++}, is regarded as having a positive valence of two. Aluminum has a positive valence of three, since it gives up three electrons, etc. In general, metals give electrons as they combine with other elements, and their valence is the number of electrons so given.

Nonmetal atoms, in general, take up electrons and have a negative valence; for example, an atom of chlorine takes up one electron to complete its outer shell of eight electrons and thus becomes a chlorine ion, Cl^-. The valence of chlorine is negative one. Sulfur atoms accept two electrons from metal atoms, becoming S^{--}, and sulfur is said to have a valence of negative two.

This type of valence in which electrons are transferred from one atom to another is called *electrovalence*.

Groups of atoms that remain together throughout a chemical change, radicals, may also have valence. Radicals as such do not exist alone as do metal or nonmetal atoms and thus strictly speaking are not electron receivers. In their formation one or more electrons are acquired to give the group functioning as a unit a net charge. Table 7 gives the common valences of various metals, nonmetals, and radicals.

TABLE 7

VALENCES OF ELEMENTS AND RADICALS

POSITIVE VALENCES: ELECTRON GIVERS			
+1	+2	+3	+4
H	Ca	Al	C
Na	Mg	Fe (ferric)	Si
K	Ba	Cr (chromic)	Sn (stannic)
Ag	Zn	As (arsenious)	Mn (manganic)
NH₄ (ammonium)	Pb	Sb	
Cu (cuprous)	Ni	Bi	
Hg (mercurous)	Fe (ferrous)		
	Cu (cupric)		
	Hg (mercuric)		
	Sn (stannous)		
	Mn (manganous)		
	Sr		
	Co		

NEGATIVE VALENCES: ELECTRON RECEIVERS			
−1	−2	−3	−4
Cl (chloride)	O (oxide)	PO₄ (phosphate)	SiO₄ (silicate)
Br (bromide)	S (sulfide)	AsO₄ (arsenate)	
I (iodide)	SO₃ (sulfite)	N	
F (fluoride)	SO₄ (sulfate)		
OH (hydroxide)	CO₃ (carbonate)		
C₂H₃O₂ (acetate)	CrO₄ (chromate)		
ClO₃ (chlorate)	C₂O₄ (oxalate)		
NO₃ (nitrate)	SiO₃ (metasilicate)		
CN (cyanide)			

It should be pointed out that an element exhibits a valence *only when it is combined with some other element*, in other words, when it is a part of a compound. Valence means a charge on the atom — an element in the free state is without charge and therefore must have a zero valence. Thus Na by itself has no valence, but when combined exhibits a valence of $+1$.

The meaning of valence is most easily explained by the theory that the outer orbit of metals gives up electrons and the outer orbit of nonmetals receives them. However, this theory of atomic structure is itself based in large part on facts observed during the formation of compounds and on the weight relations between united elements. Long before present day ideas of atomic structure were developed, chemists believed in the atomic theory and were writing formulas on the basis of that belief. Accordingly, let us study how ideas of the specific valence of various elements or radicals came to be known.

Determination of formulas from analytical data. Formulas may be derived from the results of analyzing for each of the elements present in a pure chemical compound. These results are usually expressed in terms of percentage of each element present, that is parts of each element present in 100 parts by weight of the compound. In order to arrive at the formula for the compound, it is necessary to have the relative number of *atoms* of each element present. By dividing the percentage of each element present by its atomic weight, we obtain quotients which will be in the ratio of the number of atoms of each element. This will be clarified by the example:

A compound on analysis is found to contain 1.59 per cent hydrogen, 22.2 per cent nitrogen, and 76.2 per cent oxygen. If we arbitrarily take 100 grams of the compound, then 1.59 grams will be hydrogen, 22.2 grams will be nitrogen, and 76.2 grams will be oxygen. The number of gram atoms of each of the three elements per 100 grams of compound will be: $\frac{1.59}{1} = 1.59$ gram atoms of hydrogen, $\frac{22.2}{14} = 1.59$ gram atoms of nitrogen, and $\frac{76.2}{16} = 4.77$ gram atoms of oxygen. The relative number of atoms will be in the same ratio as the number of gram atoms, namely

H	N	O
1.59	1.59	4.77

By dividing each number by the highest common divisor (1.59) of the three values, we obtain the ratio

H	N	O
1	1	3

Hence we obtain the formula, HNO_3.

The formula thus obtained is an *empirical* formula, and not necessarily the true formula, since in the foregoing example, the true formula might be any multiple of HNO_3, for example, $H_2N_2O_6$ or $H_3N_3O_9$, etc. To obtain the true formula, we need the molecular weight of the compound as additional information. (See chap. XIII for methods of determining molecular weights experimentally.) In the example above, if we knew the molecular weight of the compound to be 63, then the true formula must be HNO_3; if the molecular weight were 126, then the formula would be $H_2N_2O_6$.

In deriving a formula from percentage composition data, we may then employ the following steps:

1. Divide the percentage of each element by its atomic weight.
2. Divide the quotients obtained by the highest common divisor of all the quotients.
3. Write the simplest or empirical formula for the compound.
4. If the molecular weight or the approximate molecular weight is known, determine what multiple of the simplest formula most nearly gives the molecular weight; multiply the number of atoms of each element in the simplest formula by this multiple and write the true formula for the compound.

A further example concerns the compound aluminum fluoride which analyzes 32.14 per cent aluminum and 67.86 per cent fluorine.

$$\frac{32.14}{27 \text{ (at. wt. Al)}} = 1.19 \qquad \frac{67.86}{19 \text{ (at. wt. F)}} = 3.57$$

This gives a 1.19–3.57 or 1–3 ratio; hence simplest formula is AlF_3.

Derivation of valence from formulas. The valences of Table 7 may be worked out by a consideration of the formulas of a number of compounds which have been analyzed. If we choose hydrogen as a measuring stick of valence and assign it a valence number of positive one, we may deduce valences as follows:

Consider the formulas:

HCl, hydrogen chloride
H_2O, water
NH_3, ammonia
CH_4, methane

Each of the above compounds is made up of hydrogen and one other element. We might say that the various elements combined with hydrogen have different combining capacities for hydrogen; chlorine has the capacity to hold in combination one hydrogen atom, oxygen has the capacity to hold two hydrogen atoms, etc. Oxygen exhibits a greater holding capacity for hydrogen atoms than does chlorine; nitrogen and carbon have still greater combining capacities for hydrogen. Since all molecules are electrically neutral, we may determine the combining capacities for each of the above elements in terms of the hydrogen atom, which has been selected as the standard with a valence of positive one. In HCl, if hydrogen is $+1$, then Cl must be -1, in order that the molecule be balanced electrically. The valence of oxygen in H_2O would be -2; nitrogen in NH_3, -3; carbon in CH_4, -4. Consider the formulas of the compounds:

> NaCl, sodium chloride
> $CaCl_2$, calcium chloride
> $AlCl_3$, aluminum chloride

Although these compounds do not contain hydrogen, and we cannot determine their valence in terms of hydrogen atoms directly from the formula, the compounds do contain chlorine, which we have shown is equivalent in valence to hydrogen, but of opposite charge. Since chlorine has a valence of -1, the valence of sodium, calcium, and aluminum must be positive 1, 2, and 3 respectively. It is evident, then, that we may derive the valence of combining capacities of the elements from the formulas of their compounds by a consideration of the hydrogen atoms in the molecule, or, in those cases where hydrogen is not present, an element whose valence is known in terms of hydrogen. *Valence is a number, which for a given atom of an element is the number of hydrogen atoms said atom of the element will combine with or replace.*

Radicals are treated as units in most chemical changes. In the formula, H_2SO_4, it is obvious that the SO_4 (sulfate) radical must have a valence of -2, since one radical is combined with two hydrogen atoms.

The use of valence in writing formulas. Electrovalent compounds are made up of a combination of positive and negative units. In writing the formula for any given compound, we must balance the combining capacities of the positive and negative units in such a way that the molecule is electrically neutral; in other words, the total charge of the positive part of the molecule must balance the total charge of the negative part of the molecule. For example, the compound aluminum chloride is composed of the elements aluminum and chlorine, so we may write down the symbol for Al and the symbol for the chloride unit, thus:

Al   Cl

Aluminum has a valence of positive three, and chloride a valence of negative one (see Table 7). In order to balance electrically, it is necessary that three chlorine atoms combine with one atom of aluminum; hence, we write

$$AlCl_3$$

which must be the correct formula for aluminum chloride. Valence requires that the ratio of aluminum atoms to chlorine atoms in the compound be 1 to 3. Of course, we might write Al_2Cl_6, which shows the composition of the compound correctly, but it is customary to use the smaller numbers 1 and 3. Consider the compound aluminum sulfate, which is composed of aluminum and the sulfate radical. We write down the symbols for each of these (it is customary to write the positive part of the molecule first) thus:

$$\overset{3}{Al} \quad \overset{2}{SO_4}$$

We may for convenience write down the valence of the units above the formulas. In order to balance positive and negative charges in this compound we must use a ratio of two aluminum atoms to three sulfate groups. Two aluminum atoms then will contribute a total of six positive charges which are balanced by a total of six negative charges contributed by the three sulfate groups. The formula for aluminum sulfate then must be

$$Al_2(SO_4)_3$$

Experimental determination of valence. We have seen above that the valence of a positive or negative group is really a measure of the combining capacity of that group in terms of hydrogen atoms or the equivalent of hydrogen atoms. Metals (above hydrogen in the activity series) displace hydrogen from acids, and hence we may determine the relationship between the metal and hydrogen directly. If the metals sodium, magnesium, and aluminum are allowed to react with an acid, the following data are obtained:

1 gram atom (23 grams) of sodium displaces 1 gram atom (1 gram) of hydrogen.

1 gram atom (24.3 grams) of magnesium displaces 2 gram atoms (2 grams) of hydrogen.

1 gram atom (27 grams) of aluminum displaces 3 gram atoms (3 grams) of hydrogen.

Gram atomic weights (atomic weight in grams) of all elements contain the same number of atoms, namely 6×10^{23} (see chap. IX). It is evident then that one atom of sodium is equivalent to one atom of hydrogen; therefore, the valence of sodium must be one. Similarly, one atom of magnesium displaces two atoms of hydrogen and therefore must have a valence of two. By similar reasoning, aluminum is shown to have a valence of three.

We may arrive at the valence of the metals sodium, magnesium, and aluminum in another way from the same data above. The weight of an element which is equivalent to 1 gram of hydrogen (1 gram) is termed the *equivalent* weight of the element. From the above data, it is evident that the equivalent weight of sodium is 23, since 23 grams of sodium displace 1 gram of hydrogen. The equivalent weight of magnesium must be $\frac{24.3}{2}$ or 12.15, since 12.15 grams of magnesium would displace 1 gram of hydrogen. Twenty-seven grams of aluminum displace 3 grams of hydrogen; hence 9 grams of aluminum would displace 1 gram of hydrogen. The equivalent weight of aluminum then is 9. *The valence of an element may be calculated by dividing the atomic weight of the element by its equivalent weight.* Thus the valence of sodium is $\frac{23}{23} = 1$; the valence of magnesium is $\frac{24.3}{12.15} = 2$; the valence of aluminum is $\frac{27}{9} = 3$. The equivalent weight is always either equal to or is some simple fraction of the atomic weight.

Many of the elements do not displace hydrogen from an acid; neither do they combine directly with that element. In determining the valence of such an element, an element with which it does combine and whose valence is known may be used. For example, we know that chlorine has a valence of one, since one atom of chlorine combines with one atom of hydrogen in hydrogen chloride. If the element in question combines with chlorine, the weight of the element combining with 1 gram atom of chlorine (this would be an equivalent weight of the element) can be determined. The valence then is calculated by dividing the atomic weight of the element by its equivalent weight.

Variable valence. Many of the elements form a series of compounds in which the valence of the element is variable. For example, the element manganese forms the compounds MnO, MnO_2, Mn_2O_3, MnO_3, and Mn_2O_7, in which the valences of manganese are 2, 4, 3, 6, and 7 respectively. Other elements showing a variation in valence are phosphorus, nitrogen, chromium, chlorine, bromine, iodine, sulfur, and several of the metals. On the other hand, many elements have a single valence; for example, hydrogen, sodium, potassium, calcium, magnesium, aluminum, silver.

An element of variable valence forms as many distinct classes of compounds as it has valences. Manganese, which exhibits five different valences, forms five distinct classes of manganese compounds.

Iron exhibits two valences, a valence of two in ferrous compounds and a valence of three in ferric compounds. The suffixes -*ous* and -*ic* are used to differentiate between the two classes of compounds formed by an element of two different valences. The suffix -*ous* refers to compounds in which the element has the lower of its two valences.

The valence of an element or radical may be determined from the formula of a compound. In the formula Hg_2O, the mercury must have a valence of one, since two mercury atoms are required to balance a single oxygen atom which has a valence of -2. Since this is the lower valence of mercury, the compound is properly called mercurous oxide. The valence of iron in $FeCl_3$ is $+3$, since one atom of iron balances three chlorine atoms, each having a valence of -1. In the compound H_4SiO_4, the SiO_4 radical must have a valence of -4, since one SiO_4 radical is balanced by 4 hydrogen atoms each having a valence of positive one.

The valence of an element within a radical may also be determined from a consideration of the valence of the other elements composing the compound. Consider the valence of Mn in the compound $KMnO_4$. We might say that the one potassium atom will contribute one positive charge, since its valence is positive one. Four oxygen atoms will contribute 8 negative charges, since the valence of oxygen is negative two. In order then that the molecule be electrically neutral, the one Mn atom must possess an apparent charge of $+7$. Consider the valance of chromium in $K_2Cr_2O_7$. Two potassium atoms will contribute two positive charges (the valence of potassium is $+1$), seven oxygen atoms will contribute fourteen negative charges. To balance the compound electrically, a charge of $+12$ will be borne by the chromium in the compound. Since there are two atoms of chromium, each atom will bear six positive charges and $+6$ may be assumed to be the valence of chromium in the compound.

Actually, in the cases just cited, the high charges on the Mn and Cr atoms are more apparent than real. Ions of such high charge probably do not exist. Since the valence of an element is often associated with its ionic charge, some authors prefer to use the term *oxidation number* in assigning an apparent charge to an element in a covalent grouping of atoms. Since charge loses some significance when applied to covalent substances (see below) in which electrons are shared between atoms, the valence number or oxidation number is simply a number which corresponds to the apparent charge an atom must possess to give the compound a neutral character. We shall use the term valence or valence number to denote charge, whether it be real (ionic) or apparent (covalent groupings).

Covalence. In the union of a chemically active metal with a non-metal, there is a very decided transfer of electron or electrons from the outer orbit of the metal atom to the nonmetallic atom; electrovalency is involved. In the formation of some compounds, electrons are not so definitely transferred from one atom to another atom as chemical union takes place; there is more of a sharing of electrons between the atoms. This type of union has been referred to as covalence.

As pointed out in chapter III much of the significance of positive and negative valence is lost in covalent compounds. In the compound HCl, for example, the hydrogen and chlorine atoms share a pair of electrons. The question may arise as to which of the elements, hydrogen or chlorine, is positive. In a question of this kind we are guided by the natural tendency of the elements concerned to accept or give up electrons. Since hydrogen tends to give up an electron in some reactions, the hydrogen is regarded as being positive. Chlorine, on the other hand, usually takes up an electron and is regarded as being negative. The pair of electrons shared by the hydrogen and chlorine atoms in the compound is probably located closer to the chlorine atom than the hydrogen atom, and while there has been no actual transfer of electrons, the electron from the hydrogen has been displaced in a direction away from the hydrogen atom and nearer to the chlorine atom. We are probably justified, therefore, in assigning positive or negative values to the valences concerned in a compound of the covalent type.

Numerous compounds exist in which both electrovalence and covalence are exhibited; salts, in general, which contain a radical, exhibit both types. For example, consider the compound sodium sulfate. The salt is electrovalent and exists as sodium and sulfate ions in the crystal lattice. However, within the SO_4 radical the sulfur atom and oxygen atoms are held together by covalent linkages — electron pairs are shared mutually by sulfur and oxygen atoms. Na_2SO_4 may be represented diagrammatically:

$$2\,Na^+ + \left[\begin{array}{c} :\overset{..}{O}: \\ :\overset{..}{O}:\overset{..}{S}:\overset{..}{O}: \\ :\overset{..}{O}: \end{array} \right]^{--}$$

Polar and nonpolar bonds. In our discussions so far we have described two principal types of bonds which hold atoms together, namely the electrovalent or ionic bond and the covalent bond. Although many substances appear to fall strictly into one or the other of these classifications, others seem to exhibit a bonding which is intermediate between the two. We may look at it this way: Elements vary in their affinity for electrons. Sodium and chlorine would represent two extremes; the sodium atom has little or no affinity for electrons, as a matter of fact it readily gives up an electron. Chlorine, on the other hand has a strong affinity for electrons. The compound NaCl is definitely of the electrovalent or ionic type. The ions are held together simply by attraction of the opposite charges.

Consider now a case in which two atoms with the same electron affinity combine. Such would be the situation in the chlorine molecule, Cl_2. Each chlorine atom has the same affinity for electrons and the shared pair of electrons in the chlorine molecule would lie midway between the two atoms, giving rise to an electrically symmetrical molecule. Such a bonding of atoms may be described as *nonpolar*.

However in a combination of unlike atoms such as HCl (a covalent compound), attraction for electrons would not be equal and because of a displacement of the electron pair toward the chlorine atom, the molecule is not electrically symmetrical; the chlorine end of the molecule tends to be negative while the hydrogen end is positive. Such a molecule is described as *polar*. This situation approaches that present in ionic combinations and such a polar molecule may be considered as having some electrovalent or ionic character. The degree of polarity of the molecule depends upon the relative attractions of the combining atoms for electrons. The combinations just cited, Cl_2, HCl, NaCl represent the transition from a nonpolar to a polar and finally to an ionic substance.

Co-ordinate valence. Many examples may be cited where molecules of one compound may combine with molecules of a second compound to form a more complex compound.

EXAMPLE. The compound BCl_3 will chemically unite with the gaseous compound NH_3 to give a new crystalline compound $BCl_3 \cdot NH_3$

$$
\begin{array}{ccc}
:\overset{..}{\text{Cl}}: & \text{H} & :\overset{..}{\text{Cl}}:\text{H} \\
:\overset{..}{\underset{..}{\text{Cl}}}:\text{B} \; + :\text{N}:\text{H} \longrightarrow & :\overset{..}{\underset{..}{\text{Cl}}}:\text{B}:\overset{..}{\underset{..}{\text{N}}}:\text{H} \\
:\overset{..}{\underset{..}{\text{Cl}}}: & \text{H} & :\overset{..}{\underset{..}{\text{Cl}}}:\text{H}
\end{array}
$$

In this case the boron and the nitrogen atoms seem to share a pair of electrons, but the nitrogen atom contributes both of them. Sharing of an electron pair between atoms, where both of the electrons of the electron pair come from one of the atoms, constitutes a *co-ordinate* valence. It is apparent from the diagram formula of $BCl_3 \cdot NH_3$ that valence bonds between boron and chlorine and between nitrogen and hydrogen are covalent; whereas the boron to nitrogen bond is co-ordinate valency.

The formation of a co-ordinate valence linkage depends upon the existence of a pair of unused electrons. In the above example the nitrogen atom in the compound NH_3 has such an unused pair.

Ions as well as molecules may add to unused electron pairs; for example, ammonia may add H^+ to form ammonium ion, NH_4^+:

$$ \underset{H}{\overset{H}{H \underset{\cdot\times}{\overset{\times\cdot}{\times}} N}} : + H^+ \longrightarrow \left[\underset{H}{\overset{H}{H \underset{\cdot\times}{\overset{\times\cdot}{\times}} N}} : H \right]^+ $$

A molecule of water contains two pairs of unused electrons and readily adds a proton to form hydronium ion, H_3O^+:

$$ H \underset{\cdot\cdot}{\overset{\cdot\cdot}{\times}} \overset{\cdot\cdot}{O} \overset{\times}{} H + H^+ \longrightarrow \left[H \underset{H}{\overset{\cdot\cdot}{\times}} O \overset{\times}{} H \right]^+ $$

In résumé, electrovalence involves actual transfer of an electron or electrons from one atom to another; covalence is a sharing of an electron pair between atoms, both atoms contributing an electron to the pair; co-ordinate valence exists between atoms when one of the atoms has furnished both of the electrons of the pair.

EXERCISES

1. Prepare a form like the one below and fill in the blanks with formulas of compounds composed of the indicated positive and negative groups:

	Cl	SO₄	OH	PO₄	CO₃	SO₃	O	C₂H₃O₂	Br
Na									
Mg									
NH₄									
Ca									
Fe (ous)									
Fe (ic)									
Zn									
Al									
Cu									
K									

2. Determine the valence of the underlined elements or radicals in each of the following compounds: $Na\underline{Mn}O_4$; $Ca(\underline{N}O_2)_2$; $K_2\underline{Cr}_2O_7$; $\underline{Mn}O_2$; $H_2\underline{S}O_4$; $\underline{Sn}Cl_4$; $K_2\underline{Mn}O_4$; $K\underline{I}O_3$; $Na\underline{Br}O_2$; $Ag\underline{Cl}O_4$; $Na_2\underline{HP}O_4$; $Na\underline{Cr}O_2$; $K_3\underline{Al}O_3$; $Al(\underline{N}O_3)_3$; $H_2\underline{S}_2O_7$; $H_4\underline{Si}O_4$; $H_2\underline{Se}O_3$; $Na_2\underline{W}O_4$; $\underline{Ti}Cl_4$; $Ca(\underline{Cl}O_2)_2$. $Ca\underline{W}O_4$; $K_2\underline{Pd}Cl_6$; $\underline{U}O_2SO_4$; $Pb_3(\underline{As}O_3)_2$; $Zn_3(\underline{V}O_4)_2$.

3. Element Z forms the compound H_2Z. Element Z and element W form the compound WZ_3. What is the valence of W and Z?

4. The atomic weight of the element X is 64. 8 grams of X displace .25 grams of hydrogen from hydrochloric acid. What is the valence of element X?
Ans. 2

5. 1.2 grams of the element Y displaces 584 ml. of hydrogen (measured at S. C.) when treated with an acid. The atomic weight of the element Y is 23. What is the valence of Y? (22,400 ml. of H_2 weigh 2.016 grams.) Ans. 1

6. From the following data, calculate the valence of the elements M and N.

Element	At. Wt.	Wt. of Metal Used	Vol. of H_2 Displaced	Atmospheric Pressure	Temp. ° C.
M	36	1.2 g.	1762 ml.	700 mm.	17
N	65	0.822 g.	322 ml.	710.5 mm.	20

Ans. M–4
N–2

7. A compound analyzes 32.38 per cent sodium, 22.57 per cent sulfur, and 45.05 per cent oxygen. What is its formula? What is the valence of sulfur in the compound? Ans. Na_2SO_4

8. A white solid is found to contain 15.656 per cent magnesium, 48.262 per cent arsenic, and 36.082 per cent oxygen. What is its formula? What is the valence of arsenic in the compound? (0.322 will be the highest common divisor).

REFERENCES

S. R. Brinkley, "Application of the Electron Concept to Oxidation-Reduction Reactions in General Chemistry," *J. Chem. Ed.* **2**, 576 (1925).

C. A. Buehler, "Development of the Electronic Theory of Valency," *ibid.* **10**, 741 (1933).

J. DeVries, "Valence and Molecular Structure," *ibid.* **13**, 320 (1936).

R. L. Ebel, "Atomic Structure and the Periodic Table," *ibid.* **15**, 575 (1938).

L. H. Germer, "Optical Experiments with Electrons," *ibid.* **5**, 1041, 1255 (1928).

C. H. Kunsman, "A Comparative Study of Certain Properties of Electrons and the Ions of the Alkali Metals," *ibid.* **6**, 623 (1929).

Special Note: Table 7 of this chapter constitutes one of the fundamental a, b, c's of chemistry. Much as one cannot spell without knowledge of the alphabet, or do much arithmetic without multiplication tables, one cannot progress well in chemistry without knowing valence. Memorize Table 7.

X

Classification and Naming of Compounds

Chemistry indeed would be a tedious and monotonous subject if we were required to learn the properties and behavior of each of the many compounds which we are to use. It is fortunate that the multitude of chemical compounds can be grouped together in a few classes. Then, if we can properly classify the compound, we are at once aware of the general properties of the compound from a knowledge of the properties of that particular class or group of compounds. For example, HCl is classed as an acid, and by becoming familiar with the behavior of acids as a distinct class, we are at once aware of the general properties of the compound. We shall learn that nearly all of the compounds which we are to study may be classified as acids, bases, salts, metallic oxides, or nonmetallic oxides. Of these five classes of compounds, the first three, namely, acids, bases, and salts, are by far the most important.

Acids. We have used the term "acids" many times in our previous discussion. In the study of oxygen compounds we learned that the solution of a nonmetallic oxide in water produces an acid, *e.g.*:

$$SO_2 + H_2O \longrightarrow H_2SO_3$$
$$P_2O_5 + 3 H_2O \longrightarrow 2 H_3PO_4$$

All acids contain hydrogen; furthermore this hydrogen may be replaced by metals. The negative portion of the acid molecule is composed of a nonmetal or a radical (negative valence group). These negative valence groups (except oxide and hydroxide) are often referred to as acid radicals. All acids are covalent compounds; *i.e.*, the atoms are held together by a sharing of electrons. When an acid is dissolved in water, ions are formed as a result of the transfer of a hydrogen ion (proton) from the acid molecule to the water molecule, *e.g.*,

$$H \overset{\times}{\cdot} \overset{\cdot\cdot}{Cl} : + \; H \overset{\cdot\cdot}{\underset{\cdot\cdot}{\times O}} \overset{\times}{\cdot} H \longrightarrow \left[H \overset{\cdot\cdot}{\underset{H}{\times O}} \overset{\times}{\cdot} H \right]^{+} + \left[\overset{\cdot\cdot}{\times} \overset{\cdot\cdot}{Cl} : \right]^{-}$$

which may be written:

$$HCl + H_2O \longrightarrow H_3O^+ + Cl^-$$

This is a case of co-ordinate valence as discussed on page 129, in which an unused pair of electrons from the water molecule combines with a hydrogen ion to form a hydronium ion. The hydronium ion is a hydrated hydrogen ion or proton, $H^+ \cdot H_2O$, and while the ionization of acids in aqueous solution depends upon its formation, we shall ordinarily use the simple H^+ in writing equations. Such equations are thereby simplified and are easier to balance. (But see chap. XVIII.)

The chief characteristic of an acid is its ability to furnish hydrogen ions (protons); therefore, an acid is usually defined as "a substance which may furnish protons."

While all acids contain hydrogen, not all compounds containing hydrogen can be classed as acids. For example, methane, CH_4, has no acid characteristics and does not furnish hydrogen ions in solution.

Properties of acids. In general, acids are characterized by the following properties:

1. Sour taste. Lemons, oranges, and other citrus fruits owe their sour taste to the presence of citric acid. The taste of sour milk is due to the presence of lactic acid.

2. Turn blue litmus paper red. Litmus is a dye which has a pink color in acid solution and a blue color in basic solution. Paper which has been soaked in litmus is referred to as litmus paper. Substances of this type which enable us to determine whether a given solution is acid or basic are called indicators. Methyl orange and phenolphthalein are other examples of indicator substances frequently used in the chemical laboratory.

3. React with certain metals to produce hydrogen. Reactions of this type were studied in connection with the preparation of hydrogen.

4. React with bases to produce salts and water.

5. An acid may be either a solid, a liquid, or a gas. Many acids are water soluble.

Bases. The compounds $NaOH$, KOH, $Ca(OH)_2$, $Ba(OH)_2$ are classed as bases. These compounds are electrovalent and are thus ionized in the pure state. When these compounds are dissolved in water, the solid disappears and the ions are dispersed in the solution. The hydroxide ion, OH^-, is common to all of these solutions.

$$NaOH \longrightarrow Na^+ + OH^-$$
$$KOH \longrightarrow K^+ + OH^-$$
$$Ca(OH)_2 \longrightarrow Ca^{++} + 2\,OH^-$$

Other compounds classed as bases are $Cu(OH)_2$, $Fe(OH)_3$, $Al(OH)_3$, and NH_4OH. In each compound we find a combination of a metal (or NH_4) with the hydroxyl, OH, group. Just as the characteristic group of an acid is hydrogen, so the characteristic group of a base in water solution is hydroxyl. Later this concept of a base will be extended to include substances which do not furnish hydroxide ions in solution.

Properties of bases. In general, water solutions of metallic hydroxides (bases) exhibit the following properties:

1. Bitter taste.
2. Soapy or slippery feeling.
3. Turn red litmus paper to blue color.
4. React with acids to form salts and water.
5. Most metallic hydroxides (bases) are insoluble in water. Of the common ones, only NaOH, KOH, $Ca(OH)_2$, $Ba(OH)_2$, and NH_4OH are soluble.

Salts. An acid reacts with a base by double decomposition to produce a salt and water. Hydrogen from the acid combines with hydroxyl from the base to form water molecules:

$$NaOH + HCl \longrightarrow NaCl + HOH \qquad (1)$$
$$Mg(OH)_2 + 2\ HNO_3 \longrightarrow Mg(NO_3)_2 + 2\ HOH$$
$$2\ Al(OH)_3 + 3\ H_2SO_4 \longrightarrow Al_2(SO_4)_3 + 6\ HOH$$

The reaction of an acid with a base is called *neutralization*. If the water is removed from the solution after the reaction, the positive ions from the base combine with the negative ions from the acid to form a *salt*.

It was shown (chap. III) that the compound sodium chloride, which is classed as a salt, is ionized in the solid or crystalline state, the crystal lattice being made up of positive sodium ions and negative chlorine ions oriented in a definite pattern. In general most salts in the crystalline state are composed of ions oriented in a definite way similar to sodium chloride.

Salts are, then, in general, compounds between metallic ions and nonmetallic ions. They are the most numerous of chemical compounds, and many of them are industrially important. A few with some of their uses are: NaCl, essential food mineral; $Ca_3(PO_4)_2$, in bone and needed in making phosphate fertilizer; Na_2CO_3, washing soda; $Cu_3(AsO_3)_2$, insecticide.

Writing equations in ionic form. Since all acids, bases, and salts in aqueous solution give ions, perhaps the chemical equations in which these classes of compounds are involved should show the ions present. Actually an ionic equation is more instructive than a molecular equation since the actual chemical process is more clearly indicated. For example, if equation (1) above is represented in ionic form

$$[Na^+ + OH^-] + [H^+ + Cl^-] \longrightarrow [Na^+ + Cl^-] + H_2O$$

it is evident that the neutralization process involves only the combination of H^+ and OH^- to form water. Na^+ and Cl^- are incidental to the process. Of course if the solution after neutralization is evaporated, Na^+ and Cl^- form a crystal lattice of NaCl, and the latter may be recovered as a solid. However, as long as the NaCl remains in solution, there is no tendency for Na^+ and Cl^- to combine.

In writing ionic equations, it is necessary to adopt certain rather arbitrary conventions. For example, if an insoluble substance (*e.g.*, AgCl) is produced in a reaction, that substance is shown in molecular form, even though the solid crystal lattice is made up of ions. This convention is necessary to differentiate between a substance in which the ions are oriented in a definite pattern (the crystal lattice) and one in which the ions are free to move about in a random manner. Another convention usually employed in writing ionic equations is to show a substance in ionic form only when it gives a relatively large number of ions in solution. Such substances are termed strong electrolytes (chap. XVIII).

The whole subject of ionic reactions will be considered in detail later (chaps. XVIII and XIX). However to familiarize the student gradually with this method of writing equations, we shall henceforth represent a given reaction in both the molecular and ionic forms (if ions are involved in the reaction). A great deal more basic knowledge must be acquired by the student before he can be expected to handle ionic equations with facility.[1]

Type reactions of acids, bases, and salts. Probably most of the chemical changes of inorganic chemistry involve the interaction of acids, bases, and salts. Just as we may classify hundreds of chemical compounds into a few groups or classes, so we may also classify hundreds of chemical changes into a few types of reactions. Once we recognize to which type a given chemical change belongs we are able to predict the probable products of the reaction. The principal type chemical changes involving acids, bases, or salts are the following: Examples are given for each type.[2]

---

[1] The instructor may emphasize the use of ionic equations here or defer serious consideration of them until the writing of ordinary molecular equations has been mastered. For pedagogical reasons, some may prefer to wait until ionization as a topic is being studied.

[2] See also the reaction of "oxides" on page 140.

A. *Direct combination*

  1. Metal + Nonmetal $\longrightarrow$ Salt

$$Cu + Br_2 \longrightarrow CuBr_2$$
$$2\,Al + 3\,S \longrightarrow Al_2S_3$$

Many of the metals and nonmetals combine directly to produce salts. In general, these combinations are limited to those in which either the metal or nonmetal is at least a moderately active element.

  2. Hydrogen + Nonmetal $\longrightarrow$ Acid

$$H_2 + Cl_2 \longrightarrow 2\,HCl$$
$$H_2 + S \longrightarrow H_2S$$

Hydrogen may react directly with the more active nonmetallic elements to form acids, which give up protons in water solution to form hydronium ions.

B. *Decomposition*

  1. Salt $\xrightarrow{\text{heat}}$ Decomposition Products

$$2\,KClO_3 \longrightarrow 2\,KCl + 3\,O_2$$
$$2\,Pb(NO_3)_2 \longrightarrow 2\,PbO + 4\,NO_2 + O_2$$

Certain salts are unstable toward heat. No generalization can be made as to the decomposition products.

C. *Simple replacement*

  1. Metal (above hydrogen) + Acid $\longrightarrow$ Salt + H_2

$$Zn + H_2SO_4 \longrightarrow ZnSO_4 + H_2$$
$$Zn + [2\,H^+ + SO_4^{--}] \longrightarrow [Zn^{++} + SO_4^{--}] + H_2$$

$$2\,Al + 6\,HCl \longrightarrow 2\,AlCl_3 + 3\,H_2$$
$$2\,Al + 6\,[H^+ + Cl^-] \longrightarrow 2\,[Al^{+++} + 3\,Cl^-] + 3\,H_2$$

This displacement type of reaction was discussed in the preparation of hydrogen (chap. VII).

  2. Metal + Salt $\longrightarrow$ Metal (less active) + Salt

$$Zn + CuSO_4 \longrightarrow Cu + ZnSO_4$$
$$Zn + [Cu^{++} + SO_4^{--}] \longrightarrow Cu + [Zn^{++} + SO_4^{--}]$$

$$Fe + Ag_2SO_4 \longrightarrow 2\,Ag + FeSO_4$$
$$Fe + [2\,Ag^+ + SO_4^{--}] \longrightarrow 2\,Ag + [Fe^{++} + SO_4^{--}]$$

This type reaction was discussed in connection with the activity series (chap. VII). <u>A metal will displace a less active metal from its salt in water solution.</u> The metal displaced must be lower in the activity series than the displacing metal.

3. Nonmetal + Salt ⟶ Nonmetal + Salt

$$Cl_2 + Na_2S \longrightarrow S + 2\,NaCl$$

Similar to the action of a metal with a salt. <u>A nonmetal displaces a less active nonmetal from its salt.</u>

4. Metal (only certain ones) + Base ⟶ Salt + H_2

$$Zn + 2\,NaOH \longrightarrow Na_2ZnO_2 + H_2$$
$$Zn + 2[Na^+ + OH^-] \longrightarrow [2Na^+ + ZnO_2^{--}] + H_2$$

$$2\,Al + 6\,NaOH \longrightarrow 2\,Na_3AlO_3 + 3\,H_2$$
$$2\,Al + 6[Na^+ + OH^-] \longrightarrow 2[3\,Na^+ + AlO_3^{---}] + 3\,H_2$$

Certain metals, such as zinc and aluminum, react with strong bases, sodium and potassium hydroxides, to yield a salt and hydrogen.

D. *Double decomposition*

1. Salt + Salt ⟶ New Salt + New Salt

$$AgNO_3 + NaCl \longrightarrow AgCl \downarrow + NaNO_3$$
$$[Ag^+ + NO_3^-] + [Na^+ + Cl^-] \longrightarrow AgCl \downarrow + [Na^+ + NO_3^-]$$

$$BaCl_2 + K_2SO_4 \longrightarrow BaSO_4 \downarrow + 2\,KCl$$
$$[Ba^{++} + 2\,Cl^-] + [2\,K^+ + SO_4^{--}] \longrightarrow BaSO_4 \downarrow + 2[K^+ + Cl^-]$$

This type reaction takes place if one of the products (a salt) is insoluble and precipitates from solution. In the first reaction silver chloride is insoluble while in the second, barium sulfate is insoluble. The insoluble substance is denoted in an equation by a downward arrow.

2. Salt + Acid ⟶ New Salt + New Acid ↑

$$CaCl_2 + H_2SO_4 \longrightarrow CaSO_4 + 2\,HCl \uparrow$$
$$3\,KNO_3 + H_3PO_4 \xrightarrow{\text{heat}} K_3PO_4 + 3\,HNO_3 \uparrow$$

These reactions involve the formation of a volatile acid which is expelled from the reaction mixture. The volatile substance is indicated by the upward arrow in the equations above.

Reactions of this type are usually carried out in the absence of water, and since no ions are present in solution, the substances in the equation are represented only in molecular form.

3. Salt + Base $\longrightarrow$ New Salt + New Base

$$AlCl_3 + 3\ KOH \longrightarrow 3\ KCl + Al(OH)_3 \downarrow$$
$$[Al^{+++} + 3\ Cl^-] + 3[K^+ + OH^-] \longrightarrow 3[K^+ + Cl^-] + Al(OH)_3 \downarrow$$

This type of reaction occurs if one of the products is insoluble or is expelled from the reaction mixture as a volatile substance.

4. Base + Acid $\longrightarrow$ Salt + H_2O

$$Ca(OH)_2 + 2\ HNO_3 \longrightarrow Ca(NO_3)_2 + 2\ H_2O$$
$$[Ca^{++} + 2\ OH^-] + 2[H^+ + NO_3^-] \longrightarrow [Ca^{++} + 2\ NO_3^-] + 2\ H_2O$$

$$2\ KOH + H_2SO_4 \longrightarrow K_2SO_4 + 2\ H_2O$$
$$2[K^+ + OH^-] + [2\ H^+ + SO_4^{--}] \longrightarrow [2\ K^+ + SO_4^{--}] + 2\ H_2O$$

As pointed out previously, reactions of this type are termed neutralization reactions; the OH^- ions of the base combine with the H^+ ions of the acid to form water. On evaporation of the water, positive ions of the base combine with negative ions from the acid to form the solid salt.

The student should thoroughly familiarize himself with the type reactions just listed — and it is suggested that he write equations for further examples of all of these type reactions.

It is not meant to be implied here that the type reactions discussed above include all of the reactions which we are to study; a large share of the reactions of inorganic chemistry however fall into these types. With this background of chemical reactions, the student has a good working basis for the more complicated reactions to follow.

In order to write chemical equations successfully the student must first be thoroughly familiar with the concept of valence, secondly, he must be able to classify compounds correctly, and thirdly, he must know the more important general type reactions and be able to classify the reaction in question under the proper type.

Nomenclature of acids, salts, and bases. 1. *Naming of acids.* Due to the fact that a number of nonmetallic elements exhibit several valences, a series of acids in which a given nonmetal appears is possible. For example, chlorine forms the series: HCl; $HClO$; $HClO_2$; $HClO_3$; $HClO_4$. By replacing the hydrogen of these acids with a metal a series of salts of these acids would be obtained: $NaCl$; $NaClO$; $NaClO_2$; $NaClO_3$; $NaClO_4$. Obviously to differentiate between the acids or the salts a system of naming is required. The system which has been adopted follows:

The suffix *ic* is used to denote the common oxygen-containing acid of an element; thus $HClO_3$ is chlor-*ic* acid.

The suffix *ous* denotes the acid containing one less oxygen atom; thus $HClO_2$ is chlor-*ous* acid.

The prefix *hypo* and the suffix *ous* are used to denote the acid with two less oxygen atoms; thus $HClO$ is *hypo*-chlor-*ous* acid.

The prefix *per* and the suffix *ic* denote an acid containing one more oxygen atom than the common acid; thus $HClO_4$ is *per*-chlor-*ic* acid.

A prefix *hydro* and a suffix *ic* denote an acid with no oxygen, thus HCl is *hydro*-chlor-*ic* acid.

A slight complication in using this system results from the fact that some of the common oxygen-containing acids have three atoms of oxygen while others have four atoms of oxygen per molecule. In order to use the system, the common oxygen-containing acid must be known. A few of the common oxygen acids are:

$HBrO_3$	bromic acid	H_2SO_4	sulfuric acid
HIO_3	iodic acid	H_3PO_4	phosphoric acid
HNO_3	nitric acid	H_3AsO_4	arsenic acid
H_2CO_3	carbonic acid	H_2CrO_4	chromic acid

2. *Naming of salts.* Salts are derived from acids and are named by using the suffix *ate* for a salt of an *ic* acid; the suffix *ite* for a salt of an *ous* acid; and the suffix *ide* for a salt containing no oxygen (salt of a hydro . . . ic acid).

We may summarize the above system as follows:

	ACID	SALT
One more oxygen atom than common	per . . . ic	per . . . ate
Common oxygen-containing acid	. . . ic	. . . ate
One less oxygen atom	. . . ous	. . . ite
Two less oxygen atoms	hypo . . . ous	hypo . . . ite
No oxygen	hydro . . . ic	. . . ide

EXAMPLES

ACID		SALT	
Formula	*Name*	*Formula*	*Name*
$HBrO_4$	perbromic acid [1]	$NaBrO_4$	sodium perbromate [1]
$HBrO_3$	bromic acid	$NaBrO_3$	sodium bromate
$HBrO_2$	bromous acid	$NaBrO_2$	sodium bromite
$HBrO$	hypobromous acid	$NaBrO$	sodium hypobromite
HBr	hydrobromic acid	$NaBr$	sodium bromide

[1] Actually this compound does not exist but the analogous iodine compound does.

3. *Naming of bases.* The nomenclature of bases is much simpler than that of acids, since metals usually form no more than two hydroxides. The name of the base in which the element has the higher valence is based on a shortened form of the name of the element and the suffix *ic*. Thus $Fe(OH)_3$ is fer*ric* hydroxide. In naming the hydroxide in which the metal has the lower valence, the suffix *ous* is used. Thus $Fe(OH)_2$ is fer*rous* hydroxide. Other examples of bases in which the metal exhibits two valences are:

$Ni(OH)_2$ nickelous hydroxide	$Sn(OH)_2$ stannous hydroxide
$Ni(OH)_3$ nickelic hydroxide	$Sn(OH)_4$ stannic hydroxide

Oxides. The oxides of elements differ greatly in their physical and chemical properties. All of the metallic oxides are solids at ordinary temperatures; some of the oxides of nonmetals are gases at ordinary temperatures; others are solids. On the basis of their reactions with water, oxides may be conveniently divided into two groups, (1) nonmetallic oxides, and (2) metallic oxides.

1. *Nonmetallic oxides.* We learned in the study of oxygen that oxides of nonmetals react with water to form acids:

$$SO_2 + H_2O \longrightarrow H_2SO_3$$
$$CO_2 + H_2O \longrightarrow H_2CO_3$$
$$P_2O_5 + 3\ H_2O \longrightarrow 2\ H_3PO_4$$

A nonmetallic oxide which reacts with water to produce an acid and no other product is called an *acid anhydride*. Thus SO_2 is the anhydride of sulfurous acid, CO_2 is the anhydride of carbonic acid, etc.

An acid anhydride reacts with a base to form a salt and water in the same way that the corresponding acid acts, *e.g.*:

$$\underset{\text{base}}{Ca(OH)_2} + \underset{\text{acid}}{H_2SO_4} \longrightarrow CaSO_4 + 2\ H_2O$$

$$Ca(OH)_2 + \underset{\substack{\text{anhydride} \\ \text{of } H_2SO_4}}{SO_3} \longrightarrow CaSO_4 + H_2O$$

In writing equations of this type, the salt formed will be derived from the acid of which the oxide is the anhydride; in the above example SO_3 is the anhydride of H_2SO_4, therefore the salt must be a sulfate. If the acid anhydride were P_2O_5, what salt would be formed?

2. *Metallic oxides.* Certain metallic oxides act with water to form metallic hydroxides (bases):

$$Na_2O + H_2O \longrightarrow 2\ NaOH$$
$$CaO + H_2O \longrightarrow Ca(OH)_2$$

Oxides of metals are called *basic anhydrides*. Their formulas may be derived by subtracting water from the metallic hydroxides.

Basic anhydrides act like bases in their reactions with acids, *e.g.:*

$$Ca(OH)_2 + H_2SO_4 \longrightarrow CaSO_4 + 2\,H_2O$$
$$\underset{\text{base}}{} \quad \underset{\text{acid}}{}$$

$$CaO + H_2SO_4 \longrightarrow CaSO_4 + H_2O$$
anhydride
of $Ca(OH)_2$

The oxides of sodium, potassium, calcium, magnesium, and barium are readily soluble in water, reacting to form hydroxides. Oxides of other metals react slowly or not at all with water.

3. *Reactions between metal oxides and nonmetal oxides.*

Metal Oxide + Nonmetal Oxide $\longrightarrow$ Salt (combination)

$$CaO + CO_2 \longrightarrow CaCO_3$$
$$Al_2O_3 + 3\,SO_3 \longrightarrow Al_2(SO_4)_3$$

A gaseous nonmetal oxide, *e.g.*, CO_2, SO_3, if passed over a metallic oxide which has been ground to a powder may combine with it to form a salt. Two solid oxides when heated together may give the same type reaction, *e.g.*,

$$PbO + SiO_2 \longrightarrow PbSiO_3$$

Naming of oxides. The nomenclature of metallic oxides is similar to that of bases. The oxide in which the metal exhibits the higher valence is an *ic* oxide. Thus CuO is cup*ric* oxide. The oxide in which the metal has the lower valence is an *ous* oxide. Cu_2O is cuprous oxide. Another example is FeO, ferrous oxide; Fe_2O_3, ferric oxide.

In naming the oxides of nonmetals, a prefix is usually used to indicate the number of oxygen atoms in the molecule. Thus SO_2 is sulfur dioxide, CO_2 is carbon dioxide, SO_3 is sulfur trioxide, As_2O_3 is arsenic trioxide, P_2O_5 is phosphorus pentoxide, etc.

Acid and basic salts. It is conceivable that in the neutralization of an acid by a base, only a part of the hydrogen might be neutralized, thus

$$Na\,OH + \overset{H}{\underset{H}{SO_4}} \longrightarrow \overset{Na}{\underset{H}{SO_4}} + H_2O$$

The compound $NaHSO_4$ has acid properties, since it contains hydrogen, and is also a salt, since it contains both a metal and an acid radical. Such a salt containing acidic hydrogen is termed an *acid salt*. Phosphoric acid, H_3PO_4, might be progressively neutralized to form the salts, NaH_2PO_4, Na_2HPO_4, and Na_3PO_4. The first two are acid salts, since they contain replaceable hydrogen. A way of naming these salts is to call Na_2HPO_4 di-sodium hydrogen phosphate and NaH_2PO_4 sodium di-hydrogen phosphate. These acid phosphates are important in the blood and have much to do in control of the alkalinity of the blood. The third compound, Na_3PO_4, which contains no replaceable hydrogen, is often referred to as *normal* sodium phosphate to differentiate it from the two acid salts.

Historically some acid salts have been named making use of the prefix "bi." Thus in industry $NaHCO_3$ is called sodium bicarbonate and $Ca(HSO_3)_2$, calcium bisulfite. The "bi" is somewhat misleading, so that naming as above is preferable.

If the hydroxyl radicals of a base be progressively neutralized by an acid, *basic salts* may be formed:

$$Ca \overset{OH}{\underset{OH}{\big<}} + HCl \longrightarrow CaOHCl + H_2O$$

Basic salts have properties of a base and will react with acids to form a normal salt and water, thus

$$CaOHCl + HCl \longrightarrow CaCl_2 + H_2O$$

Further examples of basic salts are $BiOH(NO_3)_2$, $Bi(OH)_2NO_3$, and $Pb(OH)C_2H_3O_2$.

Mixed salts. If the hydrogen atoms in an acid be replaced by two or more different metals, a *mixed salt* results. Thus the two hydrogen atoms in H_2SO_4 might be replaced with sodium and potassium to yield the mixed salt, $NaKSO_4$. $NaNH_4HPO_4$ is a mixed acid salt that may be crystallized from urine.

Amphoterism. Some hydroxides have the property of acting as acids under certain conditions and as bases under other conditions. For example, $Sn(OH)_2$ may react with an acid to form a salt and water:

$$\underset{\text{base}}{Sn(OH)_2} + \underset{\text{acid}}{2\ HCl} \longrightarrow \underset{\text{salt}}{SnCl_2} + 2\ H_2O$$

In this reaction, the $Sn(OH)_2$ is functioning as a base. $Sn(OH)_2$ (this may be written as H_2SnO_2) functions as an acid in the reaction:

$$\underset{\text{base}}{2\ NaOH} + \underset{\text{acid}}{H_2SnO_2} \longrightarrow \underset{\text{salt}}{Na_2SnO_2} + 2\ H_2O$$

Such compounds are termed *amphoteric*. We have said that a base contains a metallic element while an acid contains a nonmetal. The element tin in the first reaction is acting as a metal, while in the second reaction it is acting as a nonmetal. While some of the elements are distinctly metallic and others nonmetallic, there are some which under certain conditions act as metals and under other conditions act as nonmetals. Other elements whose hydroxides are amphoteric are aluminum, zinc, chromium, and lead.

EXERCISES

1. (a) Name: $HClO_2$; $NaClO$; H_3AsO_4; $Cu_3(AsO_3)_2$; HI; Mg_3N_2; $Ni(OH)_2$; $Bi(OH)_2Cl$.

   (b) Give formulas for aluminum sulfite, nitrous acid, calcium perchlorate.

2. Write balanced equations for: potassium oxide plus water; aluminum bromide plus sulfuric acid; zinc plus silver nitrate; $H_4SiO_4 + CuCl_2$.

3. (a) Name: Zn_3P_2; $KClO$; HNO_2; H_2CO_3; $Cr(OH)_3$; $CaSO_3$.

   (b) Give formulas for sodium iodate, arsenious acid, potassium dihydrogen arsenate, bismuth dihydroxy nitrate.

4. Write equations for: arsenic oxide plus water; sodium oxide plus water; potassium sulfate plus barium iodide; aluminum plus bromine.

5. Write balanced chemical equations for five different ways of preparing $AlCl_3$. (They need not be economically practicable.)

6. Write equations other than those given in the text representing nine different ways of preparing a salt (the methods need not be practicable).

7. Classify each of the following compounds as (1) acid, (2) base, (3) normal salt, (4) acid salt, (5) basic salt, (6) acid anhydride, (7) basic anhydride, (8) mixed salt:

   (a) P_2O_5, (b) $NaNO_3$, (c) H_2SO_3, (d) NH_4Cl, (e) $CaOHCl$, (f) Na_2SO_4, (g) CuO, (h) HNO_3, (i) $MgNaPO_4$, (j) $KHSO_4$, (k) $NaHCO_3$, (l) $Mg(OH)_2$, (m) $NaNH_4HAsO_4$, (n) NH_4OH, (o) $Bi(OH)_2NO_3$, (p) $Ca(H_2PO_4)_2$, (q) $HClO$, (r) Fe_2O_3, (s) NaH_2PO_4, (t) CO_2, (u) H_2S.

8. $HBrO_3$ is bromic acid. Write formulas for (a) sodium perbromate, (b) hypobromous acid, (c) calcium bromite, (d) ferric bromate, (e) perbromic acid.

9. Write formulas of the anhydrides of the following acids and bases: (a) H_2CrO_4, (b) KOH, (c) $Fe(OH)_3$, (d) $HAsO_2$, (e) $Mg(OH)_2$, (f) $HBrO$, (g) H_3AsO_4, (h) H_4SiO_4.

10. Complete and balance the equations:

   (a) $Al + HCl \longrightarrow$ (f) $SO_2 + H_2O \longrightarrow$

   (b) $CuCO_3 + H_3PO_4 \longrightarrow$ (g) $MgF_2 + H_2SO_4 \longrightarrow$

   (c) $BaCl_2 + MnSO_4 \longrightarrow$ (h) $CO_2 + Ba(OH)_2 \longrightarrow$

   (d) $K_2O + HNO_3 \longrightarrow$ (i) $HClO + Ca(OH)_2 \longrightarrow$

   (e) $MgOHCl + HCl \longrightarrow$ (j) $Fe(NO_3)_3 + NH_4OH \longrightarrow$

REFERENCES

Committee on Inorganic Nomenclature, "Rules for Naming Inorganic Compounds," *J. Am. Chem. Soc.* **63,** 889 (1941).

W. C. Fernelius, "Some Problems of Inorganic Chemical Nomenclature," *Chem. and Eng. News,* **26,** 161 (1948).

XI

Water and the Liquid State

Water is the most familiar of liquids and in its study we shall discuss characteristics of the liquid state in general. In oceans, lakes, and rivers it covers nearly three-fourths of the earth's surface. It is a constituent of the soil and the atmosphere. The human body is more than 65 per cent water, and many of our foods contain an even larger percentage. Table 8 shows the approximate percentage of water in several familiar substances.

TABLE 8

WATER IN FAMILIAR SUBSTANCES

SUBSTANCE	PER CENT	SUBSTANCE	PER CENT
Beef	65–70	Plant tissue	50–75
Eggs	74	Tomatoes	85
Milk	87	Bacon	19
Apples	86	Butter	17
Vegetables (green)	90–95	Peanuts	9
Potatoes	78	Bread	35
Bone	50	Wheat	11
Muscle	75	Lard.	0

Physical properties of water. Pure water has a flat taste and is odorless and practically colorless in thin layers. If a deep section of it is viewed, it appears blue in color. Water has a maximum density at 4° at which temperature 1 ml. weighs 1 gram. Above or below this temperature, 1 ml. weighs less than 1 gram (Table 9). On the centigrade temperature scale, water freezes at 0° and boils at 100°.

Water has a specific heat of 1. *Specific heat* is defined as the number of calories of heat necessary to raise the temperature of 1 gram of a substance 1° C.; thus one calorie is necessary to raise the temperature of 1 gram of water 1°. The specific heat of water is one of the highest.

When ice melts (changes from a solid to a liquid), heat is absorbed. About 80 calories of heat are required to melt 1 gram of ice. When water is frozen, an equivalent amount of heat is evolved. The heat absorbed when 1 gram of solid melts is called the *heat of fusion*, and the heat evolved when 1 gram of liquid freezes is called the *heat of solidification*.

TABLE 9

DENSITY OF WATER FROM 0° TO 100°

Temp. ° C.	Density g./ml.	Temp. ° C.	Density g./ml.
0	0.99987	50	0.9881
2	0.99997	60	0.9832
4	1.0000	70	0.9778
10	0.9997	80	0.9718
20	0.9982	90	0.9653
30	0.9957	100	0.9584
40	0.9922		

The quantity of heat necessary to convert 1 gram of a liquid into a vapor is termed the *heat of vaporization*. For water this is about 539 calories; 539 calories of heat are necessary to change 1 gram of liquid water at 100° C. into vapor (steam) at 100° C. When water is condensed (changed from vapor to liquid), an equivalent amount of heat is given off. This evolved heat is termed the *heat of condensation*. The heat of condensation is an important factor in the use of steam for heating purposes. Steam is introduced into radiators, where it is condensed to the liquid state. In this condensation process, 539 calories of heat are given up to the radiator for every gram of water condensed.

Water is a particularly good solvent. Practically all substances are more or less soluble in water, and a study of aqueous solutions is of primary importance to the chemist.

Properties of the liquid state. A liquid has no definite shape but unlike a gas does occupy a more or less definite volume. Whereas a gas completely fills any container in which it is placed, a liquid does not. Molecules in the liquid state appear to be very much closer together than in a gas; that is, the free volume surrounding each molecule is much less. Evidence for this is the relatively small compressibility of liquids as compared to gases. High pressures are required to compress a liquid even a small fraction of its original volume; for example, a pressure of 3000 atmospheres (about 45,000 lb. per square inch) is necessary to compress 1 liter of water at 0° C. to 900 ml. For additional evidence we may consider the relative volumes of 1 mole of water in the liquid and gaseous states. One mole of water (18 g.) as a liquid at 100° C. occupies a volume of about 18 ml., but when vaporized as steam, it occupies a volume of about 30,000 ml.

Like a gas, molecules in the liquid state are in a constant state of motion, although the movement is much more restricted because of the close proximity of molecules. This motion explains the diffusion of one liquid into another. However, the rate of diffusion of liquids is very much lower than that of gases because of the restricted movement.

Molecules in a liquid are held together presumably by large forces of mutual attraction. This force of attraction is a function of the distance between the molecules, the smaller the distance the greater the force. When a liquid is vaporized, the distance between molecules must be greatly increased. To accomplish this, energy must be expended in overcoming the attractive forces; therefore a liquid possesses less energy than a gas. The energy required to vaporize a liquid is termed the *latent heat of vaporization.*

Evaporation of a liquid. Evaporation of a liquid means the conversion of the liquid to vapor; and condensation, the conversion of vapor to liquid. If a liquid is placed in an open container, the molecules of the liquid gradually escape into the space above the liquid — the liquid evaporates. From an open container the molecules of vapor are dispersed into the atmosphere, and more molecules change into vapor to take their place. If this process is allowed to continue, all of the liquid will eventually be converted into the vapor state; in other words, evaporation continues until the liquid has disappeared.

If a liquid is contained in a closed vessel, the situation is somewhat different, and evaporation does not seem to continue indefinitely. A certain amount of the liquid will be converted into the form of vapor; but after the atmosphere above the liquid becomes saturated with molecules, further evaporation of the liquid appears to cease. This vapor exerts a pressure and this pressure assumes a constant value at a given temperature. As the temperature of a liquid is increased, the vapor pressure increases. Let us study carefully the cause of these phenomena.

We shall try to imagine the state of affairs existing in a liquid which is contained in a closed vessel (Fig. 45). If we could see the individual molecules, we undoubtedly would observe that a number of molecules of the substance are present in the space above the liquid. These molecules are moving about in a random fashion and are in a constant state of motion. Collision of these molecules with the walls of the vessel and the surface of the liquid gives rise to the pressure exerted by the vapor (vapor pressure). Probably a somewhat similar state of affairs exists in the body of the liquid, but the molecules of the liquid are very close together, and movement of the molecules through the body of the liquid is more restricted. However, these molecules possess kinetic energy and move about through the liquid constantly. The molecules are probably held together by mutual attraction. Each molecule in the body of the liquid is attracted and held by the multitude of molecules about it. Occasionally, however, a molecule near the surface of the liquid may possess sufficient energy to break through the surface and thus pass into the space above the liquid. This molecule is thus converted from the liquid state to the vapor state. We may note, too, that some of the molecules which are in the atmosphere above the liquid are passing back into the liquid state. A molecule strikes the surface and passes into the body of the liquid. These molecules are thus condensed from the vapor state to the liquid state. Two continuous processes are occurring simultaneously, the conversion of liquid to vapor (evaporation) and the conversion of vapor to liquid (condensation). Eventually these two processes will be taking place with exactly the same speed, and the number of molecules at any given time in the form of vapor will be a constant; hence the vapor pressure of the liquid attains a constant value at a given temperature. When the rate of evaporation is exactly equal to the rate of condensation, a condition of equilibrium has been established. Equilibrium is an apparent state of rest; actually it is one in which *two opposing processes are taking place with exactly the same speed.*

Fig. 45. A liquid in a closed container soon comes to equilibrium with its vapor — the rate of evaporation is equal to the rate of condensation.

When the temperature of the liquid is increased, the kinetic energy of the molecules in the liquid increases, and more of them escape into the vapor state. Since the number of molecules determines the pressure of the vapor, the pressure must increase as the temperature is increased. Vapor pressures of liquids at various temperatures have been carefully determined. The vapor pressures of water between 0° and 100° will be found in Table 10, page 148.

When the data in Table 10 are plotted, with vapor pressure as ordinate and temperature as abscissa, the vaporization curve for water is obtained (Fig. 46).

All points on this curve represent an equilibrium between liquid

TABLE 10

PRESSURE OF WATER VAPOR, OR AQUEOUS TENSION

(In millimeters of mercury)

TEMPERATURE	PRESSURE	TEMPERATURE	PRESSURE
0° C.	4.6	65° C.	187.5
5°	6.5	70°	233.7
10°	9.2	75°	289.1
15°	12.8	80°	355.1
20°	17.5	85°	433.6
25°	23.7	90°	525.8
30°	31.7	94°	610.0
50°	92.3	97°	680.0
55°	118.0	100°	760.0
60°	149.4		

water and gaseous water. The vapor pressure at any temperature can be obtained from the curve by extending a horizontal line from the point of intersection of a perpendicular corresponding to the temperature; *e.g.*, at 70° the horizontal extension cuts the ordinate at about 230 mm. Consequently the vapor pressure of water at 70° is approximately 230 mm. (See Table 10, which gives 233.7 mm.)

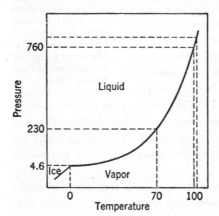

Fig. 46. **Vaporization curve for water.**

The boiling point of a liquid. When a liquid is heated in an open container, the escape of molecules from the liquid into the vapor is opposed by atmospheric pressure. As the temperature of the liquid is increased, the vapor pressure of the liquid increases and approaches the atmospheric pressure. The *temperature at which the vapor pressure of the liquid is equal to the external pressure is the boiling point of the liquid.* Thus water which boils at a temperature of 100° at a pressure of 760 mm. will boil at a temperature of 25° if the external pressure is 23.7 mm. Water boils on a mountain top at a temperature below 100°, since the pressure there is less than 760 mm. It is evident from the vaporization curve for water (Fig. 46) that if the pressure above water is greater than 760 mm., the water will boil at a temperature above 100° C.

Further application of heat at the boiling point of a liquid tends only to vaporize the liquid; the liquid absorbs heat in changing from the liquid to the vapor state. The temperature of the boiling liquid remains constant during conversion to vapor, and application of more heat only increases the speed of evaporation.

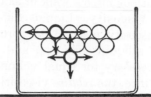

Surface tension. A molecule in the center of a liquid is subject to gravitaional pull in all directions by attraction of the molecules all around it (Fig. 47). A molecule at the surface, however, is subject to attractional pull by the molecules of liquid at all sides and below it,

Fig. 47. Molecules in the surface layer of a liquid have no upward attraction.

but not by attraction upward. This lateral attraction and downward force on surface molecules without any upward force tends to make the surface of a liquid contract, much as a sheet of rubber stretched

Hugh Spencer

Fig. 48. Insect resting on surface film.

laterally in all directions tends to contract. This helps account for a small quantity of a liquid tending to form a spherical or drop shape as there is less surface area to a sphere than to any other shape for a given weight of a liquid. A container can be with care slightly more than filled before it runs over because of the attractional tension between surface molecules. The surface membrane or skinlike layer of molecules is so tough that a small needle may be horizontally floated on it; various insects walk or skate on this surface film of molecules.

Viscosity. Liquids differ in their resistance to flow, or *viscosity*. Viscosity may be interpreted as the ease with which the molecules of a liquid slide over and by one another. By comparing the times necessary for equal volumes of two liquids to flow through a given orifice, the *relative* viscosities may be determined.

Volatile liquids. Liquids are often spoken of as being volatile or nonvolatile. Volatile means easily vaporized — easily converted from a liquid to a vapor. Volatile liquids exert relatively high vapor pressures and have relatively low boiling points. Ether (b.p. 34.5°) and alcohol (b.p. 78°) are classed as volatile liquids, since conversion of liquid to vapor (evaporation) takes place rapidly at relatively low temperatures. Perfumes owe their use to their volatile nature. Liquids of high boiling point, for example sulfuric acid (b.p. 330°) and mercury (b.p. 357°) are classed as nonvolatile liquids.

Purification of water. Natural waters usually contain dissolved mineral matter or gases. This dissolved material gives water its taste, since pure water has a flat taste. Certain waters precipitate soap or form a curd with soap because of their mineral content. Such waters are termed "hard."

Small amounts of mineral matter are desirable in drinking water, but suspended insoluble matter must be removed and bacteria must be killed. Filtration is the simplest process for removing suspended particles, and filtering water through prepared sand and gravel beds constitutes one of the main methods of treatment for drinking water supplies. Charcoal filter beds sometimes augment sand filters. Prior to passage of water through a filter bed it may be allowed to stand in some reservoir or container to allow some suspended material to settle by gravity. Chemicals such as aluminum sulfate may be added to form in the water a gelatinous aluminum hydroxide which aids in the coagulation, settling out, or filtering out of suspended matter. Since some harmful bacteria may not be retained in the filter beds, it is necessary to kill them by use of added chemicals. Ozone is bubbled into water for some European cities; chlorine to the amount of about 1 part Cl_2 per million parts of water is the principal chemical used in the United States. At times bleaching powder, $CaOCl_2$, is substituted for Cl_2 because of its convenience in handling. Use of a little $CuSO_4$ to kill algae growth in settling basin or reservoir water is also practiced.

Small quantities of water may be treated to kill bacteria by boiling or by adding one drop of household iodine per quart of water and allowing to stand a half hour.

Water is often purified by distillation. Distillation is a process in which water is boiled and the vapor subsequently condensed. The process is conveniently carried out in the apparatus shown in Figure 49. The condenser, through which cold water is circulated, changes

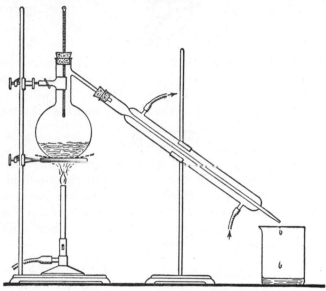

Fig. 49. Distillation of water.

the vapor (steam) to a liquid which is collected in a receiver. Mineral matter, being nonvolatile, stays behind in the distilling flask. Gases contained in the water pass over with the first portion of the distillate, which may be discarded. Water purified in this way is called "distilled water."

Chemical properties of water. Water is a relatively stable compound — a great deal of energy is required to decompose it. Even at high temperatures, water is only slightly decomposed. Slightly more than one per cent is decomposed into hydrogen and oxygen at a temperature of 2000°. At 2500° about four per cent is broken down into its elements.

We learned in the study of hydrogen (chap. VII) that certain metals act with water to form hydrogen. Only the more active metals undergo reaction.

In the study of oxygen we learned that metallic oxides act with water to form hydroxides (bases), while nonmetal oxides act to form acids.

The molecular structure of water. Studies of the molecular structure of water indicate that the hydrogen atoms in the water molecule are not arranged symmetrically about the oxygen atom but rather that they are distributed to one side of the molecule such that the angle between them is about 105°, viz.:

As a result of this arrangement, the center of negative electrical charges (at the center of the oxygen atom) is not the same point as the center of positive electrical charge. Hence, the water molecule acts as a small magnet with one pole positive and the other negative, as:

Such electrically unsymmetrical molecules are called *dipoles*. This peculiarity of structure appears to play an important role in the action of liquids as solvents for various types of solutes (see chap. XV). Because the cohesive forces between these molecules are large, it is likely that the water molecule does not exist as a single dipole, but rather two or more dipoles are associated, as:

 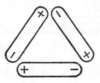

Such association would account for certain properties of water, *e.g.*, the relatively high heat of vaporization, abnormally high boiling point, and low vapor pressure in view of its low molecular weight.

Heavy water. In recent years it has been found that ordinary hydrogen is made up of two isotopes. A third isotope of hydrogen is too unstable to be detected normally in nature, but may be produced by nuclear reaction (see p. 419).

H   D   T

The names deuterium and tritium have been assigned to the heavier isotopes with the symbols D and T. In ordinary hydrogen or its compounds there is but 1 D atom to 4800 H atoms.

Consider the substitution of atoms of D and T for H in water, so that in addition to H_2O molecules of molecular weight 18, there would be D_2O, T_2O, HOD, HOT, and DOT molecules of molecular weights 20, 22, 19, 20, 21 respectively. In the electrolysis of water, ordinary hydrogen atoms are freed much more readily than hydrogen atoms of atomic weight 2. Accordingly, on long electrolysis the water residue contains a relatively high percentage of D_2O. This water is known as "heavy water." Heavy water differs somewhat from ordinary water in certain physical properties. For example, it exhibits a slightly higher freezing point and boiling point than H_2O. The principal source of heavy water has been the aqueous electrolytic baths which have been used over a long period of time.

The formation of hydrates. Many compounds combine chemically with water to form *hydrates*. For example, copper sulfate combines with water to form the hydrate of the composition $CuSO_4 \cdot 5 H_2O$:

$$CuSO_4 + 5 H_2O \longrightarrow CuSO_4 \cdot 5 H_2O$$

The hydrate thus formed is a definite chemical compound conforming to the law of definite proportions; exactly five molecules of water, no more and no less, are combined chemically with one formula weight of $CuSO_4$. The ($\cdot$) used in the formula indicates a condition of instability. The compound is readily decomposed by heating. Water held in such a combination is called *water of hydration*, or water of crystallization. Other familiar hydrates are $Na_2CO_3 \cdot 10 H_2O$ (washing soda), $Na_2SO_4 \cdot 10 H_2O$ (Glauber's salt), and $KAl(SO_4)_2 \cdot 12 H_2O$ (alum). All salts do not form hydrates, for example, NaCl, $K_2Cr_2O_7$, and KNO_3. When one buys crystalline washing soda ($Na_2CO_3 \cdot 10 H_2O$), he buys a greater weight of water than of soda.

Hydrates may be decomposed by the application of heat, the water passing off as water vapor, leaving the *anhydrous* (without water) salt:

$$CuSO_4 \cdot 5 H_2O \longrightarrow CuSO_4 + 5 H_2O$$
$$Na_2CO_3 \cdot 10 H_2O \longrightarrow Na_2CO_3 + 10 H_2O$$

These changes are reversible, since the hydrates may be re-formed by the addition of water to the anhydrous salt. All hydrates are crystalline but not all crystalline salts are hydrates.

Some hydrates are unstable when allowed to stand in contact with the atmosphere. The water of hydration is released, leaving the anhydrous salt. A hydrate which loses water to the atmosphere spontaneously is said to be *efflorescent*. $Na_2CO_3 \cdot 10 H_2O$ is an example of an efflorescent salt. Other salts take up moisture from the atmosphere to form hydrates. These salts which absorb moisture are said to be *deliquescent*. Such substances may be used as drying agents since moisture in the surrounding atmosphere is removed. $CaCl_2$ is often used for this purpose:

$$CaCl_2 + 6 H_2O \longrightarrow CaCl_2 \cdot 6 H_2O$$

Fig. 50. A desiccator.

One specific use of the comparatively cheap salt, $CaCl_2$, is in applying it to roads to keep down dust. The calcium chloride takes water from the air and the roadbed becomes somewhat moist. The salt in powder form or in a water spray has been tried for dispelling fog about landing fields.

The apparatus illustrated in Figure 50 and used for drying chemicals or for keeping them dry is called a desiccator. Commonly used drying agents are calcium chloride, concentrated sulfuric acid, and magnesium perchlorate.

Hydrogen peroxide. When certain of the chemically active metals are heated in oxygen, a peroxide is formed rather than an oxide. A peroxide of a metal contains twice as much oxygen per given weight of metal as its oxide, and in molecular bonding involves an oxygen-to-oxygen linkage. Normal oxides of these metals, Na_2O and BaO, have no oxygen-to-oxygen linkage as the bonding is direct from metal to oxygen.

If a dilute acid is added to a peroxide, *e.g.* BaO_2, hydrogen peroxide is a product:

$$BaO_2 + H_2SO_4 \text{ (dilute)} \longrightarrow BaSO_4 \downarrow + H_2O_2$$

After the above chemical change has taken place, barium sulfate may be filtered from a water solution of H_2O_2. By evaporating this water solution of H_2O_2 under reduced pressure, a concentration of the H_2O_2 to 30 per cent may be effected. Pharmaceutical hydrogen peroxide is only about 3 per cent H_2O_2. Since hydrogen peroxide has the tendency to decompose to water and oxygen, various preservatives such as acetanilide are added. Acetanilide acts as a catalyst to decrease the speed of peroxide decomposition; whereas finely divided metals, manganese dioxide, and blood hasten its decomposition.

Hydrogen peroxide is of use in the cleaning of cuts. The mild oxidizing activity of hydrogen peroxide makes it usable in bleaching feathers, wool, hair, and some silks, which substances would be injured by more vigorous bleaching agents. Hydrogen peroxide has use as an oxidizing substance in rocket fuel.

EXERCISES

1. (*a*) Calculate the volumes of hydrogen and oxygen, respectively, produced at standard conditions, when 100 grams of water is electrolyzed. (*b*) Calculate the weights of these gases.   Ans. (*b*) H_2, 11.1 g.; O_2, 88.9 g.

2. Cite evidence to prove that a hydrate is a definite chemical compound.

3. A hundred pounds of washing soda, $Na_2CO_3 \cdot 10 H_2O$, is purchased at 10 cents per pound. How much money has been invested in water?   Ans. $6.29.

4. What property of calcium chloride makes it useful for laying the dust on roads and highways?

5. Define and illustrate the terms:

   (*a*) boiling point   (*d*) efflorescent   (*g*) vapor pressure
   (*b*) deliquescence   (*e*) hydrate   (*h*) distillation
   (*c*) anhydrous   (*f*) evaporation   (*i*) volatile

6. Suggest a method for detecting the presence of water in kerosene or gasoline.

7. List methods commonly employed for the purification of water.

8. Write equations for the action of water on (*a*) potassium, (*b*) a metallic oxide, (*c*) oxide of a nonmetal, (*d*) zinc.

9. List in order of increasing weight: a 10 cm. cube of Au; a molecule of SO_2; a gram molecular weight of oxygen; a kiloliter of water; a pound of S; a milligram of Pb; a milliliter of alcohol; 22.4 liters of H_2 at standard conditions; a quart of water; an atom of Hg.

10. Below are given temperature and vapor pressure data for the liquid, benzonitrite:

TEMP. °C	VAPOR PRESSURE IN MM. OF HG
38	1
70	11
90	27
100	43
150	255
180	582
187	700
191	760
195	850

Answer the following questions and give the reason for your answer in each case:

   (*a*) Under normal atmospheric pressure, does benzonitrite have a higher or lower boiling point than water?

   (*b*) What would be the boiling point of benzonitrite at standard pressure?

   (*c*) Would boiling benzonitrite under normal pressure be suitable for processing canned meats and vegetables?

   (*d*) At an elevation of 2500 ft. the average air pressure is about 700 mm. Hg. At what temperature would benzonitrite boil at this elevation?

   (*e*) At standard pressure, benzonitrite would condense to liquid at what temperature?

11. What weight of water could be heated from 20° to 70° by the heat liberated when 1000 g. of water freezes at 0° C.   Ans. 1600 g.

12. What weight of ice could be melted at 0° by the heat liberated on condensing 100 g. of steam at 100° to liquid?   Ans. 674 g.

13. A one gram sample of hydrated zinc sulfate on being heated to expel water of hydration leaves a residue of 0.561 g. of anhydrous salt. Determine the formula for the hydrate.

14. List as many type reactions as you can think of which give water as a product.

REFERENCES

A. M. Buswell, *Chemistry of Water and Sewage Treatment*, Reinhold Publishing Co.

F. H. Getman and F. Daniels, *Outlines of Theoretical Chemistry*, John Wiley & Sons.

"Heavy Water," *J. Chem. Ed.* **18**, 552 (1941).

D. Baudisch, "Magic and Science of Natural Healing Waters," *ibid.* **16**, 440 (1939).

G. S. Forbes, "Water: Some Interpretations More or Less Recent," *ibid.* **18**, 18 (1941).

"Hydrogen Peroxide," *J. Ind. Eng. Chem.*, **22**, 1234 (1930).

Edward S. Shanley and Frank P. Greenspan, "Highly Concentrated Hydrogen Peroxide," *ibid.* **39**, 1536 (1947).

XII

The Solid State of Matter

Properties of solids. In general, the forces of attraction between atoms, molecules, or ions in solids are much stronger than the attractive forces in liquids and gases. As a consequence a solid possesses rigidity and mechanical strength. Whereas pressure and temperature greatly affect the volume of a gas and to a lesser degree the volume of a liquid, these variables have little effect on the volume of a solid. For example, if a piece of iron is heated, expansion or increase in volume does take place, but this volume change is relatively small; a high pressure would diminish the volume of a piece of iron only slightly.

Solids may be classified as *crystalline* or *amorphous*. A crystalline solid is one in which the atoms are arranged in a definite geometric pattern constantly repeated. An amorphous substance does not possess this orderly arrangement, and may be considered as simply an undercooled liquid. When a crystalline solid is heated, the transition from the solid to the liquid state is sharp and distinct; the solid changes state at a definite temperature called the melting point. On the other hand, if an amorphous substance such as glass is heated, the glass gradually softens and becomes less viscous as the temperature is raised, but no definite point of transition is recorded. In other words, a crystalline substance possesses a definite melting point; an amorphous substance does not.

Although molecules are held tightly to the surface of solids and there is little freedom of movement, nevertheless a solid may exert an appreciable vapor pressure. Solid iodine, for example, evaporates readily at ordinary temperatures. Such a change, in which the solid does not melt but passes directly to the vapor state, is called *sublimation*.

Crystal forms. The study of crystal forms and their properties is termed *crystallography*. When a substance crystallizes, the crystals

157

are bounded by plane surfaces and have a definite and characteristic form; the faces of the crystal meet at definite angles, and the edges are straight lines. This is due to the orderly arrangement of the particles of the substance to form a definite geometric structure. The

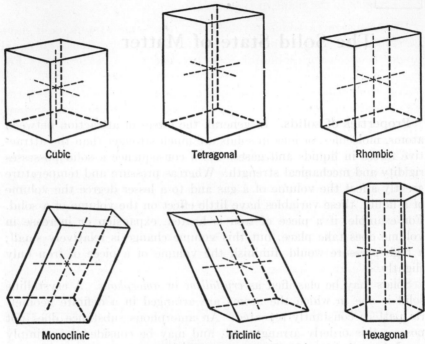

Cubic   Tetragonal   Rhombic

Monoclinic   Triclinic   Hexagonal

Fig. 51. Crystal systems.

form of the crystal is a characteristic for a given substance, and frequently a substance may be identified simply from its crystal structure. If the plane surfaces of crystals be referred to imaginary lines or axes drawn through them, all crystal forms may be resolved into the following six types (see Fig. 51):

1. *Cubic or regular system:* Three axes of equal length and all at right angles to one another.
2. *Tetragonal system:* Three axes, two of equal length, all intersecting at right angles.
3. *Rhombic system:* Three axes of unequal length, all intersecting each other at right angles.
4. *Monoclinic system:* Three axes of unequal length, two of which intersect obliquely, while the third intersects the other two at right angles.

5. *Triclinic system:* Three axes of unequal length, none of which intersect at right angles.

6. *Hexagonal system:* Three axes of equal length in one plane intersecting each other at 60° angles, and a fourth axis at right angles to the plane of the other three.

Two substances which crystallize in the same system, and have corresponding axes of approximately the same dimensions and equal angles between corresponding faces are said to be *isomorphous.* For example, the alums (chap. XXXV) are isomorphous.

A given substance may sometimes crystallize in more than one form, *e.g.,* sulfur may crystallize in the rhombic or the monoclinic system, depending upon the temperature. Such a substance is said to be *dimorphous.*

Crystal lattices. By means of X-rays it may be shown that the unit particles of a crystal, whether they be atoms, ions, or molecules, lie in parallel planes and form a definite geometric configuration. The pattern or structure thus formed is termed the *crystal lattice,* or *space lattice.* The smallest portion of the crystal which shows the complete pattern of the particles in their relative positions is called a *unit cell.*

While the cubic system is the simplest of the six crystal systems listed above, three arrangements of the particles in a crystal belonging to the cubic system are possible:

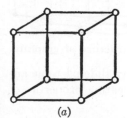 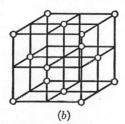 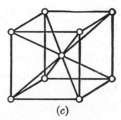

(a)   (b)   (c)

Fig. 52. (a) Simple cubic lattice; (b) face-centered lattice; (c) body-centered lattice.

1. Simple cubic lattice (Fig. 52a), in which atoms, ions, or molecules are located only at the corners of the cube.

2. Face-centered lattice (Fig. 52b), in which the unit particles are located at each corner and the center of each face of a cube. Gold, silver, and copper crystallize in this pattern.

3. Body-centered lattice (Fig. 52c), in which a unit particle is located at each of the corners of a cube and also in the center of the cube, equidistant from the eight corners. Iron, sodium, and potassium are examples of this type.

Sodium chloride crystallizes in the cubic system, the arrangement of sodium and chlorine ions in the crystal lattice being shown in Figure 24, page 50. If we select a unit of the crystal such that a sodium

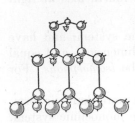

ion appears at each corner of the cube, then a chlorine ion appears in the center of each of the six faces. Six chlorine ions are equidistant from each sodium ion and likewise six sodium ions surround and are equidistant from each chlorine ion. A crystal of sodium chloride thus consists of interpenetrating simple cubic lattices of sodium and chlorine ions.

Fig. 53. Structure of diamond. Each carbon atom is bound to four other carbon atoms in a close-packed arrangement.

The crystal structure of a substance will often account for certain of its physical properties. For example, the element carbon may crystallize in two forms, diamond and graphite. In the diamond (Fig. 53) the carbon atoms are arranged as in a tetrahedron, with one atom at each of the four corners and one atom in the center of the tetrahedron. The atoms are held together by strong covalent forces and as a result, the diamond is hard, strong, and possesses a high melting point. In graphite (Fig. 54) the unit cell possesses a two-dimensional structure in which carbon atoms are arranged in the form of hexagons in planes. While the atoms in a given plane are held together by strong covalent linkages, the forces between

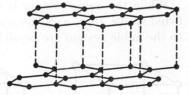

Fig. 54. Structure of graphite.

planes are weak. As a result the planes can readily slide past one another, thus explaining the flaky character and lubricating properties of the element.

The unit cell of cellulose, asbestos, and other fibrous materials has been shown by X-rays to possess a long stringlike structure.

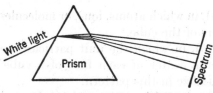

Fig. 55. Dispersion of light.

The use of X-rays in studying crystal structure. When a beam of white light strikes a prism, the light is refracted and spread out in an array of colors called a *spectrum* (Fig. 55). The white light is resolved into its component colors because of the difference in refraction of the various colors or wave lengths of light; the refraction of violet light is greater than that for red light. A diffraction grating, which is made by ruling parallel lines very close together on a metal or glass surface, like a prism resolves white light into its component colors, provided the distances between lines on the grating are of the same order as the wave length of light used.

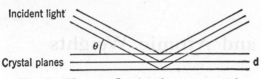

Incident light

θ

Crystal planes ═══════════════ d

Fig. 56. X-ray reflection from a crystal.

The planes of symmetry in a crystal may act as a diffraction grating when a beam of X-rays is allowed to strike the surface of the crystal. The distance between the planes in the crystal is of the same order as the wave length of the X-rays. If X-ray beams of single wave length (called monochromatic light) strike the surface of a crystal, so that the incident light is in phase, the beams of light re-enforce one another so that the reflected beam will have a high intensity (Fig. 56). The angle of incident light bears a definite relationship to the distance, d, between the planes of atoms or other units in the crystal, namely $\lambda = 2\,d\,\sin\theta$, where λ is the wave length of the incident light, and θ is the angle the incident ray makes with the surface of the crystal.

By means of this relationship, and a knowledge of the wave length of light and the angle of incidence which can be measured, the distances between the planes of atoms in the crystal may be calculated.

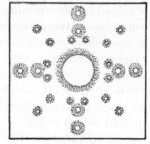

Fig. 57. X-ray diffraction pattern.

If the reflected rays from the crystal are photographed, spots of light in a definite arrangement appear on the plate (Figure 57). These spots on the plate correspond to a definite arrangement of the units in the crystal and from the nature of the arrangement, the structure of the crystal may be deduced.

REFERENCES

F. H. Getman and Farrington Daniels, *Outlines of Theoretical Chemistry*, Wiley.
C. W. Stillwell, *Crystal Chemistry*, McGraw-Hill.
J. A. Campbell, "Structural Molecular Models." *J. Chem. Ed.* **25**, 200 (1948).

XIII

Molecular and Atomic Weights

Experimental determination of molecular weights. Since a mole (gram molecular weight) of any gas at standard conditions occupies a volume of 22.4 liters, the molecular weight of a gas is easily obtained by determining the weight of a given volume of the gas at any conditions of temperature and pressure and then calculating the weight of gas which would occupy 22.4 liters at standard conditions. The weight in grams of this volume is the gram molecular weight and is numerically equal to the molecular weight. The molecular weight of solids and liquids which are easily vaporized without decomposition may also be determined by this method. For example, an experiment showed that 6 grams of chloroform (boiling point 61°) occupied a volume of 1.53 liters at 100° and 760 mm. pressure. Reduced to standard conditions, the volume would be

$$1.53 \times \tfrac{273}{373} = 1.12 \text{ l.}$$

Since the gram molecular weight (x) is the weight of 22.4 liters at standard conditions, it may be calculated by the following proportion:

$$\frac{x}{6} = \frac{22.4}{1.12}$$
$$x = 120$$

The accurate molecular weight of chloroform, $CHCl_3$, is 119.37. Hence the experimental error by this method may be less than one per cent.

The method is limited in its application since many substances are either nonvolatile or may decompose when an attempt is made to vaporize them. However, we shall learn in chapter XV that molecular weights of solids may be determined by accurately measuring the boiling and freezing points of aqueous and nonaqueous solutions.

Atomic weights. Atomic weights are determined by the analysis of pure chemical compounds. Since the atom is the reactive unit in chemical change, *the smallest weight of an element in a molecular weight of any of its compounds should be its atomic weight*. If the molecular weight of a compound of a given element is known, the weight of the element present in a mole of the compound can be determined by chemical analysis. Actually it is unnecessary to analyze all of the compounds of a given element, since a representative number of them will be sufficient to arrive at the atomic weight. Consider the compounds of chlorine in Table 11, which shows the percentage and parts by weight of chlorine in a molecular weight of several of its compounds.

The smallest weight of chlorine appearing in a molecular weight of the compounds given is 35.46. No compound of chlorine has ever been found in which a molecular weight contains less than 35.46

TABLE 11

Compound	Molecular Weight	Percentage Chlorine	Parts by Weight of Chlorine
Hydrogen chloride	36.46	97.26	35.46
Methylene chloride	84.95	83.49	70.92
Chloroform	119.40	89.10	106.38
Carbon tetrachloride	153.85	92.19	141.84
Thionyl chloride	118.98	59.69	70.92
Phosphorus pentachloride	208.28	85.13	177.30
Butyl chloride	92.57	38.31	35.46
Carbonyl chloride	98.93	71.69	70.92

parts by weight of chlorine. This value, then, must be the atomic weight of chlorine.

The main objection to this method of determining atomic weight is its dependence upon molecular weights which cannot be determined with a high degree of accuracy. The accuracy of the atomic weight of the element is limited to the accuracy of the molecular weight determinations.

Precise atomic weights. Precise atomic weights are obtained from equivalent weights, which in turn are obtained from accurate analysis and synthesis of pure chemical compounds. For emphasis let us again define the equivalent weight of an element as that weight of the element which will combine with or displace one equivalent of any other element. Since oxygen serves as the standard, the equivalent weight is defined as that weight of an element which will combine with 8 grams of oxygen. One equivalent weight of a metal will displace 1.008 grams of hydrogen from an acid. It was stated on page 28 that a simple relationship exists between the equivalent weight and the atomic weight of an element, thus

$$\text{Atomic Weight} = \text{Equivalent Weight} \times X$$

where X is a small integral number which also represents the valence of the element in the compound from which the equivalent weight was obtained. Our next problem, then, is to find the value of this small integral number.

Fortunately we have an empirical method for the determination of the approximate atomic weight of an element. If we have the approximate atomic weight, it will be an easy matter to determine the value of X in the above relationship. The relationship which allows us to calculate the approximate atomic weight of an element is due to DuLong and Petit, who found that the product of the specific heat of a solid element and its atomic weight gave a value between 6 and 7, the average value being about 6.4. They therefore stated the general rule:

$$\text{Atomic Weight} \times \text{Specific Heat} = 6.4 \text{ approx.}$$

Examination of Table 12 will show the validity of this rule.

TABLE 12

ELEMENT	SPECIFIC HEAT	ATOMIC WEIGHT	ATOMIC WEIGHT × SPECIFIC HEAT
Iron	.12	55.84	6.7
Tin	.054	118.7	6.4
Phosphorus (white)	.20	31.0	6.2
Silver	.056	107.0	6.0
Mercury	.034	200.6	6.8
Magnesium	.25	24.3	6.1
Zinc	.093	65.38	6.1
Gold	.032	197.2	6.3
Sodium	.29	23.0	6.7

It is obvious that if the specific heat of an element is known, its approximate atomic weight may be obtained by dividing 6.4 by its specific heat. Specific heat is defined as the number of calories of heat necessary to raise the temperature of 1 gram of the element 1° C. Let us consider the following examples which illustrate how atomic weights are obtained from equivalent weights, and the DuLong and Petit rule:

EXAMPLE 1. Analysis of an oxide of iron shows that 18.61 g. of iron are combined with 8 g. of oxygen. 18.61 is therefore the equivalent weight of iron in this compound.

The specific heat of iron is .12, from which we may calculate the approximate atomic weight of iron with the aid of the DuLong and Petit rule:

$$\text{Approximate Atomic Weight} = \frac{6.4}{.12} = 54$$

It is evident from inspection that the multiple of the equivalent weight (18.61) which most nearly gives 54 is 3. The exact atomic weight must therefore be

$$3 \times 18.61 = 55.83$$

EXAMPLE 2. A compound analyzes 21.23 per cent oxygen and 78.77 per cent tin.

From the above data we may calculate the equivalent weight of tin (the weight of tin combining with 8 parts by weight of oxygen) from the proportion

$$\frac{21.23}{78.77} = \frac{8}{x} \qquad x = 29.68$$

The specific heat of tin is .054, from which the approximate atomic weight is $\frac{6.4}{.054} = 118$. The smallest integral number which most nearly gives this value when multiplied by the equivalent weight is 4. The exact atomic weight then must be $4 \times 29.68 = 118.72$. The valence of tin in this compound must be 4.

EXAMPLE 3. The analysis of a compound gives 24.76 per cent chlorine and 75.24 per cent silver.

While we cannot calculate directly from these data the weight of silver which combines with 8 grams of oxygen, we can calculate the weight of silver which combines with 35.46 parts by weight of chlorine. This value, then, must be the equivalent weight of silver since we know that 35.46 is the equivalent weight of chlorine. By proportion

$$\frac{24.76}{75.24} = \frac{35.46}{x} \qquad x = 107.88$$

The specific heat of silver is .056; therefore the approximate atomic weight of silver is $\frac{6.4}{.056} = 114$.

It is evident that the valence of silver must be 1 and the atomic weight is then the same as the equivalent weight, namely, 107.88.

EXERCISES

1. 56 ml. of a gaseous compound measured at standard conditions weighed 0.26 g. What is the molecular weight of the compound?   Ans. 104.

2. .532 g. of a solid substance when vaporized occupied a volume of 118 ml. at a pressure of 694 mm. and a temperature of 94° C. Calculate the molecular weight of the substance.   Ans. 149.

3. Calculate the approximate atomic weight of an element whose specific heat is .32.

4. If the atomic weight of oxygen were 100, what would its equivalent weight be?

5. 0.134 g. of aluminum combines with 0.532 g. of chlorine. The specific heat of aluminum is .217. Calculate the valence and atomic weight of aluminum.

6. 2.25 g. of a metal of atomic weight 27 yielded 2800 ml. of H_2 gas at standard conditions. What is the valence of the metal?   Ans. 3.

7. 50 ml. of a gaseous oxide of sulfur at standard conditions weighs 0.143 g. What is its molecular weight and formula?   Ans. SO_2.

8. 0.5 g. of liquid occupies 220 ml. when volatilized at 100° and 760 mm. pressure. What is the molecular weight of the liquid?

9. 373 ml. of vapor at 100° and 760 mm. pressure on condensing forms 0.45 ml. of liquid with a density of 1.2 g./ml. Calculate the molecular weight of the vapor.   Ans. 44.

10. 0.5 g. of oxygen combines with 2 g. of a metal. Compute the equivalent weight of the metal.   Ans. 32.

11. 2.0 g. of copper is displaced from $CuSO_4$ by 0.76 g. of an unknown metal. What is the equivalent weight of the unknown metal? Equiv. weight of Cu = 31.8.   Ans. 12.1.

12. 2.5 g. of a metallic oxide contains 1.4 g. of metal. The specific heat of this metal is 0.128. Calculate the exact atomic weight.   Ans. 50.91.

13. 0.4 g. of oxygen combines with 0.6 g. of magnesium. 0.4 g. of magnesium displaces 1.05 g. of copper from a copper salt. What is the equivalent weight of copper?   Ans. 31.5.

14. Suppose you carried out an experiment and found 0.567 g. of metal would displace 700 ml. of hydrogen at standard conditions. What is the equivalent weight of the metal?   Ans. 9.

XIV

Weight and Volume Relations Between Substances in Chemical Change

As well as having a knowledge of the kinds of substances entering or resulting from chemical change, it is important from a practical standpoint to know proportionate amounts of chemicals that enter into or are formed as a result of a chemical change. Since amounts of substances may be measured by volume or by weight and by either the metric or English system, one must carefully designate the units of measurement used. Whereas solids and liquids are easily weighed, gases are not so easily weighed and frequently are measured by volume.

Volume-volume relations. Some of the simplest problems of chemistry are of a volume-to-volume nature. Their solution is based on Gay-Lussac's law of combining volumes (chap. VIII). The law, in substance, states "in a chemical change the comparative volumes of gases involved (measured under the same conditions of temperature and pressure), bear to each other a small whole-number relationship." For example, in the reaction

$$2\,CO + O_2 \longrightarrow 2\,CO_2$$

reactants and products are gases. The coefficients of the formulas give the volume relations and in this case we may say 2 unit volumes of CO react with 1 unit volume of O_2 to give 2 unit volumes of CO_2.

We might use any unit of volume such as liters, gallons, cubic feet, etc. The following examples will illustrate the solution of typical volume-volume problems. (It is assumed that all gases are under the same conditions of temperature and pressure.)

EXAMPLE 1. Calculate the volume of oxygen necessary to burn 50 liters of CO. According to the equation above, 2 liters of CO would require 1 liter of oxygen (the numbers 2 and 1 are the coefficients of CO and O_2 respectively), therefore we might set up the proportion

$$\frac{2 \text{ liters}}{50 \text{ liters}} = \frac{1 \text{ liter}}{x \text{ liters}} \qquad x = 25 \text{ liters}$$

What volume of CO_2 would be formed?

The equation tells us that 2 liters of CO would produce 2 liters of CO_2, hence 50 liters of CO would produce 50 liters of CO_2.

EXAMPLE 2. Calculate the volume of oxygen necessary to produce 1000 cubic feet of SO_2 according to the equation:

$$S + O_2 \longrightarrow SO_2$$

The coefficients of oxygen and sulfur dioxide are 1 and 1, therefore

$$\frac{1 \text{ cu. ft.}}{x} = \frac{1 \text{ cu. ft.}}{1000} \qquad x = 1000 \text{ cu. ft.}$$

We should keep in mind that Gay-Lussac's law applies *only* to substances in the gaseous state, and cannot be used with those substances which may be present as liquids or solids. For example, in the above, we cannot calculate the volume relationship between sulfur and oxygen or sulfur dioxide, since sulfur is a solid at the conditions under which this reaction is carried out.

EXAMPLE 3. How much oxygen is required for the complete combustion of 1000 cu. ft. of NH_3 according to the equation given below. Calculate also the volume of nitric oxide formed.

$$4 NH_3 + 5 O_2 \longrightarrow 4 NO + 6 H_2O$$

According to the equation 4 unit volumes of ammonia react with 5 unit volumes of oxygen to give 4 unit volumes of nitric oxide and 6 unit volumes of water (vapor). The ratio of NH_3 to O_2 being 4 to 5 by volume, we can set up the proportion

$$\frac{4}{1000 \text{ cu. ft.}} = \frac{5}{x} \qquad x = 1250 \text{ cu. ft.}$$

To calculate the volume of NO formed we may use the proportion

$$\frac{4}{1000 \text{ cu. ft.}} = \frac{4}{x} \qquad x = 1000 \text{ cu. ft.}$$

It may be noted in the latter example that the sums of the volumes on both sides of the chemical equation are not equal. Many chemical changes involving gases may show increase or decrease of volume of products over initial volume.

Weight-weight relations. In considering reactants and products of a chemical change, such questions may arise as: In what proportion should one mix the initial substances? What weight of product or products will result after chemical change from certain weights of reacting substances? Such problems are best solved with the balanced chemical equation as a guide. Just as a formula tells us very definitely the ratio of weights of the different elements present in a compound, so an equation tells us the relationship of the weights of the reactants to one another and to the products. The calculation of weights from equations can be illustrated with examples:

EXAMPLE 1. What weight of oxygen may be obtained by heating 30 grams of potassium chlorate?

The balanced equation is

$$2 \text{ KClO}_3 \longrightarrow 2 \text{ KCl} + 3 \text{ O}_2$$

ATOMIC WEIGHTS
K = 39
O = 16
Cl = 35.5

The equation tells us that 2 formula weights of potassium chlorate will give 2 formula weights of KCl and 3 formula weights of O_2; or $2 \times (39 + 35.5 + 48)$ parts by weight of KClO$_3$ will produce $2 \times (39 + 35.5)$ parts by weight of KCl and $3 \times (32)$ parts by weight of oxygen.

It is convenient to make a brief statement of the problem by putting written notes just above the formulas of the substances under consideration, thus

$$\overset{30 \text{ g.}}{\underset{2(122.5)}{2 \text{ KClO}_3}} \longrightarrow 2 \text{ KCl} + \overset{x \text{ g.}}{\underset{3(32)}{3 \text{ O}_2}}$$

The formula weights multiplied by the proper coefficients are then placed directly beneath the formulas. We are not concerned with KCl in this problem so it is unnecessary to calculate its formula weight. (This was done in this problem simply to show the full meaning of the balanced equation, but in subsequent calculations, only those formula weights which actually are needed in the solution of the problem will be used.) The proportion may be formulated:

$$\frac{30}{2(122.5)} = \frac{x}{3(32)} \qquad x = 11.75 \text{ g. of oxygen}$$

EXAMPLE 2. What weight of sulfur must combine with aluminum to prepare 600 pounds of aluminum sulfide?

This problem can be solved as a percentage composition problem or as a weight-weight problem. If one calculates the percentage of sulfur in Al_2S_3 and multiplies by 600 pounds, the needed amount of sulfur is given. As a weight-weight problem the usual procedure is best followed:

$$\underset{3(32)}{2\,Al + 3\,\overset{x\ lb.}{S}} \longrightarrow \underset{150}{\overset{600\ lb.}{Al_2S_3}}$$

$$\frac{x}{96} = \frac{600}{150} \qquad x = 384 \text{ lb. sulfur}$$

EXAMPLE 3. What weight of arsenic acid should a company use upon lime to prepare a thousand pounds of calcium arsenate insecticide material?

Once one has the balanced chemical equation for this commercial preparation, the weight-weight problem readily follows the usual pattern:

$$3\,CaO + \underset{2(142)}{2\,\overset{x\ lb.}{H_3AsO_4}} \longrightarrow \underset{398}{\overset{1000\ lb.}{Ca_3(AsO_4)_2}} + 3\,H_2O$$

$$\frac{x}{284} = \frac{1000}{398} \qquad x = 714 \text{ lb. } H_3AsO_4$$

Weight-volume relations. Gases are most commonly measured by volume, whereas liquids and solids are usually measured by weight. At times it is desirable to calculate the relationship of weight to volume in chemical changes where a gas is involved.

The fact that *22.4 liters* of any gas at standard conditions weighs *its gram molecular weight* allows one to interchange weight and volume units for a gas. By a mathematical coincidence, *22.4 cubic feet* of any gas at standard conditions weighs *its ounce molecular weight*. These facts allow calculation of the weight from volume or volume from weight of any amount of pure gas. In the event of a gas at other than standard conditions, gas law calculations of volume at standard conditions are necessary, since the equality of 22.4 liters and gram molecular weight holds only for standard conditions. The following examples will illustrate the usefulness of this relation between the weight of a gas and its volume at standard conditions:

EXAMPLE 1. What is the weight of one liter of carbon monoxide, CO, at standard conditions?

The molecular weight of CO is 28, consequently

22.4 liters of CO at s.c. = 28 grams (gram molecular weight)
1 liter of CO at s.c. = x grams

$$\frac{22.4}{1} = \frac{28}{x} \qquad x = 1.25 \text{ g.}$$

EXAMPLE 2. What is the weight of one thousand cubic feet of carbon monoxide at standard conditions?

22.4 cu. ft. of CO at s.c. = 28 ounces (ounce molecular weight)
1000 cu. ft. of CO at s.c. = x ounces

$$\frac{22.4}{1000} = \frac{28}{x} \qquad\qquad x = 1250 \text{ ounces}$$

In chemical changes involving either liquids or solids and gases, problems such as the following are encountered:

EXAMPLE 3. As sulfuric acid chemically acts on 120 grams of metallic calcium, what volume of hydrogen at standard conditions is produced?

The problem may be solved in almost identical manner to a weight-weight problem, except that for the gas one can substitute 22.4 liters in place of its gram molecular weight:

$$\underset{40 \text{ g.}}{\overset{120 \text{ g.}}{Ca}} + H_2SO_4 \longrightarrow CaSO_4 + \underset{\substack{2 \text{ g.}\\22.4 \text{ l.}}}{\overset{x \text{ liters}}{H_2}}$$

$$\frac{120}{40} = \frac{x}{22.4} \qquad\qquad x = 67.2 \text{ liters}$$

EXAMPLE 4. What volume of ammonia at standard conditions can be obtained as steam is passed over 4000 grams of calcium cyanamide?

$$\underset{80 \text{ g.}}{\overset{4000 \text{ g.}}{CaCN_2}} + 3\,H_2O \longrightarrow \underset{\substack{2(17) \text{ g.}\\2(22.4) \text{ liters}}}{\overset{x \text{ liters}}{2\,NH_3}} + CaCO_3$$

$$\frac{4000}{80} = \frac{x}{2(22.4)} \qquad\qquad x = 2240 \text{ liters}$$

EXAMPLE 5. What volume of oxygen is needed in the complete burning of 100 ounces of octane liquid?

$$\underset{2(114) \text{ oz.}}{\overset{100 \text{ oz.}}{2\,C_8H_{18}}} + \underset{\substack{25(32) \text{ oz.}\\25(22.4) \text{ cu. ft.}}}{\overset{x \text{ cu. ft.}}{25\,O_2}} \longrightarrow 16\,CO_2 + 18\,H_2O$$

$$\frac{100}{2(114)} = \frac{x}{25(22.4)} \qquad\qquad x = 245.6 \text{ cu. ft.}$$

The volume of air required for the combustion would be 5×245.6 or 1228 cu. ft. since air is approximately $\frac{1}{5}$ oxygen. A hundred ounces of octane liquid (octane approximates the average composition of gasoline) occupies a volume of about 1 gallon. It is surprising that as much as 1228 cu. ft. of air are needed in the complete combustion of 1 gallon of gasoline.

EXERCISES

1. (a) What volume of oxygen is needed to burn completely 20 liters of CH_4 gas? (Consider gases at same conditions.) (b) What volume of products will be formed?   Ans. (a) 40 l.; (b) 60 l.

2. A balloon contains 1000 cu. ft. of hydrogen. What volume of air would be used in burning the hydrogen?   Ans. 2500 cu. ft.

3. Given 0.4 liter of C_8H_{18} (octane) vapor at 100° C. (a) What volume of oxygen at 100° will be required to completely burn the gas? Products of combustion are carbon dioxide and water. (b) What volume of air (20 per cent oxygen) would be necessary? (c) What would be the total volume of the gaseous products at 100°?   Ans. (a) 5 l.

4. Four liters of nitrogen and 14 liters of hydrogen gases are mixed together. Assuming that all of the nitrogen reacts to produce ammonia gas, what gases and what volume of each would be present? Assume no change in temperature.

5. The mineral cinnabar from which most mercury is obtained is chemically HgS. What weight of mercury should be obtained from 1000 pounds of HgS?

6. What weight of chromium could theoretically be electrodeposited from a solution containing a kilogram of $Cr_2(SO_4)_3$?   Ans. 265 g.

7. (a) Sixty grams of lead dioxide on being highly heated will yield what weight of oxygen gas? (b) What would the volume of the oxygen gas be, measured at standard conditions?   Ans. (a) 4.01 g.; (b) 2.8 l.

8. What weight of H_3PO_4 can be prepared as H_2SO_4 acts on 400 pounds of $Ca_3(PO_4)_2$?   Ans. 253 lb.

9. How many pounds of silver sulfate must be used in the reaction with KBr to produce 94 pounds of silver bromide for photographic use?

10. $Bi_2(CO_3)_3$ is treated with HNO_3 to obtain $Bi(NO_3)_3$ in a step in making the medicinal bismuth subnitrate. What weight of $Bi(NO_3)_3$ can be made as excess HNO_3 acts on 1098 grams of $Bi_2(CO_3)_3$?

11. What weight of 10 per cent sulfuric acid should be used with Al_2O_3 to prepare 684 g. of $Al_2(SO_4)_3$?

12. What weight of lime (CaO) should be added to excess 10 per cent nitric acid to prepare 4920 pounds of $Ca(NO_3)_2$?   Ans. 1680 lb.

13. What is the weight of 2.8 liters of the chemical warfare gas phosgene, $COCl_2$?

14. What is the weight of 10 liters of SiF_4 at standard conditions?

15. As hydrochloric acid acts on 500 grams of iron filings, what volume of hydrogen is produced at standard conditions?   Ans. 200 l.

16. How many cubic feet of H_2S gas at standard conditions must be bubbled into a solution of $SbCl_3$ to produce 1000 pounds of the insoluble substance Sb_2S_3? (Antimony sulfide is used as a combustible substance in the preparation of matches.)

$$2\,SbCl_3 + 3\,H_2S \longrightarrow Sb_2S_3 \downarrow + 6\,HCl$$

                                                    Ans. 3170 cu. ft.

17. What volume of CO_2 measured at standard conditions would have to be cooled to produce 220 grams of "dry ice" (solid CO_2)? Ans. 112 l.

18. Eighty liters of ammonia gas at standard conditions were dissolved in water. How many grams of sodium nitrate must be treated with sulfuric acid in order to prepare enough HNO_3 to neutralize the solution?

$$NH_3 + HNO_3 \longrightarrow NH_4NO_3$$
$$2\,NaNO_3 + H_2SO_4 \longrightarrow Na_2SO_4 + 2\,HNO_3$$

Ans. 304 g.

19. How many grams of nitrogen are there in 500 liters of NO_2 at standard conditions? Ans. 313.

20. One kilogram of oxygen is pumped into a tank of 100 liters capacity. Calculate the pressure of oxygen in the tank, assuming a temperature of $0°$ C. Ans. 7 Atm.

21. What volume of Cl_2 gas at standard conditions must act on gold to form 1215 ounces of $AuCl_3$? Ans. 134.4 cu. ft.

22. When Ca_3As_2 is treated with dilute hydrochloric acid, arsine gas (AsH_3) is evolved. The residue is calcium chloride. Write the balanced equation for this reaction and then calculate the volume of arsine gas (at standard conditions) produced by the action of acid on 90 g. of Ca_3As_2 (calcium arsenide). Ans. 14.9 l.

23. What volume of HBr gas at standard conditions may be prepared as 1200 grams of $CaBr_2$ is acted on by H_3PO_4?

24. Determine the volume of acetylene gas (C_2H_2) at standard conditions produced from two gram moles of calcium carbide according to the equation:

$$CaC_2 + 2\,H_2O \longrightarrow Ca(OH)_2 + C_2H_2$$

Ans. 44.8 l.

25. Potassium chlorate may be prepared by passing chlorine gas into a hot solution of KOH, followed by cooling and crystallization of the salt. If the reaction takes place according to the equation

$$3\,Cl_2 + 6\,KOH \longrightarrow KClO_3 + 5\,KCl + 3\,H_2O$$

what weight of $KClO_3$ could be produced by the action of 100 liters of chlorine (measured at standard conditions) on an excess of KOH solution? Ans. 182 g.

26. 14.5 g. of an impure sample of ferrous sulfide yields 3.09 liters of H_2S (standard conditions) when treated with dilute HCl:

$$FeS + 2\,HCl \longrightarrow FeCl_2 + H_2S$$

Determine the percentage of FeS in the sample. Ans. 83.

27. In the presence of a platinum catalyst and at a temperature of $900°$ C., ammonia gas burns according to the equation:

$$4\,NH_3 + 5\,O_2 \longrightarrow 4\,NO + 6\,H_2O$$

Assuming all gases are at the same conditions of temperature and pressure (a) what volume of air (20% oxygen) would be required to burn 200 cubic feet of ammonia? (b) What total volume of products would remain? Ans. (a) 1250 cu. ft.; (b) 1500 cu. ft.

28. What weight of carbon is contained in 100 liters of CO_2 at a temperature of 40° C. and a pressure of 2 atmospheres?   Ans. 93.5 g.

29. One pound of dry ice (CO_2) will occupy what volume on evaporation at standard conditions?   Ans. 8.15 cu. ft.

30. A one-gram sample of Epsom salts ($MgSO_4 \cdot 7 H_2O$) when analyzed for magnesium gave 0.429 g. of $Mg_2P_2O_7$. (*a*) What was the percentage of magnesium in the original sample? (*b*) Assuming all the magnesium is present as $MgSO_4 \cdot 7 H_2O$, what is the purity of the sample?

Ans. (*a*) 9.4; (*b*) 95 per cent.

31. Calculate the weight of each of the products of the complete electrolysis of one kilogram of a 20 per cent aqueous solution of NaCl according to the equation:

$$2 \text{ NaCl} + 2 \text{ H}_2\text{O} \longrightarrow 2 \text{ NaOH} + \text{H}_2 + \text{Cl}_2$$

Ans. NaOH 137 g.; H_2 3.4 g.; Cl_2 121 g.

XV

Solutions

The water we drink is a solution of various minerals dissolved in water. Plants derive their food, in part, from the water-soluble constituents of the soil. In the digestion of food, a chemical change takes place whereby constituents of food are converted into soluble substances which can be absorbed by the blood and carried to various tissues in the body. The atmosphere we breathe is a solution of nitrogen and oxygen gases. Fish and marine life derive oxygen necessary for their life processes from oxygen dissolved in the water.

Many chemical changes take place in solution, since the rate of reaction is faster than between substances in the pure state. At least one factor in the increase in speed of reactions in solution is the better contact of the reacting substances.

What is a solution? Solutions are like compounds in that they are homogeneous and like mixtures in that the relative proportions of the constituents are variable. We may, therefore, classify solutions between mixtures and compounds:

MIXTURES	SOLUTIONS	COMPOUNDS
1. Not homogeneous	Homogeneous	Homogeneous
2. Variable proportions of constituents	Variable proportions of constituents	Fixed proportion of elements

A solution is formed when sugar is dissolved in water. It is perfectly uniform or homogeneous; if we should taste samples taken from various parts of the solution, we should find that each part has the same degree of sweetness. The amount of sugar which we can dissolve in 100 ml. of water is variable; we may dissolve one gram, ten grams, or fifty grams of sugar in the water. There is a limit, though, to the amount of sugar we can dissolve in a given amount of water at a certain temperature. This limiting amount is termed the *solubility* of sugar in water at that temperature.

If we could observe the molecules in the sugar solution, we would probably see that individual molecules of sugar are scattered throughout the solution in a uniform distribution; each unit volume of solution would contain the same number of sugar molecules. The particles of sugar are dispersed in the solution as individual molecules; the solid is said to be *molecularly dispersed*. Molecular dispersion is a characteristic of a true solution. We shall learn later (chap. XXVII) that aggregates or groups of molecules may be dispersed in a *colloidal* solution.

The above properties may be summarized in the definition: *A solution is a homogeneous mixture of two or more substances, the relative proportions of which may vary continuously within certain limits.*

Solute and solvent. The dissolved material in a solution is termed the *solute* and the dissolving medium the *solvent*. Thus in a solution of sugar in water, the sugar would be the solute, and the water the solvent. These terms, however, are arbitrary and lose their significance when applied to certain solutions. For example, in a solution of two liquids, such as alcohol and water, either the water or the alcohol might be properly classified as the solute. In situations of this kind, the constituent of the solution present in the smaller amount is usually designated as the solute.

Types of solutions. When we speak of a solution, we usually think of a solid dissolved in water. While water is the most common of solvents, other liquids are frequently employed as solvents for certain substances. Wax may be dissolved in gasoline, oil in turpentine, sulfur in carbon disulfide, etc. Solutions, however, are not confined to the solution of solids in liquids. Since there are three physical states of matter — gas, liquid, and solid — nine possibilities suggest themselves:

1. *Gases in gases.* Gases mix in all proportions, and since the particles of the gases exist as individual molecules, a mixture of any gases may be regarded as a solution. Air is essentially a solution of nitrogen and oxygen gases. Actually other gases are present in the atmosphere, and the entire system constitutes a complex solution.

2. *Gases in liquids.* The solution of oxygen in water and the solution of carbon dioxide in water (carbonated water) are examples of this type.

3. *Gases in solids.* Certain metals (platinum, palladium) absorb large volumes of hydrogen gas. In these cases, the gas may be considered as being dissolved in a solid.

4. *Liquids in gases.* Doubtful.

5. *Liquids in liquids.* Examples of this type are well known. Alcohol and water are completely *miscible* (mix with one another in all

proportions). Gasoline and kerosene dissolve in one another in all proportions. Certain liquids show incomplete solubility in one another. For example, ether and water are only partially miscible.

6. *Liquids in solids.* The solution of mercury in certain metals (amalgams) might be considered an example of this type.

7. *Solids in gases.* Doubtful.

8. *Solids in liquids.* This is the most common type of solution.

9. *Solids in solids.* If two solids are held tightly together, diffusion of each solid into the other takes place very slowly. To demonstrate this, the following experiment has been performed. A piece of lead and a piece of gold were tightly clamped together for a period of several years. On analysis, it was found that the lead contained gold in the part which had been adjacent to the piece of gold. Likewise the gold contained a small amount of lead. The experiment seems to demonstrate that, while diffusion in the solid condition is extremely slow, nevertheless, the process takes place. Certain alloys are sometimes classed as solid solutions.

Polar and nonpolar solvents. We are well aware that liquids differ greatly in their solvent action. While water is a good solvent for acids, bases, and salts — those substances which are ionic or which produce ions in solution — it is almost completely immiscible with such liquids as benzene, carbon disulfide, carbon tetrachloride, etc. On the other hand the latter liquids readily dissolve sulfur, phosphorus, wax, etc., which substances are insoluble in water. On the basis of their molecular structure, solvents may be classified as *polar* and *nonpolar*.

A polar solvent consists of dipoles (see chap. XI), *i.e.*, molecules in which the constituent atoms are unsymmetrically arranged so that the centers of positive and negative electrical charges are not located at the same point in the molecule. (Of course the molecule as a whole is electrically neutral.) Water and liquid ammonia are polar solvents. Nonpolar solvents consist of symmetrical molecules with the center of positive and negative electrical charge at the same point within the molecule. Benzene and carbon tetrachloride are examples of nonpolar liquids. Cohesive forces between molecules of polar liquids are large as compared to forces tending to hold molecules of nonpolar liquids together, since positive ends of the dipoles will tend to attract negative ends of other dipoles and hold the molecules together.

Water acts as a good solvent for electrovalent compounds since there is a definite attraction between the ions present and the dipoles of the water molecules. In crystalline sodium chloride, sodium and chloride ions are oriented in a definite pattern by electrostatic forces acting between the oppositely charged ions, thus the crystals of the compound exhibit a definite geometric pattern (NaCl crystallizes in the cubic system, see chap. XII). When NaCl dissolves, the forces holding the ions together must be overcome, so that the ions are free

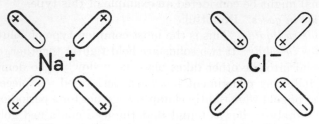

Fig. 58. Attraction between ions and water dipoles.

to move in solution. Water weakens these forces to such an extent, probably by attraction between the dipoles and ions in some such fashion as is represented by Figure 58.

These electrovalent compounds are insoluble in nonpolar liquids like benzene, since there is no electrical attraction between the ions in the compounds and the solvent molecules.

Equilibrium in solutions. When a solid is dissolved in a liquid, molecules break away from the surface of the solid and pass into the solvent, where they diffuse until a uniform distribution has been effected. Stirring or agitation will speed up the solution process. As the molecules find their way into the solvent, some of them are deflected back toward the solid due to collision with other molecules. Some of these particles which strike the solid will deposit out on the solid surface and thus are converted back to the solid form. There are thus two processes occurring: (1) the solution of molecules from the surface of the solid, (2) the deposition of molecules on the surface of the solid. If the amount of solid present is insufficient to saturate the solution, process (1) will continue until all of the solid dissolves. If there is sufficient solid to saturate the solution, the two opposing forces (1) and (2) will eventually equalize each other, and the number of molecules passing into solution will be the same as the number coming out of the solution.

Fig. 59. Equilibrium between solid and solution.

When the speed of these two processes is the same, a condition of equilibrium is reached, and the solution is said to be saturated (Fig. 59). *A saturated solution, then, is one in which the solution is in equilibrium with the undissolved solute.*

The passage of a solid into solution is analogous to the passage of liquid to vapor. Molecules of liquid break away from the surface of the liquid and pass into the atmosphere above the liquid. Molecules from the vapor may strike the liquid and condense to the liquid state. When the rate of evaporation is equal to the rate of condensation, a condition of equilibrium results. Just as a certain amount of vapor (vapor pressure) can exist in equilibrium with the liquid, so in the case of a solid dissolved in a liquid, a certain amount of solid can be present in the solution in equilibrium with the undissolved solid.

We must not think of the processes of solution and deposition (precipitation) as stopping when equilibrium has been attained. Actually the equilibrium is a dynamic one; the two opposing processes are occurring continuously. To demonstrate the dynamic nature of this equilibrium we may perform the following experiment: A hole may be bored in a crystal of solid which is in equilibrium with its saturated solution. After a time the hole becomes filled with solid and the crystal is perfectly repaired. This would seem to demonstrate that molecules are continuously passing from the solution to the solid. For every molecule which returns, a molecule must pass into solution in order that the number in the solution remain a constant. Thus the solubility of a substance is a constant value at a given temperature. As the temperature is raised, relatively more molecules of the solid may pass into solution than precipitate out, and a new condition of equilibrium is established at the higher temperature.[1]

Supersaturation. Ordinarily when a saturated solution is cooled, excess solute will crystallize out at the lower temperature. However, with certain substances it is possible to cool a saturated solution in the *absence of solid solute* without the separation of the excess solute. The cooled solution then contains more of the solute than is present in a saturated solution at that particular temperature. Such a solution is said to be *supersaturated*. These solutions are very unstable, and the excess solute immediately separates out if a tiny crystal of the solid solute is added to the solution.

Supersaturation may be demonstrated by preparing a saturated solution of sodium thiosulfate at an elevated temperature, and allowing the solution to cool carefully in the absence of undissolved solute. The solution remains perfectly clear at the lower temperature until a crystal of sodium thiosulfate is added, after which a large mass of crystals forms slowly in the solution. The solution which remains in contact with the excess solid is saturated.

---

[1] The solubility of a few substances decreases with increasing temperature.

To determine whether a given solution is saturated, unsaturated, or supersaturated, one can add a crystal of the dissolved substance. If the crystal dissolves, the solution is unsaturated; if it remains the same, the solution is saturated; and if the crystal causes the formation of more crystals, the solution is supersaturated.

Solubility. The weight of a substance dissolved by a given weight or volume of solvent is termed the solubility of the substance. Solubility varies greatly with the nature of the dissolved substances. 100 grams of water will dissolve 179 grams of sugar, or 35.7 grams of sodium chloride, or 3 grams of potassium chlorate, or 0.00009 gram of silver chloride at 0°. Sugar would be classed as very soluble, sodium chloride as moderately soluble, potassium chlorate as slightly soluble and silver chloride as practically insoluble.

The general rules for the solubility of salts and hydroxides in water are given below.

1. All nitrates, acetates, and chlorates are soluble.
2. All chlorides, bromides, and iodides are soluble except Pb, Hg (ous), and Ag.
3. All sulfates are soluble except Ba, Sr, Pb, and Ca ($CaSO_4$ is moderately soluble).
4. All oxides, hydroxides, and sulfides are insoluble except Na, K, NH_4, Ca, Ba, Mg, and Sr.
5. All phosphates, carbonates, and chromates are insoluble except Na, K, and NH_4.
6. Nearly all Na, K, and NH_4 salts are soluble.

The solubility of gases in liquids. The solubility of a gas is often expressed as the volume of gas dissolved by a certain volume of liquid. For example, .021 volume of hydrogen dissolves in 1 volume of water, or 1.71 volumes of carbon dioxide dissolve in 1 volume of water. The solubility of gases in liquids varies over a wide range and depends upon the nature of the solute and solvent. At 0° 1 volume of water may dissolve .021 volume of hydrogen, 1.71 volumes of carbon dioxide, 506 volumes of hydrogen chloride, or 1175 volumes of ammonia. Gases which are very soluble in water may be nearly insoluble in some other solvent.

The weight of a gas dissolved by a given weight of liquid is directly proportional to the pressure of the gas over the liquid. This is a statement of Henry's Law. If a certain weight of gas is dissolved by a liquid at a pressure of 1 atmosphere, then ten times that weight will dissolve if the pressure is increased to 10 atmospheres. A practical application of this law is the preparation of carbonated beverages. Carbon dioxide gas is dissolved in the liquid under pressure. When the cap of the bottle is removed, the solution effervesces (gives off gas from solution) rapidly, since the pressure has been reduced.

The solubility of a gas in a liquid is also dependent upon the temperature. The quantity of gas dissolved by a given weight of liquid decreases as the temperature is raised. If water containing dissolved air is warmed, bubbles of the air escape from the solution as the temperature increases. At the boiling point of the solvent, the gas is practically insoluble.

Effect of temperature on solubility of solids in liquids. Although the solubility of a solid in a liquid is usually increased with an increase in temperature, this is not always true. The solubilities of several salts in water are shown in Table 13 and represented graphically in Figure 60.

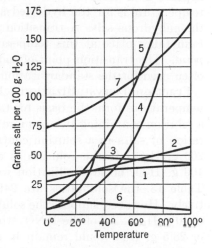

Fig. 60. Solubility curves:
(1) NaCl; (2) KCl; (3) Na_2SO_4;
(4) alum; (5) KNO_3; (6) $CaCrO_4$;
(7) $NaNO_3$.

TABLE 13

SOLUBILITY OF SALTS AT VARIOUS TEMPERATURES (g./100 g. H_2O)

Tempera-ture ° C.	Potassium Nitrate	Sodium Chloride	Potassium Alum	Calcium Chromate	Potassium Chloride	Sodium Sulfate	Sodium Nitrate
0	13	35.7	4	13	28	4.8	73
10	21	35.8	10	12		9.0	80
20	31	36	15	10.4	34	19.5	85
30	45	36.3	23	9.4		40.9	92
40	64	36.6	31	8.5	40	48.8	98
50	86	37	49	7.3		46.7	104
60	111	37.3	67	6	46	45.3	
70	139	37.9	101	5.3		44.4	
80		38.4	135	4.4	51	43.7	133
90		39.1		3.8		43.1	
100	249	39.8		3	57	42.5	163

It may be noted that in some cases an increase in temperature greatly changes the solubility, while in other cases there is very little change. The solubility of potassium nitrate increases from about 13 grams per 100 grams of water at 0° to about 139 grams at 70°. Sodium chloride increases only from 35.7 to 37.9 for the same temperature range. Calcium chromate actually decreases in solubility as the temperature is raised. A break in the solubility curve for sodium sulfate appears at a temperature of 32.7°. The solubility curve below this temperature is for the hydrated salt and above this temperature for the anhydrous salt. A transition from the hydrate to the anhydrous form takes place at this temperature which is known as a *transition point*. The transition point of sodium sulfate is so definite that it is often used for the standardization of thermometers.

Fractional crystallization. Differences of solubility at various temperatures form the basis for the selective separation of salts from a solution containing two or more dissolved salts. Consider the separation of salts in a solution containing 50 g. KNO_3, 50 g. KCl, and 200 g. H_2O. If the solution is evaporated at 100° to a weight of 100 g. H_2O, no crystallization would be effected, since according to Table 13, the solubilities are 249 g. KNO_3 and 57 g. KCl respectively. However, suppose the solution is evaporated at 100° to a weight of 50 g. H_2O. All of the KNO_3 would remain in solution but only $\frac{57}{2}$ or 28.5 g. KCl would remain in solution. The excess KCl above a saturated solution, namely $50 - 28.5 = 21.5$ g. KCl, would crystallize out. If the hot liquid was poured off from the crystallized KCl, 21.5 g. of fairly pure KCl would be left; not entirely pure since the adhering liquid would still contain a small amount of KNO_3. If the crystals were redissolved and the process repeated a purer fraction of KCl crystals could be obtained. Such a process is an example of fractional crystallization.

Concentration. Sometimes we speak of a solution as being "dilute" or "concentrated." These are qualitative terms to designate whether a solution contains relatively little solute or a relatively large amount. Thus a solution containing one gram of sugar in 100 ml. of water would be "dilute" while a solution containing 50 g. of sugar in 100 ml. of water would be "concentrated." The concentration of a solution represents the weight of solute dissolved in a given weight or volume of the solution. Several methods are available for expressing the concentration of a solution. The weight of a solute in a given weight of the solution may be expressed in terms of percentage. Thus a solution containing 5 grams of solute and 95 grams of solvent would be a 5 per cent solution, since 5 parts of 100 are solute.

Molarity. Another means of expressing concentration which has been adopted by the chemist involves expression of the concentration in terms of moles of solute in 1 liter of the solution. A solution containing one mole of solute in 1 liter of solution is termed a *molar* (1 *M*) solution. A solution containing 2 moles of solute in a liter of solution would be 2 molar (2 *M*), one containing 0.5 mole in a liter would be 0.5 molar (0.5 *M*), etc. In other words,

$$\text{Molarity} = \frac{\text{Number of Moles}}{\text{Number of Liters}}$$

In order to become more familiar with this method of expressing concentration, consider the following illustrative problems.

PROBLEM 1. Calculate the molarity of a solution containing 10 grams of sulfuric acid in 500 ml. of solution.

Since molarity is defined in terms of moles, we must first convert grams to moles. Remembering that a mole is the molecular weight in grams, to convert grams to moles we must divide the weight in grams by the molecular weight. Since the molecular weight of sulfuric acid is 98, $\qquad 10 \text{ g.} = \frac{10}{98} = 0.102 \text{ mole}$

0.102 mole of sulfuric acid in 500 ml. would be the same as $2 \times 0.102 = 0.204$ mole in $2 \times 500 = 1000$ ml. or 1 liter. The molarity is thus 0.204.

PROBLEM 2. Calculate the weight in grams of sulfuric acid in 2 liters of 0.1 molar solution.

One liter of a molar solution of sulfuric acid would contain 1 mole of sulfuric acid or 98 grams. One liter of a $\frac{1}{10}$ molar solution would contain $\frac{1}{10}$ of 98 or 9.8 grams. Two liters of the solution, then, would contain $2 \times 9.8 = 19.6$ g.

Normal solutions. The equation

$$H_2SO_4 + 2\,NaOH \longrightarrow Na_2SO_4 + 2\,H_2O$$

shows that one mole of sulfuric acid reacts with two moles of sodium hydroxide. It is evident that if the solutions of H_2SO_4 and NaOH were of the same molarity it would require twice the volume of NaOH as of H_2SO_4 for the neutralization. One liter of 1 *M* H_2SO_4 will require 2 liters of 1 *M* NaOH, or 1 liter of 2 *M* NaOH.

In the reaction of NaOH and HCl, equal volumes of molar solutions will exactly neutralize one another. The difficulty, that in some reactions equal volumes, in other cases different volumes, must be used, can be avoided by making up the solutions in terms of equivalent weights rather than molecular weights.

One equivalent of a substance is the weight (1) which (as an acid) contains 1 gram atom of replaceable hydrogen, or (2) which (as a base) reacts with a gram atom of hydrogen, or (3) which (as a salt) is produced in a reaction involving 1 gram atom of acid hydrogen. Thus, **36.5 g**. of HCl contains 1 g. atom of replaceable hydrogen, hence is an equivalent weight; 40 g. of NaOH will react with 36.5 g. of HCl which contains 1 g. atom of hydrogen, hence 40 g. of NaOH is an equivalent weight; 58.5 g. of NaCl is formed in the reaction involving 36.5 g. of HCl, hence is an equivalent weight; 98 g. of H_2SO_4 contains two gram atoms of hydrogen, so $\frac{98}{2} = 49$ g. is one equivalent.

A solution containing one equivalent of a solute in one liter of solution is a *normal* solution; one containing 2 equivalents in one liter is two normal (2 N), etc. The normality of any solution is given by the expression

$$\text{Normality} = \frac{\text{Equivalents of Solute}}{\text{Liters of Solution}}$$

Equal volumes of solutions of the same normality are equivalent; for example, 1 liter of a normal solution of any acid will react with exactly 1 liter of a normal solution of any base.

Study the following examples involving the calculation of normalities:

EXAMPLE 1. Calculate the normality of a solution containing 2.45 grams of sulfuric acid in 2 liters of solution.

One equivalent of H_2SO_4 (mol. wt. 98) would be 49 grams, since one molecule of acid contains two atoms of replaceable hydrogen. The solution in this problem contains 2.45 g. in 2 liters, or 1.225 g. per liter. The normality would then be $\frac{1.225}{49} = 0.025$ N.

EXAMPLE 2. How many grams of sulfuric acid are there in 3 liters of 0.5 N solution?

There are 49 grams of H_2SO_4 (one equivalent) in 1 liter of a normal solution. In 1 liter of .5 N solution there would be 24.5 g., in 3 liters, $3 \times 24.5 = 73.5$ g.

Standard solutions and titrations. Very often in analytical work it is necessary to determine the acidity or basicity of an unknown solution. This may be accomplished with the aid of a *standard solution* of an acid or a base — a solution whose concentration is accurately known. The operation of analyzing an unknown solution by means of a standard solution is known as *titration*. The determinations are usually carried out with the aid of burets (Fig. 60x), which are devices for accurately measuring the volumes of solutions used. Acids neutralize bases, and the endpoint of a titration is reached when *equivalent quantities* of acid and base have been brought together. A certain volume of solution from one buret is collected in a beaker and then solution from the other buret is added carefully until equiva-

Fig. 60x. Titrating a solution in a metallurgical laboratory.

lent quantities of the two solutions have been brought together. The latter is determined by an indicator which changes in color at the endpoint. Knowing the volumes of the two solutions used and the normality of either the acid or base, we may calculate the normality of the other solution and thereby determine its acidity or basicity.

The concentration of a standard solution is usually expressed in terms of normality, *i.e.*

$$\text{Normality } (N) = \frac{\text{Equivalents } (E)}{\text{Liters } (L)}$$

or

$$E = N \times L$$

Since equivalent quantities of acid and base must be present at the endpoint of the titration, $E_{acid} = E_{base}$; therefore

Normality of Acid $\times$ Volume of Acid = Normality of Base $\times$ Volume of Base

If three of the above four factors are known, the fourth may be calculated. Volumes may be expressed in milliliters or liters. Study the following sample calculations:

EXAMPLE 1. Calculate the volume of 0.3 N base necessary to neutralize 3 liters of .01 N acid.

Substituting in the formula

$$\text{Normality} \times \text{Volume of Acid} = \text{Normality} \times \text{Volume of Base}$$
$$.01 \times 3 \text{ liters} = 0.3 \times x$$
$$x = \frac{.01 \times 3}{.3} = 0.1 \text{ liter or } 100 \text{ ml.}$$

EXAMPLE 2. If 20 ml. of 0.50 N salt solution is diluted to 1 liter, what is the new concentration?

$$\text{Normality} \times \text{Volume} = \text{Normality} \times \text{Volume}$$
$$.50 \times 20 \text{ ml.} = N \times 1000 \text{ ml.}$$
$$N = \frac{.50 \times 20}{1000} = .01$$

Molal solutions. In the study of properties of solutions which depend upon the ratio of number of solute particles to number of solvent particles (colligative properties), concentrations are expressed in terms of *molality*. A molal solution is one which contains 1 mole of solute in 1000 g. of solvent. Such solutions are independent of temperature changes. In dilute solutions molar and molal solutions are very nearly identical, but in more concentrated solutions wide differences may be expected.

The boiling point of solutions. We have learned that the boiling point of a liquid is the temperature at which the vapor pressure of the liquid is equal to the external pressure (usually the atmospheric pressure). The addition of a substance like sugar or salt lowers the vapor pressure of the liquid because the solute molecules interfere with the escape of molecules of the solvent from the liquid to the vapor state. Molecules of the solvent will collide with solute molecules and thus the speed at which the solvent molecules escape from solution is diminished, resulting in a decreased vapor pressure. *The lowering of the vapor pressure by a nonvolatile solute is proportional to the concentration of the solute in the solution.* This is a statement of Raoult's Law.

A decreased vapor pressure means a rise in the boiling point of the liquid, since a higher temperature will be necessary to bring the vapor pressure up to the external pressure. From a kinetic standpoint, it would seem that the rise of the boiling point would depend directly upon the number of solute particles, since the escape of solvent molecules (the vapor pressure) is influenced by the number of solute particles. The following facts indicate the validity of this speculation. 342 grams of sugar (1 gram molecular weight) dissolved in 1000 grams of water raises the boiling point 0.52°, in other words the solution would boil at 100.52°; 60 grams of urea (1 gram molecular weight) dissolved in 1000 grams of water gives exactly the *same* elevation of the boiling point. It has been found that 1 gram molecular weight of other substances gives the same elevation of the boiling point. There is no relation between the weight in grams of substance and the boiling point elevation, since 60 grams of urea produces the same effect as 342 grams of sugar. However, a gram molecular weight of each of these substances contains exactly the same number of molecules. This seems to indicate beyond doubt that the boiling point of a solution is dependent upon the number of solute particles in solution. The normal elevation of the boiling point of a liquid containing 1 gram molecular weight of dissolved substance in 1000 grams is called the boiling point constant. For water this constant is 0.52°. The elevation of the boiling point of water containing 3 moles of solute in 1000 grams of water would be 3×0.52 or $1.56°$.

We shall find in the study of ionization (chap. XVIII) that solutions of acids, bases, and salts have abnormal boiling points. These abnormalities will be explained at that time.

Solutions of volatile solutes. What we have said above does not apply to solutions in which the solute has a vapor pressure of its own. A solution of alcohol and water boils below the boiling point of water. It is probable that the vapor pressures of alcohol and water are separately reduced by the presence of the other, but the additive reduced vapor pressures exceed the vapor pressure of the water alone.

In Figure 61 is shown the liquid and vapor curves for solutions of two volatile liquids *A* and *B*. The lower curve shows the boiling points of solutions of *A* and *B* of varying composition from 100 per cent *A* to 100 per cent *B*. *O* is the boiling point of pure *A*, and *P* the boiling point of pure *B*. The broken curve shows the compositions of vapor in equilibrium with various solutions of *A* and *B*. The composition can be determined by a perpendicular drawn to the composition axis.

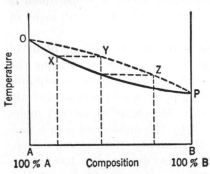

**Fig. 61. Boiling point diagram of
two volatile liquids.**

Suppose a solution of composition *X* is distilled. The composition of the vapor is represented by *Y* — the vapor is richer in the lower boiling component *B*. As the solution is boiled, the temperature rises and the solution becomes richer in the higher boiling component *A*. If the vapor at *Y* be condensed to liquid and subsequently redistilled, the composition of the vapor would be that represented by point *Z*. Thus by distilling a solution and collecting several fractions boiling at different temperatures and repeating the distillation of the fractions perhaps several times, an almost complete separation of the two components may be effected. This process is termed *fractional distillation* and is invaluable in separation of the components of such complex mixtures as petroleum.

The freezing point of solutions. Solutes lower the freezing point of water. Alcohol and other antifreeze mixtures are added to the water in our car radiators to prevent them from freezing. Just as the boiling point of a solution is dependent upon the number of solute particles, so is the freezing point of a solution a function of the number of particles in solution. 1 mole of a substance (except those substances which ionize) dissolved in 1000 grams of water lowers the freezing point 1.86°. This number 1.86 is called the freezing point constant for water. Thus a solution containing 1 gram molecular weight of alcohol (46 grams) in 1000 grams of water will freeze 1.86° below the freezing point of water (0°), that is at −1.86°. A solution containing 2 moles of alcohol in 1000 grams of water would freeze at

$-(2 \times 1.86) = -3.72°$, etc. From these facts,[1] we can calculate the concentration of an antifreeze necessary to prevent our car radiator from freezing at a given temperature.

PROBLEM. Calculate the composition of an alcohol-water mixture which will not freeze above a temperature of $-30°$ C. Molecular weight of alcohol is 46.

Let x = number of moles of alcohol per 1000 g. H_2O in mixture.
Since 1 mole alcohol in 1000 g. H_2O freezes at $-1.86°$
then x moles alcohol in 1000 g. H_2O freezes at $-30°$

$$\frac{1}{x} = \frac{-1.86}{-30} \qquad x = \frac{-30}{-1.86} = 16.1 \text{ moles}$$

16.1 moles = 16.1×46 g. = 741 g. alcohol per 1000 g. H_2O

Osmotic pressure. If a U-shaped tube as shown in Figure 62 were filled with water on one side and a sugar solution on the other side, in time the sugar molecules would have diffused throughout so that a uniform concentration of sugar would be present on both sides of the tube. If, however, a semipermeable membrane, such as an animal or vegetable membrane that will allow water to pass through it, but not the solute molecules, is placed across the bottom of the U-tube and the U-tube is again filled with water on one side and sugar solution on the other to the same level, then it will be noted that water will flow through the semipermeable membrane from the water side of the tube to dilute the sugar solution on the other side. As a result the level of solution on the sugar side will rise while the level on the pure water side will be depressed. If evaporation is prevented, the system will remain indefinitely at these new levels. The difference in levels between the two arms of the U-tube,

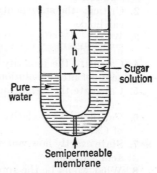

Fig. 62. Apparatus for demonstrating osmotic pressure.

h, is a measure of the pressure tendency of the water to go through the membrane and dilute the solution. This pressure which may be thought of as that sufficient to prevent the flow of pure solvent through a semipermeable membrane into a solution is called *osmotic pressure*. This pressure is proportional to the concentration of the solution. Like the boiling point elevation and freezing point depression of a solvent as well as the vapor pressure of a solution, the osmotic pressure is

[1] It should be pointed out that this relationship between freezing point and concentration does not hold very well for concentrated solutions.

a property dependent upon the *number* of dissolved particles and is independent of the nature of the dissolved particles. Such properties which are dependent upon *number* but *not kind* of dissolved particles are termed *colligative* properties.

Osmosis is the passage of a solvent through a semipermeable membrane from a solution of lesser concentration to one of higher concentration. Osmosis through plant and animal membranes is of prime importance in many physiological processes.

Determination of molecular weights of dissolved substances. Since a mole (molecular weight in grams) of a substance in 1000 grams of water gives a definite and known lowering of the freezing point (1.86°) we can, by determining the freezing point of a solution of known concentration, calculate the molecular weight of the dissolved substance. For example, suppose the freezing point of a solution containing 30 grams of solute in 1000 grams of water is $-.62°$. The molecular weight of the dissolved substance must be $\frac{1.86}{.62} \times 30 = 90$.

EXERCISES

1. Differentiate clearly between unsaturated, saturated, and supersaturated solutions.
2. Criticize the statement: A saturated solution contains as much solute as it can hold.
3. What is the effect of temperature and pressure upon the solubility of gases in liquids?
4. Calculate the molarity of a solution which contains .049 gram of sulfuric acid per liter of solution. Ans. .0005.
5. Calculate the weight in grams of NaCl in 5 liters of 0.25 molar solution. Ans. 73.1.
6. Calculate the molarity of a solution, 100 ml. of which contains .037 gram of $Ca(OH)_2$.
7. State exactly how you would proceed to prepare 250 ml. of 0.2 molar sulfuric acid solution.
8. What would be the approximate freezing point of a solution which contains 250 grams of alcohol, C_2H_5OH, dissolved in one liter of water? Ans. $-10°$.
9. A solution which contains 50 grams of solute in 500 g. of water freezes at a temperature of $-0.93°$ C. What is the molecular weight of the solute? Ans. 200.
10. A saturated solution of KNO_3 at 60° containing 150 grams of water is cooled to a temperature of 20°. Calculate the weight of KNO_3 which will crystallize from the solution from the solubility data on page 181. Ans. 120 g.
11. Explain the effects of the addition of a solute on the freezing and boiling points of water.
12. Calculate the approximate boiling and freezing points of a solution which contains 150 grams of glucose, $C_6H_{12}O_6$, dissolved in 300 grams of water.
13. Two beakers contain sugar solutions (a) and (b). A lump of sugar is dropped into each and thoroughly stirred. In (a) the lump disappears and in (b) it grows larger. Give the appropriate term descriptive of solutions (a) and (b).

14. Would it be possible for a certain solution to be both *saturated* and *dilute?* Explain briefly.

15. The concentration of dissolved air in the waters of a mountain lake is not the same as in a lake at sea level at the same temperature. In which is the concentration greater? Explain.

16. What is the normality of a solution containing 1.11 grams of $Ca(OH)_2$ per liter of solution?   Ans. .03.

17. Explain in detail how you would make up a 0.1 normal solution of the salt Ag_2SO_4.

18. A sulfuric acid solution has a density of 1.8 and is 90 per cent H_2SO_4. What weight of H_2SO_4 is present in 500 ml. of solution?   Ans. 810 g.

19. Suppose you wished to dissolve as much as possible of (1) a gas in a liquid, (2) a solid in a liquid. In a general way, how would you proceed?

20. In the following statements indicate whether the missing word should be "increases" or "decreases":

   (a) Solubility of a solid in solvent, in general, . . . with increase in temperature.

   (b) Solubility of a gas in water . . . with increase in temperature.

   (c) Solubility of a gas in a liquid . . . as pressure of the given gas over the liquid increases.

   (d) Partial pressure of a gas . . . as the percentage by weight of the gas in a gaseous mixture increases.

   (e) Chemical union of a gas with its solvent . . . its apparent solubility.

   (f) Vapor pressure of a liquid . . . as soluble solid is added.

   (g) In the fractional distillation of a 17 per cent alcohol-water solution the percentage of alcohol in the successive distilled fractions. . . .

   (h) Speed of dissolving . . . as a solution approaches saturation.

   (i) Boiling point of pure water . . . with decreasing atmospheric pressure.

   (j) Density of water . . . from 4° C. to 0° C.

21. Refer to the solubility data on page 181. A solution containing 40 g. NaCl, 100 g. $NaNO_3$ and 150 g. H_2O is evaporated to 100 g. H_2O at 100°. (a) What solid will crystallize from solution and how much? (b) If the solution is allowed to cool to 50°, what solid will crystallize and how much? (c) If the solution from (b) after filtering off the solid is concentrated to 50 g. H_2O and cooled to 20°, what would be the composition of the solid crystallizing out? Ans. (a) NaCl, 0.2 g. (c) NaCl, 19 g.; $NaNO_3$, 57.5 g.

22. With the aid of the solubility curves on page 181, answer the following questions:

   (a) At what approximate temperature would the solubilities of NaCl and KCl be the same?

   (b) At what approximate temperature would the solubilities of KCl and KNO_3 be the same?

   (c) Under what conditions would KCl exhibit a greater solubility than KNO_3?

   (d) If separate saturated solutions of $NaNO_3$ and NaCl are made up at 50° and cooled to 0°, will the weight of $NaNO_3$ separating out be less or greater than the weight of NaCl crystallizing out?

   (e) Which of the salts in the diagram is most soluble at 50°?

   (f) If a saturated solution of $CaCrO_4$ at 50° is cooled to 20°, will solid crystallize? If this solution is heated to 100°, what happens?

(g) If separate saturated solutions of the salts NaCl, KCl, KNO₃, and NaNO₃ are made up at 100° in 100 g. H₂O, what weight of each salt would be crystallized from solution on cooling to 20°?

(h) What are the relative rates of increase in solubility of all the salts for which solubility curves are given in Figure 60?

(i) How would you proceed to prepare a supersaturated solution of calcium chromate?

23. Calculate the (a) molarity and (b) normality of solutions of each of the following containing 10 g. of the solute per liter of solution: (1) KOH, (2) H_3PO_4, (3) $MgCl_2$, (4) Na_2SO_4, (5) $Al_2(SO_4)_3$.

24. 7.29 g. of a certain nonelectrolyte was dissolved in 100 g. of water. The resulting solution was found to have a freezing point of −0.396°. What is the molecular weight of the nonelectrolyte?

25. What weight of glucose must be added to 100 g. of a 10 per cent solution of glucose to give a 25 per cent solution?   Ans. 20 g.

26. The solubilities of nitrogen and oxygen gases at 15° C. and one atmosphere pressure in water are:

> Nitrogen   0.002085 g. per 100 g. water
> Oxygen   0.004802 g. per 100 g. water

Determine the volume of these weights of gas in 100 g. of water at 15° and one atmosphere pressure.   Ans. N₂, 1.76 ml.; O₂, 3.55 ml.

27. Considering the solubilities of nitrogen and oxygen in water from the previous exercise and assuming that air is 20 per cent oxygen and 80 per cent nitrogen, what would be the percentage of oxygen by volume in a sample of dissolved air at a temperature of 15° and a pressure of one atmosphere?
                                                               Ans. 33.

28. The solubility of carbon dioxide at 0° and one atmosphere pressure is 0.3346 g. per 100 g. water. (a) What volume of CO₂ does this represent at standard conditions? (b) What weight of CO₂ would be dissolved in 100 g. of water at 0° and 5 atmospheres pressure? (c) What volume would be dissolved at 0° and 5 atmospheres pressure?
                       Ans. (a) 170 ml. (b) 1.673 g. (c) 170 ml.

29. State the law which applies to the previous exercise.

30. The molar depression of the freezing point of urethane, i.e., the depression obtained by dissolving one mole of a solute in 1000 g. of urethane, is 5.14° C. The melting point of urethane is 50°. If a solution of 20 g. of a substance dissolved in 250 g. of urethane freezes at 39.7° C., what is the molecular weight of the substance?   Ans. 40.

31. Indicate in a general way how you would proceed to separate the components of a

(a) mixture of two immiscible liquids.
(b) solution of a nonvolatile solute.
(c) solution of volatile solute.
(d) solution of gases.

32. What properties of compounds are useful in predicting solubilities in polar and nonpolar solvents?

33. From the following list of water soluble compounds, select (a) 5 pairs which when brought together in aqueous solution will not form a precipitate; (b) 5 pairs which will give a precipitate. Write equations for part (b) reactions.

$AgNO_3$; $NaCl$; K_3PO_4; $BaCl_2$; NH_4OH; HBr; $CuSO_4$; KOH; Na_2CrO_4; $(NH_4)_2CO_3$; $Zn(C_2H_3O_2)_2$; $Ca(ClO_3)_2$; $NaNO_3$; K_2S.

34. Determine the normality of the following solutions which contain the indicated amount of dissolved substance per liter of solution:

(a) 100 g. NaOH
(b) 2.45 g. H_2SO_4
(c) 1.62 g. HBr
(d) 6.84 g. $Ba(OH)_2$
(e) 2.85 g. $Al_2(SO_4)_3$ Ans. (a) 2.5 (b) .05 (e) .05.

35. Calculate the weight of solute needed to prepare each of the following solutions:

(a) 250 ml. 0.1 N H_2SO_4
(b) 2 liters 0.25 N NaOH
(c) 100 ml. 0.01 N $Ba(OH)_2$
(d) 10 ml. 5 N H_3PO_4
(e) 1 liter 0.3 N KOH   Ans. (a) 1.23 g. (b) 20 g. (e) 16.8 g.

36. What would be the normality of a solution of acid, 30 ml. of which exactly neutralizes 20 ml. of 0.15 base?   Ans. 0.1.

37. 15 ml. of HCl solution is exactly neutralized by 20 ml. of NaOH solution. After neutralization, the solution is evaporated to dryness and the weight of NaCl produced was found to be 0.234 g. Calculate (a) normality of the HCl solution, (b) normality of the NaOH solution. (c) If 10 ml. of this acid neutralizes 25 ml. of some unknown basic solution, what is the normality of the unknown base?   Ans. (a) 0.267 (b) 0.20 (c) 0.107.

38. 40 ml. of an acid solution neutralized 0.212 g. of solid Na_2CO_3 according to the equation:

$$Na_2CO_3 + 2\,H^+ \longrightarrow 2\,Na^+ + CO_2 + H_2O$$

What is the normality of the acid solution?   Ans. 0.1.

REFERENCES

C. J. Engelder, *Textbook of Elementary Qualitative Analysis*, Wiley.
E. G. Mahin, *Quantitative Analysis*, McGraw-Hill.
Willard and Furman, *Elementary Quantitative Analysis*, Van Nostrand.

XVI

The Halogens

$$_9F^{19} \quad _{17}Cl^{35.46} \quad _{35}Br^{79.9} \quad _{53}I^{126.9}$$

Halogen	Symbol	Color and Physical State at Standard Conditions	Melting Point	Boiling Point	Formula	Valence
Fluorine .	F	pale-yellow gas	−223	−187	F_2	1
Chlorine .	Cl	yellowish-green gas	−101.6	−34.5	Cl_2	1
Bromine .	Br	deep red-brown liquid	−7.3	58.7	Br_2	1
Iodine . .	I	gray solid	113	184	I_2	1

The elements fluorine, chlorine, bromine, and iodine constitute a group or family of elements called the "halogens," a term which means "salt formers." The elements are very active nonmetals, and are very much alike in their chemical properties. That there should be a marked similarity in chemical properties of these elements is predicted from their atomic structure. Each of the elements possesses seven valence electrons and thus exhibits a valence of −1.

Although these elements are markedly alike chemically, nevertheless, a gradual change in properties is shown as the atomic weight of the element increases. Fluorine, having the lowest atomic weight is the most active of the family, followed by chlorine of next higher atomic weight, then bromine, and finally iodine with the highest atomic weight. In physical properties, too, a gradual change may be noted. For example, fluorine and chlorine are gases at ordinary temperatures, bromine is a liquid, and iodine is a solid.

Because of their extreme activity, the halogens are not found in the free state, but are widely distributed in nature as halide salts. All are found in sea water in the form of salts.

Chlorine is by far the most important of the halogens and will be studied in somewhat more detail than the other members of the family. What we have to say regarding this element will in general apply to the other halogens.

CHLORINE

History. Scheele, a Swedish chemist, is credited with the discovery of chlorine in 1774. Scheele observed that a heavy, yellowish-green gas was obtained when manganese dioxide was allowed to act on hydrochloric acid. He believed the gas to be a compound, however, and it remained for Davy in 1810 to establish the substance as an element and to give it the name "chlorine" because of its color.

Occurrence. Chlorine is found in combination with many of the metals as chlorides, by far the most abundant of which is NaCl. Sea water contains nearly 3 per cent of this compound. Evaporation of inland bodies of water has produced large and extensive deposits of it. The Great Salt Lake in Utah contains nearly 20 per cent. Large deposits of rock salt, which is the impure compound, are found in the states of New York, Michigan, Louisiana, Kansas, Oklahoma, and Texas.

In addition to sodium chloride, sea water contains smaller percentages of magnesium chloride, potassium chloride, and calcium chloride. Compounds of chlorine are found in the body — sodium chloride in the blood, and hydrochloric acid in the gastric juice, where it aids in digestion.

Preparation. (*a*) *Electrolysis of brine.* Chlorine is prepared commercially by the electrolysis of an aqueous sodium chloride solution. The processes taking place during electrolysis may be illustrated by means of the diagram (Fig. 63). Sodium chloride is ionized in the solid and when the compound is dissolved in water, the sodium and chlorine ions are dispersed in the solution. Water itself ionizes slightly into hydrogen ions and hydroxyl ions. Thus, in the solution, four ions are present, two cations and two anions. When the electric

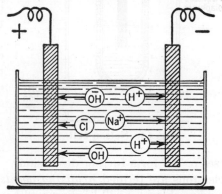

Fig. 63. Electrolysis of an aqueous sodium chloride solution yields hydrogen at the cathode and chlorine at the anode.

current is passed through the solution, chlorine ions and hydroxyl ions migrate toward the anode (positive pole), while the sodium ions and hydrogen ions move toward the cathode (negative pole). Since hydrogen ions accept electrons more readily than sodium ions, the former ions are discharged at the cathode and form hydrogen atoms. Two hydrogen atoms then combine to form a molecule of hydrogen which escapes from the solution as a gas. At the anode, chlorine ions are discharged in preference to hydroxyl ions, since the former give up electrons more readily than the latter. As a result, free chlorine is formed at the anode. The solution contains an excess of sodium and hydroxyl ions which may be recovered in the form of solid sodium hydroxide by evaporation of the water present. The equation for the electrolysis process is

$$2\ NaCl + 2\ H_2O \xrightarrow{\text{electric current}} 2\ NaOH + H_2 + Cl_2$$

In the actual commercial process it is necessary to keep the chlorine separated from the aqueous sodium hydroxide solution, since chlorine reacts with the latter to form sodium hypochlorite. This may be accomplished by separating the anode and cathode compartments by means of a porous diaphragm. This is effectively done in the Nelson cell (Fig. 64), which is widely used at the present time.

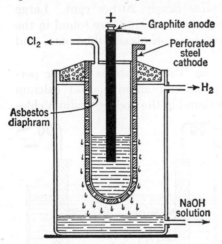

Fig. 64. Nelson cell.

(b) *Oxidation of chlorides.* Free chlorine may be obtained by the removal of an electron from the chloride ion:

$$Cl^- \longrightarrow Cl + e \quad \text{oxidation}$$

The removal of electrons from a substance is termed *oxidation* (see p. 267 for a further discussion). Substances capable of removing electrons are termed *oxidizing agents.* A few substances which may oxidize chlorides will be discussed here.

Hydrogen chloride reacts slowly with oxygen at ordinary temperatures

$$4\ HCl + O_2 \longrightarrow 2\ Cl_2 + 2\ H_2O$$

and is the basis for the Deacon process which was used extensively at one time, but which has now been replaced by cheaper methods of production. In this process hydrogen chloride and oxygen gases are passed through a chamber heated to about 400° which contains pumice impregnated with a copper salt to act as a catalyst.

In the laboratory, manganese dioxide is usually employed as the oxidizing agent. The chlorine is collected by the displacement of air (Fig. 65):

$MnO_2 + 4 HCl \longrightarrow$
$\qquad MnCl_2 + 2 H_2O + Cl_2$

Instead of the hydrochloric acid, sodium chloride and sulfuric acid may be used with the manganese dioxide. This change is essen-

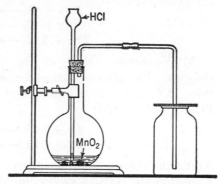

Fig. 65. Laboratory preparation of chlorine.

tially the same as the one above since the sulfuric acid first acts with the salt to form hydrogen chloride which is then oxidized by the manganese dioxide:

$$2 NaCl + 2 H_2SO_4 + MnO_2 \longrightarrow MnSO_4 + Na_2SO_4 + Cl_2 + 2 H_2O$$

Other oxidizing agents may be employed. The equations for the reactions of a few are:

$$2 KMnO_4 + 16 HCl \longrightarrow 2 KCl + 2 MnCl_2 + 5 Cl_2 + 8 H_2O$$
$$K_2Cr_2O_7 + 14 HCl \longrightarrow 2 KCl + 2 CrCl_3 + 3 Cl_2 + 7 H_2O$$
$$HNO_3 + 3 HCl \longrightarrow NOCl + Cl_2 + 2 H_2O$$
$$KClO_3 + 6 HCl \longrightarrow KCl + 3 Cl_2 + 3 H_2O$$
$$PbO_2 + 4 HCl \longrightarrow PbCl_2 + Cl_2 + 2 H_2O$$

Physical properties. Chlorine is a greenish-yellow gas at ordinary temperatures and has a sharp, disagreeable odor. It is very irritating to the mucous lining of the lungs, and its inhalation in large quantities might prove fatal. This irritating quality was taken advantage of in the use of chlorine as a war gas. The gas is moderately soluble in water, 2.26 volumes dissolving in 1 volume of water at 20°. The gas condenses to a liquid at a temperature of $-34.5°$ at a pressure of one atmosphere and freezes to a solid at $-101.6°$.

Chemical properties. Because of its great activity, chlorine reacts with a great number of elements and compounds, some of the more important of which will be listed here:

(a) *Metals.* Chlorine combines directly with practically all of the metallic elements to form chlorides. The more active metals unite vigorously. Powdered antimony when sprinkled into a jar containing chlorine bursts into flame with the formation of a white cloud of antimony chloride. A few typical unions with metals are:

$$2\,Na + Cl_2 \longrightarrow 2\,NaCl$$
$$Zn + Cl_2 \longrightarrow ZnCl_2$$
$$2\,Sb + 3\,Cl_2 \longrightarrow 2\,SbCl_3$$

(b) *Nonmetals.* Most of the nonmetals combine directly with chlorine. Phosphorus burns in chlorine forming phosphorus trichloride, PCl_3, a colorless liquid, and with an excess of chlorine forms PCl_5, a yellow solid:

$$2\,P + 3\,Cl_2 \longrightarrow 2\,PCl_3$$
$$2\,P + 5\,Cl_2 \longrightarrow 2\,PCl_5$$

Sulfur and chlorine combine at an elevated temperature to form sulfur monochloride, S_2Cl_2, a yellow liquid:

$$2\,S + Cl_2 \longrightarrow S_2Cl_2$$

Chlorine and hydrogen combine slowly in the dark, but unite explosively in strong light with the formation of hydrogen chloride:

$$H_2 + Cl_2 \longrightarrow 2\,HCl$$

(c) *Compounds of hydrogen.* Chlorine readily removes hydrogen from hydrocarbons (compounds of carbon and hydrogen) to form hydrogen chloride and carbon in each case. If a lighted jet of methane gas (this gas is the main constituent of natural gas) is introduced into an atmosphere of chlorine, combustion continues with the formation of a black sooty deposit of carbon:

$$CH_4 + 2\,Cl_2 \longrightarrow C + 4\,HCl$$

A piece of filter paper which has been saturated with turpentine, $C_{10}H_{16}$, inserted into a jar of chlorine rapidly takes fire with the formation of a deposit of carbon on the sides of the vessel:

$$C_{10}H_{16} + 8\,Cl_2 \longrightarrow 10\,C + 16\,HCl$$

Other hydrocarbons act similarly with free chlorine.

(d) *Water.* Chlorine with water forms a solution of hydrochloric and hypochlorous acids:

$$Cl_2 + H_2O \rightleftharpoons HCl + HClO$$

Hypochlorous acid is quite unstable and breaks down on exposure to sunlight:

$$2\,HClO \longrightarrow 2\,HCl + O_2$$

As a result, the equilibrium above is displaced to the right and eventually the reaction becomes complete to the right when the hypochlorous acid has completely decomposed.

Courtesy E. I. du Pont de Nemours & Co.

Fig. 66. Machines used in the chlorine process of bleaching rayon.

(e) *Bases.* Since a solution of two acids is produced when chlorine is dissolved in water, we might suppose that the addition of a base to such a solution would result in the neutralization of the acids to form salts. This is the case with the formation of a chloride salt and a hypochlorite salt:

$$Cl_2 + 2\,NaOH \longrightarrow NaCl + NaClO + H_2O$$

Uses. Chlorine is used extensively as a bleaching agent. If a piece of colored calico is dipped into a water solution of chlorine, bleaching of the color takes place rapidly. The hypochlorous acid which is present in the solution seems to be the active bleaching agent as dry chlorine is not very effective. Chlorine is too corrosive to be used with fibers of animal origin (wool, silk, etc.). Much of the chlorine produced commercially is used for bleaching wood pulp which is used in the production of paper and rayon.

Chlorine combines with gold to form gold chloride. Advantage is taken of this property in extracting gold from low-grade ores, from which the salt can be leached out after the treatment with chlorine.

Pathogenic organisms are destroyed in water containing as little as one or two parts of chlorine per million; hence chlorine finds extensive use in the sterilization of drinking water.

Chlorine to be used for bleaching purposes is often transported in the form of bleaching powder, which is produced from lime and chlorine:

$$CaO + Cl_2 \longrightarrow CaOCl_2$$

The chlorine is readily liberated from this compound by treatment with dilute acid:

$$CaOCl_2 + H_2SO_4 \longrightarrow CaSO_4 + H_2O + Cl_2$$

Chlorine was the first of the war gases to be used in World War I. The gas was liberated when the wind was in the proper direction, and since the gas is nearly two and one-half times as heavy as air, it remained close to the ground where it was most effective. Most of the poisonous gases developed later in the war were chlorine compounds. Among the more effective gases were *mustard* gas $(CH_2ClCH_2)_2S$, *phosgene*, $COCl_2$, and *chlorpicrin*, CCl_3NO_2.

In addition to the preparation of chlorides of many of the elements, chlorine also finds use in the preparation of dyes and drugs.

A particularly effective new insecticide is a chlorine compound $(C_6H_4Cl)_2C_2HCl_3$, named dichloro-diphenyl-trichloro-ethane (DDT).

BROMINE

History and occurrence. Balard, in 1826, isolated a heavy dark brown liquid from sea salt. The liquid proved to be an element and was given the name "bromine" from the Greek word *bromos*, meaning stench. Bromides are found in natural salt brines and in deposits from such brines. The Stassfurt salt deposits in Germany, and brines from wells near Midland, Michigan, furnish small quantities of the element. Bromides are also found in sea water from which the element is extracted on a commercial scale.

Preparation. Since chlorine is more active than bromine, the latter may be liberated from its salts by treatment with chlorine water:

$$2 \, NaBr + Cl_2 \longrightarrow 2 \, NaCl + Br_2 \qquad (1)$$

Similar to chlorine, it may also be prepared by electrolysis of bromides or by the oxidation of hydrobromic acid.

It is frequently prepared in the laboratory by treating a bromide salt with an oxidizing agent and sulfuric acid, *e.g.*

$$2 \, NaBr + MnO_2 + 2 \, H_2SO_4 \longrightarrow Na_2SO_4 + MnSO_4 + Br_2 + 2 \, H_2O$$

Commercially, bromine is obtained from sea water by displacement of the bromide present with free chlorine according to equation (1) above. Sea water is pumped into large towers, where it is circulated in contact with chlorine. The liberated bromine is swept upward in the towers by an air stream and collected in a solution of sodium carbonate:

$$3 \, Br_2 + 3 \, Na_2CO_3 \longrightarrow 5 \, NaBr + NaBrO_3 + 3 \, CO_2$$

Bromine is readily liberated from the solution by treatment with sulfuric acid:

$$5 \, NaBr + NaBrO_3 + 3 \, H_2SO_4 \longrightarrow 3 \, Na_2SO_4 + 3 \, H_2O + 3 \, Br_2$$

Properties and uses. Bromine is a heavy, red-brown liquid at ordinary temperatures with a high vapor pressure which is evidenced by the brown vapor which is always present above a sample of the liquid. The vapors are particularly irritating to the eyes and to the respiratory system. Liquid bromine produces severe burns if spilled on the skin. These burns are very slow to heal.

Bromine boils at 58.7°, and freezes to solid at −7.3°. Bromine water is produced by dissolving bromine in water, in which it is moderately soluble. Bromine dissolves readily in carbon disulfide, carbon tetrachloride, ether, and alcohol. In testing for the presence of bromine, one of these liquids is usually added, since the bromine is much more soluble in these liquids than in water; hence the element is concentrated in the added liquid and the color is intensified.

Bromine is used in the manufacture of dyes, drugs, and medicinals. Potassium bromide added to silver nitrate precipitates silver bromide, which is used extensively in the preparation of photographic films as

Fig. 67. The bromides are important in photography.

the compound is very sensitive to light. The compound $C_2H_4Br_2$ is admixed with tetraethyl lead and added to gasoline for improved "antiknock" quality.

In chemical properties the element is very similar to chlorine. It is somewhat less active than chlorine, but nevertheless combines directly with most of the metals and nonmetals to form bromides.

IODINE

History and occurrence. Iodine was discovered in 1812 by Courtois, who extracted crystals of the violet solid from the ashes of seaweed. Two years later, Gay-Lussac proved this substance to be an element and gave it the name "iodine" from the Greek, meaning violet.

The principal source of iodine is sodium iodate, $NaIO_3$, which occurs in small amounts in Chile saltpeter, $NaNO_3$. Free iodine is liberated from the former compound by reduction with $NaHSO_3$.

Iodine in the form of sodium iodide is found in very small amounts in sea water. Certain seaweeds called *kelp* also contain small quantities and have been employed as a commercial source of the element.

Preparation. Iodine is prepared in the laboratory by the methods usually employed for the preparation of chlorine and bromine:

$$2\,NaI + MnO_2 + 2\,H_2SO_4 \longrightarrow Na_2SO_4 + MnSO_4 + I_2 + 2\,H_2O$$

Iodides are more easily oxidized than either chlorides or bromides.

Since iodine is less active than chlorine or bromine, both of these elements displace iodine from iodides:

$$2\,NaI + Br_2 \longrightarrow 2\,NaBr + I_2$$
$$2\,NaI + Cl_2 \longrightarrow 2\,NaCl + I_2$$

Properties and uses. Iodine is a dark gray or black solid at ordinary temperatures. When heated rapidly, iodine does not melt but changes directly from the solid to vapor. The gas, on being cooled, does not pass through the liquid state, but condenses directly to the solid. The property of a substance of changing directly from solid to gas and from gas to solid without going through the liquid state is termed *sublimation*.

Iodine is only slightly soluble in water, but is readily soluble in a solution which contains potassium iodide because of the combination:

$$I_2 + KI \longrightarrow KI \cdot I_2 \text{ or } KI_3$$

It is readily soluble in alcohol, carbon tetrachloride, and ether, and as is the case with bromine, these solvents are often used in extracting the element from water solutions. Starch forms an unstable blue compound with iodine. The latter is used as a test for the presence of free iodine.

Although less active than the other halogens, iodine nevertheless combines with most of the metals and many of the nonmetals to form iodides.

You are all familiar with the use of iodine as an antiseptic. A solution of iodine in alcohol is known as "tincture" of iodine. Silver iodide, like silver bromide, is sensitive to light and finds use in the photographic industry.

The presence of iodine in the body seems to be essential for good health. Iodine appears to perform a vital function in the thyroid gland, in which it is found in the compound, iodothyrin. If the body is not furnished with iodine in some form, this vital gland does not function properly. Under normal circumstances, sufficient iodine is derived from the foods we eat. Butter, spinach, beans, and particularly sea foods are sources of iodine.

FLUORINE

History and occurrence. Although fluorine compounds are fairly common and have been known for several centuries, the element itself was not isolated until 1886 by Moissan, a French chemist. Among the more common minerals of fluorine are *fluorspar*, CaF_2; *cryolite*, Na_3AlF_6; and *apatite*, $CaF_2 \cdot 3 Ca_3(PO_4)_2$. It was shown in the seventeenth century that fluorspar treated with acids yielded a substance capable of etching glass. This substance has since been proved to be hydrogen fluoride.

Preparation and properties. The fact that fluorine was the last of the halogens to be prepared in the free state may be attributed to its extreme activity. Because of its activity its compounds are very stable, and the methods used in the liberation of the other halogens from their compounds are not applicable.

Attempts to liberate the element by means of oxidizing agents fail, since fluorine is more active than oxygen. Fluorine reacts vigorously with water according to the equation

$$2 F_2 + 2 H_2O \longrightarrow 4 HF + O_2$$

hence the electrolysis of water solutions of fluorides is unsuccessful. Moissan was finally able to isolate the element in 1886 by electrolyzing an anhydrous solution of potassium fluoride in liquid hydrofluoric acid. The mixture is a good conductor of the current and fluorine is liberated at the anode. The composition of the container and the electrodes to be used in the electrolysis process presents a problem, since fluorine is so extremely active. At the present time containers are made of Monel metal, an alloy of copper and nickel, which is resistant to the action of fluorine. The anode is composed of graphite.

In chemical properties the element is similar to the other halogens. It is the most active of the family and consequently will displace any of the others from their salts.

Fluorine is a pale yellow gas at ordinary conditions, very irritating and extremely poisonous. The element has no large use at the present time although many of its compounds are important commercially.

THE HYDROHALOGENS

The compounds HF, HCl, HBr, and HI are termed the *hydrohalogens* and their water solutions are known as *hydrofluoric, hydrochloric, hydrobromic,* and *hydriodic acids* respectively. All are colorless gases at ordinary temperatures and all are very soluble in water.

These compounds may be prepared by direct combination of the elements. The rate of reaction varies from an extremely rapid reaction with fluorine to a slow and incomplete reaction with iodine. In general this method of preparation is not applicable in the laboratory.

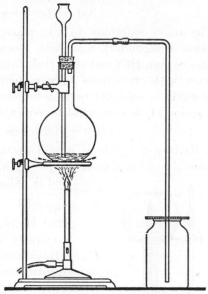

Fig. 68. Hydrogen chloride generator.

Preparation of hydrogen chloride and hydrogen fluoride. The usual method employed for the preparation of any volatile acid is to *treat a salt of the desired acid with a less volatile acid and distil over the desired acid.* If NaCl is treated with concentrated sulfuric acid, a nonvolatile acid (Fig. 68), hydrogen chloride, which is a gas at ordinary temperatures and therefore volatile, passes into the delivery tube and may be collected by displacement of air. The reaction may proceed in two steps:

$$NaCl + H_2SO_4 \longrightarrow NaHSO_4 + HCl \uparrow$$

If excess salt is present and the mixture is heated, a second reaction takes place:

$$NaCl + NaHSO_4 \longrightarrow Na_2SO_4 + HCl \uparrow$$

Hydrogen fluoride is prepared from fluorspar, CaF_2, and concentrated sulfuric acid:

$$CaF_2 + H_2SO_4 \longrightarrow CaSO_4 + 2 HF \uparrow$$

The reaction is usually carried out in a lead container which is resistant to the action of HF. Glass vessels cannot be used as the acid attacks the constituents in the glass. Hydrofluoric acid is stored in wax containers.

Action of concentrated sulfuric acid on bromides and iodides.

We might expect that the reaction of concentrated sulfuric acid with bromides and iodides would be similar to its action with chlorides and fluorides:

$$NaBr + H_2SO_4 \longrightarrow NaHSO_4 + HBr \tag{1}$$
$$NaI + H_2SO_4 \longrightarrow NaHSO_4 + HI \tag{2}$$

The above reactions do take place, but the products are impure because of secondary reactions. Both HBr and HI are better reducing agents than HCl and after their formation in the reactions above, they react with the excess sulfuric acid present. Some of the hydrogen bromide is oxidized to free bromine and as a result the product of reaction (1) is somewhat brown in color:

$$2\,HBr + H_2SO_4 \longrightarrow Br_2 + SO_2 + 2\,H_2O \tag{3}$$

Hydrogen iodide is a still better reducing agent than hydrogen bromide and is almost completely oxidized to free iodine; the sulfuric acid is reduced to hydrogen sulfide:

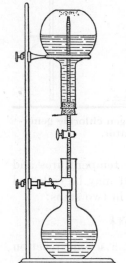

$$8\,HI + H_2SO_4 \longrightarrow 4\,I_2 + H_2S + 4\,H_2O \tag{4}$$

That HI is a better reducing agent than HBr is evident from reactions (3) and (4). While HBr reduced the valence of sulfur from $+6$ in sulfuric acid to $+4$ in sulfur dioxide, HI reduces the valence of sulfur from $+6$ to -2 in hydrogen sulfide.

Preparation of pure hydrogen bromide and hydrogen iodide.

Pure hydrogen bromide and hydrogen iodide are usually prepared by the action of water on phosphorus tribromide and phosphorus triiodide respectively:

$$PBr_3 + 3\,H_2O \longrightarrow H_3PO_3 + 3\,HBr$$
$$PI_3 + 3\,H_2O \longrightarrow H_3PO_3 + 3\,HI$$

Fig. 69. Hydrogen chloride fountain.

The phosphorus halides may be prepared by direct combination of the elements. Double decomposition reactions such as those above in which water is one of the reactants are termed *hydrolysis* reactions.

Physical properties. The hydrohalogens are colorless gases at ordinary temperatures and are extremely soluble in water.[1] All

---

[1] The extreme solubility of the hydrohalogens in water may be demonstrated by the following experiment (Fig. 69): The upper flask is filled with hydrogen chloride gas and the lower flask with water. When the stopcock is opened, hydrogen chloride begins dissolving in water. The solution process is slow at first because a small surface of water is exposed to the gas. As the gas dissolves a partial vacuum is produced in the upper flask and

possess a sharp, irritating odor. Other physical properties are tabulated below.

TABLE 14
PHYSICAL PROPERTIES OF HYDROHALOGENS

Formula	Molecular Weight	Boiling Point	Freezing Point	Solubility in Water: Volumes of Gas in 1 Volume of Water
HF	20 (above 90°)	19.4	−92	
HCl . . .	36.5	−84	−112	507 at 0°
HBr . . .	81	−67	−89	610 at 0°
HI	128	−35	−51	425 at 10°

At temperatures above 90°, determinations of densities of hydrogen fluoride indicate the formula to be HF, while at temperatures below 90° the molecules are associated to correspond with the formula H_2F_2. It is likely that an equilibrium between the two forms exists:

$$2\,HF \rightleftharpoons H_2F_2$$

Above 90° the equilibrium is displaced almost completely to the left while at ordinary temperatures the reverse is true. A still higher degree of association is indicated in liquid hydrogen fluoride.

Chemical properties of hydrogen chloride. While a water solution of hydrogen chloride exhibits all the properties of a strong acid, pure hydrogen chloride is relatively unreactive. Litmus is scarcely affected by the dry gas, neither do metals react rapidly with the anhydrous substance. This contrast in properties may be explained on the basis of the reaction of hydrogen chloride with water. Pure hydrogen chloride is a covalent compound and is therefore un-ionized. When the compound dissolves in water, the reaction

$$HCl + H_2O \rightleftharpoons H_3O^+ + Cl^-$$

takes place, resulting in the formation of ions. These ions appear to be responsible for the greater activity of hydrogen chloride in water solution.

An aqueous solution of hydrogen chloride exhibits the characteristic properties of an acid, turns litmus red, reacts with metals above hydrogen in the activity series to form hydrogen, reacts with bases to form salts, etc., *e.g.*:

$$Zn + 2\,HCl \longrightarrow ZnCl_2 + H_2$$
$$NaOH + HCl \longrightarrow NaCl + H_2O$$
$$CuO + 2\,HCl \longrightarrow CuCl_2 + H_2O$$
$$Na_2CO_3 + 2\,HCl \longrightarrow 2\,NaCl + CO_2 + H_2O$$

water flows up the vertical tube into the upper flask. The rate of solution increases until finally water sprays rapidly into the upper flask, and the gas seems to dissolve almost at once.

Gaseous HCl reacts with gaseous ammonia to form a white cloud of solid ammonium chloride (enough water vapor is present to render the gas active): $NH_3 + HCl \longrightarrow NH_4Cl$

Uses of hydrochloric acid. As an acid, hydrochloric acid is second only to sulfuric acid in importance. It finds extensive use in "pickling baths" for cleaning iron and steel objects before the latter are plated. Iron and steel become coated with a layer of oxide of the metal which is soluble in hydrochloric acid. Large quantities are used in the hydrolysis of starch to glucose in the manufacture of corn sirup. Other major uses are in the manufacture of textiles, dyes, and chemicals. Hydrochloric acid appears to play an important role in the stomach, where it aids in digestion.

Hydrofluoric acid and fluorides. Hydrofluoric acid possesses the unique property of reacting with silica, SiO_2, to form *silicon tetrafluoride*, SiF_4, a gas at ordinary temperatures:

$$SiO_2 + 4\,HF \longrightarrow SiF_4 \uparrow + 2\,H_2O$$

Glass, which is a mixture of sodium and calcium silicates, is readily attacked by the acid, the following reactions taking place:

$$Na_2SiO_3 + 6\,HF \longrightarrow SiF_4 + 2\,NaF + 3\,H_2O$$
$$CaSiO_3 + 6\,HF \longrightarrow SiF_4 + CaF_2 + 3\,H_2O$$

Because of these reactions, hydrofluoric acid finds extensive use in the etching of glass. A glass object to be etched is coated with paraffin after which a design is cut into the paraffin. The object is then exposed to the action of hydrofluoric acid. Burets, pipets, graduated cylinders, and other pieces of chemical apparatus are thus etched.

Hydrofluoric acid is a weak acid, while the other hydrohalogen acids are very strong. As a result its reactions with metals and bases are very slow. Salts of the acid are extremely poisonous and find limited use. *Sodium fluoride* and *sodium aluminum fluoride* are used as insecticides. *Sodium fluosilicate*, Na_2SiF_6, is used as a germicide and deodorant. Several fluorine compounds have been used recently as refrigerants, one of the more common ones being CCl_2F_2 which has been given the trade name Freon.

OXYGEN COMPOUNDS OF THE HALOGENS

Oxides. Although the halogens do not combine directly with oxygen, several oxides have been prepared indirectly. Generally speaking, these compounds are unstable and difficult to preserve. Cl_2O, *chlorine monoxide*, a yellowish gas which may be condensed to a liquid at 4° is the anhydride of HClO, and may be distilled from a solution of the acid under reduced pressure. The gas readily explodes when heated. ClO_2, *chlorine dioxide*, is a yellowish gas, liquefying at 10°. It may be produced by the action of a strong acid on a chlorate and since the ClO_2 is very unstable the reaction may occur with explosive violence, *e.g.*:

$$6\ KClO_3 + 3\ H_2SO_4 \longrightarrow 2\ HClO_4 + 4\ ClO_2 + 2\ H_2O + 3\ K_2SO_4$$

The oxide acts as a mixed anhydride as its solution in water produces both chlorous and chloric acids:

$$2\ ClO_2 + H_2O \longrightarrow HClO_3 + HClO_2$$

Cl_2O_7, *chlorine heptoxide*, the anhydride of perchloric acid, is a colorless oily liquid with a boiling point of 82°. It readily explodes when struck or heated above its boiling point. It may be prepared by dehydration of $HClO_4$ with P_2O_5:

$$2\ HClO_4 + P_2O_5 \longrightarrow Cl_2O_7 + 2\ HPO_3$$

A few other oxides of the halogens, *e.g.*, F_2O and Br_3O_8, have been prepared but are relatively unimportant.

Oxyacids of the halogens. The halogens with 7 electrons in the outer shell of their atoms are capable of exhibiting several valences by sharing of electrons with oxygen, and as a consequence form series of oxygen-containing acids with several acids in each series. The oxyacids are listed in Table 15.

TABLE 15

HALOGEN OXYACIDS

Name	Valence of Halogen	Fluorine	Chlorine	Bromine	Iodine
Per . . . ic	7	. . .	$HClO_4$	. . .	HIO_4
. . . ic	5	. . .	$HClO_3$	$HBrO_3$	HIO_3
. . . ous	3	. . .	$HClO_2$	. . .	. . .
Hypo . . . ous	1	. . .	$HClO$	$HBrO$	HIO

The electronic configurations of the oxyacids of chlorine are given below:

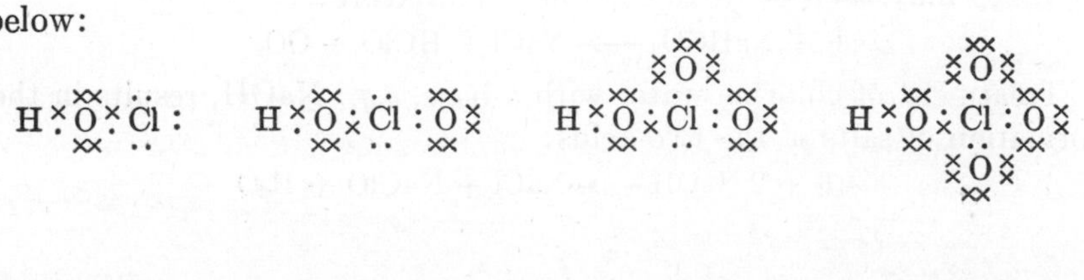

The stability of the oxyacids increases with increase of oxygen content, thus $HClO_4$ is the most stable of the oxyacids of chlorine, $HClO$ the least stable. There is a tendency for every substance to change to a more stable state. When such a change does occur, the change does not take place directly but rather in several steps to the most stable state. Thus $HClO$, the least stable of the oxyacids, changes first to $HClO_2$, which is more stable. $HClO_2$ in turn changes to still more stable $HClO_3$; and finally $HClO_3$ changes to $HClO_4$, the most stable of the oxyacids. Ostwald was the first to discover this principle, which is often referred to as Ostwald's Law of Successive Reactions and is stated as follows: *A system does not pass directly from the least stable to the most stable state, but does so through a series of gradually increasing stable states.*

$$2\,HClO \longrightarrow HClO_2 + HCl$$

In this reaction one atom of chlorine gains in valence at the expense of the other, which loses in valence. Such a change in which like atoms gain and lose electrons within a given substance simultaneously is termed *auto-oxidation*.

Hypochlorous acid. $HClO$ is formed when chlorine is dissolved in water:
$$Cl_2 + H_2O \rightleftharpoons HCl + HClO$$

The bleaching action of chlorine which is effective only in the presence of water is due presumably to the oxidizing properties of hypochlorous acid produced.

A water solution of chlorine gradually deteriorates on standing, particularly in sunlight; a fact that may be readily accounted for by the instability of hypochlorous acid which decomposes:

$$2\,Cl_2 + 2\,H_2O \longrightarrow 2\,HCl + 2\,HClO$$
$$\!\!\longrightarrow 2\,HCl + O_2$$

The reaction is displaced to the right as the decomposition proceeds until eventually only HCl is left in the solution.

Hypochlorous acid is a weak acid in contrast to hydrochloric acid produced at the same time when chlorine is dissolved in water. Advantage is taken of this difference in acid strengths in separation of the two acids; the strong acid may be neutralized with $NaHCO_3$ or $CaCO_3$ leaving free hypochlorous acid in solution. A dilute solution of $HClO$ may then be distilled from the mixture:

$$Cl_2 + NaHCO_3 \longrightarrow NaCl + HClO + CO_2$$

Treatment of chlorine water with a base, *e.g.*, $NaOH$, results in the formation of salts of the two acids:

$$Cl_2 + 2\,NaOH \longrightarrow NaCl + NaClO + H_2O$$

The resulting solution containing sodium chloride and sodium hypochlorite is called *Javelle water*, widely used as a bleaching agent. The solution may also be prepared directly by the electrolysis of an aqueous NaCl solution, provided the solution is continuously stirred so that chlorine liberated at the anode may come in contact with sodium hydroxide left in solution as a result of the electrolysis.

Dakin's solution, which was very effective in World War I for sterilization of deep wounds, is essentially a solution of NaClO.

Bleaching powder. Although liquid chlorine is now used extensively in bleaching operations, available chlorine as a solid powder of the composition $CaOCl_2$, called *bleaching powder*, has long been used. Easily made, transported, and convenient to use as desired, its manufacture constitutes a large industry.

Bleaching powder is produced when chlorine gas is passed over layers of slaked lime, $Ca(OH)_2$:

$$\text{Ca}\begin{matrix}\diagup\text{OH}\\\diagdown\text{OH}\end{matrix} + \begin{matrix}\text{Cl}\\|\\\text{Cl}\end{matrix} \longrightarrow \text{Ca}\begin{matrix}\diagup\text{Cl}\\\diagdown\text{OCl}\end{matrix} + \text{HOH}$$

Note that the compound is a mixed salt, containing both the chloride and hypochlorite acid radicals. It may be considered to be a mixture of the two salts $CaCl_2$ and $Ca(ClO)_2$ present in equal molecular proportions. Chlorine is readily liberated by treatment with an acid:

$$\text{Ca}\begin{matrix}\diagup\text{Cl}\\\diagdown\text{OCl}\end{matrix} + \text{H}_2\text{SO}_4 \longrightarrow \text{CaSO}_4 + \underbrace{\text{HOCl} + \text{HCl}}_{\text{Cl}_2\ +\ \text{H}_2\text{O}}$$

Chloric acid, $HClO_3$. Chloric acid is a colorless liquid which explodes violently when heated. It is most readily prepared by addition of dilute sulfuric acid to barium chlorate:

$$\text{Ba(ClO}_3)_2 + \text{H}_2\text{SO}_4 \longrightarrow \text{BaSO}_4 \downarrow + 2\,\text{HClO}_3$$

Sulfuric acid is added in exact amount necessary for reaction and insoluble $BaSO_4$ is filtered from the solution. Concentration of the dilute solution to about 40 per cent $HClO_3$ may be accomplished by distillation below 40° under reduced pressure. The acid is an active oxidizing agent.

Chlorates. Sodium and potassium chlorates are the most important salts of chloric acid. They find extensive use as laboratory oxidizing agents and are widely used in production of matches, fireworks, and explosives. An oxidizable substance such as wood or charcoal burns brilliantly and rapidly when dropped into the molten salt. Potassium chlorate may be prepared by passing chlorine gas into a hot concentrated solution of KOH or by electrolysis of KCl solution. The reactions occurring in both cases may be summarized in the equation

$$6 \, KOH + 3 \, Cl_2 \longrightarrow KClO_3 + 5 \, KCl + 3 \, H_2O$$

Since potassium chlorate is much less soluble than the potassium chloride produced, it may be recovered by crystallization from the cooled solution.

Sodium chlorate is used as a weed killer, but as such should be used in the absence of oxidizable dust since combustion once started proceeds with great vigor.

When potassium chlorate is heated strongly the reaction takes place:

$$2 \, KClO_3 \longrightarrow 2 \, KCl + 3 \, O_2$$

This is a source of oxygen as prepared in the laboratory. It may be recalled that the decomposition is slow unless the salt is brought to the boiling point or a catalyst is added. If the salt is maintained at a temperature just above the melting point, auto-oxidation proceeds with the formation of potassium perchlorate:

$$4 \, KClO_3 \longrightarrow KCl + 3 \, KClO_4$$

Perchloric acid and perchlorates. Perchloric acid is a colorless liquid which decomposes explosively if heated strongly. Its preparation is similar to that of chloric acid, *i.e.*, treatment of a perchlorate, preferably barium perchlorate, with dilute sulfuric acid followed by distillation under reduced pressure. It is one of the strongest acids, being comparable in strength to HCl and HNO_3. As a 60–70 per cent solution it is used in the analytical separation of potassium, since potassium perchlorate is one of the few slightly soluble salts of potassium.

Magnesium perchlorate is an effective desiccant or drying agent, having the capacity to absorb up to 30 per cent of its own weight of water.

Other oxyacids. Several oxyacids of bromine and iodine are known; in general their properties and methods of preparation are similar to the oxyacids of chlorine. Iodic acid, HIO_3, and its salt, KIO_3, are used as oxidants in analytical titrations. HIO_3 may be prepared by oxidation of free iodine with concentrated nitric acid:

$$I_2 + 10 \, HNO_3 \longrightarrow 2 \, HIO_3 + 10 \, NO_2 + 4 \, H_2O$$

Crystals of the acid are recovered by evaporation of the solution.

EXERCISES

1. From the standpoint of atomic structure, why would you expect the members of the halogen family to be very similar in chemical properties?
2. The halogens are never found in the uncombined or free state. Explain.
3. What products are always obtained upon the oxidation of hydrochloric acid?
4. Write balanced equations for the action of four different oxidizing agents on hydrochloric acid.
5. Describe an experiment which you could carry out in the laboratory to show the relative activity of the halogens.
6. Give two or three reasons why chlorine was effective in the early part of World War I as a war gas.
7. State clearly in your own words a definition of *sublimation*.
8. Why cannot fluorine be prepared in a similar manner to the other halogens? Show by diagram and equations what products would be formed during the electrolysis of an aqueous hydrofluoric acid solution.
9. List several similarities and several dissimilarities of members of the halogen group.
10. Explain clearly why concentrated sulfuric acid cannot be used in the preparation of pure hydrogen bromide and hydrogen iodide.
11. What is the general method for the preparation of a volatile acid? Write equations to illustrate for (a) nitric acid; (b) acetic acid.
12. Explain how you might test a sample of table salt for the presence of iodide.
13. A sample of chlorine water on exposure to the sunlight gradually loses its effectiveness as a bleaching agent. Explain.
14. Despite the fact that hydrogen chloride contains the element hydrogen in addition to chlorine, a liter of hydrogen chloride weighs less than a liter of chlorine. Explain.
15. Calculate the weight of 100 liters of hydrogen chloride at standard conditions.
16. Calculate the theoretical quantity of chlorine which is obtainable by the electrolysis of 200 pounds of a 20 per cent sodium chloride solution. What other products would be obtained and what weight of each?
17. Complete and balance:

   (a) $Mg + HCl \longrightarrow$
   (b) $NH_4OH + HI \longrightarrow$
   (c) $F_2 + H_2O \longrightarrow$
   (d) $MnO_2 + HBr \longrightarrow$
   (e) $H_2 + F_2 \longrightarrow$
   (f) $Fe + Cl_2 \longrightarrow$
   (g) $I_2 + KOH \longrightarrow$
   (h) $AlBr_3 + H_3PO_4 \longrightarrow$
   (i) $CuO + HCl \longrightarrow$
   (j) $Al_2O_3 + HBr \longrightarrow$
   (k) $Cl_2 + NaOH \longrightarrow$
   (l) $K + Br_2 \longrightarrow$

18. In those cases where a reaction occurs, write the equation. If no action takes place, indicate such:

   (a) Chlorine water is added to (i) potassium bromide, (ii) sodium fluoride, (iii) calcium iodide, (iv) a solution of potassium hydroxide, (v) hydriodic acid.
   (b) Hydrochloric acid solution is added to (i) copper, (ii) ferric oxide, (iii) tin, (iv) SiO_2, (v) sodium hydroxide, (vi) manganese dioxide, (vii) mercury.
   (c) Bromine water is added to (i) potassium chloride, (ii) magnesium, (iii) tin, (iv) sodium iodide, (v) calcium fluoride, (vi) hydrochloric acid, (vii) sodium hydroxide solution.

19. How many grams of bromine are necessary to liberate 50 grams of iodine from sodium iodide? Ans. 31.5.
20. 500 grams of chlorine are mixed with 25 grams of hydrogen gas and the mixture exploded. What gases remained after the explosion, and how many grams of each?
21. The refrigerant liquid Freon is CCl_2F_2. What is its percentage composition?
22. How many liters of hydrogen chloride (measured at standard conditions) may be obtained by the action of concentrated sulfuric acid on 200 grams of sodium chloride? What would be the weight of this volume of HCl?
23. Calculate the volume of HCl necessary to exactly neutralize 100 liters of NH_3. (Gases measured at standard conditions.) Ans. 100 l.
24. Calculate the weight and volume of all gases produced during the electrolysis of 500 grams of an aqueous solution of sodium chloride.
25. 4480 cubic feet of chlorine gas were bubbled into sodium hydroxide to make a laundry bleach. What weight of NaClO was formed? Ans. 931 lb.
26. A plant manufacturing phosgene, $COCl_2$, made its own CO gas but bought chlorine as a liquid under pressure in large cylinders. As 142 pounds of chlorine were used, what volume (at standard conditions) of CO was needed to make $COCl_2$? Ans. 717 cu. ft.
27. What weight of silver sulfate must be added to a solution of NaBr to prepare 824 pounds of AgBr?
28. Astatine (At), a member of the halogen family, was only recently discovered. From known properties of other members of the family, predict some of the properties of this element, such as melting point, boiling point, solubility in water, color, chemical activity, stability of compounds, etc.
29. Describe tests which you might use to differentiate between the four white salts: NaF, NaCl, NaBr, NaI.
30. Complete and balance:

    (a) $SiO_2 + HF$
    (b) $CaF_2 + H_2SO_4$
    (c) $C_{10}H_{16} + Cl_2$
    (d) $K_2Cr_2O_7 + KBr + H_2SO_4$
    (e) $KClO_3 + HBr$

31. How would you proceed in the laboratory to differentiate between aqueous solutions of HCl, HNO_3, and H_2SO_4?
32. Write equations to show the preparation of pure samples of HBr and HI.
33. Calculate the volume of HCl gas at standard conditions obtainable from 22.2 g. of $CaCl_2$. Ans. 8.96 l.
34. The halogens show progressive differences in properties with increasing atomic weights. What change in the following properties occurs with increasing atomic weight: (a) color of the element, (b) activity of the element, (c) stability of the hydrohalides, (d) color of hydrohalides, (e) ease of separation of the elements from compounds?
35. Chlorine may be prepared in the laboratory by the reaction:

$$2 KMnO_4 + 16 HCl \longrightarrow 2 KCl + 2 MnCl_2 + 5 Cl_2 + 8 H_2O$$

(a) What volume of chlorine gas (standard conditions) would be produced by using 6.32 g. $KMnO_4$ with excess HCl? (b) What weight of $MnCl_2$ would be produced in (a)? Ans. (a) 2.24 l. (b) 5.04 g.

REFERENCES

T. B. Brighton, "Salt Making on the Great Salt Lake," *J. Chem. Ed.* **9,** 407 (1932).

C. C. DeWitt, "Recovery of Iodine from Waste Iodide Solutions," *ibid.* **14,** 215 (1937).

D. M. Yost and J. B. Hatcher, "The Chemistry of Fluorine," *ibid.* **10,** 330 (1933).

F. R. Lowdermilk, R. G. Danehower, and H. C. Miller, "Pilot Plant Study of Fluorine and Its Derivatives," *ibid.* **28,** 246 (1951).

"Bromine from Sea Water," *ibid.* **46,** 771 (1939).

"Handling Hydrofluoric Acid," *ibid.* **47,** 542 (1940).

Humphry Davy, "The Elementary Nature of Chlorine," *Alembic Club Reprints,* No. 9.

G. M. Dyson, "Industrial Aspects of Bromine and Its Compounds," *Chemical Age* **23,** 425 (1930).

A. Rogers, *Manual of Industrial Chemistry,* Van Nostrand.

T. Midgley, Jr., and A. L. Henne, "Organic Fluorides as Refrigerants," *Ind. and Eng. Chem.* **22,** 542 (1930).

G. R. Robertson, "New American Iodine Industry," *ibid.* **26,** 376 (1934).

L. C. Stewart, "Commercial Extraction of Bromine from Sea Water," *ibid.* **26,** 361 (1934).

R. C. Dawning, *et al.,* "Electrolytic Cells for Production of Fluorine," *ibid.* **39,** 259 (1947).

Lucius A. Bigelow, *et al.,* "Fluorine as a Halogen," *ibid.* **39,** 360 (1947).

C. C. Brunbaugh, *et al.,* "Synthesis and Recovery of Hydrogen Chloride Gas," *ibid.* **41,** 2165 (1949).

W. H. MacIntire, *et al.,* "Effects of Fluorine in Tennessee Soils and Crops," *ibid.* **41,** 2466 (1949).

Walter C. Schumb and Maurice A. Lynch, Jr., "Iodine Hepta Fluoride," *ibid.* **42,** 1383 (1950).

H. C. Miller and J. F. Gall, "Inorganic Compounds Containing Sulfur and Fluorine," *ibid.* **42,** 2223 (1950).

W. H. MacIntire, *et al.,* "Effect of Fluorine Carriers on Crops and Drainage Waters," *ibid.* **43,** 1797 (1951).

XVII

Chemical Equilibrium

Examples of physical equilibrium. We have encountered several examples of physical equilibria in our study thus far. A saturated solution is one which is in equilibrium with the undissolved solute. In such a solution two processes are occurring in opposite directions with the same speed; namely, molecules of solid are continually passing into solution, and at the same time molecules from the solution are precipitating or depositing out as solid. Since these processes are taking place at the same speed, no apparent change in the solution is observed and at a given temperature the solubility is a constant.

A liquid placed in a closed container soon comes to an equilibrium with its vapor. Molecules from the liquid are continually escaping from the surface of the liquid and passing into the vapor state; and at the same time molecules from the vapor state are passing into the liquid state. When equilibrium has been attained, these two processes are taking place with the same speed, *i.e.*, the rate of evaporation is equal to the rate of condensation.

A chemical equilibrium is like a physical equilibrium in that two opposing processes are occurring simultaneously with the same speed. However, there is this difference between physical equilibria and chemical equilibria: in the former, only a physical change occurs and there is no change in composition of the substances involved, whereas in a chemical equilibrium, a chemical change does occur — the reactants undergo a change in composition to form the products, which in turn are reconverted to the original reacting substances.

Reversible and irreversible changes. Under certain conditions the products of a chemical change may react to re-form the original substances. Such chemical changes are said to be *reversible*. When mercuric oxide is heated to a temperature of 600°–700°, decomposition of the compound takes place, yielding mercury and oxygen as products:

$$2\,HgO \longrightarrow 2\,Hg + O_2$$

This change is reversible, since at a temperature of 300° mercury will combine with oxygen to form mercuric oxide:

$$2 \, Hg + O_2 \longrightarrow 2 \, HgO$$

Although most chemical changes are reversible many must be classed as *irreversible*. When sugar ($C_{12}H_{22}O_{11}$) is heated, decomposition into carbon and water takes place:

$$C_{12}H_{22}O_{11} \longrightarrow 12 \, C + 11 \, H_2O$$

Under no conditions known at present will carbon combine with water to form sugar. Hence the decomposition is irreversible; the products will not react to re-form the original substance. The following are other examples of irreversible reactions:

$$2 \, Mg + O_2 \longrightarrow 2 \, MgO$$
$$2 \, KClO_3 \longrightarrow 2 \, KCl + 3 \, O_2$$
$$C_2H_5OH + 3 \, O_2 \longrightarrow 2 \, CO_2 + 3 \, H_2O$$
$$wood + oxygen \longrightarrow ashes + gases$$

Equilibrium in reversible changes. In discussing the action of steam on iron filings (p. 96) it was shown that the following reaction takes place:
$$3 \, Fe + 4 \, H_2O \text{ (steam)} \longrightarrow Fe_3O_4 + 4 \, H_2 \qquad (1)$$

This reaction is reversible since the passage of hydrogen gas over Fe_3O_4 results in the formation of iron and steam:

$$Fe_3O_4 + 4 \, H_2 \longrightarrow 3 \, Fe + 4 \, H_2O \qquad (2)$$

In both of these cases a gas has been passed over a solid, in the first, steam over iron; in the second, hydrogen over iron oxide. Let us now modify the conditions by enclosing iron filings and steam in a container so that no gaseous substance can escape. Reaction (1) above will proceed fairly rapidly at first, reaction (2) cannot take place since no Fe_3O_4 and H_2 are initially present, but as these two products are formed as a result of reaction (1), then reaction (2) will start. At first reaction (2) is slow as the concentration of reactants is small but gradually increases in speed until reactions (1) and (2) are taking place with the same speed. Under these conditions the amounts of Fe, H_2O, Fe_3O_4 and H_2 remain unchanged and the system is said to be in *equilibrium*.

To discuss the general case of equilibrium, consider the reaction:

$$A + B \longrightarrow C + D$$

If the reaction is reversible, then C must react with D to re-form the reactants A and B:
$$C + D \longrightarrow A + B$$

If the two reactions above occur at the same time and at the same speed, a chemical equilibrium results and may be represented thus:

$$A + B \rightleftharpoons C + D$$

When this condition results, no apparent change is taking place; analysis of the system would show that at all times constant amounts of reactants and products would be present. *Chemical equilibrium is an apparent state of rest in which two opposing chemical reactions are proceeding in opposite directions at the same speed.*

It should be pointed out that an equilibrium may be approached from either direction; in the above it would make no difference whether we started with A and B or C and D as reactants, the same final condition of equilibrium would result.

Factors which influence the speed of reactions. Since speed is an important factor in the determination of chemical equilibrium, let us discuss briefly those factors which may affect the speed of chemical change.

(a) *Nature of the reacting substances.* Substances differ in activity and hence differ in the speed with which they react with other substances. The active metals displace hydrogen vigorously and rapidly from acids, while the less active metals act slowly if at all. Metals differ in their rates of corrosion because of differences in speed of combination with oxygen and other elements. Inert elements like nitrogen combine very slowly with other elements; in contrast to these the halogens comprise a group of active nonmetals which combine with most of the other elements readily.

(b) *Temperature.* The speed of all chemical changes increases as the temperature rises. Hydrogen and oxygen combine very slowly at ordinary temperatures but do so rapidly at high temperatures. The same is true of a piece of coal which burns readily in air when the temperature is raised sufficiently. *In general, the speed of a chemical change is approximately doubled for each ten degrees rise in temperature.*

(c) *Catalysts.* Catalysts may alter the speed of chemical changes. The decomposition of potassium chlorate is speeded up by the addition of the catalyst, manganese dioxide. A catalyst may also reduce the speed; for example, acetanilide decreases the speed of decomposition of hydrogen peroxide. Catalysis is extremely important in the preparation of many industrial products. The success of many processes from a commercial standpoint depends upon the rate at which the desired products may be produced, which in turn may depend upon the speed of certain chemical changes. The addition of a catalyst may so speed up a chemical change as to make it commercially feasible.

(d) *Concentration.* From a kinetic standpoint, chemical change takes place as a result of collisions of molecules. The greater the number of collisions in unit time, the greater the conversion of initial substances into products in unit time, *i.e.*, the greater the speed of reaction. If the concentrations of reactants are high (a large number of molecules in a given volume) the chance for collision is much better. The chance for collision between couples on a dance floor is much greater if the floor is crowded (high concentration) than if only a few couples occupy the same area.

The student should not infer from the above that all collisions of molecules necessarily result in chemical change. In some cases, a relatively large percentage of collisions may result in atomic rearrangements (chemical change) while in other cases possibly only a small percentage of collisions will be effective. It is necessary, however, that actual contact be made between the interacting substances to produce chemical reaction.

The law of mass action. Gulberg and Waage in 1807 expressed the relationship between mass or concentration and speed of reaction in the Law of Mass Action: *The speed of a chemical reaction is proportional to the product of the concentrations (or active masses) of the reacting molecules.* Consider the reaction

$$A + B \longrightarrow C + D$$

The rate at which A reacts with B will depend upon the number of collisions between A and B molecules. Suppose we have one molecule each of A and B in one liter of solution. We may say that the chance for collision is 1; that is, $1 \times 1 = 1$. If we double the number of molecules of A, then we have doubled the chance for collision between A and B molecules; hence the chance for collision is $2 \times 1 = 2$. If the number of B molecules is also doubled (the concentration of B is doubled), then the chance for collision becomes $2 \times 2 = 4$, etc. The number of collisions, then, is proportional to the product of the concentrations of reacting substances. Since the speed at which A combines with B is dependent upon the number of collisions between A and B, it follows that the speed of reaction is proportional to the concentrations of A and B. If we denote the concentration of A molecules as C_A and the concentration of B molecules as C_B, this may be expressed:

Speed $\propto C_A \times C_B$ ($\propto$ means proportional)

or   Speed $= k \times C_A \times C_B$

where k is a constant. This k is termed a *velocity constant,* and it includes the effects of temperature, pressure, catalyst, and nature of the reactants — all the factors other than concentration which influence the speed of reaction. Since the reaction takes place between molecules, concentrations are expressed in terms of molarity, *i.e.*, moles per liter.

If we apply the above relation to the reaction

$$H_2 + Cl_2 \longrightarrow 2\,HCl$$
then $\qquad$ Speed $= k \times C_{H_2} \times C_{Cl_2}$

where C_{H_2} and C_{Cl_2} represent the molar concentrations of H_2 and Cl_2 respectively.

In the reaction

$$H_2 + H_2 + O_2 \longrightarrow 2\,H_2O$$

two molecules of hydrogen react with one molecule of oxygen and therefore

$$\text{Speed} = k \times C_{H_2} \times C_{H_2} \times C_{O_2}$$
or $\qquad$ Speed $= k \times C^2_{H_2} \times C_{O_2}$

In the reaction

$$N_2 + H_2 + H_2 + H_2 \longrightarrow 2\,NH_3$$
$$\text{Speed} = k \times C_{N_2} \times C^3_{H_2}$$

In the reaction

$$3A + 4B \longrightarrow C + D$$
$$\text{Speed} = k \times C^3_A \times C^4_B$$

It may be noted that the concentration of each substance is raised to the power which corresponds to the number of reacting molecules. Thus in the above, three molecules of A enter into the reaction, and the concentration of A is raised to the third power; four molecules of B react, hence the concentration of B must be raised to the fourth power, etc.

The equilibrium constant. Consider the reaction

$$A + B \rightleftharpoons C + D$$

in which an equilibrium exists between the four substances, A, B, C, and D. Two reactions are proceeding, one to the right in which A and B react to form C and D, and the other to the left in which C and D react to form A and B. According to the law of mass action

$$\text{Speed to the Right} = k_1 \times C_A \times C_B$$
and $\qquad$ Speed to the Left $= k_2 \times C_C \times C_D$

At the beginning of the reaction, if we start with A and B, the concentrations of A and B will be high and consequently reaction to the right will proceed rapidly. At the start no reaction to the left is possible, since C and D are not as yet present. But as C and D are formed, reaction to the left will begin slowly and gradually increase in speed as C and D accumulate. Meanwhile the reaction to the right is slowing down as A and B are being used up. Equilibrium results when the speed in the two directions is equal, that is

$$\text{Speed Right} \xrightarrow{\hspace{1cm}} = \text{Speed Left} \xleftarrow{\hspace{1cm}}$$

Consequently at equilibrium

$$k_1 \times C_A \times C_B = k_2 \times C_C \times C_D$$

or

$$\frac{k_1}{k_2} = \frac{C_C C_D}{C_A C_B}$$

or since the ratio of the two constants $\dfrac{k_1}{k_2}$ is also a constant we may write

$$K = \frac{C_C C_D}{C_A C_B}$$

where K is termed the *equilibrium constant*. We must keep in mind that equilibrium conditions may be approached from either direction. If we had started with C and D as reactants instead of A and B, the same final situation of equilibrium would result.

In the event that more than one molecule of a substance is used as a reactant or formed as a product, the number of molecules as shown in the chemical equation must appear as the exponent of the concentration in the formulation of the equilibrium constant; thus in the equilibrium

$$mA + nB \rightleftharpoons rC + sD$$

where m, n, r, s represent the coefficients of A, B, C, D respectively in the balanced equation, the formulation for K becomes

$$K = \frac{C^r_C \times C^s_D}{C^m_A \times C^n_B}$$

Summarizing, we may say: *In a chemical equilibrium, the product of the concentrations of products divided by the product of concentrations of reactants — each concentration raised to that power whose exponent is the coefficient of the substance in the balanced chemical equation — is a constant.*

K has a constant numerical value for any given reaction at a given temperature. It is determined by actual analysis of an equilibrium mixture to find out the concentration of each of the substances. If the concentration of one of the substances in the mixture is changed, the concentrations of other substances must change in such a way that the ratio

$$\frac{C_C C_D}{C_A C_B}$$

retains the same numerical value.

Suppose, for example, in the equilibrium

$$A + B \rightleftharpoons C + D$$

the concentration of A is increased. We should expect the speed of reaction between A and B to increase, since now there are more possible collisions between A and B molecules. As a result, the equilibrium is shifted to the right; the concentrations of C and D become larger. From an inspection of the formula for the equilibrium constant, it is evident that an increase of C_A must result in an increase of C_C and C_D and a decrease in C_B, if K is to retain its value.

It should be evident from the expression for an equilibrium constant that if K has a large value, the numerator must be large as compared to the denominator; consequently the concentrations of C and D are relatively high. This indicates that the reaction is more nearly complete to the right. On the other hand, a small value of K would show that the chemical change to the right has not proceeded very far.

The equilibrium constant is very important in chemistry, since it shows the extent to which a reaction may take place. In the preparation of substances from a commercial standpoint, it is desirable to choose a reaction in which K has a high value, since this would mean a high proportion of products.

The extent to which a reaction takes place is often roughly indicated by varying the length of the arrows appearing in the equilibrium equation. $\rightleftharpoons$ would indicate an equilibrium displaced far to the right, *i.e.*, a high proportion of products; $\rightleftharpoons$ one far to the left, *i.e.*, a high proportion of reactants; intermediate stages may be represented by arrows of approximately the same length, *i.e.*, $\rightleftharpoons$. A single arrow $\longrightarrow$ indicates a complete reaction to the right; $\longleftarrow$ indicates no reaction.

Chemical changes which go to completion. Reactions which proceed in only one direction are *complete*, while those in which an equilibrium exists are *incomplete*. Irreversible reactions (p. 217) are of necessity complete; also every reaction becomes complete if one of the products is removed as fast as it is formed. There are three conditions under which a chemical change may proceed practically to completion.

(*a*) *Formation of a gas.* It is evident that removal of one of the products, as fast as it is formed, would preclude reaction in the reverse direction. Thus:

$$A + B \longrightarrow C + D\uparrow$$

Suppose that D is a gas and escapes from the mixture. There is then no possibility of reaction between C and D, and the chemical change becomes complete to the right. In certain cases, the evolution of gas will depend upon the conditions under which the process is carried out. If solid NaCl is treated with concentrated H_2SO_4 and heated

$$NaCl + H_2SO_4 \longrightarrow NaHSO_4 + HCl \uparrow$$

hydrogen chloride is evolved as a gas, and the change is complete to the right. This is the laboratory preparation of HCl. However, if a solution of NaCl in H_2O is used instead of solid salt the reaction is incomplete, since the hydrogen chloride which may be formed remains in the solution (HCl is very soluble in water) and an equilibrium results:

$$NaCl + H_2SO_4 \rightleftharpoons NaHSO_4 + HCl$$

Now if the mixture is heated, the hydrogen chloride distils off and the change becomes complete to the right.

(b) *Formation of a precipitate.* A chemical change is essentially complete if one or more of the products precipitates from solution. When silver nitrate is added to a sodium chloride solution, insoluble silver chloride is produced which precipitates from solution:

$$AgNO_3 + NaCl \longrightarrow AgCl \downarrow + NaNO_3$$

In this case one of the products is effectively removed from what we might term the "sphere of chemical action," and thus the change proceeds only to the right. It should be pointed out, however, that such reactions are not entirely complete, since all substances are soluble to a greater or lesser extent, and thus the soluble part would bring about a slight reverse action. The more insoluble the product, the more nearly the reaction is complete.

In preparing a product in the laboratory it is desirable to choose a chemical change which is essentially complete, since separation of the desired product is simplified. For example, a sample of $NaNO_3$ might be made according to the above. If the proper amounts of reactants have been used, only AgCl and $NaNO_3$ remain. Since AgCl is insoluble, it may be filtered out, leaving $NaNO_3$ in solution. Solid $NaNO_3$ may then be obtained by evaporation of the water from the solution of the salt. The above reaction would be preferable to the following

$$KNO_3 + NaCl \rightleftharpoons KCl + NaNO_3$$

in which $NaNO_3$ is also a product. Since the latter reaction is incomplete, the four salts, KNO_3, NaCl, KCl, and $NaNO_3$, would all be present in the reaction mixture (all of these salts are soluble in water), and the separation of $NaNO_3$ from the other three would be a tedious and difficult procedure. The student should familiarize himself with the solubility of salts (see solubility rules on page 180). A knowledge of solubility rules enables one to predict whether or not a given reaction in which a salt is a product will proceed to completion.

(c) *Formation of water, an un-ionized substance.* Chemical changes between acids and bases in which water is a product are essentially complete. This may be attributed to the fact that water is a very slightly ionized substance. We shall elaborate on this particular type of reaction in the next chapter.

Le Chatelier's principle. A principle of universal application to systems in equilibrium has been stated by Le Chatelier as follows: *If a stress is placed upon a system in equilibrium whereby the equilibrium is altered, that change will take place which tends to relieve or neutralize the effect of the added stress.* Consider the equilibrium reaction

$$A + B \rightleftharpoons C + D$$

We learned that an increase in concentration of any of the reactants or products would result in a shift in the equilibrium. An increase in concentration may be considered as an added stress or force. For example, if more A is added to the system, thereby increasing the concentration or stress of A, the equilibrium is shifted to the right, since by doing so A is used up in the reaction and consequently the stress (increase in concentration of A) is relieved or diminished. On the other hand, if A be removed (the concentration of A decreased), the equilibrium will shift to the left resulting in the formation of more A. The stress in this case is the removal of A, and the system tends to relieve or diminish this stress by forming more of A. Other stresses which may be imposed upon a system are additions of heat (increase of temperature) and application of pressure.

Effect of pressure upon a system in equilibrium. Consider a reaction in which a relatively large change in volume occurs, for example,

$$N_2 + 3 H_2 \rightleftharpoons 2 NH_3$$

The reactants N_2 and H_2 and the product NH_3 are all gaseous at ordinary temperatures. According to the equation, one volume of nitrogen reacts with three volumes of hydrogen to produce two volumes of ammonia. It is evident, then, that four volumes of reactants produce only two volumes of products, a decrease in volume as the reaction proceeds from left to right. We may readily predict the effect of increased pressure on this system from Le Chatelier's principle. If the pressure on the system be increased, the reaction will proceed in the direction of smaller volume, *i.e.*, to the right, because a decrease in volume will tend to relieve the added stress (pressure). If the added stress be a decrease of pressure, the reaction will be favored in which there is a volume increase, since an increase in volume will tend to offset or neutralize the decrease in pressure. This would result in a displacement of equilibrium to the left. A high pressure would be favorable in the production of ammonia by the above process, since the higher the pressure, the greater will be the displacement of the equilibrium to the right. A decrease in pressure would have the opposite effect, *i.e.*, the equilibrium would be displaced to the left. A greater proportion of the reaction mixture, then, would be composed of the reactants, N_2 and H_2.

Certain gaseous reactions involve no change in volume, for example,

$$H_2 + I_2 \text{ (gas)} \rightleftharpoons 2\,HI$$

A total of two volumes (one of hydrogen and one of iodine) of reactants produce two volumes of products (two volumes of hydrogen iodide). Pressure has no effect upon such a system as there is no volume change in the reaction.

The effect of temperature upon an equilibrium. All chemical changes are accompanied by changes in energy; certain reactions are exothermic, *i.e.*, heat is produced during the reaction; others are endothermic, *i.e.*, heat is absorbed. In the reaction

$$N_2 + 3\,H_2 \rightleftharpoons 2\,NH_3 + 24{,}000 \text{ calories}$$

nitrogen and hydrogen, in combining to form ammonia, produce heat which is arbitrarily designated by a $+$ sign. When ammonia undergoes decomposition into nitrogen and hydrogen (the reverse of the reaction) an equivalent amount of heat must be taken up or absorbed. Heat absorbed will be designated by a $-$ sign. When the system is at equilibrium, no heat change is taking place.

Let us apply Le Chatelier's principle to an equilibrium in which heat is added to the system (increase of temperature). To relieve the strain (increase of temperature) the system will absorb heat, since by absorbing heat the tendency is to use up the added heat. Consider an equilibrium mixture of ice and water. A solid in melting absorbs heat. If an equilibrium mixture of ice and water be heated, the ice melts and absorbs heat, and the temperature does not rise above

0° until all of the ice is melted. The equilibrium proportions of ice and water shift so as to use up the newly applied heat.

In the reaction above in which ammonia is produced, an increase of temperature would favor the reaction to the left, *i.e.*, the formation of nitrogen and hydrogen from ammonia, since that is the reaction which absorbs heat.

It should be realized that Le Chatelier's principle has considerable significance from a practical standpoint. If ammonia were being produced commercially by the method above, it would be desirable to have the equilibrium displaced as far to the right as possible, since this would mean a greater yield of ammonia. In order to accomplish this, a high pressure and a low temperature would be desirable. Ammonia is actually produced commercially (Haber process) by this reaction at a pressure of several hundred atmospheres and a temperature of 400°–500°. This temperature might seem to be rather high; however, it is the minimum temperature which is feasible for the process, as the reaction between H_2 and N_2 to attain equilibrium takes place too slowly at lower temperatures.

If N_2 and H_2 gases are mixed at ordinary temperature, reaction between them is so slow that thousands of years might elapse before equilibrium proportions of N_2, H_2, and NH_3 would be reached. Time to attain equilibrium at low temperatures is very slow for this reaction. However, at 400°–500° equilibrium proportions are reached in a matter of minutes. Although the equilibrium proportions at the higher temperature are not quite so favorable as at ordinary temperature, time to attain equilibrium is very much reduced. It is economically feasible to obtain a 17.6 per cent yield of NH_3 by using 400°–500° temperature and 200 atmospheres pressure in a matter of minutes, and thence condense out the NH_3 and recycle the unused N_2 and H_2. It is not economically feasible to use room temperature and 200 atmospheres pressure to attain a much greater percentage of NH_3, for it would require ages of time.

Catalysts and equilibrium. A catalyst cannot displace an equilibrium, but may greatly reduce the time necessary for the establishment of equilibrium. This is extremely important from an industrial standpoint, since the speed at which a product can be produced is a primary consideration. Catalysts may be effectively used in many reactions which allow conversion of only a small percentage of reactants into products (equilibrium far to the left). From a production standpoint, it is more important to obtain a small yield in a few minutes than to obtain a larger yield if the latter required several days. A catalyst by its presence adds no energy to a system, and thus cannot alter equilibrium proportions.

EXERCISES

1. How does chemical equilibrium differ from physical equilibrium?
2. Differentiate between reversible and irreversible reactions.
3. What factors influence the speed of a reaction?
4. List the factors which may displace an equilibrium.
5. Under what conditions do reactions proceed to completion?
6. Write equations for four different methods of preparing KCl. Reactions must go to completion.
7. The following salts are soluble in water: $BaCl_2$, Na_3PO_4, $Al(NO_3)_3$, $CuSO_4$, KCl, $(NH_4)_2CO_3$, $ZnBr_2$, CaS, $Mg(C_2H_3O_2)_2$. (*a*) From this list select five pairs which brought together in solution form a precipitate. Write the equations. (*b*) Select five pairs which form no precipitate.
8. What is the effect of change in pressure upon a system in equilibrium? State Le Chatelier's principle.
9. How does change in temperature affect a system in equilibrium?
10. What is the effect of increased temperature and pressure on the following systems in equilibrium? All reactants and products are in the vapor state.

   (*a*) $2 X_2 + Y_6 \rightleftharpoons 2 X_2Y_3 - 200$ calories
   (*b*) $H_2 + I_2 \rightleftharpoons 2 HI - 630$ calories
   (*c*) $CO + Cl_2 \rightleftharpoons COCl_2 + 48,770$ calories
   (*d*) $N_2 + 3 H_2 \rightleftharpoons 2 NH_3 + 24,000$ calories
   (*e*) $N_2 + O_2 \rightleftharpoons 2 NO - 43,200$ calories

11. Given the following equilibrium mixture of gases at a temperature of 200° C., underline the right answer.

$$4 NH_3 + 7 O_2 \rightleftharpoons 6 H_2O + 4 NO_2 + \text{heat}$$

   (*a*) Increased pressure will shift the equilibrium (left, right, not at all).
   (*b*) Increased temperature will shift the equilibrium (left, right, not at all).
   (*c*) Adding excess NH_3 will shift the equilibrium (left, right, not at all).
   (*d*) Adding excess O_2 will shift the equilibrium (left, right, not at all).
   (*e*) Adding a drying agent to absorb the water will shift the equilibrium (left, right, not at all).

12. Phosphorus pentachloride dissociates according to the equation:

$$PCl_5 \rightleftharpoons PCl_3 + Cl_2$$

At a given temperature the dissociation is 20 per cent (to the right). (*a*) If we start with 0.5 mole PCl_5 in 1 liter, what will be the equilibrium concentrations of the three constituents? (*b*) Calculate the value for the equilibrium constant.   Ans. (*a*) PCl_5 0.4 mole
PCl_3 0.1 mole
Cl_2 0.1 mole
(*b*) 0.025.

13. $$N_2 + 3 H_2 \rightleftharpoons 2 NH_3$$

An equilibrium mixture of the above was analyzed and found to contain 0.4 mole N_2, 0.2 mole H_2 and 0.1 mole NH_3 in one liter. Calculate the value for the equilibrium constant.   Ans. 3.1.

14. If HI is 25 per cent dissociated according to the equation

$$2 HI \rightleftharpoons H_2 + I_2$$

at a given temperature (a) calculate the equilibrium concentrations of HI, H_2, and I_2 if we start with 10 moles of HI in a one liter container, (b) calculate the value for the equilibrium constant.

15.
$$N_2 + 3 H_2 \rightleftharpoons 2 NH_3$$

At a given temperature this reaction is 20 per cent complete to the right. If 1000 molecules of nitrogen and 3000 molecules of hydrogen are mixed and heated to this given temperature, how many molecules of each of these gases will be present at equilibrium?

16.
$$2 SO_2 + O_2 \rightleftharpoons 2 SO_3$$

A reaction vessel with a capacity of one liter, in which the above reaction had reached a state of equilibrium was found to contain 0.6 mole of SO_3, 0.2 mole of SO_2, and 0.3 mole of O_2. Calculate the equilibrium constant.

17. From the list of available starting materials select suitable compounds from which $MgCl_2$ may be prepared and show by balanced equations the reactions employed. Reactions must be complete. Available starting materials: $MgSO_4$; $FeCl_3$; HCl; $NaNO_3$; H_2SO_4; MgO; Mg; $BaCl_2$.

REFERENCES

F. H. Getman and Farrington Daniels, *Outlines of Theoretical Chemistry*, Wiley.

T. R. Hogness and W. C. Johnson, *Qualitative Analysis and Chemical Equilibrium*, Holt.

J. H. Hildebrand, "Approach to Equilibrium," *J. Chem. Ed.* **23,** 589 (1946).

XVIII

The Theory of Ionization

Introduction. Modern theory of atomic structure (chap. III) has familiarized us with the nature of atoms, molecules, and ions. Ions are atoms or atomic groups which have either an excess or a deficiency of electrons.

The theory of ions originated with Faraday in 1832 and was extended by the Swedish chemist, Arrhenius, in 1887, many years prior to the modern concepts of atomic structure. The theory has undergone considerable modification since that time and is now successful in interpreting many hitherto inexplicable phenomena.

It will be recalled from chapter I that theories are designed to explain facts obtained by experimentation. The modern scientist obtains experimental data and then seeks to explain the results obtained. These experimental facts may be explained by means of certain assumptions which are not subject to direct experimentation. This set of assumptions and its explanation of facts constitute the theory. As more data are obtained which are not readily explained by the assumptions, the theory will undergo modification.

In the sections to follow, we shall first outline the experimental evidence upon which the theory is based, secondly the assumptions of the theory, and finally we shall be interested in seeing how the theory explains the experimental facts.

Facts leading to the ionization theory. (1) *Aqueous solutions of acids, bases, and salts are conductors of the electric current.* With the aid of an apparatus as shown in Figure 70, the conductivity of solutions may be conveniently studied.

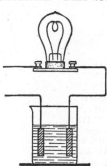

Fig. 70. Apparatus for measuring electrical conductance of solutions.

The apparatus consists of two electrodes (copper wires may be used) connected in series with a 110-volt alternating-current source and an ordinary electric light bulb. The electrodes are immersed in the solution whose conductivity is to be tested. If a current flows across the solution between the electrodes, the bulb will light, and the degree of conduction of the electric current is roughly indicated by the intensity of light shown in the bulb. If the solution is a good conductor (that is, if the resistance offered to the passage of the current is small), the bulb will show a bright light. On the other hand, a solution whose resistance is high will not allow the current to pass through the solution readily, and a dim light or no light at all will be obtained. In Table 16 are summarized the results obtained with several substances in aqueous solutions.

Those substances which in aqueous solution conduct the electric current are referred to as *electrolytes,* and those showing no conduction are said to be *nonelectrolytes.* From an inspection of Table 16, we note that acids, bases, and salts may be classified as electrolytes. Although the table shows the results of a study with a limited number of compounds, a more complete study would show this classification to be correct. We may note, too, from Table 16 that compounds differ in their degree of conduction, *e.g.,* hydrochloric acid is a very good conductor, while acetic acid is a fair conductor only, etc. Although acids, bases, and salts may show different degrees of conduction, nevertheless, in aqueous solution, these classes of compounds all conduct the current to a greater or less extent. Even tap water shows some conduction because of dissolved mineral salts.

TABLE 16

CONDUCTIVITY OF SOLUTIONS (AQUEOUS)

SUBSTANCE	LIGHT INTENSITY	CLASSIFICATION AS CONDUCTOR
HCl	bright	very good
NaOH	bright	very good
NH$_3$	dim	fair
HC$_2$H$_3$O$_2$	dim	fair
Sugar	none	nonconductor
HCl (in toluene)	none	nonconductor
Alcohol	none	nonconductor
Water (distilled)	none	nonconductor
Water (tap)	very dim	poor
NaCl	bright	very good
CuSO$_4$	bright	very good

We may ask the questions: Why do acids, bases, and salts in aqueous solution conduct an electric current, while other substances in solution do not? Why are certain electrolytes better conductors of the current than others? We shall soon find the answers to these questions.

(2) *Aqueous solutions of acids, bases, and salts show abnormal boiling points and freezing points.* In the study of solutions it was pointed out that one mole of a substance (nonelectrolyte) dissolved in 1000 grams of water (this would be a 1 molal solution) produced an elevation of the boiling point of 0.52° and a depression of the freezing point of 1.86°. One mole of any substance contains about 6×10^{23} molecules. It follows that the elevation of the boiling point 0.52° and the depression of the freezing point 1.86° are produced by this number of particles or molecules in 1000 grams of water. A solution containing twice this number of molecules (12×10^{23}) gives a boiling elevation of $2 \times 0.52° = 1.04°$, and a freezing point depression of $2 \times 1.86° = 3.72°$. These properties, then, are dependent upon the number of dissolved particles; 0.52° is referred to as a normal elevation of the boiling point and 1.86° as a normal depression of the freezing point of water.

Inspection of Table 17 reveals that electrolytes in aqueous solution exhibit abnormalities with respect to the boiling point elevation and freezing point depression. For example, sodium chloride produces almost double the expected effect, calcium chloride almost three times the normal effect, etc.

TABLE 17

EFFECT OF SOLUTES ON THE BOILING AND
FREEZING POINTS OF WATER

SUBSTANCE (1 mole in 1000 g. H_2O)	ELEVATION OF B.P.	DEPRESSION OF F.P.
$CO(NH_2)_2$ (urea)	.52° (normal)	1.86° (normal)
$C_{12}H_{22}O_{11}$	.52° (normal)	1.86° (normal)
NaCl	.97° (abnormal)	3.49° (abnormal)
$CaCl_2$	1.3° (abnormal)	4.83° (abnormal)
$AlCl_3$	1.73° (abnormal)	5.68° (abnormal)

Since the boiling point elevation is a function of the number of dissolved particles, it would seem that a mole of sodium chloride must furnish about twice as many particles in solution as a mole of a substance like sugar, which shows a normal effect on the boiling and freezing points of water. Since calcium chloride produces about three times the normal effect, about three times as many particles would be necessary, etc. How can we account for the apparent increase in the number of particles present in aqueous solutions of acids, bases, and salts? We note that those substances which produce abnormal boiling and freezing points are the same substances which conduct the electric current in aqueous solution.

(3) *Reactions in solution.* Acids, bases, and salts in general show characteristic properties only in solution. For example, solid sodium chloride shows no tendency to react with solid silver nitrate when the two dry substances are mixed. However, if, to a solution of sodium chloride, is added a solution of silver nitrate, reaction takes place immediately according to the equation

$$NaCl + AgNO_3 \longrightarrow AgCl \downarrow + NaNO_3$$

Likewise, other substances which do not react in the pure state readily do so when dissolved in water.

Acids and bases exhibit their characteristic properties only in solution in water or certain other liquids. Pure HCl has little or no effect on litmus, but a water solution of hydrogen chloride turns blue litmus paper red. Similarly, pure sodium hydroxide has no effect on litmus; a water solution shows the characteristics of a base, turns litmus blue, tastes bitter, etc.

(4) *Molten salts are conductors.* Many molten salts are good conductors of the electric current — indeed the electrolysis of molten sodium chloride is a commercial means of producing metallic sodium.

Assumptions of the ionization theory. In order to explain the facts which have just been listed, the following assumptions are made (the original assumptions of Arrhenius have been modified somewhat to adequately explain experimental evidence which was not known at the time the theory was proposed):

(*a*) Electrolytes (acids, bases, salts) in aqueous solution produce two or more charged parts, called ions. A given electrolyte may form one or more positive ions and one or more negative ions. The total positive charge on the ions is equal to the total negative charge on the ions.

Acids produce ions by the transfer of a proton from the acid molecule to a water molecule, *e.g.*:

$$HCl + H_2O \longrightarrow \underset{\substack{\text{hydro-} \\ \text{nium ion}}}{H_3O^+} + Cl^-$$

$$HNO_3 + H_2O \longrightarrow H_3O^+ + NO_3^-$$
$$H_2SO_4 + 2 H_2O \longrightarrow 2 H_3O^+ + SO_4^{--}$$

Although water plays an important role in the ionization of acids in producing the hydrated hydrogen ion (hydronium ion), the ionization of acids will ordinarily be shown as giving the simple hydrogen ion, *i.e.*,

$$HCl \rightleftharpoons H^+ + Cl^-$$

This is justified since there is considerable uncertainty as to the degree of hydration of the hydrogen ion, the amount of water per hydrogen ion is probably more than one molecule. In simplifying the ionization process, however, we should not lose sight of the fact that free hydrogen ions probably do not exist in aqueous solution but are hydrated in some degree.

Metallic hydroxides (bases) in aqueous solution produce metallic ions (or NH_4^+) and hydroxyl ions:

$$NaOH \longrightarrow Na^+ + OH^-$$
$$Ca(OH)_2 \longrightarrow Ca^{++} + 2\ OH^-$$
$$NH_4OH \longrightarrow NH_4^+ + OH^-$$

Salts yield metallic ions (or NH_4^+) and acid radical ions:

$$NaCl \longrightarrow Na^+ + Cl^-$$
$$CaCl_2 \longrightarrow Ca^{++} + 2\ Cl^-$$
$$K_2SO_4 \longrightarrow 2\ K^+ + SO_4^{--}$$

Not all compounds in aqueous solution are ionized — for example, sugar and other solutes which do not give a conducting solution form no ions.

(*b*) The number of charges on an ion is equal to its valence.

(*c*) Ionization of acids is not complete — in all cases, undissociated molecules are in equilibrium with the ions as, for example,

$$HCl + H_2O \rightleftharpoons H_3O^+ + Cl^-$$
or simply
$$HCl \rightleftharpoons H^+ + Cl^-$$

The extent of ionization (the degree of completeness of the above reaction to the right) is dependent upon both the solute and solvent.

(*d*) In general, salts and soluble metallic hydroxides are completely ionized, even in the solid state.

Let us now interpret the facts which we have outlined in terms of the assumptions just given.

The conduction of the electric current. The fact that electrolytes in water solution conduct the electric current is explained by assuming that the ions act as carriers of the current across the solution between the electrodes. Electrolysis consists in the discharge of ions at the electrodes of a cell through which a current is passing. During the electrolysis of a copper chloride solution, for example

(Fig. 71), Cu^{++} ions move toward the negative pole of the cell (the cathode) and the Cl^- ions move toward the positive pole (the anode).

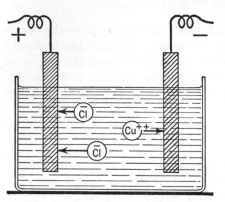

Accordingly positively charged ions are called *cations*, and negatively charged ions *anions*. At the anode the Cl^- ion loses its charge and becomes a chlorine atom. When two chlorine atoms are liberated, they unite to form a chlorine molecule (Cl_2). At the cathode each Cu^{++} ion is discharged and forms a copper atom. Thus free chlorine is formed at the anode and metallic copper is produced at the cathode.

Fig. 71. When an aqueous solution of cupric chloride is electrolyzed, metallic copper is plated out on the cathode, and chlorine gas is liberated at the anode.

The conductivity of a solution depends upon two factors: (1) the number of ions present and (2) the speed at which the ions move through the solution. The greater the number of ions and the greater the speed at which they travel, the better the conductivity of the solution.

We noted that some electrolytes were better conductors than others. For example, hydrochloric acid was classed as a very good conductor, while acetic acid was classed as only fair. We may explain the better conduction of the former by assuming that more ions are produced when mole quantities of hydrogen chloride are dissolved in water than when mole quantities of acetic acid are dissolved in water. That is, hydrochloric acid is more highly ionized than acetic acid.

The fraction of molecules which break up into ions is referred to as the *degree of ionization*. Thus if one half of the molecules dissolved in solution break up into ions, the electrolyte is said to be 50 per cent ionized, a degree of ionization of 0.5.

Since the conductivity of a solution depends upon the number of ions, electrical conductivity measurements have been used to determine an apparent degree of ionization. The conductance of a mole of electrolyte in dilute solution is greater than the conductance of a mole of the same electrolyte in concentrated solution. Hence the molar conductance increases with dilution and would reach a maximum value in an infinitely dilute solution in which the ionization would presumably be 100 per cent. The degree of ionization at any concentration of electrolyte then may be calculated from the expression

$$\text{Apparent Degree of Ionization} = \frac{\text{Conductance at a Given Concentration}}{\text{Conductance at Infinite Dilution}}$$

A degree of ionization obtained by this method would be a true value only if no factors other than number of ions were responsible for conduction. As will be shown later other factors are involved and hence the degrees of ionization obtained here are termed *apparent degrees of ionization.*

TABLE 18

DEGREE OF IONIZATION OF ELECTROLYTES IN AQUEOUS SOLUTION [1]

Compound	Ionization	Concentration of Solution (Normality)	Apparent Degree of Ionization
HCl	$H^+ + Cl^-$	1.0	0.78
HCl	$H^+ + Cl^-$	0.5	0.88
HBr	$H^+ + Br^-$	0.5	0.90
HNO$_3$	$H^+ + NO_3^-$	1.0	0.82
H$_2$SO$_4$	$2 H^+ + SO_4^{--}$	1.0	0.51
H$_3$PO$_4$	$3 H^+ + PO_4^{---}$	0.5	0.17
KOH	$K^+ + OH^-$	1.0	0.77
NaOH	$Na^+ + OH^-$	1.0	0.73
NH$_4$OH	$NH_4^+ + OH^-$	1.0	0.004
KCl	$K^+ + Cl^-$	0.1	0.86
BaCl$_2$	$Ba^{++} + 2 Cl^-$	0.1	0.72
K$_2$SO$_4$	$2 K^+ + SO_4^{--}$	0.1	0.72
CuSO$_4$	$Cu^{++} + SO_4^{--}$	0.1	0.45

Table 18 shows the apparent degree of ionization of several electrolytes as calculated from conductivity data.

Abnormal boiling points and freezing points of aqueous solutions. Reference to Table 17 (p. 231) shows that NaCl produces about double the expected or normal effect in lowering the freezing point and raising the boiling point of water. Since these properties are dependent upon the number of dissolved particles, we must assume that almost twice as many particles are present. This is easily accounted for if we assume that most units of NaCl produce two ions:

$$NaCl \longrightarrow Na^+ + Cl^-$$

Calcium chloride produces nearly three times the normal effect on the boiling and freezing points of water and this fact is likewise easily

[1] Data taken from *Handbook of Chemistry and Physics*, Chemical Rubber Publishing Co.

explained if we assume that each unit of $CaCl_2$ produces one calcium ion and two chloride ions, a total of three ions per unit:

$$CaCl_2 \longrightarrow Ca^{++} + 2\ Cl^-$$

On this basis we would expect an electrolyte which furnishes four ions to depress the freezing point of water four times the normal (1.86°); if five ions are produced, the effect would be five times the normal, etc.

However, we may note from Table 17 that the effects are not quite twice, three, and four times the normal effect, *e.g.*, a molal solution of NaCl freezes at — 3.49° which is not quite twice the expected effect, $2 \times - 1.86° = - 3.72°$. The logical explanation of this might seem to be that the ionization of NaCl is not complete, *i.e.*, not all NaCl units produce Na^+ and Cl^-. This was the explanation as originally given by Arrhenius. However, present-day evidence indicates that NaCl and other salts are 100 per cent ionized and we must seek another explanation of the fact that boiling points and freezing points are not what might be expected.

Ionization of salts. Debye and Hückel in 1922 extended the theory, earlier suggested by A. A. Noyes and others, that strong electrolytes are 100 per cent ionized. Recent studies have shown that many substances in the solid state consist of ions. Consequently ions

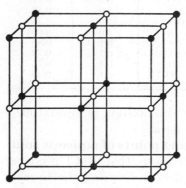

may be present before the substance is dissolved in solution. Solution is not necessary for the ionization process; for example, X-rays have shown that sodium chloride in the solid state is composed of ions (Fig. 72); each sodium atom has given up one electron and each chlorine atom has gained an electron. In the sodium chloride crystal, each sodium ion is surrounded by six chlorine ions (Fig. 72). If a sodium atom occupies the center of a cube, then a chloride ion would appear in the center of each one of the six faces

Fig. 72. Dots represent Na^+. Circles represent Cl^-.

of the cube. Similarly, each chlorine ion is surrounded by six sodium ions. This definite orientation or position of the ions in a salt crystal makes up a crystal lattice as shown in Figure 72.

Other lines of evidence also point to the existence of ions in the pure state, *e.g.*, many molten salts conduct the electric current.

Dissolving of electrovalent compounds in water. When an electrovalent compound such as NaCl is brought into contact with water, the forces of attraction between the ions in the crystal lattice are so weakened by the attraction of water dipoles (see chap. XI) that the ions separate from the lattice and are dispersed in the solvent. Positive sodium ions are attracted by the negative ends of the water dipoles; likewise the negative chloride ions are attracted to the positive ends of water dipoles so that each ion becomes surrounded with a shell of water molecules as shown below, where $\oplus\ominus$ represents a water molecule dipole.

$$
8\,\underset{}{\oplus\ominus} +
\begin{array}{ccc}
-\text{Na}^+ - & \text{Cl}^- - & \text{Na}^+ - \\
-\text{Cl}^- - & \text{Na}^+ - & \text{Cl}^- - \\
-\text{Na}^+ - & \text{Cl}^- - & \text{Na}^+ -
\end{array}
\longrightarrow
\begin{array}{cc}
-\text{Na}^+ - & \text{Cl}^- - \\
-\text{Cl}^- - & \text{Na}^+ - \\
-\text{Na}^+ - & \text{Cl}^- - \text{Na}^+ -
\end{array}
\ + \
\begin{array}{c}
\oplus \\ \ominus \\
\oplus\ominus\,\text{Na}^+\,\ominus\oplus \\
\oplus \\ \ominus \\
\ominus\oplus\,\text{Cl}^-\,\oplus\ominus \\
\oplus \\ \ominus
\end{array}
$$

The *dielectric constant* is a measure of this ability of a solvent to weaken the forces of attraction between ions. Water has a dielectric constant of about 80 as compared to air as 1. This means that the force of attraction between ions in a water medium is only about $\frac{1}{80}$ as great as between ions in a medium of air. The high dielectric constant for water explains the relatively greater solubility of salts in water than in other solvents of lower dielectric constant.

Apparent and true degrees of ionization. Arrhenius explained the conductivity of electrolytes on the basis of the number of ions produced in a solution. A solution of sodium chloride shows only about 90 per cent of the conduction that might be expected if it were completely dissociated into ions. Arrhenius explained this by assuming that the NaCl is 90 per cent ionized; that is, 90 out of every 100 molecules of NaCl are dissociated into ions, the remaining 10 molecules are undissociated and in equilibrium with the ions:

$$\text{NaCl} \rightleftharpoons \text{Na}^+ + \text{Cl}^- \quad \text{(Arrhenius)}$$

According to the modern theory NaCl is completely ionized:

$$\text{NaCl} \longrightarrow \text{Na}^+ + \text{Cl}^- \quad \text{(Debye-Hückel)}$$

The latter theory explains the conductivity on the basis of the speed at which the ions move through the solution. When NaCl is dissolved, the sodium and chloride ions are further separated than in the crystal but tend to retain their position or orientation. That is, each ion is surrounded by six ions of opposite charge. An ionic atmosphere of opposite charge is thus formed about each ion, and this results in a restricted movement of the ions; the ions cannot act independently of one another in the solution. The attractive force of the ions of opposite charge tends to exert a "drag" on the ion which is moving; consequently the mobility or speed of the ion is decreased. Therefore NaCl acts as if it were 90 per cent ionized; that is, the salt gives the same conductance as would a solution in which 90 out of every 100 ions were unrestricted in their movement through a solution.

Likewise, we may explain the apparent degree of ionization of a salt solution from freezing and boiling point studies. NaCl does not produce quite twice the effect on the boiling and freezing points of water (Table 17) since the ions are not entirely independent of their neighbors. If movement of the ions was unrestricted, then we should expect NaCl to produce exactly *twice* the normal depression of the freezing point of water. Calcium chloride would produce three times the effect; aluminum chloride, four times; etc.

The strength of electrolytes. In aqueous solution, according to the ionic theory, all acids produce H^+ (H_3O^+) and this ion is responsible for the chief characteristics of an acid, namely, the sour taste, effect on litmus, etc. In like manner the similar properties of metallic hydroxides in aqueous solution are readily explained on the basis of OH^- ions, the OH^- ions being responsible for the bitter taste, soapy slippery feeling, effect on litmus, etc.

The strength of any electrolyte is measured by the concentration of ions produced in solution, thus a strong acid would be one which furnishes a high concentration of H^+ ions. HCl is classed as a strong acid, since it is about 90 per cent ionized; that is, 90 out of every 100 molecules of HCl produce H^+ and Cl^- ions. Acetic acid is a weak acid, since it is only about 1 per cent ionized; only one molecule out of every 100 produces H^+ and $C_2H_3O_2^-$ ions.

A strong metallic hydroxide which is a special case of the more general term, base, is one which produces a high concentration of OH^- ions in aqueous solution. The common strong bases are NaOH, KOH, $Ca(OH)_2$, and $Ba(OH)_2$; most others are weak.

In general, salts would be classed as strong electrolytes.

Neutralization reactions. It was pointed out (chap. X) that an acid reacts with a metallic hydroxide (base) in aqueous solution to form a salt and water — a type of reaction called neutralization. Let us examine a few reactions of this type from an ionic standpoint:

$$NaOH + HCl \longrightarrow NaCl + H_2O \text{ (molecular equation)}$$
$$Na^+ + OH^- + H^+ + Cl^- \longrightarrow Na^+ + Cl^- + H_2O \text{ (ionic equation)}$$

NaOH, which is a strong base, gives Na^+ and OH^- ions in solution; HCl, a strong acid, furnishes H^+ ions as a result of its reaction with water. Water is written in the molecular form in the ionic equation since it is only slightly ionized:

$$2 KOH + H_2SO_4 \longrightarrow K_2SO_4 + 2 H_2O \text{ (molecular equation)}$$
$$2 K^+ + 2 OH^- + 2 H^+ + SO_4^{--} \longrightarrow 2 K^+ + SO_4^{--} + 2 H_2O \text{ (ionic equation)}$$

Note that in the two ionic equations above all ions except H^+ and OH^- ions may be canceled so that the essential change in the neutralization process is

$$H^+ + OH^- \longrightarrow H_2O$$

Further evidence to show that this is the fundamental reaction of neutralization is gained from thermal studies of the reactions of strong acids and bases, *e.g.*:

$$KOH + HCl \longrightarrow KCl + H_2O + 13,700 \text{ calories}$$
$$NaOH + HNO_3 \longrightarrow NaNO_3 + H_2O + 13,700 \text{ calories}$$

Other reactions of strong acids and bases produce the same thermal change — 13,700 calories per gram equivalent of acid or base neutralized. From an ionic standpoint all of these reactions involve simply the combination of H^+ and OH^- ions to form water, hence this thermal change must be the heat of the reaction:

$$H^+ + OH^- \longrightarrow H_2O + 13,700 \text{ calories}$$

The neutralization of a strong base by a weak acid, *e.g.*, sodium hydroxide and acetic acid, might at first appear confusing to the student.

$$NaOH + HC_2H_3O_2 \longrightarrow NaC_2H_3O_2 + H_2O$$

According to the equation, 1 mole of NaOH reacts with 1 mole of acetic acid. Since sodium hydroxide is highly ionized and acetic acid only weakly ionized, it might appear that a large excess of OH^- ions would be present in the solution, and reaction would stop after the relatively few hydrogen ions from acetic acid were neutralized. However, the neutralization is complete because as H^+ ions are used up in reaction with OH^- ions, more acetic acid ionizes, producing more H^+ ions. This process continues until the acetic acid has completely ionized. Likewise in the neutralization of a weak base, OH^- ions would continue to be formed until neutralization was complete.

Other reactions in aqueous solution. The fact that certain reactions which do not take place between pure substances do proceed in aqueous solution is explained by assuming that the reaction takes place between ions which are free to move about in the solution. Although solid NaCl and solid $AgNO_3$ do not react, when these are dissolved in water and the solutions mixed, a reaction takes place immediately with the formation of insoluble silver chloride. From an ionic standpoint

$$Ag^+ + NO_3^- + Na^+ + Cl^- \longrightarrow AgCl\downarrow + Na^+ + NO_3^-$$

In solution the ions are free to move about and collide with other ions. In the above equation it is evident that the actual reaction is between Ag^+ and Cl^- ions to form AgCl. Na^+ and NO_3^- ions appear on both sides of the equation and may be canceled out. These latter ions are incidental to the primary reaction and may be replaced by other ions, *i.e.*, nitrate ion might be replaced with acetate or sulfate ion, and sodium ion might be replaced with any metal ion whose chloride is soluble. Hence the essential reaction of any soluble chloride salt and any soluble silver salt should be

$$Ag^+ + Cl^- \longrightarrow AgCl\downarrow$$

It will be recalled from the study of chlorides that Ag^+ ions constitute a test for their presence. All chlorides act with Ag^+ ions to give insoluble AgCl as shown above.

The molecular formula is used to show the silver chloride even though the solid is composed of ions. This convention will henceforth be used to differentiate between a solid electrolyte and a solution of its ions. Sodium chloride, for example, in the solid state will be written as NaCl, but in solution will be shown as $Na^+ + Cl^-$.

Many other precipitation reactions similar to the one described above will be encountered subsequently. From an ionic standpoint the fundamental reaction will always be a union of the ions of which the precipitate is composed.

Double salts. A number of naturally occurring crystalline minerals have formulas that correspond to a combination of two salts. For example, there are the minerals carnallite, $KCl \cdot MgCl_2 \cdot 6 H_2O$, and schönite, $K_2SO_4 \cdot MgSO_4 \cdot 6 H_2O$. As a solution of mixed salts crystallizes there is frequently formed between them a crystalline compound of fixed composition. Some commonly prepared compounds of this nature are Mohr's salt, $(NH_4)_2SO_4 \cdot FeSO_4 \cdot 6 H_2O$, and an alum, $Na_2SO_4 \cdot Al_2(SO_4)_3 \cdot 24 H_2O$. Salts of this kind which in solution give the individual metal ions and nonmetal (or negative radical) ions are called *double salts*. Such salts in solution exhibit chemical changes appropriate for each respective ion.

Complex salts. Certain crystalline compounds that may by composition appear to be double salts do not adhere to the above definition of a double salt. A formula for a compound that could be written $4 \: KCN \cdot Fe(CN)_2$ is usually written $K_4Fe(CN)_6$. There is definite experimental evidence to prove that little Fe^{++} is present in its water solution. It ionizes as follows:

$$K_4Fe(CN)_6 \longrightarrow 4 \: K^+ + Fe(CN)_6^{----}$$

Other examples are:

$$PbSiF_6 \longrightarrow Pb^{++} + SiF_6^{--}$$
$$Na_3AlF_6 \longrightarrow 3 \: Na^+ + AlF_6^{---}$$
$$Na_2PtCl_6 \longrightarrow 2 \: Na^+ + PtCl_6^{--}$$
$$Na_3AsS_4 \dashrightarrow 3 \: Na^+ + AsS_4^{---}$$

These compounds are called *complex salts* since in their ionization but two kinds of ions are formed, a single element ion and a complex ion. Since complex ions play an important role in chemistry in understanding many type reactions, some solubility phenomena, and certain metal ion separations, they will now be discussed briefly.

Complex ions. Simple ions may sometimes combine with other ions or neutral molecules to form complex ions, which in general have a high stability. Ordinarily the units in such a complex ion are held together by co-ordinate bonds of valence, *i.e.*, a pair of electrons furnished by one of the ions or neutral molecules. The hydronium ion, H_3O^+, and the ammonium ion, NH_4^+, might be considered as complex ions, since a neutral molecule of water or ammonia furnishes a pair of electrons to combine with a proton (p. 130).

More common examples of complex ion formation are those in which a metallic ion, such as Cu^{++}, Co^{+++}, Ag^+, etc., combines with a molecule or another ion to form a complex. Ammonia forms complex ions with a number of metallic ions, *e.g.*:

$$Cu^{++} + 4 \: NH_3 \rightleftharpoons Cu(NH_3)_4^{++}$$
$$Co^{+++} + 6 \: NH_3 \rightleftharpoons Co(NH_3)_6^{+++}$$
$$Ag^+ + 2 \: NH_3 \rightleftharpoons Ag(NH_3)_2^+$$

If NH_4OH is added to a solution of Cu^{++}, $Cu(OH)_2$ is first precipitated but redissolves as more NH_4OH is added because of the formation of $Cu(NH_3)_4^{++}$. The latter ion has a deep blue color. $Cu(OH)_2$ which is insoluble in water is therefore readily soluble in an aqueous solution containing free ammonia. Other hydroxides are soluble in NH_4OH

if the metallic ion forms a complex with NH_3. Consequently the formation of complex ions may be important in solubility considerations. In many cases, the number of molecules or ions combined with a simple ion is double the valence of the simple metallic ion. Thus Cu^{++} usually co-ordinates four such groups, Ag^+ two, and Co^{+++} six, etc. The number of molecules or ions grouped about a central ion is referred to as the *co-ordination number*.

In qualitative chemical analysis complex sulfide salts or ions thereof are encountered in various separations. Factually HgS will dissolve in a Na_2S solution, whereas PbS will not. This is typical of a separation of metal compounds or ions. The reaction is written

$$HgS + Na_2S \longrightarrow Na_2S \cdot HgS \quad or \quad Na_2HgS_2$$
or
$$HgS + S^{--} \longrightarrow HgS_2^{--}$$

Similarly

$$As_2S_5 + 3\,Na_2S \longrightarrow 3\,Na_2S \cdot As_2S_5 \quad or \quad 2\,Na_3AsS_4$$
$$As_2S_5 + 3\,S^{--} \longrightarrow 2\,AsS_4^{---}$$

Cyanide ion, CN^-, readily forms complexes with several metallic ions, *e.g.:*

$$Ag^+ + 2\,CN^- \longrightarrow Ag(CN)_2^-$$
$$Fe^{+++} + 6\,CN^- \longrightarrow Fe(CN)_6^{---}$$

Silver cyanide, AgCN, which is insoluble in water, is readily soluble in excess CN^- because of the formation of the complex $Ag(CN)_2^-$.

Halide ions frequently act similarly to form complex ions, *e.g.*, $AuCl_4^-$, $CuCl_4^{--}$, SiF_6^{--}, $SbCl_6^{---}$, $PtCl_6^{--}$, AlF_6^{---}, etc.

The structures of the $Cu(NH_3)_4^{++}$, $AuCl_4^-$, and AsS_4^{---} complex ions are shown below.

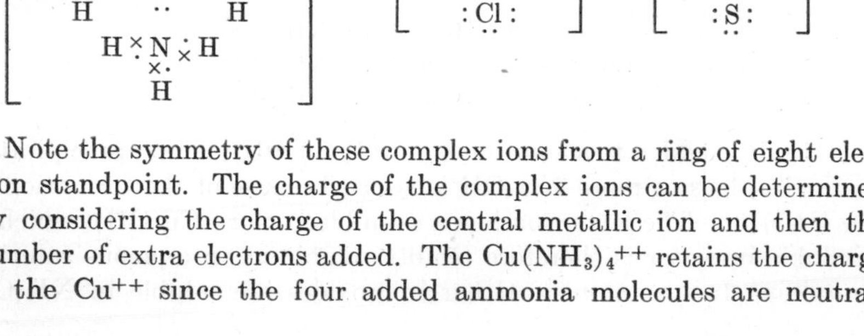

Note the symmetry of these complex ions from a ring of eight electron standpoint. The charge of the complex ions can be determined by considering the charge of the central metallic ion and then the number of extra electrons added. The $Cu(NH_3)_4^{++}$ retains the charge of the Cu^{++} since the four added ammonia molecules are neutral.

The $AuCl_4^-$ has its mononegative charge as the Au^{+++} has had 4 Cl^- added. The AsS_4^{---} can be construed as an As^{+++++} with 4 S^{--} added.

The above examples represent a central metallic ion with a coordination number of 4. In many complex ions, the central ion exhibits a co-ordination number of 6. Spatially, these may be pictured as the co-ordinating groups occupying the corners of an octahedron with the metallic ion in the center. Examples are $Co(NH_3)_6^{+++}$, $PtCl_6^{--}$, and $Co(NH_3)_3(H_2O)_3^{+++}$.

The subject of amphoterism (p. 142) can now be explained on the basis of complex ion formation. Certain metal hydroxides which, of course, dissolve in acid will also dissolve in basic solution.

$$Al(OH)_3 + OH^- \longrightarrow Al(OH)_4^- \quad \text{or} \quad AlO_2^- \cdot 2\,H_2O$$
$$Zn(OH)_2 + 2\,OH^- \longrightarrow Zn(OH)_4^{--} \quad \text{or} \quad ZnO_2^- \cdot 2\,H_2O$$
$$Sn(OH)_4 + 2\,OH^- \longrightarrow Sn(OH)_6^{--} \quad \text{or} \quad SnO_3^{--} \cdot 3\,H_2O$$

EXERCISES

1. How do vapor pressure and boiling point effects show that there is a greater number of particles per mole in solutions of acids, bases, and salts than in solutions of nonelectrolytes such as sugar?

2. How may the nature of the charge borne by an ion be experimentally determined?

3. Explain why solutions of certain acids and bases are better conductors than others.

4. What would be the approximate freezing point of a solution which contains 234 grams of sodium chloride per 1000 grams of water?   Ans. $-14°$.

5. How do the assumptions of the ionic theory explain the fact that some solutions are conductors of the electric current while others are not?

6. What is meant by "degree of ionization" or "extent of ionization"?

7. What is the difference between an ion and an atom? an ion and a molecule?

8. Although the compounds, chloroform, $CHCl_3$, and potassium chlorate contain chlorine, no precipitate is obtained with silver nitrate solution. Explain.

9. Of what unit particles are crystalline salts composed?

10. What are the essential differences between the Arrhenius and Debye-Hücke theories of ionization?

11. Write formulas of the ions present in aqueous solutions of the compounds: $NaCl$; Li_2SO_4; HBr; $Ca(OH)_2$; $Al(NO_3)_3$.

12. Write ionic equations for the following reactions in aqueous solution:
    (a) $CaCl_2 + Ag_2SO_4$
    (b) $Ba(NO_3)_2 + H_2SO_4$
    (c) $PbCl_2 + K_2CrO_4$
    (d) $Ba(OH)_2 + HBr$
    (e) $HCl + KOH$

13. Discuss briefly why we believe that electrolytes exist in aqueous solution as ions. Include at least three lines of evidence to support this belief.

14. Give approximate boiling points at sea level for the following: molal H_2SO_4; suspension of 200 g. of powdered glass in a liter of water; 3.03×10^{23} glycerin molecules per liter; 0.5 molal NaCl solution.

15. How would you make an ethylene glycol in water solution which would freeze at about $-9.3°$ C.? (The formula for ethylene glycol is $C_2H_4(OH)_2$.) About how much radiator glycol would you buy for a car radiator of 12 qt. capacity to withstand the mentioned temperature? Assume the density of glycol to be 1.

16. List the following in order of increasing boiling points: $1 M$ H_2SO_4; 3.03×10^{23} molecules NaCl in 1000 g. H_2O; 171 g. sugar in 1000 g. H_2O; twice the gram molecular weight of glycerin per liter; 200 g. suspended finely ground sand; molal solution of a nonelectrolyte.

17. Arrange the following solutions in order of increasing boiling point (assume almost complete ionization of the electrolytes): 18.18×10^{23} molecules of glycerin per 1000 g. H_2O; molal NaI; ten molal alcohol; 3.03×10^{23} molecules of sugar (mol. wt. 342) in 1000 g. H_2O; 0.1 molal HBr; molal K_2SO_4; normal H_2SO_4.

18. 25 g. of a nonelectrolyte in 125 g. of water gave a solution which boils at $100.78°$ C at standard pressure. What is the approximate molecular weight of the substance?   Ans. 133.

19. 6 g. of a nonelectrolyte in 200 g. H_2O gave a freezing point of $-0.93°$ C. What is the molecular weight of the substance?   Ans. 60.

REFERENCES

H. T. Briscoe, *General Chemistry for Colleges*, Houghton Mifflin.

"The Foundations of the Theory of Electrolytic Dissociation," *Alembic Club Reprints*, No. 19.

XIX

Ionic Equilibria

The ionization of covalent compounds. Atoms of the elements in covalent molecules are held together by sharing of electrons and the structural units of the substance carry no charge. All acids are of this type and thus are not ionized in the pure state. Since ions are produced when an acid is dissolved in an appropriate solvent, *e.g.*, water, it follows that the solvent plays an important role in producing ionization. When HCl is dissolved in water the following reaction takes place:

$$HCl + H_2O \rightleftharpoons H_3O^+ + Cl^-$$

Similarly other acids react with water to form hydrated hydrogen ions, $H^+ \cdot H_2O$, usually written as H_3O^+ and called *hydronium* ions.

Writing the electronic configuration for the above reaction

$$H : \overset{..}{\underset{..}{Cl}} : + H : \overset{..}{\underset{..}{O}} : H \rightleftharpoons \left[H : \overset{\overset{\textstyle H}{..}}{\underset{..}{O}} : H \right]^+ + \left[: \overset{..}{\underset{..}{Cl}} : \right]^-$$

we note that a hydrogen ion (a hydrogen atom which has lost its electron), which is a proton, has been transferred from the acid to the solvent molecules. An acid is usually defined as a substance which can furnish protons in a reaction — thus an acid is a *proton donor*.

The ionization of polyprotic acids. An acid which can furnish more than one proton per molecule is termed a *polyprotic* (also called polybasic) acid. Thus H_2SO_4 is a *diprotic* acid, H_3PO_4 a *triprotic* acid, etc. When these acids are dissolved in water, ionization takes place in successive stages, *e.g.*, H_2SO_4 shows two stages of ionization:

$$H_2SO_4 + H_2O \rightleftharpoons H_3O^+ + HSO_4^- \tag{1}$$
$$HSO_4^- + H_2O \rightleftharpoons H_3O^+ + SO_4^{--} \tag{2}$$

or more simply

$$H_2SO_4 \rightleftharpoons H^+ + HSO_4^-$$
$$HSO_4^- \rightleftharpoons H^+ + SO_4^{--}$$

The first reaction is much more complete than the second, *i.e.*, the equilibrium is displaced much farther to the right. Both H_2SO_4 and HSO_4^- are acting as acids above since each liberates or releases a proton to a water molecule. H_2SO_4 is said to be a stronger acid than HSO_4^- since reaction (1) is more complete than reaction (2). In general, if an acid ionizes in successive stages, each succeeding stage is less complete than the preceding one.

Definition of a base. Up to the present time we have referred to a base as a metallic hydroxide which furnishes OH^- ions in solution. In neutralization of a metallic hydroxide with an acid the fundamental reaction takes place:

$$OH^- + H^+ \longrightarrow H_2O$$

We might say that the base has accepted a proton in the reaction. Such is the modern definition of a base — a substance which accepts a proton — a *proton acceptor*. Although strictly speaking the actual base is the OH^- ion, nevertheless in common usage, metallic hydroxides which furnish OH^- ions are referred to as bases. However, the definition does not restrict bases to substances furnishing hydroxyl ions, for instance, in the reaction of an acid with water

$$HCl + H_2O \rightleftharpoons H^+ \cdot H_2O + Cl^- \qquad (1)$$
$$(H_3O^+)$$

the water takes up a proton and could therefore be considered to be a base. This definition of an acid as a proton donor and a base as a proton acceptor allows an extension of acid-base reactions to solvents other than water. For example, HCl reacts with liquid ammonia in a manner analogous to its reaction with H_2O:

$$HCl + NH_3 \rightleftharpoons H^+ \cdot NH_3 + Cl^- \qquad (2)$$
$$(NH_4^+)$$

In this case NH_3 acts as the base as it accepts a proton from HCl to form ammonium ion.

In general, a proton donor reacts with a base according to the general reaction, where A is an anion:

$$\underset{\text{acid}}{HA} + \underset{\text{base}}{B} \rightleftharpoons H^+ \cdot B + A^-$$

By far the most common usage of this concept of a base will be in water solutions where the base is OH^- ion.

Other acid-base reactions. Consider the reverse of equation (1) above:

$$\underset{\text{acid}}{H^+ \cdot H_2O} + \underset{\text{base}}{Cl^-} \rightleftharpoons \underset{\text{acid}}{HCl} + \underset{\text{base}}{H_2O}$$

The hydronium ion $H^+ \cdot H_2O$ is giving up a proton to a Cl^- ion to form HCl. Thus H_3O^+ is acting as an acid, since it is here a proton donor. Cl^- ion is a base, since it accepts a proton. The reverse of equation (2) above is analogous:

$$\underset{\text{acid}}{H^+ \cdot NH_3} + \underset{\text{base}}{Cl^-} \rightleftharpoons \underset{\text{acid}}{HCl} + \underset{\text{base}}{NH_3}$$

According to this concept, then, acids and bases may be either molecular or ionic. From the above two reactions, we may tabulate the acids and bases:

ACIDS	BASES
H_3O^+	Cl^-
HCl	H_2O
NH_4^+	NH_3

The Lewis theory. A concept of acids and bases which is more general in its application is that introduced by G. N. Lewis. According to the Lewis theory any substance which has an unused pair of electrons (such as NH_3) may be considered as a base, while any substance which may attach itself to such an available pair of electrons would be classed as an acid. For example, in the reaction of an acid anhydride with a basic anhydride to form a salt:

$$SO_3 + CaO \longrightarrow CaSO_4$$

$$\begin{matrix} O \\ \ddot{S}:O \\ O \end{matrix} + \ddot{:}\ddot{O}\ddot{:}Ca \longrightarrow \left[\begin{matrix} O \\ O:\ddot{S}:O \\ O \end{matrix} \right]^{--} Ca^{++}$$

CaO would be considered a base and SO_3 an acid. In the Lewis theory, a base is an *electron pair donor* and an acid an *electron pair acceptor*.

Strength of acids and bases. The strength of an acid is measured by its ability to release protons. In the reaction

$$(0.1\,M)\ HCl + H_2O \rightleftharpoons H_3O^+ + Cl^-$$

the reaction is about 90 per cent complete to the right; that is, for every 100 molecules of HCl that enter into reaction, approximately 90 molecules give up protons. HCl is said to be a strong acid, since it readily donates protons. On the other hand, acetic acid is a weak acid, since the reaction

$$(0.1\,M)\ HC_2H_3O_2 + H_2O \rightleftharpoons H_3O^+ + C_2H_3O_2^-$$

is only about 1 per cent complete to the right; only one molecule in every 100 of acetic acid gives up a proton.

Water may act as an acid or as a base, since it gives up and accepts protons in the reaction

$$\underset{\text{acid}}{H_2O} + \underset{\text{base}}{H_2O} \rightleftharpoons H_3O^+ + OH^-$$

It acts as a very weak acid, however, because the ionization is slight, *i.e.*, the reaction proceeds only slightly to the right.

Ammonia functions in an analogous manner:

$$\underset{\text{acid}}{NH_3} + \underset{\text{base}}{NH_3} \rightleftharpoons NH_4^+ + NH_2^-$$

It is evident from the above that certain substances may function as either acids or bases, in other words they are *amphoteric*.

A strong base is one which exerts considerable affinity for a proton. Compare the reactions:

$$HCl + H_2O \rightleftharpoons H_3O^+ + Cl^-$$
$$HC_2H_3O_2 + H_2O \rightleftharpoons H_3O^+ + C_2H_3O_2^-$$

The first reaction produces relatively more hydronium ions than the second. Since HCl gives up protons more readily than does $HC_2H_3O_2$, we conclude that $C_2H_3O_2^-$ ion is acting as a stronger base than Cl^- ion. We might say that an acetate ion clings more tightly to a proton than does a chloride ion. Hydroxyl ion is a strong base in water solution, since very few protons are released from the water molecule.

The anion of a strong acid is a weak base; protons are released easily by the acid, as they are not held tightly by the anion. The anions SO_4^{--}, NO_3^-, Cl^-, are weak bases, since sulfuric, nitric, and hydrochloric acids readily give up protons in water solution. The converse is also true; anions of weak acids are strong bases; thus $C_2H_3O_2^-$, PO_4^{---}, and S^{--} are classed as strong bases.

Ionization constants. The law of mass action is applicable to ionic as well as molecular reactions, and we may write an expression for the equilibrium constant for these reactions. In these cases the equilibrium constant is usually written as K_i and termed the *ionization* or *dissociation constant*. Thus in the ionization of acetic acid, which is a weak electrolyte,

$$HC_2H_3O_2 + H_2O \rightleftharpoons H_3O^+ + C_2H_3O_2^-$$

or

$$HC_2H_3O_2 \rightleftharpoons H^+ + C_2H_3O_2^-$$

we may write

$$K_i = \frac{C_{H^+} \times C_{C_2H_3O_2^-}}{C_{HC_2H_3O_2}}$$

In other words, at a given temperature, the product of the concentrations of H^+ and $C_2H_3O_2^-$ ions divided by the concentration of undissociated acetic acid must have a constant numerical value.[1] A small value for K_i means that the numerator is small as compared to the denominator, which, of course, means that the concentrations of H^+ ions and $C_2H_3O_2^-$ ions are relatively small as compared with the concentration of undissociated acetic acid. Thus the ionization constant is a measure of the extent of the dissociation and in the case of acids would be a measure of their strength, since the strength of an acid is determined by its ability to produce H^+ ions.

Obviously, if the concentrations of ions and undissociated molecules are known, K_i may be calculated. For example, in .1 molar acetic acid solution at 25° C. the acid ionizes to the extent of about 1.3 per cent. Since each molecule of acetic acid which ionizes produces one H^+ ion and one $C_2H_3O_2^-$ ion, the concentrations in the solution would be

$$C_{H^+} = .1 \times .013 = .0013 \text{ mole per liter}$$

and

$$C_{C_2H_3O_2^-} = .1 \times .013 = .0013 \text{ mole per liter}$$
$$C_{HC_2H_3O_2} = .1 - .0013 = .0937 \text{ mole per liter}$$

Substituting in the above formulation for K_i

$$K_i = \frac{C_{H^+} \times C_{C_2H_3O_2^-}}{C_{HC_2H_3O_2}} = \frac{.0013 \times .0013}{.0937} = .000018$$

usually written as 1.8×10^{-5}.

Below are given the ionization constants of a number of acids:

ACID	K_i
Acetic	1.86×10^{-5}
Benzoic	6.6×10^{-5}
Carbonic K_1	3×10^{-7}
Carbonic K_2	6×10^{-11}
Formic	2.1×10^{-4}
Iodic	1.9×10^{-1}
Phosphoric K_1	1.1×10^{-2}
Phosphoric K_2	2×10^{-7}
Phosphoric K_3	3.6×10^{-13}
Trichloracetic	2×10^{-1}

[1] In the equilibrium

$$HC_2H_3O_2 + H_2O \rightleftharpoons H_3O^+ + C_2H_3O_2^-$$

the concentration of H_2O in dilute solutions is essentially a constant, and this concentration term is embodied in the ionization constant, K_i, which is expressed as

$$K_i = \frac{C_{H^+} \times C_{C_2H_3O_2^-}}{C_{HC_2H_3O_2}}$$

The larger the value of K_i the stronger the acid; thus of the acids listed above, trichloracetic acid is the strongest and phosphoric acid the weakest.

It may be noted that two constants are given for carbonic acid and three for phosphoric acid. It will be recalled that acids with more than one replaceable hydrogen ionize in steps. Each successive step of the ionization is an equilibrium and thus would have a value for K. K_1 is for the first ionization step, K_2 for the second, etc. In the case of H_3PO_4

$$H_3PO_4 \rightleftharpoons H^+ + H_2PO_4^- \qquad K_1 = 1.1 \times 10^{-2}$$
$$H_2PO_4^- \rightleftharpoons H^+ + HPO_4^{--} \qquad K_2 = 2 \times 10^{-7}$$
$$HPO_4^{--} \rightleftharpoons H^+ + PO_4^{---} \qquad K_3 = 3.6 \times 10^{-13}$$

Thus H_3PO_4 is a stronger acid than $H_2PO_4^-$ which in turn is stronger than HPO_4^{--}.

The ionization of bases and their equilibrium constants would follow a similar pattern, the larger the value for the ionization constant, the stronger the base, etc.

Common ion effect. At a given temperature the relationship given above for acetic acid

$$K_i = \frac{C_{H^+} \times C_{C_2H_3O_2^-}}{C_{HC_2H_3O_2}}$$

must hold for all solutions of acetic acid. If the equilibrium is disturbed by changing the concentration of either H^+, $C_2H_3O_2^-$, or $HC_2H_3O_2$, the concentrations of the other two will adjust themselves in such a way that K retains its constant value. For example, if more acetate ion were added, the value for the concentration of H^+ would necessarily have to decrease, which in turn would cause an increase in the value of concentration of $HC_2H_3O_2$ in order that K remain constant. The addition of an ion which is the same as one already present in the equilibrium is termed the *common ion effect*. Thus in the above the acetate is the common ion and its effect is to shift the equilibrium resulting in a decrease of concentration of H^+ ions. Assuming that sodium acetate is the source of added acetate ion, the equations may be represented:

$$HC_2H_3O_2 \rightleftharpoons H^+ + \boxed{C_2H_3O_2^-}$$
$$NaC_2H_3O_2 \longrightarrow Na^+ + \boxed{C_2H_3O_2^-}$$

The ionization of acetic acid is repressed and since the hydrogen ion concentration is decreased, the acidity of the solution is decreased.

By regulating the amount of sodium acetate added to a solution of acetic acid, the acidity may readily be controlled. Careful control of acidity is extremely important in many chemical processes and often *common ion effect* is the basis for such control.

In a similar manner the addition of a common ion to a weak base reduces the alkalinity of the solution. For example, if NH_4Cl is added to a solution of NH_4OH, the concentration of OH^- is decreased:

$$NH_3 + H_2O \rightleftharpoons \boxed{NH_4^+} + OH^-$$
$$NH_4Cl \longrightarrow \boxed{NH_4^+} + Cl^-$$

Study the following sample calculations.

EXAMPLE 1. The ionization constant for acetic acid is 1.8×10^{-5}.
(a) Calculate the concentration of H^+ ions in a 0.1 molar solution of acetic acid

$$K_i = \frac{C_{H^+} \times C_{C_2H_3O_2^-}}{C_{HC_2H_3O_2}} = 1.8 \times 10^{-5}$$

Since each molecule of $HC_2H_3O_2$ which ionizes produces one H^+ ion and one $C_2H_3O_2^-$ ion,

$$C_{C_2H_3O_2^-} = C_{H^+}$$

Substituting in the above

$$K_i = \frac{C_{H^+} \times C_{H^+}}{0.1} = 1.8 \times 10^{-5}$$
$$C^2_{H^+} = (1 \times 10^{-1})(1.8 \times 10^{-5}) = 1.8 \times 10^{-6}$$
$$C_{H^+} = \sqrt{1.8 \times 10^{-6}} = 1.34 \times 10^{-3}$$

(b) Calculate the concentration of H^+ ions in a 0.1 molar solution of acetic acid in which the concentration of acetate ions has been increased to 1 molar by addition of sodium acetate.

$$K_i = \frac{C_{H^+} \times C_{C_2H_3O_2^-}}{C_{HC_2H_3O_2}} = 1.8 \times 10^{-5}$$

$$C_{H^+} = ? \qquad C_{C_2H_3O_2^-} = 1 \qquad C_{HC_2H_3O_2} = 0.1$$

Substituting

$$\frac{C_{H^+} \times 1}{0.1} = 1.8 \times 10^{-5}$$
$$C_{H^+} = (1.8 \times 10^{-5})(1 \times 10^{-1}) = 1.8 \times 10^{-6}$$

The concentration of H^+ has been decreased from 1.34×10^{-3} to 1.8×10^{-6} mole per liter by the common ion effect.

EXAMPLE 2. The ionization constant for NH_4OH is 1.76×10^{-5}. (a) Calculate the concentration of OH^- ions in a 1.0 molar solution of NH_4OH.

$$K_i = \frac{C_{NH_4^+} \times C_{OH^-}}{C_{NH_4OH}} = 1.76 \times 10^{-5}$$

$$C_{NH_4^+} = C_{OH^-} \qquad C_{NH_4OH} = 1$$

Substituting

$$K_i = \frac{C_{OH^-} \times C_{OH^-}}{1} = 1.76 \times 10^{-5}$$

$$C^2_{OH^-} = 1.76 \times 10^{-5} \quad \text{or} \quad 17.6 \times 10^{-6}$$

$$C_{OH^-} = \sqrt{17.6 \times 10^{-6}} = 4.2 \times 10^{-3}$$

(b) Calculate the concentration of OH^- ions in a 1.0 molar solution of NH_4OH to which 0.1 mole of NH_4Cl is added to one liter of solution.

$$K_i = \frac{C_{NH_4^+} \times C_{OH^-}}{C_{NH_4OH}} = 1.76 \times 10^{-5}$$

Since NH_4Cl is a salt and 100 per cent ionized, 0.1 mole of NH_4Cl would give 0.1 mole of NH_4^+.

Then

$$C_{NH_4^+} = 0.1 \qquad C_{NH_4OH} = 1 \qquad C_{OH^-} = ?$$

Substituting

$$K_i = \frac{0.1 \times C_{OH^-}}{1} = 1.76 \times 10^{-5}$$

$$C_{OH^-} = \frac{1.76 \times 10^{-5}}{1 \times 10^{-1}} = 1.76 \times 10^{-4}$$

The concentration of OH^- has been decreased from 4.2×10^{-3} to 1.76×10^{-4} moles per liter by the common ion effect.

NOTE: In the above the relatively small concentration of NH_4^+ present from the ionization of NH_4OH is neglected, since it is small in comparison to the 0.1 mole of NH_4^+, added as NH_4Cl.

Buffer solutions. An important application of the common ion principle is the preparation of buffer solutions. They may be prepared from a combination of a weak acid and a salt of the weak acid, e.g., acetic acid and sodium acetate, or a weak base and a salt of the base, e.g., NH_4OH and NH_4Cl. Such solutions are resistant to changes in acidity or basicity. Consider the addition of a strong acid, e.g., HCl, to a solution of $HC_2H_3O_2$ and $NaC_2H_3O_2$.

$$NaC_2H_3O_2 \longrightarrow Na^+ + \boxed{\begin{array}{c} C_2H_3O_2^- \\ H^+ \end{array}}$$
$$HCl \rightleftharpoons Cl^- +$$
$$\downarrow$$
$$HC_2H_3O_2$$

Even though a relatively high concentration of H^+ is added, the hydrogen ion concentration of the solution cannot be altered appreciably since the excess $C_2H_3O_2^-$ ions in the solution react with the added H^+ ions to form slightly ionized acetic acid. Thus the acidity remains essentially unchanged. In a somewhat similar way, the addition of OH^- ions to this same solution would not appreciably alter the acidity since the added OH^- ions would combine with H^+ ions to form undissociated H_2O molecules.

$$HC_2H_3O_2 \rightleftharpoons \boxed{\begin{array}{c} H^+ \\ OH^- \end{array}} \begin{array}{c} + C_2H_3O_2^- \\ + Na^+ \end{array}$$
$$NaOH \longrightarrow$$
$$\downarrow$$
$$H_2O$$

Although the number of H^+ ions in the solution is relatively small, they would be produced as needed by the dissociation of the acetic acid present.

The student should reason out for himself how a solution of a weak base and a salt of that base would act in resisting a change in alkalinity on addition of either H^+ or OH^- ions.

Buffers are important in many biological processes. Phosphates in the blood act as buffer salts since excess acid is neutralized by formation of relatively undissociated phosphoric acid. Thus the H^+ concentration of the blood is maintained at a nearly constant value.

Hydrogen ion concentration. The hydrogen ion concentration is a measure of the acidity of a solution and is usually expressed in terms of moles per liter of solution.

In the biological sciences, the pH[1] method for expressing hydrogen ion concentration is employed. We may best illustrate this method with some actual examples: Let us consider the hydrogen ion concentration in solutions of hydrochloric acid. Hydrochloric acid is a strong acid and therefore nearly completely ionized. Assuming complete ionization, a solution of .01 M HCl will produce a 0.01 molar concentration of hydrogen ions; a solution of 0.001 M HCl gives a hydrogen ion concentration of 0.001 molar, etc. These concentrations may be expressed as 10^{-2} and 10^{-3} (.01 $= 10^{-2}$ and .001 $= 10^{-3}$) respectively. The pH of the solution is taken as the exponent with its sign reversed.[2] Thus a solution of hydrogen ion concentration 10^{-2}

---

[1] pH was originally proposed as a measure of hydrogen ion concentration. Although the term "hydrogen ion concentration" is still in common usage, the ion which is actually responsible for acidity is the hydronium ion, i.e., the hydrated H^+, H_3O^+.

[2] pH is defined as the negative logarithm of the hydrogen ion concentration, i.e., $pH = -\log C_{H^+}$. Thus if $C_{H^+} = 10^{-2}$, $pH = -\log 10^{-2} = -(-2) = 2$.

would have a pH of 2, a solution of hydrogen ion concentration 10^{-3} has a pH of 3, etc. Note that a change of one unit in pH corresponds to ten times the change in hydrogen ion concentration. The solution of pH 2 contains ten times the concentration of hydrogen ions as the solution pH 3. A study of Table 19 will further reveal the relationship between hydrogen ion concentration and pH. It may be noted from the table that the pH of the solution increases as the concentration of hydrogen ion decreases.

TABLE 19

HYDROGEN ION CONCENTRATIONS OF SOLUTIONS OF HCl

CONCENTRATION OF HCl IN MOLES PER LITER	CONCENTRATION OF HYDROGEN ION	pH
0.1	$0.1 = 10^{-1}$	1
0.01	$0.01 = 10^{-2}$	2
0.001	$0.001 = 10^{-3}$	3
0.0001	$0.0001 = 10^{-4}$	4
0.00001	$0.00001 = 10^{-5}$	5
0.000001	$0.000001 = 10^{-6}$	6
0.0000001	$0.0000001 = 10^{-7}$	7

The ionization of water. Pure water is classed as a very poor conductor of electricity. This is emphasized by the fact that liquid mercury is about 25,000,000 times as good a conductor as water. The low conductivity of water may be attributed to its very slight ionization in accordance with the reaction:

$$H_2O \rightleftharpoons H^+ + OH^-$$

Evidence indicates that but one molecule of water in 555,000,000 is ionized. This corresponds to 1 mole of H^+ and also 1 mole of OH^- per 10,000,000 liters of water. Consequently in pure water

$$C_{H^+} = C_{OH^-} = \frac{1 \text{ mole}}{10,000,000 \text{ liters}} = \frac{1}{10^7} = 1 \times 10^{-7} \text{ mole per liter}$$

Hence the pH of pure water is 7, and since equal numbers of H^+ and OH^- ions are present, this pH represents a neutral solution.

Applying the law of mass action to the above equilibrium,

$$K_1 = \frac{C_{H^+} \times C_{OH^-}}{C_{H_2O}}$$

The concentration of H_2O can usually be considered a constant in dilute solutions; hence $K_1 \times C_{H_2O}$ is a constant and may be represented by another constant K_w. The value of K_w at ordinary temperatures is 10^{-14}. This value is the product of the concentrations of hydrogen ion and hydroxyl ion in any water solution.

$$K_w = C_{H^+} \times C_{OH^-} = 1 \times 10^{-14}$$

Let us suppose that an acid is added to water until the hydrogen ion concentration is 10^{-3} ($pH = 3$). The increase in hydrogen ion concentration displaces the equilibrium above to the left and results in a decrease in the concentration of OH^-. The value of the concentration of OH^- in the solution must be 10^{-11}, since $10^{-3} \times 10^{-11} = 10^{-14}$. Students frequently think of an acid as containing hydrogen ions but no hydroxyl ions. It is evident from the above that any aqueous solution of an acid also contains hydroxyl ions. Likewise, any basic or alkaline solution contains not only hydroxyl ions but hydrogen ions as well. A solution in which the concentration of OH^- is 10^{-4} must have a hydrogen ion concentration of 10^{-10}. The pH of this latter solution would be 10, and since the C_{OH^-} is greater than C_{H^+}, the solution is basic. Summarizing, a solution of pH 7 is neutral; a solution of pH less than 7 is acid; and one of pH greater than 7 is alkaline.

```
        Increasing Acidity        Increasing Basicity
    0 ◄─────────────────── 7 ───────────────────► 14
                        Neutral
```

A careful control of pH is important in many biological processes. Most of the body fluids in a healthy individual have a pH very near to 7. The gastric juice is an exception, having a pH of about 2 which means it is quite acid. pH is important in the growth of bacteria, certain pH values representing optimum conditions for growth. The utility of soil for growing certain crops depends upon its acidity or alkalinity (its pH). Technicians use the so-called pH meter, which measures pH with an accuracy approaching 0.01, and in the range 0–14. This device is essentially an electrolytic cell, in which the voltage varies with H^+ concentration.

Indicators. Certain organic substances undergo a change in color at rather definite pH values. For example, methyl orange has a red or orange color in solutions with a pH of 3 or less and a yellow color in solutions of pH more than 4. Phenolphthalein changes from colorless to red violet at a pH of 9 to 10. Such substances are called *indicators* and may be used to determine the approximate pH of a solution. Some of the more common indicators and color changes at various pH values are shown in Table 20.

TABLE 20

COLOR CHANGES IN INDICATORS AT VARIOUS pH VALUES [1]

INDICATOR	0	1	2	3	4	5	6	7	8	9	10	11	12	13	14
Methyl violet	Y	///	BV	BV	BV	BV	V	V	V	V	V	V	V	V	V
Meta-cresol purple	R	R	///	Y	Y	Y	Y	Y	///	Pu	Pu	Pu	Pu	Pu	Pu
Thymol blue	R	R	///	Y	Y	Y	Y	Y	Y	///	B	B	B	B	B
Methyl orange	R	R	R	R	///	Y	Y	Y	Y	Y	Y	Y	Y	Y	Y
Congo red	B	B	B	B	///	R	R	R	R	R	R	R	R	R	R
p-Nitrophenol	C	C	C	C	C	C	///	Y	Y	Y	Y	Y	Y	Y	Y
Rosolic acid	A	A	A	A	A	A	A	P	P	P	P	P	P	P	P
Phenolphthalein	C	C	C	C	C	C	C	C	C	///	V	V	V	V	V
Malachite green	BG	BG	LG	BG	BG	BG	BG	BG	BG	BG	BG	BG	///	C	C

A	amber	C	colorless	R	red
B	blue	P	pink	V	violet
BG	blue green	Pu	purple	Y	yellow
BV	blue violet				

[1] The shading in the squares signifies that the indicator is changing in color, and shows the pH range over which the color change takes place.

To illustrate the use of indicators in determining approximate pH, suppose a given solution gives no color with p-nitrophenol and a red color with congo red indicator. Inspection of Table 20 shows that the pH of the solution must be approximately 5.

In order to choose the proper indicator to use in any given titration of acids and bases, one must know the pH of the solution when equivalent amounts of the acid and base are present. For example, the pH of the solution resulting from neutralization of acetic acid with sodium hydroxide is 8.5, the same as would be obtained if pure sodium acetate were dissolved in water. Phenolphthalein changes color at a pH of about 9 and may be used satisfactorily in this titration. Actually in the titration of strong acids and strong bases, any indicator which changes in a pH range of 5 to 9 may be used, but in the titration of weak acids and weak bases, the indicator must be carefully chosen to insure accuracy of a determination.

Solubility product principle. If solid AgCl is shaken with water, Ag^+ and Cl^- ions from the crystal lattice of the solid pass into solution until the solution becomes saturated. In the saturated solution thus formed an equilibrium exists between the ions in solution and the ions present in the solid crystal lattice:

$$AgCl_{\text{solid}} \rightleftharpoons Ag^+ + Cl^-$$

The amount of AgCl dissolved depends upon the temperature; at a given temperature the solubility of a substance is a constant.

Applying the law of mass action to the above equilibrium we may write:

$$K = \frac{C_{Ag^+} \times C_{Cl^-}}{C_{AgCl}}$$

The term in the denominator refers to the concentration of solid AgCl and as used here may be considered a measure of the tendency of the solid to pass into solution. Since this tendency at a given temperature is independent of the amount of solid AgCl present, this term may be incorporated in the constant K to give a new constant $K_{s.p.}$.

$$K_{s.p.} = C_{Ag^+} \times C_{Cl^-}$$

where $K_{s.p.}$ is the *solubility product constant*. In other words the product of the concentrations of ions in a saturated solution of a relatively insoluble salt, such as AgCl, at a given temperature is a constant. This is known as the *solubility product principle*.

The numerical value for $K_{s.p.}$ can readily be calculated if the concentrations of ions in the saturated solution are known. If a saturated solution of AgCl is prepared at 25° the solubility by analysis is found to be 1.06×10^{-5} mole per liter. AgCl is completely ionized, hence each AgCl will give one Ag^+ and one Cl^- ion in solution; consequently the concentration of Ag^+ ions will be 1.06×10^{-5} mole per liter and likewise the concentration of Cl^- ions will be 1.06×10^{-5} mole per liter. Substituting these concentrations in the solubility product formulation

$$K_{s.p.} = C_{Ag^+} \times C_{Cl^-}$$
$$K_{s.p.} = (1.06 \times 10^{-5})(1.06 \times 10^{-5}) = 1.1 \times 10^{-10}$$

The value for $K_{s.p.}$ is a measure of the solubility of a substance; the larger the value of $K_{s.p.}$ the greater must be the concentrations of ions and hence the greater the solubility of the substance. Likewise the smaller the value of $K_{s.p.}$ the more insoluble the substance.

In the event that more than two ions are produced from the ionization, two or more of which are alike, the concentration of that particular ion must be raised to that power which corresponds to the coefficient of the ion in the balanced equation as called for by the law of mass action. To illustrate

$$PbCl_2 \rightleftharpoons Pb^{++} + 2\,Cl^-$$
$$K_{s.p.} = C_{Pb^{++}} \times C^2_{Cl^-}$$

The solubility of $PbCl_2$ in water at 20° is 10.84 g. per liter. Since the molecular weight of $PbCl_2$ is 278

$$10.84 \text{ g.} = .039 \text{ mole}$$
$$C_{Pb^{++}} = 3.9 \times 10^{-2} \text{ mole per liter}$$

Since each $PbCl_2$ yields two Cl^-

$$C_{Cl^-} = 2 \times .039 = 7.8 \times 10^{-2} \text{ mole per liter}$$
$$K_{s.p.} = (3.9 \times 10^{-2})(7.8 \times 10^{-2})^2 = 2.4 \times 10^{-4}$$

A partial list of solubility product constants is given in Table 21.

TABLE 21

SOLUBILITY PRODUCT CONSTANTS

Compound	$K_{s.p.}$	Compound	$K_{s.p.}$
AgCl	1.1×10^{-10}	BaSO$_4$	1.0×10^{-10}
PbCrO$_4$	1.7×10^{-14}	HgS	4.0×10^{-53}
Fe(OH)$_3$	1.1×10^{-36}	CuS	8.5×10^{-45}
BaCrO$_4$	2.3×10^{-10}	CdS	3.6×10^{-29}
CaC$_2$O$_4$	3.9×10^{-9}	PbS	4.2×10^{-28}
SrSO$_4$	3.6×10^{-7}	ZnS	1.2×10^{-23}
PbCl$_2$	2.4×10^{-4}	FeS	1.5×10^{-19}
AgBr	4.0×10^{-13}	MnS	1.4×10^{-15}

Application of solubility product principle to formation of precipitates. The formation of a precipitate depends first upon the formation of a saturated solution; only when the solubility of the substance is exceeded can a precipitate form. $K_{s.p.}$ is directly related to the solubility of a substance since it is equal to the product of ion concentrations in a saturated solution. Any solution in which the product of the ion concentrations exceeds $K_{s.p.}$ is supersaturated and precipitation will occur until the solution is saturated, in which case the product of ion concentrations attains the value of $K_{s.p.}$. Any solution in which the ion product is less than $K_{s.p.}$ is unsaturated and is capable of dissolving more of the solute.

In the case of AgCl, when the product of the concentration of Ag^+ ions and the concentration of Cl^- ions exceeds 1.1×10^{-10}, the salt will precipitate. In a water solution of AgCl the concentrations of Ag^+ and Cl^- ions are the same, namely, 1.06×10^{-5} mole per liter. However, it is not necessary that the concentrations of the ions have equivalent values to bring about precipitation, so long as the product of these ion concentrations exceeds $K_{s.p.}$.

Suppose we know the concentration of Ag^+ ions in a certain solution to be 1×10^{-7} mole per liter. We can calculate the concentration of Cl^- ions necessary to bring about precipitation. Substituting in the equation

$$K_{s.p.} = C_{Ag^+} \times C_{Cl^-} = 1.1 \times 10^{-10}$$

solving for C_{Cl^-}

$$C_{Cl^-} = \frac{1.1 \times 10^{-10}}{1 \times 10^{-7}} = 1.1 \times 10^{-3}$$

This concentration of Cl^- ions will just form a saturated solution, but any value of the concentration of Cl^- ions larger than 1.1×10^{-3} will cause a precipitate of AgCl to form.

It was shown above that the solubility of AgCl in water was 1.06×10^{-5} mole per liter, while the solubility in a solution in which the concentration of Cl^- ions is 1.1×10^{-3} is only 1×10^{-7} mole per liter; in other words, by using an excess of Cl^- the solubility of the salt has been decreased nearly a hundredfold. In the precipitation of ions from solution in qualitative and quantitative analysis, a large excess of the precipitating ion is used to reduce markedly the solubility of the substance and cause it to precipitate. Study the following illustrations:

EXAMPLE 1. With the aid of Table 21 above, calculate the minimum concentration of Br^- ion necessary to bring about precipitation of AgBr from a solution in which the concentration of Ag^+ ion is 1×10^{-5} mole per liter.

$$K_{s.p.} \text{ for AgBr} = C_{Ag^+} \times C_{Br^-} = 4 \times 10^{-13}$$

Substituting for C_{Ag^+}

$$(1 \times 10^{-5})(C_{Br^-}) = 4 \times 10^{-13}$$
$$C_{Br^-} = \frac{4 \times 10^{-13}}{1 \times 10^{-5}} = 4 \times 10^{-8}$$

This value for the concentration of Br^- would just form a saturated solution, but any value larger than this would cause precipitation of AgBr.

EXAMPLE 2. Will precipitation occur if .01 mole of Ba^{++} is added to a liter of solution containing .05 mole of SO_4^{--}?

$$K_{s.p.} \text{ for BaSO}_4 = C_{Ba^{++}} \times C_{SO_4^{--}} = 1 \times 10^{-10}$$
$$C_{Ba^{++}} = .01 \text{ mole per liter} = 1 \times 10^{-2} \text{ mole per liter}$$
$$C_{SO_4^{--}} = .05 \text{ mole per liter} = 5 \times 10^{-2} \text{ mole per liter}$$
$$\text{Trial product } (1 \times 10^{-2})(5 \times 10^{-2}) = 5 \times 10^{-4}$$

5×10^{-4} is larger than 1×10^{-10}, hence precipitation of $BaSO_4$ will take place.

EXAMPLE 3. After precipitation of $BaSO_4$ from a liter of solution which originally contained .01 mole of Ba^{++}, the concentration of SO_4^{--} was found to be .1 mole per liter. How much $BaSO_4$ was precipitated?

First calculate the concentration of Ba^{++} in the solution after precipitation:

$$K_{s.p.} = C_{Ba^{++}} \times C_{SO_4^{--}} = 1 \times 10^{-10}$$

$$C_{Ba^{++}} \text{ left in solution} = \frac{1 \times 10^{-10}}{.1} = 1 \times 10^{-9} \text{ mole per liter}$$

Number of moles precipitated $= .01 - .000000001 = .009999999$

The solubility product principle is applicable only to solutions of slightly soluble salts. Experimental studies show that it does not hold for soluble or moderately soluble salts.

The dissolving of precipitates. Just as a precipitate is formed when the product of ion concentrations exceeds $K_{s.p.}$, so a precipitate must dissolve when the ion concentrations are decreased sufficiently to give an ion product less than $K_{s.p.}$. Anything which will lower the concentrations of ions in the solution will disturb the equilibrium with the undissolved solid. To re-establish equilibrium by replenishing the supply of ions, more solid will pass into solution. This process will continue until all the solid has dissolved, providing the concentrations of ions are continuously lowered. Decreasing the concentration of ions in solution may be accomplished in the following ways:

(a) Dilution; as a solution is diluted, the concentrations become less and more solid passes into solution.

(b) Addition of a reagent which forms an undissociated substance with one of the ions of the solid, e.g., addition of HCl to a precipitate of calcium oxalate forms slightly dissociated oxalic acid:

$$\begin{array}{l} CaC_2O_4 \underset{\text{solid}}{\rightleftharpoons} Ca^{++} + \boxed{\begin{array}{l} C_2O_4^{--} \\ \\ 2\,H^+ \end{array}} \\ 2\,HCl \longrightarrow 2\,Cl^- + \\ \qquad\qquad\qquad\qquad \searrow H_2C_2O_4 \end{array}$$

As $C_2O_4^{--}$ ions are removed by combination with H^+ ions, more CaC_2O_4 passes into solution to replenish the supply of $C_2O_4^{--}$ ions; if sufficient HCl is present all of the precipitate will dissolve.

(c) Addition of a reagent which reacts with the solid to form a gas which is insoluble and escapes from solution; e.g., ferrous sulfide is soluble in HCl:

$$\text{FeS} \rightleftharpoons \text{Fe}^{++} + \boxed{\text{S}^{--} \quad \longrightarrow \text{H}_2\text{S}}$$
$$\underset{\text{solid}}{} \quad 2\,\text{HCl} \longrightarrow 2\,\text{Cl}^- + \boxed{2\,\text{H}^+}$$

Hydrolysis. Although water is only slightly ionized according to the equation

$$\text{H}_2\text{O} \rightleftharpoons \text{H}^+ + \text{OH}^- \tag{1}$$

the few H^+ ions and OH^- ions produced may become of primary importance in aqueous solutions of certain salts. As long as the number of H^+ ions is equal to the number of OH^- ions the solution is neutral. However, if something is added which furnishes either of the ions or which uses up either of the ions, then one of the two ions is present in excess — if excess H^+ ions are present the solution is acid; if excess OH^- ions are present then the solution is basic.

Ions of salts may disturb the equilibrium in aqueous solution and as a result the solution is actually acidic or basic depending on whether H^+ or OH^- ions are present in excess. This reaction of the ions of a salt with water is termed *hydrolysis*. We may illustrate hydrolysis with a few examples:

(*a*) *Sodium carbonate.* An aqueous solution of this salt tests basic toward litmus indicating an excess of OH^- ions present in the solution. This may readily be explained as follows: Sodium carbonate, a salt derived from the strong base, sodium hydroxide, and the weak acid, carbonic acid, is completely ionized into Na^+ and CO_3^{--}. CO_3^{--} ions have a great affinity for protons to form the weak (slightly ionized) acid, HCO_3^-; consequently protons are removed from solution by the reaction

$$\text{H}^+ + \text{CO}_3^{--} \longrightarrow \text{HCO}_3^-$$

As a result the equilibrium in (1) above is shifted in the direction of a higher concentration of OH^- ions which gives the solution an alkaline reaction. Meanwhile there has been no tendency for Na^+ and OH^- ions to combine since NaOH is a strong base. The equation for the reaction may be represented

$$2\,\text{Na}^+ + \text{CO}_3^{--} + \text{H}_2\text{O} \rightleftharpoons 2\,\text{Na}^+ + \text{OH}^- + \text{HCO}_3^- \tag{2}$$
or
$$\text{CO}_3^{--} + \text{H}_2\text{O} \rightleftharpoons \text{OH}^- + \text{HCO}_3^-$$

since Na^+ ions may be canceled out. A solution of Na_2CO_3 is only weakly alkaline as the equilibrium in (2) above is far to the left. The extent of hydrolysis is said to be slight.

(b) *Ammonium chloride.* The ions present in the solution are H^+, OH^-, NH_4^+, Cl^-. There is very little tendency for H^+ to unite with Cl^- since HCl is a strong acid. However NH_4^+ readily combines with OH^-, since NH_4OH (or $NH_3 + H_2O$) is a weak base. Accordingly an excess of H^+ ions are left in solution, which reacts acid to litmus. The reaction may be represented

$$NH_4^+ + Cl^- + H_2O \rightleftharpoons NH_4OH + H^+ + Cl^- \qquad (3)$$

or

$$NH_4^+ + H_2O \rightleftharpoons NH_4OH + H^+$$

since Cl^- may be canceled out.

(c) *Sodium chloride.* Ions present in the solution are Na^+, Cl^-, H^+, OH^-. Since both NaOH and HCl are strong electrolytes, there is little if any tendency for either to be formed. Hence the concentrations of H^+ and OH^- ions remain about equal and the resulting solution is approximately neutral. The hydrolysis of a salt derived from a strong acid and strong base is negligible.

(d) *Ammonium acetate.* The aqueous solution contains NH_4^+, $C_2H_3O_2^-$, H^+, and OH^- ions. This salt is highly hydrolyzed (reaction far to the right) since both acetic acid and ammonium hydroxide are weak electrolytes:

$$NH_4^+ + C_2H_3O_2^- + H_2O \rightleftharpoons NH_4OH + HC_2H_3O_2 \qquad (4)$$

Both ammonium hydroxide and acetic acid are of about the same strength as electrolytes, consequently about the same number of H^+ and OH^- ions are left in solution, which is approximately neutral.

(e) *Copper sulfate.* Salts of most of the heavy metals contain hydrated ions and such ions may furnish protons to the solution and give it an acidic reaction. For example, copper sulfate in solution gives $Cu(H_2O)_4^{++}$ and SO_4^{--} ions. There would be little tendency for SO_4^{--} to combine with H^+ since H_2SO_4 is a strong acid. However, the hydrated cupric ions may react with water to form H^+ ions:

$$Cu(H_2O)_4^{++} + H_2O \rightleftharpoons Cu(H_2O)_3OH^+ + H_3O^+ \ (H^+ + H_2O) \qquad (5)$$

Thus a solution of this salt is slightly acidic because of the excess H^+ ions present.

It is evident from the above that whether or not the aqueous solution of a salt is acidic, basic, or neutral depends upon the strength of the acid and base from which the salt may be considered to be derived. A knowledge of the strength of acids and bases, therefore, is essential in predicting the effects of hydrolysis. Of the common acids, only HNO_3, H_2SO_4, and the hydrohalogen acids (except HF) are strong.

Likewise the strong bases in aqueous solution are KOH, NaOH, $Ca(OH)_2$, and $Ba(OH)_2$; others are weak. We may summarize the possible hydrolysis effects as follows:

1. Salt of strong acid and strong base. Solution is approximately neutral, pH about 7.
2. Salt of weak acid and weak base. Solution is approximately neutral, pH about 7. The pH will depend upon the relative strengths of the weak acid and the base.
3. Salt of weak acid and strong base. Alkaline solution, pH greater than 7.
4. Salt of strong acid and weak base. Acid solution, pH less than 7.

Conventions used in writing ionic equations. Certain arbitrary conventions must be adopted in writing ionic equations, since both molecules and ions for a given substance may exist in the aqueous solution. It is customary to show the substance in its predominate form, unless it is desired to emphasize either the molecular or ionic form of the substance. Therefore, weak electrolytes which are only slightly ionized will be shown in the equation in molecular form unless particular attention wants to be drawn to the relatively few ions from these substances. For example, H_2O, $HC_2H_3O_2$, NH_4OH, H_3PO_4, etc. will ordinarily be shown in molecular form. Of course, in the consideration of equilibrium constants such as were discussed earlier in this chapter, the relatively few ions in solution are of paramount importance and the equilibrium in solution between molecules and ions must be shown.

It is also customary to represent a substance which is not in solution, *e.g.*, a solid or gas, in molecular form. Thus sodium chloride in the solid state would be represented as NaCl, whereas in solution it would be shown as Na^+ and Cl^-. A substance precipitating from solution would be shown in molecular form and its insolubility is usually designated by a downward arrow, *e.g.*, $AgCl \downarrow$. Substances other than electrolytes, of course, are never shown in ionic form.

It is probable that all ions in aqueous solution are hydrated to some degree. In general, however, the exact amount of water of hydration is not known. Consequently we shall ordinarily show the ion in its anhydrous form; particular attention has already been called to the hydrated hydrogen ion or hydronium ion.

In writing ionic equations, some instructors prefer to show in the equation all the ions present in the system, even though some of them may not actually take part in the reaction; others prefer to show only the ions which enter into the chemical change. The latter has advantages in that the equations are considerably simplified and furthermore a single equation may represent a number of chemical changes; for example, as already pointed out, the simple combination of H^+ and OH^- to form H_2O represents the actual change in neutralization reactions. A disadvantage of not showing all the ions present is that a subsequent treatment of the system might involve some ions not taking part in the primary reaction. Under such conditions it would be desirable to have information on all ions or molecular species present in a system.

EXERCISES

1. What determines the strength of an acid? a base?

2. Define the terms acid and base from the modern viewpoint.

3. Explain the effect of the addition of ammonium acetate to a solution containing acetic acid.

4. List five salts whose water solutions test acid to litmus; five whose water solutions test basic to litmus.

5. How would water solutions of the following salts test with litmus?

(a) $KC_2H_3O_2$
(b) $(NH_4)_3PO_4$
(c) $CuBr_2$
(d) $NaCN$
(e) $ZnSO_4$
(f) KCl
(g) $BiCl_3$
(h) Na_2S
(i) $Al(C_2H_3O_2)_3$
(j) $Zn(NO_3)_2$

6. Explain how indicators may be used to determine the approximate pH of a solution.

7. What would be the effect of adding each of the following to a solution of ammonium hydroxide: (a) solid NH_4Cl; (b) HCl; (c) solid KOH?

8. Explain with the aid of an equation or equations how acids produce ions in a solution.

9. Write an ionic equation for:

(a) the neutralization of phosphoric acid with potassium hydroxide.
(b) the reaction of silver nitrate and ferric chloride solutions.
(c) the addition of hydrogen chloride gas to water.
(d) the reaction between zinc and hydrochloric acid.

10. After copying (a)–(j), complete and balance the equations and by use of one of the following sets of arrows indicate comparative concentration of chemicals involved at equilibrium.

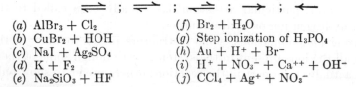

(a) $AlBr_3 + Cl_2$
(b) $CuBr_2 + HOH$
(c) $NaI + Ag_2SO_4$
(d) $K + F_2$
(e) $Na_2SiO_3 + HF$
(f) $Br_2 + H_2O$
(g) Step ionization of H_3PO_4
(h) $Au + H^+ + Br^-$
(i) $H^+ + NO_3^- + Ca^{++} + OH^-$
(j) $CCl_4 + Ag^+ + NO_3^-$

11. From the following ionization constants, indicate the strongest acid and the weakest:

Nitrous acid: 4×10^{-4} Butyric acid: 1.5×10^{-5}
Arsenious acid: 6×10^{-10} Fumaric acid: 1×10^{-3}

12. Calculate the concentration of hydrogen ion in one liter of .3 molar acetic acid to which .1 mole of sodium acetate has been added. K_i for $HC_2H_3O_2 = 1.8 \times 10^{-5}$.   Ans. 5.4×10^{-5}.

13. Calculate the concentration of hydroxyl ion in one liter of .25 molar NH_4OH which contains .05 mole NH_4Cl. K_i for $NH_4OH = 1.75 \times 10^{-5}$.
     Ans. 8.7×10^{-5}.

14. Calculate the hydrogen ion concentration of .1 molar lactic acid $(HC_3H_5O_3)$ solution. K_i for lactic acid $= 1.4 \times 10^{-4}$.   Ans. 3.7×10^{-2}.

15. Calculate the concentration of OH^- in .01 molar NH_4OH solution. K_i for $NH_4OH = 1.75 \times 10^{-5}$.   Ans. 4.2×10^{-4}.

16. Given $K_{s.p.}$ for the following compounds:

COMPOUND	$K_{s.p.}$
$PbCrO_4$	1.8×10^{-14}
MnS	1.4×10^{-15}
ZnS	1.2×10^{-73}
CuS	8.5×10^{-45}
$PbCO_3$	3.3×10^{-14}

List the compounds according to increasing solubility, placing the least soluble compound first.

17. $K_{s.p.}$ for $CaSO_4 = 6 \times 10^{-15}$. If .02 mole of Na_2SO_4 is added to a liter of solution containing 4×10^{-3} mole of calcium chloride, will $CaSO_4$ precipitate? Give reason for your answer.

18. Calculate the minimum concentration of Cl^- necessary to precipitate $AgCl$ from a solution in which the concentration of Ag^+ is 5×10^{-2}. $K_{s.p.}$ for $AgCl = 1.1 \times 10^{-10}$.   Ans. 2×10^{-9}.

19. A hypothetical acid, HA, ionizes in solution $HA \rightleftharpoons H^+ + A^-$. A salt, MA, is added to a solution of the above acid. In the resulting solution, the total hydrogen ion concentration is 1×10^{-4} gram ions per liter and the total anion concentration from the acid and salt is 5×10^{-2}. If the concentration of the undissociated acid is 2×10^{-1} mole/liter, what is (a) the ionization constant of the acid? (b) the pH of the solution? (c) the concentration of OH^- in the solution?   Ans. (a) 2.5×10^{-5} (b) 4.

20. A solution of a hypothetical salt MX_2 contains an excess of M^{++} ions and the solution is in equilibrium with solid MX_2. If the concentration of M^{++} is 2×10^{-3} gram ions per liter, and the concentration of X^- is 5×10^{-8} gram ions per liter, calculate the solubility product of the salt, MX_2.
     Ans. 5×10^{-18}.

21. A hypothetical weak base ionizes according to the equation, $MOH \rightleftharpoons M^+ + OH^-$. A salt M_2SO_4 is added. The concentration of the base is 0.01 molar and the salt 0.005 molar. Calculate (a) concentration of OH^- in the solution, (b) concentration of H^+, (c) pH of the solution.

22. Would $Fe(OH)_3$ precipitate if the ferric ion concentration in a solution is 3×10^{-24} mole per liter and hydroxyl ion is added to make an OH^- concentration of 1×10^{-5}? $K_{s.p.}$ for $Fe(OH)_3 = 1.1 \times 10^{-38}$. Explain your answer.

23. The ionization constant for an acid HX of concentration 0.01 M is 6.4×10^{-11} at 25°. Calculate the hydrogen ion concentration. What is the approximate pH of the solution?   Ans. 4.

24. Calculate the solubility product constant for Ag_2SO_4 where the molar solubility is 1.4×10^{-2} mole/liter.   Ans. 1.1×10^{-5}.

25. The ionization constant for acetic acid is 1×10^{-5}. What would be the approximate pH of a 0.1 molar acetic acid solution which contains .01 mole of sodium acetate per liter of solution?   Ans. 4.

26. The solubility of PbS in water is 2×10^{-14} mole per liter. Assuming 100 per cent ionization, what is the solubility product constant for PbS?
   Ans. 4×10^{-28}.

27. $K_{s.p.}$ for $BaSO_4$ is 1×10^{-10}. (a) Calculate the solubility of $BaSO_4$ in water. (b) What would be the solubility of $BaSO_4$ in a solution which is .01 molar with respect to sulfate ion? (c) By what factor is the solubility decreased from part (a) to part (b) above?   Ans. (a) 1×10^{-5}
   (b) 1×10^{-8} (c) .001.

28. After precipitation of $Bi(OH)_3$ from a solution of $BiCl_3$ by the addition of NH_4OH, the concentration of OH^- in the solution is 5×10^{-4} mole/liter. (a) What is the concentration of Bi^{+++} remaining in the solution? $K_{s.p.}$ for $Bi(OH)_3 = 4 \times 10^{-30}$. (b) What is the approximate pH of the solution?
   Ans. (a) 3×10^{-20} (b) 11.

29. Given the following solubility product constants

$BaSO_4$	1×10^{-10}	$PbSO_4$	2×10^{-8}
$SrSO_4$	3×10^{-7}	$RaSO_4$	1×10^{-18}
$CaSO_4$	2×10^{-5}		

If the concentration of sulfate ion is 1×10^{-7} mole/liter and the concentration of each of the above cations is .01 mole per liter, which of the cations will precipitate as the insoluble sulfate?

30. Assuming 100 per cent ionization, what would be the pH of .001 M NaOH?
   Ans. 11.

31. Give approximate pH for: 0.001 N NaOH; $Cu(NO_3)_2$ solution; a dilute solution of sugar in water; CO_2 in water; Na_3PO_4 solution; 0.001 N H_2SO_4.

32. Give approximate pH values for water solutions of: NH_3, SO_3, SO_2, O_2, CO_2.

33. In an aqueous solution of $AlCl_3$ there are: more H^+ than OH^-; more OH^- than H^+; the same number of H^+ and OH^-; neither H^+ nor OH^-.

REFERENCES

H. N. Alyea, "A Résumé of the Proton Transfer Concept of Acids and Bases," *J. Chem. Ed.* **18**, 206 (1941).

N. F. Hall, "Systems of Acids and Bases," *ibid.* **17**, 124 (1940).

L. P. Hammett, "The Theory of Acids and Bases in Analytical Chemistry," *ibid.* **17**, 131 (1940).

W. C. Johnson, "The Advantages of the Older Methods," *ibid.* **17**, 132 (1940).

K. J. Radimer, "Solution of Problems Involving Equilibrium Constants," *ibid.* **27**, 251 (1950).

Donald D. DeFord, "The Bronsted Concept in Calculations Involving Acid-Base Equilibria," *ibid.* **27**, 554 (1950).

H. T. Briscoe, "Teaching the New Concepts of Acids and Bases in General Chemistry," *ibid.* **17**, 128 (1940).

XX

Oxidation-Reduction

Chemical changes may be classified into two large groups, (1) those involving no change in valence; (2) those in which a change of valence occurs (oxidation-reduction).

Double decomposition reactions involve no change in valence and thus are in the first group. Combinations and replacements among atoms of elements do involve valence change. Many of the elements may have more than one valence and in chemical reaction change from one valence to another. Valence increase by one atom is always accompanied by an equivalent valence loss by a different atom. All chemical changes involving change in valence are termed *oxidation-reduction* reactions.

Since valence is intimately related to the electronic configuration of an atom, oxidation-reduction processes are those which involve a change in the arrangement of the electrons of an atom. Consider the combination of sodium and chlorine:

$$2\,\mathrm{Na} + \mathrm{Cl_2} \longrightarrow 2\,\mathrm{NaCl}$$

We assign a valence of zero to the elements sodium and chlorine, since the atoms in themselves are neutral and possess no charge, either positive or negative. In the chemical change, however, an electron is transferred from a sodium atom to a chlorine atom, which results in the formation of ions, Na^+ and Cl^-, in the compound, sodium chloride.

As a result of the electron interchange, sodium gains in valence, while chlorine loses in valence. That process in which an atom gives electrons (gains in positive valence) is termed *oxidation*, while the process in which an atom gains electrons (loses in positive valence) is termed *reduction*.

Oxidation and reduction are mutually dependent processes; it is obvious that if electrons are taken up by one substance, they must be

267

given up by another. There can be no oxidation without reduction, nor reduction without oxidation, taking place simultaneously.

We might represent the change above as taking place in two steps, where e represents an electron:

$$2\,\text{Na} \longrightarrow 2\,\text{Na}^+ + 2\,e\ \text{(oxidation)}$$
$$\text{Cl}_2 + 2\,e \longrightarrow 2\,\text{Cl}^-\ \text{(reduction)}$$

The first change is the oxidation step; the second the reduction step. By adding up the two steps and canceling the electrons, we obtain the net reaction which was written above in a single step. Note that each step is balanced both atomically and electrically.

Oxidizing and reducing agents. In oxidation-reduction reactions, that which is oxidized is termed the *reducing agent*, and that which is reduced is termed the *oxidizing agent*. Thus above, sodium is the reducing agent and chlorine is the oxidizing agent.

In the combination $\qquad \text{Fe} + \text{S} \longrightarrow \text{FeS}$

the iron changes in valence from 0 to $+2$ and the sulfur from 0 to -2. The two electrons which are given up by the atom of iron are taken up by the atom of sulfur in forming the compound ferrous sulfide. The iron is the reducing agent, since it has given up electrons, and the sulfur is the oxidizing agent, since it has taken up electrons. In brief:

> Oxidizing Agent = Electron Receiver = Valence Loser
> Reducing Agent = Electron Giver   = Valence Gainer

In the replacement:

$$\text{Zn} + \text{CuSO}_4\ \text{solution} \longrightarrow \text{ZnSO}_4\ \text{solution} + \text{Cu}$$
$$\text{Zn} + \text{Cu}^{++} + \text{SO}_4^{--} \longrightarrow \text{Zn}^{++} + \text{SO}_4^{--} + \text{Cu}$$

Cu^{++} is oxidizing agent — receives 2 electrons — loses 2 in valence.
Zn is reducing agent — gives 2 electrons — gains 2 in valence.

Oxidation-reduction applied to covalent compounds. We should differentiate between chemical changes in which ions are involved and those changes involving only molecules. In the former case electrons are actually transferred from one atom to another, while in changes involving molecules (covalent compounds) electrons are shared rather than transferred. Are we justified, then, in saying that covalent compounds may undergo oxidation or reduction?

Carbon combines with oxygen to form carbon dioxide:

$$\text{C} + \text{O}_2 \longrightarrow \text{CO}_2$$

It is evident from the electronic configuration of the atoms involved that no actual transfer of electrons has taken place. Four electrons of the carbon atom have been shared with two electrons from each of two oxygen atoms. We have pointed out previously that in compounds formed by sharing of electrons (covalence), while there is actually no transfer of electrons, there is likely a displacement of electrons toward one atom or the other depending upon the electropositive or electronegative character of the atoms concerned. In the compound carbon dioxide, the shared pairs of electrons probably lie closer to the oxygen atoms than to the carbon atom. On that basis we are justified in assigning carbon a valence number of $+4$ and an oxygen atom a valence number of -2. If our definition of oxidation-reduction is based on a change of valence rather than on an actual transfer of electrons, then we may properly classify reactions of covalent compounds as oxidation-reduction.

In the above change, carbon has gained in positive valence (from 0 to 4) and has therefore been oxidized; each oxygen atom has lost in positive valence (from 0 to -2) and has been reduced.

Balancing oxidation-reduction equations. In the foregoing changes we noted that electrons were given up by one substance and accepted by another. In order to balance an equation in which the arrangement of electrons is disrupted, it is necessary to balance the gain and loss of electrons. In other words, the total number of electrons given up must be equal to the number of electrons taken up. From the standpoint of valence change, the total gain in positive valence must equal the total loss in positive valence. In the reaction

$$\overset{\text{gain of 2 } e}{\underset{\text{loss of 1 } e}{2 \text{ Na} + \text{Cl}_2 \longrightarrow 2 \text{ NaCl}}}$$

it is at once evident that two sodium atoms are necessary to yield two electrons required by the chlorine molecule since each atom of chlorine needs one electron to form a chlorine ion. A neutral sodium atom on giving an electron away becomes a sodium ion and with a chlorine ion constitutes a unit in the compound sodium chloride.

Consider the reaction

$$\overset{\text{loss of 2 } e}{\underset{\text{gain of 1 } e}{\text{FeCl}_3 + \text{H}_2\text{S} \longrightarrow \text{FeCl}_2 + \text{HCl} + \text{S}}}$$

Each atom of iron loses one in positive valence, or from an electronic standpoint gains one electron. Each atom of sulfur meanwhile gains two in positive valence (loses two electrons). To balance the gain and loss, it is evident that two molecules of FeCl_3 will lose a total of two in positive valence, and one molecule of H_2S will gain two in positive valence. Thus the ratio of FeCl_3 to H_2S must be 2 to 1.

$$\overset{\overset{\text{—loss of 2 } e\text{—}}{\overbrace{}}}{\underset{\underset{\text{—gain of 1 } e\text{—}}{\underbrace{}}}{2\,FeCl_3 + H_2S}} \longrightarrow 2\,FeCl_2 + 2\,HCl + S$$

Having obtained the ratio of the oxidizing agent, $FeCl_3$, to the reducing agent, H_2S, it is an easy matter to complete the balancing of the equation. We may note in this reaction that the change in valence of the sulfur (two) is made the coefficient of the $FeCl_3$, while the change in valence of the iron (one) is made the coefficient of H_2S.

In general, we may employ the following steps in balancing oxidation-reduction equations:

1. Write the valence of each of the elements in each compound above the symbol of the element in the equation.
2. Determine which elements have changed in valence and the amount of the change. Two elements will be found to change in valence; one element gains in valence, the other loses.
3. Balance the gain and loss of valence or the gain and loss of electrons. This may be accomplished automatically by placing the number representing the change in the oxidizing agent in front of the formula for the reducing agent, and vice versa.
4. Complete the balancing of the equation, keeping in mind that the ratio of oxidizing agent to reducing agent as determined from the change in valence may not be changed. Balance hydrogen and oxygen only after all other elements have been balanced.

Let us illustrate the outlined steps by balancing an equation:

$$\overset{0 \quad +1+5-2 \quad +1+5-2 \quad +2-2 \quad +1-2}{P + HNO_3 \longrightarrow HPO_3 + NO + H_2O}$$

$$\underset{\underset{\text{—loss 5 } e\text{—}}{\underbrace{}}}{\overset{\overset{\text{gain 3 } e}{\overbrace{}}}{\overset{0 \qquad +5 \qquad\quad +5 \qquad +2}{P + HNO_3 \longrightarrow HPO_3 + NO + H_2O}}}$$

$$3\,P + 5\,HNO_3 \longrightarrow HPO_3 + NO + H_2O$$

$$3\,P + 5\,HNO_3 \longrightarrow 3\,HPO_3 + 5\,NO + H_2O \text{ (balanced)}$$

Oxidation-reduction equations are more difficult to balance by ordinary trial and error methods than those equations which involve no change of valence, since the former type may require larger coefficients of the formulas. The change of valence method for balancing oxidation-reduction equations is rapid and accurate. To illustrate further the application of the principle, we may balance several more equations:

EXAMPLE 1:

$$\underset{\underset{\text{gain of 5 } e}{\underbrace{}}}{\overset{\overset{\text{loss of 2 } e}{\overbrace{}}}{\overset{+1\,-2 \quad +1+7-2 \quad +1-1 \quad\quad 0 \quad +1-1 \quad +2-1 \quad +1-2}{H_2S + KMnO_4 + HCl \longrightarrow S + KCl + MnCl_2 + H_2O}}}$$

Mn in $KMnO_4$ undergoes a change in valence of 5 units, while the sulfur atom in H_2S changes by two units. Thus the number 5 is made the coefficient of H_2S and the number 2 is made the coefficient of $KMnO_4$:

$$5 H_2S + 2 KMnO_4 + HCl \longrightarrow S + KCl + MnCl_2 + H_2O$$

The ratio of H_2S to $KMnO_4$ must be 5 to 2 as determined by the rule of change in valence. Since this ratio fixes the number of sulfur, potassium, and manganese atoms in the equation, those elements should be balanced on the right side of the equation,

$$5 H_2S + 2 KMnO_4 + HCl \longrightarrow 5 S + 2 KCl + 2 MnCl_2 + H_2O$$

Since 6 chlorine atoms are required on the right side; 6 molecules of HCl will be necessary to furnish these 6 atoms. The hydrogen and oxygen atoms are balanced last:

$$5 H_2S + 2 KMnO_4 + 6 HCl \longrightarrow 5 S + 2 KCl + 2 MnCl_2 + 8 H_2O$$

EXAMPLE 2:

$$\overset{+1\ -2 \qquad 0 \qquad\quad +1-2 \quad +4\ -2}{\underset{\text{gain 2 }e\text{ per atom or 4 }e\text{ per molecule}}{H_2S\ +\ O_2 \longrightarrow H_2O + SO_2}}$$

loss of 6 e

Since 2 atoms of oxygen are present per molecule, the change per molecule is 4 (2 for each atom), and the ratio of H_2S to O_2 becomes 4 to 6 or 2 to 3.

$$2 H_2S + 3 O_2 \longrightarrow 2 H_2O + 2 SO_2$$

EXAMPLE 3:

$$Cu + HNO_3 \longrightarrow Cu(NO_3)_2 + NO + H_2O$$

From change in valence, the ratio of the reducing agent, Cu, to the oxidizing agent, HNO_3, must be 3 to 2:

gain 3 e

$$\overset{0 \qquad +1+5\,-2 \qquad\quad +2+5-2 \qquad\quad +2-2\ +1-2}{3 Cu + 2 HNO_3 \longrightarrow 3 Cu(NO_3)_2 + 2 NO + H_2O}$$

loss 2 e

We note that part of the nitric acid undergoes no change in valence in forming the salt cupric nitrate; however, 3 $Cu(NO_3)_2$ call for 6 more atoms of nitrogen which must be furnished by the nitric acid. This requires six additional molecules of HNO_3 to be added to the 2 molecules which have been reduced to nitric oxide. The completed equation becomes

$$3 Cu + 2 HNO_3 + 6 HNO_3 \longrightarrow 3 Cu(NO_3)_2 + 2 NO + 4 H_2O$$

or
$$3 Cu + 8 HNO_3 \longrightarrow 3 Cu(NO_3)_2 + 2 NO + 4 H_2O$$

The change in valence gives only the part which undergoes oxidation and reduction and gives no information relative to the amount of a reagent used in some capacity other than oxidation-reduction. Thus in the above, the ratio of reducing agent to oxidizing agent is 3 to 2, but due to the fact that part of the nitric acid is used in another capacity, the number of molecules of HNO_3 used in this other capacity must be added to those used for oxidation purposes. It is evident from the equation that only $\frac{1}{4}$ of the HNO_3 (2 molecules of 8) act in an oxidizing capacity; the other $\frac{3}{4}$ acting as a salt former (formation of copper nitrate). The student should bear in mind that change of valence gives information only with regard to the parts undergoing oxidation-reduction.

After a little practice, the student may determine the valence changes by inspection and place the correct coefficients in the equation. Occasionally it may be necessary to double the numbers corresponding to the valence changes; however, the ratio must be maintained and if one number is doubled the second must also be doubled. For example in the reaction

$$\overbrace{KMnO_4 + FeSO_4 + H_2SO_4 \longrightarrow K_2SO_4 + MnSO_4}^{\text{gain 5 } e} + Fe_2(SO_4)_3 + H_2O$$

$$\underbrace{}_{\text{loss 1 } e}$$

2 atoms of Fe are necessary on the left side, so the numbers used in the final balancing must be 10 and 2 (which is the same ratio as 5 : 1), thus

$$2\,KMnO_4 + 10\,FeSO_4 + 8\,H_2SO_4 \longrightarrow K_2SO_4 + 2\,MnSO_4 + 5\,Fe_2(SO_4)_3 + 8\,H_2O$$

Ionic oxidation-reduction equations. Having balanced a molecular equation as above by electron interchange (or by valence gain or loss) it may thence be written in an ionic form.

$$2\,MnO_4^- + 10\,Fe^{++} + 16\,H^+ \longrightarrow 2\,Mn^{++} + 10\,Fe^{+++} + 8\,H_2O$$

Note that the ions not taking part in the chemical change have been omitted, they would merely cancel each other on either side of the equation if written. Other molecular equations from the previous section rewritten in ionic form follow:

$$3\,Cu + 2\,NO_3^- + 8\,H^+ \longrightarrow 3\,Cu^{++} + 2\,NO + 4\,H_2O$$
$$2\,Fe^{+++} + H_2S \longrightarrow 2\,Fe^{++} + 2\,H^+ + S$$
$$5\,H_2S + 2\,MnO_4^- + 6\,H^+ \longrightarrow 5\,S + 2\,Mn^{++} + 8\,H_2O$$

It is often preferable to write and balance a chemical change involving ions without first writing the molecular equation. The equation is balanced by a consideration of electron transfer as explained above for molecular equations:

$$\overset{\displaystyle \overset{\text{each N gains 3 } e}{\longleftarrow \quad \longrightarrow}}{\underset{\text{each Ag loses 1 } e}{3 \text{ Ag} + 4 \text{ H}^+ + \text{NO}_3^- \longrightarrow 3 \text{ Ag}^+ + \text{NO} + 2 \text{ H}_2\text{O}}}$$

or

$$\overset{\text{each As loses 2 } e}{\underset{\text{each Mn gains 5 } e}{2 \text{ MnO}_4^- + 5 \text{ AsO}_3^{---} + 6 \text{ H}^+ \longrightarrow 2 \text{ Mn}^{++} + 5 \text{ AsO}_4^{---} + 3 \text{ H}_2\text{O}}}$$

It is to be noted in all of these balanced ionic equations that the net positive or negative charge on one side of an equation balances that on the other side.

The step ion-electron method of balancing equations. This method is applicable only to ionic reactions; however, since most of our reactions in solution are between ions, the method proves convenient and useful. The method takes into account only those ions in solution which actually enter into reaction; in other words, only the net reaction is shown. Those ions which remain unaltered in the solution do not appear in the equation. The oxidation-reduction equation is broken down into two partial equations or steps; one equation represents the oxidation step, the other the reduction step. The number of electrons transferred in each step is indicated and each equation is balanced both atomically and electrically. The gain and loss of electrons is then balanced by multiplying each step by the appropriate number. For example:

$$\text{FeCl}_3 + \text{SnCl}_2 \longrightarrow \text{FeCl}_2 + \text{SnCl}_4$$

From an ionic standpoint, we should write down only the ions which enter into the chemical change, namely Fe^{+++}, which is reduced to Fe^{++}, and Sn^{++}, which is oxidized to Sn^{++++}. The two partial reactions would be

$$\text{Sn}^{++} \longrightarrow \text{Sn}^{++++} + 2 e \quad \text{(oxidation)}$$
$$\text{Fe}^{+++} + e \longrightarrow \text{Fe}^{++} \quad \text{(reduction)}$$

Each step is now balanced electrically as well as atomically. Since two electrons appear in the first step, we may balance electrons by multiplying the second equation by two

$$2 \text{ Fe}^{+++} + 2 e \longrightarrow 2 \text{ Fe}^{++}$$

Now the two steps may be added (electrons are canceled) and we obtain the net ionic reaction:

$$Sn^{++} \longrightarrow Sn^{++++} + 2e$$
$$2\,Fe^{+++} + 2e \longrightarrow 2\,Fe^{++}$$
$$\overline{Sn^{++} + 2\,Fe^{+++} \longrightarrow Sn^{++++} + 2\,Fe^{++}}$$

Note that the final step is also balanced electrically; the net charge on each side of the equation is positive eight.

Copper reacts with dilute nitric acid to form cupric nitrate, water, and nitric oxide. Applying the ion-electron method to this reaction, copper is oxidized from the free state to cupric ion:

$$Cu \longrightarrow Cu^{++} + 2\,e \quad \text{(oxidation)} \tag{1}$$

Meanwhile, nitric acid is reduced to NO and H_2O, the latter two substances being un-ionized:

$$H^+ + NO_3^- \longrightarrow NO + H_2O$$

The latter equation is balanced atomically as follows:

$$4\,H^+ + NO_3^- \longrightarrow NO + 2\,H_2O$$

The equation is balanced atomically but not electrically, since the net charge on the left is positive three, and the net charge on the right side is zero. The addition of 3 e to the left side will balance the step electrically:

$$3\,e + 4\,H^+ + NO_3^- \longrightarrow NO + 2\,H_2O \quad \text{(reduction)} \tag{2}$$

To balance the gain and loss of electrons, equation (1) may be multiplied by three and equation (2) by 2, then:

$$3\,Cu \longrightarrow 3\,Cu^{++} + 6e$$
$$6e + 8\,H^+ + 2\,NO_3^- \longrightarrow 2\,NO + 4\,H_2O$$
$$\overline{3\,Cu + 8\,H^+ + 2\,NO_3^- \longrightarrow 3\,Cu^{++} + 2\,NO + 4\,H_2O}$$

It is further assumed in the ion-electron method that H^+, OH^-, and H_2O are available for balancing each step of the equation atomically. To illustrate, permanganate ion will oxidize sulfide ion to free sulfur in acid solution

$$S^{--} \longrightarrow S + 2\,e \tag{3}$$

and the permanganate ion is reduced to manganous ion

$$MnO_4^- \longrightarrow Mn^{++}$$

To balance the latter step atomically, we may add eight hydrogen ions to the left side, in which case four molecules of water will appear on the right side:

$$8 \, H^+ + MnO_4^- \longrightarrow Mn^{++} + 4 \, H_2O$$

Five electrons are then necessary on the left side to balance electrically:

$$5 \, e + 8 \, H^+ + MnO_4^- \longrightarrow Mn^{++} + 4 \, H_2O \tag{4}$$

Combining steps (3) and (4) and balancing gain and loss of electrons,

$$5 \, S^{--} \longrightarrow 5 \, S + \cancel{10 \, e}$$
$$\underline{\cancel{10 \, e} + 16 \, H^+ + 2 \, MnO_4^- \longrightarrow 2 \, Mn^{++} + 8 \, H_2O}$$
$$5 \, S^{--} + 16 \, H^+ + 2 \, MnO_4^- \longrightarrow 5 \, S + 2 \, Mn^{++} + 8 \, H_2O$$

EXERCISES

1. From the standpoint of modern atomic theory, define the following terms: (a) oxidation; (b) reduction; (c) oxidizing agent; (d) reducing agent.
2. From a consideration of change of valence or electron transfer, balance the following equations and indicate the oxidizing agent and reducing agent:
   - (a) $FeCl_3 + H_2S \longrightarrow FeCl_2 + HCl + S$
   - (b) $Bi(OH)_3 + Na_2SnO_2 \longrightarrow Bi + Na_2SnO_3 + H_2O$
   - (c) $SnCl_2 + H_2SO_3 + HCl \longrightarrow SnCl_4 + H_2S + H_2O$
   - (d) $H_2S + HNO_3 \longrightarrow H_2SO_4 + NO_2 + H_2O$
   - (e) $KIO_3 + KI + HC_2H_3O_2 \longrightarrow KC_2H_3O_2 + H_2O + I_2$
   - (f) $Fe + HNO_3 \longrightarrow Fe(NO_3)_3 + NO + H_2O$
   - (g) $HMnO_4 + AsH_3 + H_2SO_4 \longrightarrow H_3AsO_4 + MnSO_4 + H_2O$
   - (h) $As_4 + HNO_3 \longrightarrow HAsO_3 + NO + H_2O$
   - (i) $Sb_2S_5 + HNO_3 \longrightarrow Sb_2O_5 + H_2SO_4 + NO + H_2O$
   - (j) $KMnO_4 + H_2C_2O_4 + H_2SO_4 \longrightarrow K_2SO_4 + CO_2 + MnSO_4 + H_2O$
   - (k) $MnBr_2 + HNO_3 + PbO_2 \longrightarrow HMnO_4 + Br_2 + Pb(NO_3)_2 + H_2O$
3. Complete and balance the following equations in the steps indicated, using the ion-electron method:
   - (a) $Zn \longrightarrow Zn^{++}$
     $Cl_2 \longrightarrow Cl^-$
   - (b) $CuS \longrightarrow Cu^{++} + S$
     $H^+ + NO_3^- \longrightarrow H_2O + NO$
   - (c) $Fe^{+++} \longrightarrow Fe^{++}$
     $Sn^{++} \longrightarrow Sn^{++++}$
   - (d) $Mn^{++} + H_2O \longrightarrow MnO_4^- + H^+$
     $H^+ + PbO_2 \longrightarrow Pb^{++} + H_2O$
   - (e) $Bi(OH)_3 \longrightarrow Bi + OH^-$
     $OH^- + SnO_2^{--} \longrightarrow SnO_3^{--} + H_2O$
   - (f) $Fe^{++} \longrightarrow Fe^{+++}$
     $Cr_2O_7^{--} + H^+ \longrightarrow Cr^{+++} + H_2O$
   - (g) $Sb^{+++} \longrightarrow Sb$
     $Fe \longrightarrow Fe^{++}$
   - (h) $As + OH^- \longrightarrow H_2AsO_4^- + H^+$
     $H^+ + NO_3^- \longrightarrow H_2O + NO_2$
   - (i) $Zn \longrightarrow Zn^{++}$
     $HAsO_2 + H^+ \longrightarrow AsH_3 + H_2O$

(j) $Pt + Cl^- \longrightarrow PtCl_6^{--}$

$H^+ + Cl^- + NO_3^- \longrightarrow NOCl + H_2O$

(k) $Bi_2O_5 + H^+ \longrightarrow Bi^{+++} + H_2O$

$Cl^- \longrightarrow Cl_2$

(l) $Fe^{++} \longrightarrow Fe^{+++}$

$H_2O_2 + H^+ \longrightarrow H_2O$

4. Complete and balance:

   (a) $Na_2C_2O_4 + KMnO_4 + H_2SO_4 \longrightarrow$

   (b) $FeSO_4 + HNO_3 + H_2SO_4 \longrightarrow$

5. Write the two above equations ionically.

6. Write balanced ionic equations for:

   (a) Bismuth trisulfide plus nitric acid yielding trivalent bismuth ion, sulfur, nitric oxide, and water.

   (b) Sulfite ion plus permanganate ion yielding sulfate ion, divalent manganese ion, and water.

7. The following electronic equations are to be balanced. Where necessary add H^+, OH^-, or H_2O. Break the reaction down into the oxidation part and the reduction part, balancing each part by the ion-electron method. Then add the two parts to get the single step equation. In the event that H^+ appear on one side of the finished equation and OH^- on the other, these must be combined to form H_2O molecules, since these two ions are not compatible in the same solution.

   (a) $Fe + H^+ + NO_3^- \longrightarrow Fe^{+++} + NO + H_2O$

   (b) $Co(OH)_2 + O_2^{--} \longrightarrow Co(OH)_3 + OH^-$

   (c) $NiS + Cl^- + NO_3^- \longrightarrow NiCl_4^{--} + S + NO$

   (d) $H_2O_2 + MnO_4^- + H^+ \longrightarrow O_2 + Mn^{++} + H_2O$

   (e) $Mn^{++} + ClO_3^- \longrightarrow MnO_2 + ClO_2$

   (f) $MnO_4^- + NO_2 + H^+ \longrightarrow Mn^{++} + NO_3^- + H_2O$

   (g) $I_2 + H_2O + Cl_2 \longrightarrow IO_3^- + H^+ + Cl^-$

   (h) $H_2SO_3 + MnO_4^- + H^+ \longrightarrow HSO_4^- + Mn^{++}$

   (i) $Zn + CNS^- \longrightarrow Zn^{++} + H_2S + HCN$

REFERENCES

C. W. Bennett, "Balancing Equations by the Valence-Change Method," *J. Chem. Ed.* **12,** 189 (1935).

W. T. Hall, "Oxidation-Reduction Reactions," *ibid.* **6,** 479 (1929).

M. S. Kharasch, O. Reinmuth, and F. Mayo, "The Electron in Organic Chemistry," *ibid.* **8,** 1703 (1931); **11,** 82 (1934).

B. Park, "A Rational Method for Balancing Exceptional Chemical Equations," *ibid.* **6,** 1136 (1929).

Lawrence P. Eblin, "Oxidation Number in Auto-Redox Reactions," *ibid.* **28,** 221 (1951).

XXI

Nitrogen and the Atmosphere

$$_7\mathbf{N}^{14.01}\ {}^{1\ 1}_{2\ 5}\ {}^{1}_{1}$$

History. In 1772, Rutherford, a Scottish botanist, showed that an inert substance incapable of sustaining life remained after the combustion of various substances in air. The nature of this inert substance remained obscure until Lavoisier recognized it as an elementary substance. Because of its inertness, it was given the name "azote," which means "lifeless." Later the name was changed to nitrogen since the element is a constituent of "niter," now known as potassium nitrate.

Importance of nitrogen. Nitrogen is characterized by its tendency to remain in the uncombined state. Because of its inactivity, we may think of it as being a relatively unimportant component of the atmosphere. However, a careful study of the ways in which nitrogen and its compounds influence our lives will convince us of the vital importance of this element. The air we breathe is approximately 80 per cent nitrogen, 20 per cent oxygen, and 0.04 per cent carbon dioxide. Exhaled air still contains about 80 per cent nitrogen; the oxygen content is about 16 per cent and carbon dioxide content 4 per cent. We use, then, only about 4 per cent of the air we breathe in; our lungs do a great lot of pumping in and out of inert nitrogen.

Combustion of fuel would be extremely rapid were it not for the nitrogen present in the air. A glowing cigarette placed into pure oxygen bursts into flame and quickly burns up. No smoking would be the rule if the atmosphere were pure oxygen. Corrosion of metals would proceed at a rapid rate, so rapid as to make many of them impractical for use. All oxidation processes in which air is the oxidizing agent would be difficult to control were it not for the fact that inert nitrogen is present.

Certain nitrogen compounds are essential for the growth of plants and animals. Proteins, complex organic compounds containing nitrogen, are present in every living cell. A study of the element, then, is important to the biologist. Very few plants have the ability to utilize nitrogen from the atmosphere; consequently we must replenish the supply in soil with nitrogen-containing fertilizer. Hence nitrogen is important to those engaged in agriculture.

Nitrogen is a constituent of many of our foods and as such plays an important part in processes of animal metabolism. Nitrogen compounds are used extensively in the production of drugs and dyestuffs and are present in practically all explosives. The success of a nation at war depends directly upon its access to nitrogen compounds, not only in the form of explosives, but also as foods and fertilizers.

The occurrence of nitrogen. Tremendous quantities of free nitrogen are found in the atmosphere; it has been estimated that there are more than 20 million tons over each square mile of the earth's surface. Certain natural gases contain a small percentage of the free element. Relatively little nitrogen is found as compounds. The main concentrated source of combined nitrogen is sodium nitrate (Chile saltpeter), fairly large deposits of which are found in Chile. Small deposits of potassium nitrate (saltpeter) are also known. Proteins constitute another source of combined nitrogen. Small quantities of nitrate or ammonium salts are naturally present in all soils.

Laboratory preparation. (*a*) *From the air.* The problem of obtaining nitrogen from the atmosphere is one of separating the two principal constituents of air, namely, nitrogen and oxygen. This may be accomplished by physical means (see p. 84) or by removing the oxygen by chemical means, leaving nitrogen. Since oxygen is quite an active substance and nitrogen very inert, we may take advantage of this difference in activity as a basis for separation. Phosphorus readily combines with oxygen in the air to form phosphorus pentoxide. Since nitrogen does not combine with phosphorus, the separation of nitrogen from oxygen can be carried out very effectively by means of the following procedure: A piece of phosphorus may be burned in air which is enclosed in a bottle inverted over water. The oxygen is removed by combination with the phosphorus, leaving essentially nitrogen gas in the bottle. The phos-

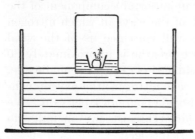

Fig. 74. Obtaining nitrogen from air.

phorus pentoxide dissolves in the water forming phosphoric acid. The changes which occur are shown by the equations:

$$4 P + 5 O_2 \longrightarrow 2 P_2O_5$$
$$P_2O_5 + 3 H_2O \longrightarrow 2 H_3PO_4$$

Certain metals, such as heated copper, may be used to remove the oxygen from the air in much the same manner as phosphorus. Nitrogen prepared by this method is not pure, as it contains a small amount of water vapor, and the rare gases present in the atmosphere. However, it is sufficiently pure for a study of its common properties.

(b) *From certain compounds of nitrogen.* Chemically pure nitrogen is conveniently prepared by heating together solutions of sodium nitrite and ammonium chloride:

$$NaNO_2 + NH_4Cl \longrightarrow NaCl + NH_4NO_2$$
$$ \longrightarrow N_2 + 2 H_2O$$

This is a double decomposition reaction between two salts, the ammonium nitrite formed, being unstable toward heat, breaks down to yield nitrogen and water. A combination of any nitrite salt and any ammonium salt would give a reaction similar to that above.

If ammonia is passed over hot copper oxide, the following reaction takes place:

$$3 CuO + 2 NH_3 \longrightarrow 3 Cu + 3 H_2O + N_2$$

Cupric oxide acts as an oxidizing agent, ammonia as a reducing agent.

Commercial preparation. Commercial nitrogen is prepared by liquefaction of air and subsequent fractional distillation. This process has been described in the commercial preparation of oxygen (p. 84). The nitrogen obtained by this process contains about one per cent of other substances, chief of which is argon. Argon is also inactive chemically, so its presence does not interfere in the use of the product.

Properties of nitrogen. Nitrogen is an odorless, colorless, and tasteless gas at ordinary temperatures. The boiling point under atmospheric pressure is $-195.8°$, and its freezing point, $-209.9°$. Because of its low boiling point, nitrogen is difficult to liquefy. 22.4 liters of the gas at standard conditions weigh 28 grams; hence its formula is N_2, two atoms of nitrogen being held together in each molecule by covalent linkages. The gas is relatively insoluble in water, a little more than 2 ml. dissolving in 100 ml. of water at standard conditions.

Chemically, nitrogen is an inert substance. It combines with few elements and then only with difficulty. We shall refer to these reactions later in discussing the compounds of nitrogen.

NITROGEN FIXATION

Nitrogen in the combined state, that is, in compounds, is far more useful and important than in the free state. Unfortunately, animals and plants (with a few exceptions) cannot utilize nitrogen in the free state, but rather must depend upon nitrogen compounds for their supply of this essential element. It becomes the problem, then, of the chemist to convert elementary nitrogen into nitrogen compounds, a form in which it can be utilized. Any process by which elementary nitrogen is converted into nitrogen compounds is termed *nitrogen fixation*.

Nitrogen compounds are essential to plant and animal life in building up proteins, complex organic substances containing the elements carbon, hydrogen, oxygen, and nitrogen, and sometimes phosphorus and sulfur. Animals must eat protein directly, as the body is incapable of building up proteins from other nitrogen compounds. Beans, peas, and meat contain considerable protein. The plant, on the other hand, can synthesize plant protein from ammonium salts or nitrate salts which it derives from the soil. The soil may get some nitrogen compounds from the decay of plants, leaves, and other organic matter. Farm soil must be frequently replenished with fertilizer in the form of animal refuse matter, manure, or compounds of nitrogen, such as ammonium sulfate, calcium nitrate, etc.

Methods for the fixation of nitrogen can be divided into two groups: (1) natural fixation and (2) artificial fixation.

Natural fixation. (*a*) Certain plants called *legumes* are equipped with nodules which contain nitrogen-fixing organisms. These organisms are able to assimilate nitrogen directly from the atmosphere, converting free nitrogen into nitrogen compounds. Peas, beans, alfalfa, and clover are leguminous plants. To replenish the soil with nitrogen, one of the above may be grown on the depleted soil. The plants may be plowed under, in which case decomposition occurs, furnishing fixed nitrogen to the soil. A system of crop rotation, using leguminous plants for maintaining soil fertility is now an approved practice.

(*b*) One of nature's principal methods of replenishing the supply of nitrogen compounds in the soil occurs as a result of electrical discharges in air and subsequent rainfall. At the high temperature associated with lightning bolts or other arc discharges, nitrogen and oxygen gases combine to form nitrogen oxides. These oxides with air moisture form nitrous and nitric acids which come to the earth in rainfall. A person out in a thunder shower is being subjected to a shower of very dilute nitric acid. As these acids act on soil minerals, soluble nitrogen-containing salts are formed in soil waters. For example, as the very dilute nitric acid acts on limestone, $CaCO_3$, calcium nitrate is formed; this salt is a common soil mineral. Considering the bulk of the atmosphere as a factory for HNO_3 production and geologic time of operation, one can account for millions of tons of nitrate compound formation.

Artificial fixation. Man's methods of fixation of nitrogen will be discussed in detail in a study of the compounds of nitrogen. The important processes may be listed as follows:

1. Haber process
2. Birkeland-Eyde process
3. Cyanamide process

The nitrogen cycle. It might occur to us that since nitrogen is continually being fixed from the air by natural and artificial methods, the supply of nitrogen in the atmosphere would decrease. Careful analysis of the air, however, shows that this is not the case; the percentage of nitrogen in the air remains nearly constant. This is due to the fact that a balance between free and combined nitrogen is maintained as a result of decomposition of nitrogen compounds, yielding elementary

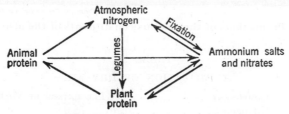

Fig. 75. The nitrogen cycle.

nitrogen. The cycle of changes which nitrogen undergoes can best be shown by the diagram (Fig. 75). This series of changes is referred to as the *nitrogen cycle* of nature. Although the process is more complex and involves more steps than indicated in the diagram, nevertheless, it will represent the essential changes taking place.

We may start with elementary nitrogen and trace some of the possible changes. A nitrogen atom in the free state may be fixed by (1) legumes into plant protein or (2) lightning discharges into ammonium or nitrate salts or (3) artificial processes into ammonium or nitrate salts. A plant may then utilize the salts for production of plant protein. The plant may serve as a food for animals in which case the original nitrogen atom may become a part of animal protein; or degradation of the plant may again produce ammonium salts. Animal protein in undergoing decay or degradation may be converted either into ammonium salts or into free nitrogen which finds its way back into the atmosphere where it is again ready to start another cycle of changes.

OTHER GASES OF THE ATMOSPHERE

Although nitrogen and oxygen are the most abundant constituents of the atmosphere, small quantities of water vapor, carbon dioxide, dust particles, argon, and other inert gases are present. The average composition of dry air by volume is shown in Table 22.

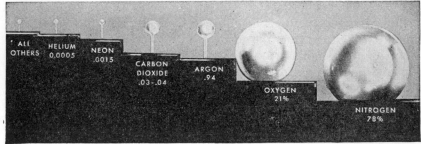

Courtesy The Linde Air Products Company

Fig. 76. Proportions of the gaseous constituents of the atmosphere.

TABLE 22

COMPOSITION OF DRY AIR

Component	Percentage by Volume
Nitrogen	78.0
Oxygen	21.0
Argon	.94
Carbon dioxide	.03 — .04
Hydrogen	.01 or less
Neon	.0015
Helium	.0005
Krypton	.00005
Xenon	.000006

The quantity of oxygen in the atmosphere remains essentially a constant; this despite the fact that large quantities are continually being used in the processes of respiration, combustion, decay, and oxidation. The constancy of the oxygen content of the atmosphere is no doubt in a large measure due to the action of plants which utilize carbon dioxide and produce oxygen in the process.

TABLE 23

COMPOSITION OF AIR AT VARIOUS ELEVATIONS [1]

HEIGHT IN KILOMETERS	NITROGEN	WATER VAPOR	OXYGEN	CARBON DIOXIDE	HYDROGEN	TOTAL PRESSURE IN MM.
0 . . .	77.08	1.20	20.75	.03	.01	760
5 . . .	77.89	.18	20.95	.03	.01	405
11 . . .	78.02	.01	20.99	.03	.01	168
40 . . .	86.42	.06	12.61	—	.67	1.84
80 . . .	32.18	.17	1.85	—	64.70	.0123
100 . . .	2.95	.05	0.11	—	95.58	.0067
140 . . .	.01	—	—	—	99.15	.0040

[1] Data from *International Critical Tables*.

Air is a mixture. In ancient times air was regarded as an elementary substance, and this idea prevailed until Lavoisier showed that air contained an active ingredient, oxygen, which was responsible for combustion, and an inert substance which is now called nitrogen. Since the composition of the air is so nearly a constant, it might be suspected that air is a compound substance. A number of lines of evidence, however, prove that air is a mixture:

1. The composition of the atmosphere is not a constant, especially as regards the proportions of water vapor and carbon dioxide. Even the proportions of nitrogen and oxygen are variable within narrow limits. Air in the country has a lower proportion of carbon dioxide than in urban centers. The fact that air at high altitudes (Table 23) has a different composition is further proof that air is not a compound.

2. A compound substance boils at a definite temperature. When liquid air boils, the nitrogen boils off first, leaving essentially pure oxygen. During this process the boiling point increases from about $-196°$ to about $-183°$.

3. When air is dissolved in water, relatively more oxygen dissolves than nitrogen, so that the dissolved air contains a higher percentage of oxygen than ordinary air. When a compound dissolves, it dissolves as a whole, and the composition of the dissolved phase is the same as that of the compound.

4. No energy change is involved in mixing nitrogen and oxygen in the proportions in which they are present in the atmosphere. If a chemical change had taken place, energy would have been evolved or absorbed.

5. Known compounds of nitrogen and oxygen exhibit properties very different from those of air.

Carbon dioxide in the air. Analysis of air shows an average carbon dioxide content of about 0.035 per cent (Table 22). This carbon dioxide is produced as a result of the respiration processes of man and animals, decay and rotting, and the combustion of coal, wood, gasoline, and other fuels. The content of carbon dioxide in urban centers is usually appreciably higher than in the country because of the concentration of population and industrial activity. In poorly ventilated rooms the content may run as high as 3 per cent. About one-fifth of the oxygen taken into the lungs from the air is exhaled as carbon dioxide.

We might ask why the content of carbon dioxide in the air does not increase due to the continued processes mentioned above. Actually, a nearly constant balance is maintained between the carbon dioxide and the other constituents of the atmosphere. The answer lies in the fact that plants utilize carbon dioxide of the atmosphere in building up sugars, starches, cellulose, and plant tissue. In plant tissue, water and carbon dioxide combine to form those complex compounds — a process called *photosynthesis*. The reactions are catalyzed by chlorophyll, the green coloring matter of plants. The reaction producing starch may be represented as

$$6\ CO_2 + 5\ H_2O \longrightarrow C_6H_{10}O_5 + 6\ O_2$$

Note that oxygen is also produced in the reaction, this oxygen being released to the atmosphere. Energy for the above reaction is derived from the sun. While animals use oxygen and liberate carbon dioxide in respiratory processes, plants do just the opposite in photosynthesis — they use carbon dioxide and liberate oxygen.

Millions of years ago in the Carboniferous era, vegetation was abundant and tropical over most of the land surface. Coal beds of arctic regions are remnants of marked plant growth of long, long ago. Such luxurious plant growth is explained by belief that the CO_2 content of the air was much higher — perhaps 2 or 3 per cent rather than the .035 per cent of today and also the fact that the temperature of the earth's surface was higher.

Water vapor in the atmosphere. Water in the atmosphere is produced as a result of evaporation from oceans, lakes, and streams over the earth's crust. For every temperature there is a saturation pressure of water vapor in the air, and this saturation pressure is the vapor pressure of water at the temperature in question. Thus at 20° the air is saturated with water when the pressure of water vapor in the air is 17.5 mm. (Table 10, p. 148.) Usually the pressure of water vapor in the air is less than this saturation pressure. The ratio of the pressure of the water vapor in the air to the saturation pressure at any given temperature is called the *humidity*. Suppose the pressure of water vapor in the air is 10 mm. at 20°. Then the humidity is $\frac{10}{17.5} = 57.1$ per cent. Of course, if the pressure of water vapor were 17.5 mm., the humidity would be 100 per cent.

When the atmosphere is cooled during the night, the cooling may progress to the point where the pressure of water vapor in the air becomes greater than the saturation pressure. When this occurs, dew or fog is formed as a result of condensation of water vapor from the air. Clouds are produced as a result of the rising and subsequent cooling of moist warm air. The formation of large droplets may result in precipitation of rain.

Ventilation and air conditioning. The condition of the air in dwellings determines the comfort and health of the occupants. Proper air conditioning involves the three factors, *temperature, humidity,* and *circulation.* At one time it was supposed that circulation of the air was the main factor to be considered, but we now know that humidity and temperature are equally important. Humidity is important because it controls the rate of evaporation of moisture from the skin. When the water vapor content of the air becomes high, the rate of evaporation from the skin is slowed up, resulting in discomfort. This may result in crowded places where respired air containing water vapor will increase the water vapor content. In the winter, the water vapor content of the air is usually low. In heated buildings, moisture evaporates rapidly from the skin. This evaporation is attended by absorption of heat from the body, and if the rate of evaporation is high, the result is a feeling of coldness. The rate of evaporation may be slowed down by increasing the humidity of the air. At a temperature of about 70° F., the humidity should be maintained between 35 and 50 per cent for comfort. In winter it is usually necessary to provide for increased humidity, since the humidity of the outside air is relatively low. Modern air conditioning properly regulates temperature, humidity, and circulation of the air.

THE INERT GASES

Lord Rayleigh and William Ramsay in 1894 discovered an inert gas in the atmosphere which they called *argon*, meaning " inert." The discovery came as a result of studies of the atomic weight of nitrogen. Nitrogen derived from the atmosphere invariably gave a higher atomic weight than nitrogen derived by chemical means. These studies led to the conclusion that air contained some inert substance besides nitrogen which was more dense than nitrogen. Further investigation resulted in the isolation of argon from the atmosphere. Argon is present in the air to the extent of nearly one per cent. Since the discovery of argon, other rare gases have been isolated from the atmosphere, including helium, neon, krypton, and xenon.

$$_2\text{He}^4 \begin{smallmatrix} | \\ 2 \\ | \end{smallmatrix} \quad _{10}\text{Ne}^{20.2} \begin{smallmatrix} | & | \\ 2 & 8 \\ | & | \end{smallmatrix} \quad _{18}\text{A}^{39.94} \begin{smallmatrix} | & | & | \\ 2 & 8 & 8 \\ | & | & | \end{smallmatrix} \quad _{36}\text{Kr}^{83.7} \begin{smallmatrix} | & | & | & | \\ 2 & 8 & 18 & 8 \\ | & | & | & | \end{smallmatrix}$$

$$_{54}\text{Xe}^{131.3} \begin{smallmatrix} | & | & | & | & | \\ 2 & 8 & 18 & 18 & 8 \\ | & | & | & | & | \end{smallmatrix} \quad _{86}\text{Rn}^{222} \begin{smallmatrix} | & | & | & | & | & | \\ 2 & 8 & 18 & 32 & 18 & 8 \\ | & | & | & | & | & | \end{smallmatrix}$$

Gas	Symbol	Boiling Point	Freezing Point	Critical Temp.	Quantity in Air: Parts Per Million
Helium	He	− 269	———	− 268	4
Neon	Ne	− 246	− 249	− 229	12
Argon	A	− 186	−− 189	− 122	9400
Krypton . . .	Kr	− 152	− 169	− 63	.5
Xenon	Xe	− 109	− 140	− 17	.06
Radon	Rn	− 62	− 71	——	

The inactivity of these elements (Group VIII of the periodic table) may be explained on the basis of their atomic structure. Each of these elements has a stable outer configuration of electrons in its atoms. Helium has two electrons in the first orbit (its outer orbit), which represents a stable configuration. The other elements have eight electrons in the outermost orbit, which represents a stable state. The atom is completely satisfied as regards electrons, there being no tendency to give up, take up, or share electrons. As a result, we would not expect them to form compounds or undergo chemical change. The molecules of these gases are monatomic, the atoms of the elements having no tendency to combine with one another.

Helium is unique among the chemical elements, as it was discovered in the atmosphere around the sun before being found on the earth. The main source of helium is from certain natural gas wells in Kansas and Texas, the per cent by volume of helium sometimes being as high as two. Helium has the lowest boiling point of any substance known; consequently it may be separated from the other constituents of natural gas by lowering the temperature sufficiently to liquefy or freeze the other components. The boiling point of helium is −268.5°; its freezing point, −272° at 26 atmospheres pressure, is just a degree above the absolute zero temperature.

The main use of helium is in balloons and other lighter-than-air craft. While helium is somewhat heavier [1] than hydrogen, it has the important advantage that it is noncombustible. Another advantage of helium over hydrogen lies in its lower rate of diffusibility. Helium is also used in diving bells to lessen the danger of caisson disease. This results from a too rapid escape of nitrogen from the blood stream of divers coming to the surface. At the high pressures in diving bells the solubility of nitrogen of the air in the blood increases, and if the pressure is decreased too rapidly, gas bubbles may develop in the blood stream as a result of escape of the nitrogen gas. Since the solubility of helium in blood is much less than that of nitrogen, it may advantageously be mixed with oxygen for use under high pressures.

One of the important uses of the inert gases, particularly neon, is that of producing colored light in discharge tubes. Although these gases do not form ions in ordinary chemical changes, ions may be produced by removal of electrons in a discharge tube under a high alternating current potential. The gas is enclosed in a tube at a low pressure (5–10 mm.) where the application of several thousand volts produces ions and renders the gas a conductor of the current. Light of a characteristic color is emitted due to "activation" of the atoms through a displacement of electrons. Neon produces the familiar orange-

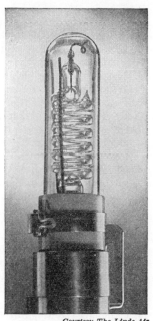

Courtesy The Linde Air Products Company

Fig. 77. The xenon-filled flash tube can be used repeatedly.

red color of neon signs, argon gives a purple color, krypton and xenon produce a blue light. By mixing the gases and using different colored glasses, various shades of color may be obtained.

---

[1] Although helium is twice as heavy as hydrogen, its lifting power is almost as good. The lifting power of a gas in a balloon depends upon the difference between the density of the gas on the inside and the air on the outside.

$$22.4 \text{ cu. ft. } H_2 = 2 \text{ oz.}$$
$$22.4 \text{ cu. ft. } He = 4 \text{ oz.}$$
$$22.4 \text{ cu. ft. air} = 29 \text{ oz.}$$

Lifting power

$$22.4 \text{ cu. ft. } H_2 = 29 - 2 = 27 \text{ oz.}$$
$$22.4 \text{ cu. ft. } He = 29 - 4 = 25 \text{ oz.}$$

Thus helium is $\frac{25}{27}$ or about 93 per cent as effective as hydrogen in lifting power.

Argon is used in filling electric light bulbs. It seems to have certain advantages over nitrogen in prolonging the life of the filaments.

Radon or niton will be considered in chapter XXXI. Its only uses depend upon its radioactivity.

EXERCISES

1. Review the evidence which indicates that air is a solution and not a compound.
2. What is meant by "nitrogen fixation"? Why was nitrogen fixation of greater importance to Germany than to England during World War I?
3. If a liquid mixture of the constituents of the atmosphere be warmed, in what order would the various constituents distil off?
4. List four plants which have the ability to fix nitrogen from the atmosphere. What agents are responsible for this fixation process?
5. Calculate the weight of 100 liters of nitrogen gas at standard conditions.
6. Devise a means of determining the molecular weight of nitrogen.
7. Calculate the weight of nitrogen obtainable by the action of ammonium chloride on 100 g. of sodium nitrite. What volume would this weight of nitrogen occupy at standard conditions?   Ans. 40.6 g.; 32.5 l.
8. Of what importance is the "nitrogen cycle"? Trace the changes which a nitrogen atom might undergo in progressing through the nitrogen cycle.
9. Give one important use of each of the following rare gases: helium, neon, argon.
10. What are the essentials of proper air conditioning?
11. Explain the formation of dew and fog.
12. Calculate the weight of 50 liters of nitrogen enclosed in a steel cylinder under a pressure of 100 atmospheres and a temperature of 0°.   Ans. 6.25 kg.
13. Diagram the nitrogen atom. Show how three atoms of hydrogen may combine with one atom of nitrogen to form NH_3. Is the linkage covalent or electrovalent?
14. Calculate the weight of nitrogen produced by passing 100 liters of ammonia gas at standard conditions over cupric oxide, according to the equation:

$$3\,CuO + 2\,NH_3 \longrightarrow 3\,Cu + N_2 + 3\,H_2O \qquad \text{Ans. 62.5 g.}$$

15. Diagram the structure of the elements, He, Ne, and A. On the basis of atomic structure, why would you expect these three elements to show similarities in chemical behavior?

REFERENCES

Contemporary Developments in Chemistry, Columbia University Press.

J. E. Crane, "Development of the Synthetic Ammonia Industry in the United States," *Ind. and Eng. Chem.* **22**, 795 (1930).

W. E. Snyder and R. R. Bottoms, "Properties and Uses of Helium," *ibid.* **22**, 1189 (1930).

H. A. Curtis, *Fixed Nitrogen*, Reinhold.

William Ramsay, *The Gases of the Atmosphere*, Macmillan.

W. C. Fernelius and W. C. Johnson, "Liquid Ammonia as a Solvent and the Ammonia System of Compounds, Pt. I," *J. Chem. Ed.* **5**, 664 (1928).

E. Berl, "Fritz Haber," *ibid.* **14**, 203 (1937).

XXII

Compounds of Nitrogen

Although nitrogen is an inert substance in the elementary state, it forms a number of compounds. Among the more important are ammonia and nitric acid, which we shall study in some detail. Nearly all nitrogen compounds are covalent — the atoms are held together by sharing of electrons. The nitrogen atom with five electrons in the outer orbit readily shares electrons with other atoms. In the compound NH_3, three electrons are shared with three hydrogen atoms, while in the compound HNO_3, electrons are shared with three oxygen atoms. We may say that the valence of nitrogen in ammonia is negative three, since the nitrogen atom is more negative than hydrogen, and the electron pairs probably lie closer to the nitrogen atom than to the hydrogen atoms. In the compound HNO_3, the opposite is probably true. The oxygen, being more negative than nitrogen, will show a greater attraction for the electrons, causing the electrons to be closer to the oxygen atoms. In this case the valence of nitrogen is considered as positive five. The valence of nitrogen in these two compounds represents the extremes of positive and negative valence for nitrogen. This illustrates again the direct connection between the maximum valence change and the number of electrons in the outermost orbit of the atom.

AMMONIA AND AMMONIUM SALTS

Decay of nitrogenous matter in the absence of air produces ammonia. The decomposition may be brought about with the aid of heat or in the presence of putrefying bacteria. Ammonia at one time was produced by distilling animal horns and hoofs, giving rise to the name "spirits of hartshorn." As a result of the action of bacteria on nitrogen compounds, small quantities of ammonia gas may be present in the air. Because of the great solubility of ammonia in water, however, it rapidly finds its way to the soil by the action of rain and snow. Here it may be converted into other compounds.

Laboratory preparation of ammonia. (*a*) *From ammonium salts.*
Ammonia is most conveniently prepared in the laboratory by the action
of a strong base on an ammonium salt, as for example:

$$NH_4Cl + NaOH \longrightarrow NH_4OH + NaCl$$
$$NH_4OH \longrightarrow NH_3 \uparrow + H_2O$$

The reaction is caused to go to completion by the use of heat, since
ammonium hydroxide is unstable and breaks down to give water and
ammonia, the ammonia escaping as a gas. The gas is collected by the
displacement of air. Since the gas is extremely
soluble in water it cannot be collected by water
displacement. (See Fig. 78.) The above reaction
is a typical one for the preparation of ammonia.
Any ammonium salt and strong base may be
employed. $Ca(OH)_2$ is usually used instead of
sodium hydroxide because it is cheaper:

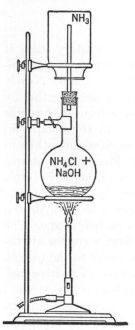

$$(NH_4)_2SO_4 + Ca(OH)_2 \longrightarrow CaSO_4 + 2\,NH_4OH$$
$$\downarrow$$
$$2\,NH_3 \uparrow + 2\,H_2O$$

(*b*) *From nitrides.* The action of water on a
nitride produces ammonia:

$$Mg_3N_2 + 6\,H_2O \longrightarrow 3\,Mg(OH)_2 + 2\,NH_3 \uparrow$$

These reactions of nitrides are of theoretical
interest only.

Commercial preparation of ammonia.
(*a*) *From coal.* Coal, a product of the decomposition of vegetation, contains a small percentage of combined nitrogen. When coal is
heated in the absence of air (destructively dis-

**Fig. 78. Ammonia
may be collected by
upward displacement
of air.**

tilled) in the production of coke, an ammoniacal liquor is produced as a by-product.
Ammonia is recovered from this liquor by distillation and subsequent absorption in water.
The ammonium hydroxide solution thus produced may be converted
into ammonium salts by the addition of acids. Most of the supply
of ammonium sulfate which is used as a fertilizer is prepared in this
manner.

(*b*) *Haber process.* When nitrogen and hydrogen gases are heated
together in the presence of certain catalysts, some ammonia is formed
according to the reaction:

$$N_2 + 3\,H_2 \rightleftharpoons 2\,NH_3 + 24,000\ cal.$$

The reaction is very incomplete at ordinary conditions, equilibrium being established when the ammonia content is less than one per cent. Since the reaction is exothermic, it is evident from a consideration of Le Chatelier's principle (p. 224) that a low temperature is favorable to the formation of ammonia. However, if the temperature is below

Courtesy Spencer Chemical Company

Fig. 79. Spherical tanks used for storing synthetic ammonia.

about 500° the combination of nitrogen and hydrogen occurs so slowly as to be impractical as a commercial means of preparation. Applying Le Chatelier's principle, we note that an increase of pressure will shift the equilibrium to the right; that is, toward the formation of ammonia. An increase of pressure from 1 atmosphere at 500° to 200 atmospheres at 500° increases the equilibrium yield of ammonia in the above reaction from 0.13 per cent to 17.6 per cent. The process is ordinarily carried out at a temperature of approximately 500° and at a pressure of 200 atmospheres in the presence of a catalyst mixture such as Fe_3O_4 and $K_2O \cdot Al_2O_3$. Ammonia is liquefied from the equilibrium mixture by rapid refrigeration of the gas mix, and the residual N_2 and H_2 is counterpassed back to the high-pressure catalyst chamber. Since large supplies of nitrogen compounds are essential in making explosives, the above process was particularly vital to German interests during World War I. Germany's access to the Chilean deposits was cut off by the British blockade, and it is certain that had Germany been unable to utilize nitrogen from the air in producing explosives, the conflict would have lasted for only a few months. Haber, a German

Fig. 80. Oven room in a Muscle Shoals fixed nitrogen plant.

chemist, perfected the process just before the beginning of World War I in 1914. In World War II Germany again had to rely on synthetic nitrogen compounds.

Examine flow sheet for ammonia synthesis on page 566.

(c) *The cyanamide process.* The United States built several plants during the war years of 1914–1918 for the production of synthetic ammonia by the cyanamide process. The largest of these was located at Muscle Shoals, Alabama. The process depends for its success upon the development of cheap electric power. The first step in the preparation of ammonia consists in heating lime, CaO, and carbon together in an electric furnace to a temperature of approximately 3000°. The carbon reduces the lime to form calcium carbide:

$$CaO + 3\,C \longrightarrow CaC_2 + CO$$

Nitrogen obtained from the liquefaction of air is passed over the crushed calcium carbide at a temperature of about 1000°. *Calcium cyanamide*, $CaCN_2$, is produced:

$$CaC_2 + N_2 \longrightarrow CaCN_2 + C$$

The cyanamide is then treated with steam under pressure, forming ammonia and calcium carbonate:

$$CaCN_2 + 3\,H_2O \longrightarrow CaCO_3 \downarrow + 2\,NH_3$$

Cyanamide itself may be used directly as a fertilizer, as this last reaction proceeds slowly in soil.

Properties of ammonia. Ammonia is a colorless gas at ordinary temperatures. It is easily liquefied, forming a colorless liquid, the boiling point of which is −33°. The gas possesses a sharp, irritating odor. 22.4 liters of the gas at standard conditions weigh 17 grams; hence its formula is NH_3. The gas is extremely soluble in water, 1 liter of water dissolving more than 1000 liters of the gas at 0°. Its extreme solubility in water may be demonstrated by placing a small piece of ice on the surface of mercury in a tube filled with ammonia gas, as shown in Figure 81. As the ice melts, the ammonia dissolves and the mercury rapidly rises and almost fills the tube.

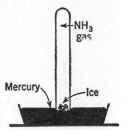

Fig. 81. Solubility of NH₃ in water.

When ammonia is dissolved in water, it reacts with the water to form a basic solution:

$$NH_3 + H_2O \rightleftharpoons NH_4{}^+ + OH^-$$

This is an equilibrium reaction; the change to the right takes place to only a slight extent. Consequently ammonium hydroxide is referred to as a weak base. Concentrated ammonium hydroxide contains about 28 per cent of ammonia at ordinary conditions of temperature and pressure.

Since it has basic properties, ammonium hydroxide reacts with acids to form ammonium salts:

$$NH_4OH + HCl \longrightarrow NH_4Cl + H_2O$$
$$2\,NH_4OH + H_2SO_4 \longrightarrow (NH_4)_2SO_4 + 2\,H_2O$$

Ammonia acts like a basic anhydride, reacting with acids to form ammonium salts:

$$NH_3 + HCl \longrightarrow NH_4Cl$$
$$2\,NH_3 + H_2SO_4 \longrightarrow (NH_4)_2SO_4$$

Reaction of ammonia with acid gases in the laboratory produces the familiar white salt deposits on laboratory glassware, windows, etc.

Ammonium salts have one characteristic which in general is not possessed by other salts. If an ammonium salt such as NH_4Cl is heated, it is dissociated according to the reaction:

$$NH_4Cl \longrightarrow NH_3 + HCl$$

The gases, ammonia and hydrogen chloride, recombine on cooling, forming solid ammonium chloride.

Ammonia readily burns in pure oxygen in the presence of a catalyst, forming nitric oxide and water:

$$4\,NH_3 + 5\,O_2 \longrightarrow 6\,H_2O + 4\,NO$$

This reaction represents one step in the preparation of nitric acid from the air by the Ostwald process (p. 297).

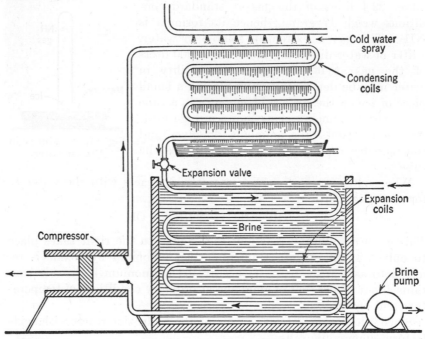

Fig. 82. Ice machine. Liquid ammonia is allowed to vaporize and expand through the expansion valve into the coils immersed in the brine solution, thereby cooling the brine. The gaseous ammonia then is compressed to liquid which takes place with evolution of heat. The heat of compression is removed by passing through coils over which cold water is sprayed. Ice may be produced by immersing tanks of water in the brine.

Uses of ammonia and ammonium salts.
Ammonia is used extensively as a refrigerant. If liquid ammonia is allowed to evaporate,

Courtesy Caterpillar Tractor Co.

Fig 82x. Fertilizing with ammonia gas.

much heat is absorbed from the surroundings. The gas may then be compressed and liquefied again, after which it again goes through the cycle of evaporation and liquefaction (Fig. 82).

Large quantities of ammonia are converted into ammonium salts, which are used as fertilizers. A solution of ammonia in water is used as a cleansing agent and as a water softener. Ammonia is also used in the Solvay process (chap. XXIX) for the production of soda.

A recent development of applying ammonia gas directly to the soil is receiving widespread attention of farmers. Spectacular results have been obtained in its use on irrigated lands in the West. The equipment consists essentially of tractor-mounted tanks of liquid ammonia and a battery of several steel tubes welded to the backs of cultivator shovels for injecting the gas into the soil. These tubes are connected with hoses to the ammonia tanks from which the flow of ammonia gas can be controlled with a meter. Very little loss occurs if the gas is placed about six inches below the surface. The practice of feeding the ammonia gas directly into irrigation streams is also successful.

Other compounds of nitrogen and hydrogen. Two additional nitrogen-hydrogen compounds merit mention. A compound H_2N-NH_2, or N$_2$H$_4$, is a liquid called *hydrazine*. Its water solution acts as a weak base and on neutralization can form salts such as N$_2$H$_5$Cl and N$_2$H$_6$Cl$_2$. A compound HN$_3$ (note formula difference from NH$_3$) is called *hydrazoic acid*. The water insoluble salts of this acid, silver azide, AgN$_3$, and lead azide, PbN$_6$, are very sensitive explosives; consequently they are used as detonators to initiate the explosion of less sensitive explosives.

NITRIC ACID AND NITRATES

Nitric acid was prepared by the alchemists from saltpeter (KNO$_3$) and concentrated H$_2$SO$_4$. It was used for separating gold and silver, the silver being soluble and the gold insoluble. The acid was called *aqua fortis* from the Latin, meaning "strong water."

Laboratory preparation. We learned in chapter XVI that a general method of preparing an acid is to treat a salt of the desired acid with sulfuric acid and distil. Since nitric acid is volatile and can be distilled easily, we may use the above method for its preparation. Sodium nitrate (Chile saltpeter) is the salt employed:

$$2\ NaNO_3 + H_2SO_4 \longrightarrow Na_2SO_4 + 2\ HNO_3 \uparrow$$

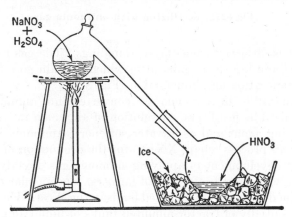

Fig. 83. Preparation of nitric acid.

Since the acid is active and attacks rubber, an all-glass apparatus is essential in the distillation (Fig. 83). The nitric acid distils over and may be condensed in a beaker or flask cooled by ice water. This same reaction is used for the preparation of nitric acid on a commercial scale, but large iron retorts are used. Due to the fact that nitric acid is slightly decomposed by impurities to form nitrogen dioxide, the acid produced by this method is not pure. The nitrogen dioxide may be removed, however, by bubbling air through the acid.

Commercial preparation. (*a*) *The same as laboratory preparation above.*

(*b*) *Haber-Ostwald process.* This is the process which enabled Germany, during 1914–1918, to fix nitrogen from the atmosphere and convert it into nitric acid for use in the manufacture of explosives. Nitrogen is first converted into ammonia by the Haber process, previously described (p. 290). Ammonia and air in the proportions of one volume of ammonia to about ten volumes of air are passed over a platinum catalyst at a temperature of about 700°. The ammonia is oxidized to nitric oxide (a colorless gas):

$$4\ NH_3 + 5\ O_2 \longrightarrow 4\ NO + 6\ H_2O$$

The NO readily combines with oxygen to form nitrogen dioxide, NO_2 (a brownish-red gas):

$$2\ NO + O_2 \longrightarrow 2\ NO_2$$

The nitrogen dioxide is then dissolved in water to produce nitric acid and nitric oxide:

$$3\ NO_2 + H_2O \longrightarrow 2\ HNO_3 + NO$$

The NO produced is again mixed with air and converted to NO_2. The acid produced by this method is about 50 per cent by weight and may be concentrated by distillation. This method of preparing nitric acid is widely used in the world today.

(*c*) *Birkeland-Eyde process.* Many years ago man learned how to hasten artificially one of nature's methods of nitrogen fixation. Cavendish discovered that nitrogen and oxygen would combine if air was passed through an electric discharge:

$$N_2 + O_2 \longrightarrow 2\ NO - 43{,}200\ calories$$

Since this reaction is endothermic, it is favored by high temperatures (Le Chatelier's principle). The electric arc used in the process produces a temperature of 3000° or greater. The nitric oxide produced is allowed to cool and then is converted into nitric acid by the same reactions as those in the Ostwald process. Birkeland and Eyde of Norway perfected this process, and its successful commercial use depends upon the production of cheap electricity. At the present time it is used only in those countries where large quantities of cheap hydroelectric power are available.

Properties of nitric acid. Nitric acid is a colorless liquid when pure, has a density of 1.5 and a boiling point of 86°. The nitric acid of commerce is about 68 per cent HNO_3 by weight and has a density of about 1.4. A product called "fuming nitric acid" is formed when nitrogen dioxide is dissolved in nitric acid.

Chemically, nitric acid is characterized both by its acid and oxidizing properties. As an acid it is highly ionized in dilute aqueous solution. It exhibits typical acid reactions, reacting with metallic oxides and bases to form salts.

In addition to its acid properties, nitric acid acts as a powerful oxidizing agent:

(*a*) *Action with metals.* Nitric acid reacts with practically all of the metals, even those below hydrogen in the activity series. This would seem to be contradictory to the rule that only metals above hydrogen react with acids. Nitric acid reacts with metals below hydrogen *not* because of its acid properties but because of its oxidizing action:

$$3\,Cu + 8\,HNO_3 \longrightarrow 3\,Cu(NO_3)_2 + 2\,NO + 4\,H_2O$$

or

$$3\,Cu + 8\,H^+ + 2\,NO_3^- \longrightarrow 3\,Cu^{++} + 2\,NO + 4\,H_2O$$

Other metals react similarly. Platinum and gold resist the oxidizing action. The reduction product of nitric acid depends somewhat on the concentration of the acid. Thus dilute acid produces nitric oxide, while concentrated acid produces nitrogen dioxide:

$$Cu + 4\,HNO_3 \longrightarrow Cu(NO_3)_2 + 2\,NO_2 + 2\,H_2O$$

or

$$Cu + 4\,H^+ + 2\,NO_3^- \longrightarrow Cu^{++} + 2\,NO_2 + 2\,H_2O$$

Metals above hydrogen in the activity series react with nitric acid to produce hydrogen *only* if the acid is very dilute and cold.

(*b*) *Action with nonmetals.* Hot concentrated nitric acid oxidizes several of the nonmetals, as shown by the equations:

$$S + 4\,HNO_3 \longrightarrow SO_2 + 4\,NO_2 + 2\,H_2O$$
$$P + 5\,HNO_3 \longrightarrow H_2O + H_3PO_4 + 5\,NO_2$$
$$C + 4\,HNO_3 \longrightarrow CO_2 + 4\,NO_2 + 2\,H_2O$$

(*c*) *Action with hydrochloric acid.* A mixture of three moles of hydrochloric acid to one mole of nitric acid is called *aqua regia* from the Latin "royal water." Aqua regia dissolves gold and platinum, these metals being inactive in either of the acids alone. The nitric acid oxidizes the hydrochloric acid to free chlorine, which is probably the active oxidizing agent in reactions with gold and platinum:

$$6\,HCl + 2\,HNO_3 \longrightarrow 3\,Cl_2 + 2\,NO + 4\,H_2O$$
$$2\,Au + 3\,Cl_2 \longrightarrow 2\,AuCl_3$$

(d) *Explosives manufacture.* Nitroglycerin is prepared by the action of a concentrated nitric-acid–sulfuric-acid mix on glycerin. (The concentrated H_2SO_4 acts as a dehydrating agent.)

$$C_3H_5(OH)_3 + 3\ HNO_3 \longrightarrow C_3H_5(NO_3)_3 + 3\ H_2O$$
$$\text{glycerin} \qquad\qquad\qquad \text{nitroglycerin}$$

Trinitrotoluene, commonly called TNT, is produced by a similar reaction:

$$C_6H_5CH_3 + 3\ HNO_3 \longrightarrow C_6H_2CH_3(NO_2)_3 + 3\ H_2O$$

Cellulose reacts with nitric acid to produce cellulose nitrate, or *guncotton.*

Most of the compounds formed by the action of nitric acid on organic compounds are explosive in character. *Dynamite* consists of nitroglycerin absorbed in a mixture such as sawdust and nitre. "Smokeless gunpowder" is essentially guncotton.

An explosion occurs as a result of a rapid chemical reaction attended by the formation of a large volume of gas. When nitroglycerin explodes, the volume of gas produced is many times the volume of the liquid nitroglycerin.

We may arrive at the approximate change in volume during the explosion of nitroglycerin from the following calculations:

$$4\ C_3H_5(NO_3)_3 \longrightarrow 12\ CO_2 + 10\ H_2O + 6\ N_2 + O_2$$

908 oz. of liquid nitroglycerin (about 1 cu. ft.) produces about $(12 + 10 + 6 + 1) \times 22.4 = 650$ cubic feet of gaseous products measured at standard conditions. Furthermore, the heat of explosion will expand the formed gases to a much larger volume. If the explosive products tend to be confined as in an artillery projectile or in a hole in rock, a disruptive pressure results as the small volume of initial explosive material, on detonation, forms so much gaseous product.

The crystalline substance NH_4NO_3 may be termed an explosive, and it is mixed in high percentage with other explosive materials. As the other materials explode, the shock brings about the instant decomposition of NH_4NO_3 into gaseous nitrogen, water, and oxygen.

Other uses of nitric acid include the manufacture of certain dyes and drugs. Nitrates are used as fertilizers.

Action of heat on nitrates. All nitrates decompose when heated. Sodium and potassium nitrates yield oxygen and the nitrite of the metal:

$$2\ NaNO_3 \longrightarrow 2\ NaNO_2 + O_2$$

The nitrates of the heavy metals produce oxygen, nitrogen dioxide, and the oxide of the metal:

$$2\ Pb(NO_3)_2 \longrightarrow 2\ PbO + 4\ NO_2 + O_2$$

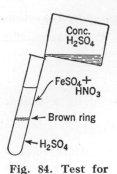

Fig. 84. Test for nitrate ion.

Test for the nitrate ion. If concentrated sulfuric acid is slowly added to a test tube containing a solution of nitric acid or a nitrate together with ferrous sulfate, a brown ring is formed at the junction of the two liquids (Fig. 84).

$$2\,NaNO_3 + H_2SO_4 \longrightarrow Na_2SO_4 + 2\,HNO_3$$

$$2\,HNO_3 + 6\,FeSO_4 + 3\,H_2SO_4 \longrightarrow$$
$$3\,Fe_2(SO_4)_3 + 2\,NO + 4\,H_2O$$

$$NO + FeSO_4 \longrightarrow FeSO_4 \cdot NO$$
nitrosyl ferrous
sulfate (brown)

OXIDES OF NITROGEN

Five oxides of nitrogen are well known:

> Nitrous oxide, N_2O, a colorless gas
> Nitric oxide, NO, a colorless gas
> Nitrogen dioxide, NO_2, a reddish brown gas
> Nitrogen trioxide, N_2O_3, a liquid boiling at 3°
> Nitrogen pentoxide, N_2O_5, a white solid

Nitrous oxide. The gas is produced by cautiously heating ammonium nitrate:

$$NH_4NO_3 \longrightarrow N_2O + 2\,H_2O$$

For laboratory study, it may be collected by displacement of hot water, since the gas is moderately soluble in cold water (61 cc. dissolves in 100 cc. water at 24° C.). Like oxygen, nitrous oxide supports combustion; a glowing splint burns vigorously when thrust into a bottle of the gas. Likewise phosphorus or sulfur burn vigorously in the gas.

Nitrous oxide has a sweet, pleasant odor and because of the exhilarating effect when inhaled is often referred to as "laughing gas." It is widely used as an anesthetic in dentistry and in minor surgical operations.

Nitric oxide. As pointed out earlier, nitric oxide is a reduction product of dilute nitric acid and is conveniently prepared by the action of dilute acid on a metal, *e.g.*

$$3\,Cu + 8\,HNO_3 \longrightarrow 3\,Cu(NO_3)_2 + 2\,NO + 4\,H_2O$$

The gas is colorless and relatively insoluble in water. It is the most stable of the oxides of nitrogen. A glowing splint thrust into the gas will go out; however, if vigorously burning phosphorus is placed in nitric oxide, it will continue to burn, leaving free nitrogen.

Nitrogen dioxide. When colorless nitric oxide is brought into contact with air or oxygen, reddish brown nitrogen dioxide is rapidly formed:

$$2\,NO + O_2 \longrightarrow 2\,NO_2$$

It may also be obtained by the action of concentrated nitric acid on metals, *e.g.*,

$$Cu + 4\,HNO_3 \longrightarrow Cu(NO_3)_2 + 2\,NO_2 + 2\,H_2O$$
$$Cu + 4\,H^+ + 2\,NO_3{}^- \longrightarrow Cu^{++} + 2\,NO_2 + 2\,H_2O$$

When heated, the reddish brown color becomes more intense; when cooled, the color fades to a pale yellow. Density studies show that an equilibrium exists in the gas between colorless N_2O_4 and brown NO_2:

$$\underset{\text{colorless}}{N_2O_4} \rightleftharpoons \underset{\text{red-brown}}{2\,NO_2} - x \text{ calories}$$

Since the reaction to the right is endothermic, an increase of temperature will shift the equilibrium to form more NO_2. When cooled, the reaction to the left forming N_2O_4 is favored. Thus the gradations of color with temperature change are explained on the basis of a shift in the equilibrium.

Nitrogen dioxide is an intermediate compound formed in the preparation of nitric acid by the Haber-Ostwald process (p. 297). When dissolved in water, oxidation and reduction take place within the molecules of NO_2 (called auto-oxidation) to form nitric acid and nitric oxide:

$$3\,NO_2 + H_2O \longrightarrow 2\,HNO_3 + NO$$

It is evident from the equation that two-thirds of the compound is oxidized to nitric acid while simultaneously one-third is reduced to nitric oxide. Thus two molecules are oxidized at the expense of the reduction of one molecule.

Nitrogen dioxide also plays an important role in the preparation of sulfuric acid by the lead chamber process (p. 325).

Nitrogen trioxide. N_2O_3 is the anhydride of nitrous acid, and may be produced by the action of sulfuric acid on a nitrite salt:

$$2\,NaNO_2 + H_2SO_4 \longrightarrow Na_2SO_4 + 2\,HNO_2$$
$$\qquad\qquad\qquad\qquad\qquad \hookrightarrow N_2O_3 + H_2O$$

The gas obtained in this reaction appears to be a mixture of equimolecular proportions of NO and NO_2, but when cooled to 3° it becomes a liquid which has a composition as represented by the formula, N_2O_3.

Nitrogen pentoxide. N_2O_5 is the anhydride of nitric acid and may be produced by the dehydration of that acid with phosphorus pentoxide:

$$2\,HNO_3 + P_2O_5 \longrightarrow 2\,HPO_3 + N_2O_5$$

The product, a white solid, melting at 30°, may be separated from the reaction mixture by low temperature distillation. The anhydride reacts vigorously with water to form nitric acid.

EXERCISES

1. List the various processes for the fixation of atmospheric nitrogen.
2. What is the general method for preparation of ammonia in the laboratory?
3. Ammonium carbonate, used as smelling salt, gives a strong odor of ammonia, while other ammonium salts do not. Explain.
4. Complete and balance:

   (a) $NH_3 + H_2O \longrightarrow$
   (b) $NH_3 + H_2SO_4 \longrightarrow$
   (c) NH_4NO_2 (heat) $\longrightarrow$
   (d) $(NH_4)_2SO_4 + Ca(OH)_2 \longrightarrow$
   (e) $SO_2 + NH_4OH \longrightarrow$

   (f) $HNO_3 + Ag \longrightarrow$
   (g) $HNO_3 + C_2H_4(OH)_2 \longrightarrow$
   (h) $S + HNO_3$ (conc.) $\longrightarrow$
   (i) $MgO + HNO_3 \longrightarrow$
   (j) $N_2O_5 + H_2O \longrightarrow$

5. Write equation or equations for the preparation of NH_4NO_3 from NH_4Cl and other needed chemicals.
6. Calculate the weight of ammonia obtainable from 100 g. of $(NH_4)_3PO_4$.

   Ans. 34.2 g.
7. Suggest a method for the determination of the molecular weight of NH_3.
8. Why cannot HNO_3 be prepared by the reaction

$$NaNO_3 + HCl \longrightarrow NaCl + HNO_3$$

9. Calculate the weight of 100 liters of ammonia at standard conditions.

   Ans. 76 g.
10. Why was the Haber process of vital importance to Germany during the two world wars?
11. By means of equations, show that:

    (a) HNO_3 may act as an acid.
    (b) HNO_3 may act as an oxidizing agent.
    (c) NH_3 may act as a reducing agent.
    (d) NH_3 neutralizes acids.

12. From the equations for the cyanamide process, calculate the quantities of lime (CaO), coke (C), and nitrogen necessary to produce one pound of ammonia.
13. Describe how you would proceed to test a sample of fertilizer for the presence of ammonium salts.
14. What volume of NH_3 measured at standard conditions must bubble into and react with H_3PO_4 to prepare 596 g. of $(NH_4)_3PO_4$?
15. "Rain during a thunderstorm is very dilute nitric acid." Write equations to explain this phenomenon.

REFERENCES

C. L. Parsons, "Nitric Acid from Ammonia," *Ind. and Eng. Chem.* **19,** 789 (1927).

George A. Sands, "Transportation and Storage of Strong Nitric Acid," *ibid.* **40,** 1937 (1948).

F. S. Lodge, "Fertilizer Chemistry," *ibid.* **43,** 311 (1951).

E. R. Riegel, *Industrial Chemistry*, Reinhold.

Robert Taft, "The Beginning of Liquid Ammonia Research in the United States," *J. Chem. Ed.* **10,** 34 (1933).

"Nitrogen from Tanks," *The Farm Quarterly* **6,** No. 1, 30 (1951).

Other Elements of the Nitrogen Family

$$_{15}P^{31} \quad _{33}As^{74.9}$$

$$_{51}Sb^{121.8} \quad _{83}Bi^{209}$$

ELEMENT	SYMBOL	COLOR AND PHYSICAL STATE	SP. GR.	MELTING POINT, °C.	BOILING POINT, °C.	VALENCE
Phosphorus .	P	yellow solid	1.8	44	280	3, 5
Arsenic . .	As	gray solid	5.7	sublimes	——	3, 5
Antimony .	Sb	silvery solid	6.7	631	1440	3, 5
Bismuth . .	Bi	silvery solid	9.8	271	1450	3, 5

In addition to nitrogen the elements phosphorus, arsenic, antimony, and bismuth appear in Group V of the periodic table. Although these elements show some similarities to nitrogen, there are many marked differences in chemical properties. As the atomic weight increases a gradual change from distinct nonmetallic properties to metallic properties is observed. Nitrogen and phosphorus are distinctly nonmetallic in character, while antimony and arsenic exhibit properties of both a metal and a nonmetal. Bismuth exhibits characteristic metallic properties.

Atoms of these elements contain five electrons in the outer shell and thus exhibit a maximum positive valence of five. Compounds of the elements are covalent, *i.e.*, the atoms are held together by a sharing of electrons. The elements form many similar compounds as will be evident from the following:

HYDRIDES	CHLORIDES	OXIDES	ACIDS
NH_3	NCl_3	N_2O_3; N_2O_5	HNO_2; HNO_3
PH_3	PCl_3	P_2O_3; P_2O_5	H_3PO_3; H_3PO_4
AsH_3	$AsCl_3$	As_2O_3; As_2O_5	H_3AsO_3; H_3AsO_4
SbH_3	$SbCl_3$	Sb_2O_3; Sb_2O_5	$HSbO_2$; H_3SbO_4
BiH_3	$BiCl_3$	Bi_2O_3	$HBiO_3$

PHOSPHORUS

History and occurrence. Brand, a German alchemist, in quest of the philosopher's stone accidentally prepared the element in 1669 while experimenting with urine. On distilling a mixture of urine, sand, and charcoal, and heating the residue he obtained a substance which glowed in the dark. The substance was subsequently shown to be an element and was given the name *phosphorus*, which means "light bearer."

The element is never found in the free state, but its compounds are widely distributed. The most abundant mineral is *phosphate rock* or *phosphorite* which is largely $Ca_3(PO_4)_2$. Deposits are found in Montana, Idaho, and several of the southern states. Bones of man and animals have a high percentage of calcium phosphate; many body proteins contain phosphorus, particularly nerve tissues and brain cells. In all, the human body contains about one per cent of the element.

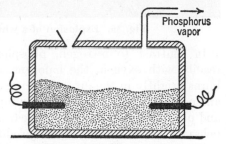

Fig. 85. **Phosphorus furnace.**

Preparation. Phosphorus is prepared by heating a mixture of phosphate rock, sand, and coke to a high temperature in an electric furnace (Fig. 85). Heat is produced by the resistance to the passage of current between the electrodes near the bottom of the furnace. The reaction probably takes place in two steps:

$$Ca_3(PO_4)_2 + 3 SiO_2 \longrightarrow 3 CaSiO_3 + P_2O_5$$
$$P_2O_5 + 5 C \longrightarrow 2 P \uparrow + 5 CO$$

Molten calcium silicate (slag) collects at the bottom and may be drawn off. Phosphorus leaves the furnace as a vapor which is condensed to a liquid. The liquid is further cooled and cast into sticks.

Properties. Phosphorus as prepared above is a soft, white, wax-like solid which gradually turns yellow in color. When exposed to air, oxidation takes place slowly with the evolution of heat, and the element spontaneously ignites at a temperature of 40° to 45°. The glowing action of phosphorus in the dark is due to the light emitted during the slow oxidation.

The element is insoluble in water but readily dissolves in carbon disulfide and certain other organic solvents. For storage and handling it is placed under water. Great care should be exercised in handling the element; it should always be picked up with tongs or forceps and never with the fingers. Warmth from the fingers may be sufficient to raise the temperature to the kindling point followed by spontaneous ignition. Phosphorus burns are painful and slow to heal.

Fig. 86. Explosion of a white-phosphorus bomb.

In contrast to nitrogen, phosphorus is fairly active, combining readily with oxygen, the halogens, and certain metals. Phosphorus burns brightly in the air, producing dense white fumes of the trioxide and pentoxide. In moist air these fumes form droplets of phosphorous and phosphoric acids which appear as a fog or mist. Because of this behavior, the element is used in production of smoke screens in warfare.

When yellow phosphorus is heated in the absence of air to a temperature of 250–300° it changes to a modification called *red* phosphorus. The latter variety is nonpoisonous in contrast to the extremely poisonous character of the yellow form. Red phosphorus ignites in air only at a high temperature and is insoluble in carbon disulfide.

Uses. Due to its low kindling temperature, phosphorus finds use as a medium for starting fires. As such it is used in incendiaries and tracer bullets, although its principal use is in the manufacture of matches. At one time yellow phosphorus was employed; its use, however, is now prohibited since factory workers inhaling air containing poisonous phosphorus vapor developed a dreadful disease causing decay of the bones of the jaw. A compound of phosphorus, phosphorus sesquisulfide, P_4S_3, has been found to be as effective as yellow phosphorus in match manufacture, and since it is nonpoisonous, workers may handle it in safety.

The essential ingredients of a match are (1) phosphorous sesquisulfide, which ignites at a low temperature; (2) a combustible substance such as paraffin, rosin, antimony sulfide, etc.; (3) an oxidizing agent like potassium chlorate or lead dioxide; (4) glue to bind the ingredients; (5) wood stick. For the "strike anywhere" match the above ingredients constitute the head; friction with a rough surface produces enough heat to ignite the phosphorus compound which initiates the reaction of the combustible substance and oxidizing agent. The flame produced is finally transmitted to the wood stick. The "safety" match contains no phosphorus in the head but instead the phosphorus compound is placed on the striking surface of the box along with ground glass and glue. Friction causes a bit of the phosphorus to ignite the ingredients of the head which are the same (except for phosphorus) as the "strike anywhere" match.

COMPOUNDS OF PHOSPHORUS

Phosphine. The hydride of phosphorus, PH_3, a colorless gas with an offensive odor resembling that of decaying fish, is the analog of ammonia, NH_3. Unlike ammonia it cannot be prepared by direct combination of the elements. It may be obtained by the action of water on calcium phosphide

$$Ca_3P_2 + 6 H_2O \longrightarrow 3 Ca(OH)_2 + 2 PH_3 \uparrow$$

or by the reaction

$$3 NaOH + 4 P + 3 H_2O \longrightarrow 3 NaH_2PO_2 + PH_3 \uparrow$$
$$\text{sodium}$$
$$\text{hypophosphite}$$

The gas is but slightly soluble in water and prepared as above ignites spontaneously on contact with the air to form smoke ring clouds of phosphoric acid (Fig. 87):

$$PH_3 + 2 O_2 \longrightarrow H_3PO_4$$

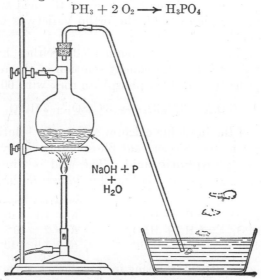

NaOH + P
+
H_2O

Fig. 87. Preparation of phosphine.

Oxides of phosphorus. The most important oxides are the trioxide, P_2O_3, and the pentoxide, P_2O_5, both white solids. They are obtained by the combustion of phosphorus in air, the trioxide being formed in a limited supply of air, and the pentoxide in an excess of air. The oxides are anhydrides of phosphorous and phosphoric acids respectively:

$$P_2O_3 + 3\ H_2O \longrightarrow 2\ H_3PO_3$$
$$P_2O_5 + 3\ H_2O \longrightarrow 2\ H_3PO_4$$

The latter reaction is particularly vigorous; advantage is taken of this behavior in the use of phosphorous pentoxide as an effective dehydrating agent.

Phosphoric acids. Phosphorous pentoxide is the anhydride of three phosphoric acids, the acids differing from one another only in degree of hydration of the oxide. The relationship between the three acids is shown below:

$$P_2O_5 + 3\ H_2O \longrightarrow 2\ H_3PO_4 \quad \text{(orthophosphoric acid)}$$
$$P_2O_5 + 2\ H_2O \longrightarrow H_4P_2O_7 \quad \text{(pyrophosphoric acid)}$$
$$P_2O_5 + H_2O \longrightarrow 2\ HPO_3 \quad \text{(metaphosphoric acid)}$$

The most hydrated of the acids is named the *ortho* acid, the least hydrated the *meta* acid, while the *pyro* acid represents an intermediate degree of hydration. Of these acids, orthophosphoric acid is the one obtained when phosphorous pentoxide is dissolved in water under ordinary conditions. When the ortho acid is heated to relatively high temperatures, the pyro and meta varieties of the acid are formed. In using the term phosphoric acid, the ortho variety is implied unless otherwise specified.

Phosphoric acid is obtained commercially either by ignition of phosphorus in the air and subsequent solution of the resulting oxide in water or by the treatment of phosphate rock with 60 per cent sulfuric acid:

$$Ca_3(PO_4)_2 + 3\ H_2SO_4 \longrightarrow 3\ CaSO_4 + 2\ H_3PO_4$$

After filtering off the insoluble calcium sulfate the solution is concentrated to approximately 85 per cent phosphoric acid by evaporation.

Ionization of phosphoric acid. The acid is triprotic, *i.e.*, has three replaceable hydrogen atoms, and thus ionizes in three steps:

IONIZATION CONSTANT

$$H_3PO_4 \rightleftharpoons H^+ + H_2PO_4^- \qquad K = 1.1 \times 10^{-2}$$
$$H_2PO_4^- \rightleftharpoons H^+ + HPO_4^{--} \qquad K = 2 \times 10^{-7}$$
$$HPO_4^{--} \rightleftharpoons H^+ + PO_4^{---} \qquad K = 3.6 \times 10^{-13}$$

As is the case with all acids ionizing in stages, each stage of the ionization is less complete than the preceding one; this is evidenced by the

Fig. 88. Barreling phosphates for industrial use.

ionization constants. Although H_3PO_4 is the strongest of the three, even it is a relatively weak acid. $H_2PO_4^-$ would be classed as a very weak acid and HPO_4^{--} as a very, very weak acid. Salts of all the three acids are known, e.g., the three sodium salts:

NaH_2PO_4 sodium dihydrogen phosphate
Na_2HPO_4 disodium hydrogen phosphate
Na_3PO_4 normal or trisodium phosphate

The latter compound is used extensively as a water softener and as a cleansing agent. A mixture of the sodium acid phosphates has much to do in maintaining a constant acidity of the blood.

Superphosphate. Phosphorus is an element vital to the growth of plants and must necessarily be present in fertile soils for successful plant propagation. Depleted soils must be furnished with fertilizers containing phosphorus. One of the most important of these is *superphosphate*, a mixture of primary calcium phosphate and calcium sulfate, which is prepared by the action of sulfuric acid on rock phosphate according to the equation:

$$Ca_3(PO_4)_2 + 2\,H_2SO_4 \longrightarrow Ca(H_2PO_4)_2 + 2\,CaSO_4$$
$$\text{superphosphate}$$

Whereas rock phosphate itself is too insoluble to be utilized by plants, the acid salt is soluble, but yet not soluble enough to be quickly washed from soil; thus it is available for plant metabolism. The sulfuric acid simply renders the phosphorus available by formation of the acid salt. Calcium acid phosphate is also used in certain baking powders (see chap. XXIX).

ARSENIC

Occurrence and preparation. Although arsenic is found in small quantities in the free state, its principal occurrence is as sulfides: *arsenopyrite*, $FeAsS$; *orpiment*, As_2S_3; and *realgar*, As_2S_2. Small quantities of arsenic are usually associated with most sulfide ores; as a matter of fact nearly all of the arsenic produced is recovered as a by-product from the flues of smelters utilizing sulfide ores of zinc, copper, lead, etc. During the roasting process, the arsenic is converted to arsenious oxide, As_2O_3, which is volatile and is condensed in the flues as a finely divided solid. The element is easily obtained from the oxide by reduction with carbon:

$$As_2O_3 + 3\,C \longrightarrow 2\,As + 3\,CO$$

Properties and uses. The element is a gray crystalline solid with a metallic luster. The solid sublimes to a yellowish, poisonous vapor which has the odor of garlic. The principal use of arsenic is in hardening lead shot. The latter is made by pouring molten lead through a screen which breaks up the liquid into small drops. The presence of arsenic lengthens the time of solidification, thereby allowing the drops to attain a more nearly spherical shape, and at the same time the arsenic alloys with the lead to produce a harder product.

Compounds of arsenic. Arsenic is very similar to phosphorus in many of its reactions. The oxides of arsenic, arsenic trioxide and arsenic pentoxide, dissolve in water to form arsenious and arsenic acids respectively. *Arsine*, AsH_3, a very poisonous gas of garlic odor, is the analog of ammonia and phosphine. It is an unstable compound and decomposes when moderately heated into metallic arsenic and hydrogen:

$$2 AsH_3 \longrightarrow 2 As + 3 H_2$$

Arsenic trioxide, a white solid commonly called "white arsenic" or simply "arsenic," is the starting material in the preparation of most of the compounds of arsenic. It has a sweet taste and is highly poisonous.[1] Its principal use is in the preparation of insecticides, some of the more common of which are: *lead arsenate*, $Pb_3(AsO_4)_2$, used as a spray for fruits and vegetables; *sodium* and *calcium arsenates* for killing boll weevil in cotton fields; *paris green*, $3 Cu(AsO_2)_2 \cdot Cu(C_2H_3O_2)_2$, an insecticide. *Scheele's green*, $CuHAsO_3$, finds limited application as a paint pigment.

While most arsenic compounds are very poisonous, a few have a definite medicinal value in small doses. The most notable of these is *salvarsan*, a complex arsenic-containing organic compound which is specific in the treatment of syphilis.

Marsh test. This test is used for detecting the presence of small quantities of arsenic. It is based on the formation of arsine by the reduction of arsenic compounds with nascent or atomic hydrogen. An apparatus as shown in Figure 89 is employed, consisting essentially of a hydrogen generator, drying tube, and a long glass tube which can be heated. The material to be tested is placed in the hydrogen generator, and if arsenic is present, arsine will be formed by reduction with hydrogen. The arsine gas is passed through the glass tube and there, because of its unstable character, may be decomposed into metallic arsenic and hydrogen by moderate heat. The arsenic deposits as a bright silvery mirror on the inside of the tube.

---

[1] One of the most wicked women of history, Lucretia Borgia, used arsenic oxide to poison many men. Roman ladies ate minute quantities of "white arsenic" to enhance the whiteness of their skin and pink of their cheeks. They gradually built up an immunity to the poisonous effects of the arsenic oxide and ultimately could safely take a dose that would "kill a horse."

Since arsenic compounds are so commonly used in fruit tree spraying, rigid state food control laws are enforced so that fruit is washed to practically free it of the poisonous arsenic-containing spray residue. Control tests for small amounts of residual arsenic are made by a modified Marsh test called a "Gutzeit test." A sample of macerated fruit peelings is put in a small flask and zinc and acid added as in the Marsh test. Instead of heating to break down the escaping arsine

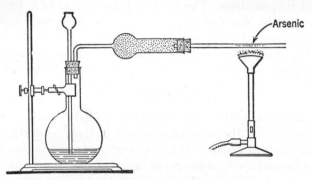

Fig. 89. Marsh test for arsenic.

gas, the possible arsine-containing gas passes by a thin strip of paper into which has been soaked a mercury salt. Arsine will turn the mercury salt to a reddish-yellow color. The length of the color band gives a measure of the amount of arsine from a given weight of sample; the amount of arsenic residue on the fruit may be determined down to as little as a few parts per million. Stomach liquid of a poisoned man or animal can be analyzed for arsenic in the same way.

Traces of arsine gas passed over a white crystal of silver nitrate will turn the crystal first yellow and then black; this likewise can be used in making a quick test for arsenic.

ANTIMONY

Occurrence and preparation. The chief source of antimony is the mineral *stibnite*, Sb_2S_3, although small quantities of the element are found in the free state. Antimony may be recovered from stibnite by heating with finely divided iron:

$$Sb_2S_3 + 3\,Fe \longrightarrow 3\,FeS + 2\,Sb$$

The molten products separate into two layers with the lighter ferrous sulfide layer on top.

Stibnite may also be roasted to the oxide, followed by reduction with carbon:

$$2 Sb_2S_3 + 9 O_2 \longrightarrow 2 Sb_2O_3 + 6 SO_2$$
$$Sb_2O_3 + 3 C \longrightarrow 2 Sb + 3 CO$$

Properties and uses. The element is more metallic in appearance and in properties than arsenic. It is brittle and a poor conductor of heat and electricity. The element is not metallic enough in character to displace hydrogen from hydrochloric acid but reacts with nitric acid to form the tri- and pentoxides. Direct combination of the element with sulfur and the halogens takes place readily.

The principal use of antimony is in the preparation of alloys. The addition of antimony to lead gives a much harder product, useful in making bullets and shrapnel. Type metal is an alloy of lead, tin, and antimony which expands on solidification, thereby filling all parts of the mold to produce a sharp and distinct casting.

Compounds of antimony. Compounds of antimony are closely related to those of arsenic. *Stibine*, SbH_3, is prepared in a manner similar to arsine. Like arsine, it is a poisonous gas which is unstable toward heat. The oxides, Sb_2O_3, Sb_2O_4, and Sb_2O_5, are known. These oxides are more basic than the corresponding oxides of phosphorus and arsenic as would be expected from the increasingly metallic character of the elements of Group V with increasing atomic weight. The tri- and pentoxides are amphoteric, dissolving in acids to form antimonous and antimonic salts and in strong bases to form antimonites and antimonates.

Antimony chloride, $SbCl_3$, called "butter of antimony" because of the soft, mushy appearance of the crystals is made by direct combination of the elements. This salt, as well as most of the other salts of antimony, is highly hydrolyzed to produce an insoluble basic salt:

$$SbCl_3 + H_2O \rightleftharpoons SbOCl + 2 HCl$$

When hydrogen sulfide is passed into a solution containing antimony ions, a reddish-orange precipitate of the sulfide is formed, a reaction which is often used in testing for the presence of antimony.

BISMUTH

Occurrence and preparation. Bismuth occurs in both the free and combined states. Naturally occurring compounds are *bismuth glance*, Bi_2S_3, and *bismite*, $Bi_2O_3 \cdot 3 H_2O$. Like arsenic and antimony, bismuth may be obtained from the sulfide ore by roasting followed by reduction with carbon. A good deal of bismuth is recovered as a by-product of lead smelters and refineries.

Properties and uses. Bismuth is distinctly a metallic element, which is hard, brittle and has a silvery luster with a reddish tinge. Bismuth burns when highly heated in air to form the trioxide, Bi_2O_3, and combines directly with the halogens to form halide salts, although the latter reactions are not vigorous. Unlike the other members of the group, bismuth dissolves in nitric acid to form a nitrate salt.

Bismuth is used in the preparation of several low-melting alloys, e.g., *Rose's metal* (Sn, Pb, Bi), melting point 94°, and *Wood's metal* (Pb, Cd, Sn, Bi), melting point 71°. These alloys find use in electrical fuses, automatic fire sprinklers, safety plugs for boilers, automatic fire alarms, etc.

Compounds. The oxide and hydroxide of bismuth are distinctly basic in character. $BiCl_3$ like $SbCl_3$ is highly hydrolyzed to form water insoluble basic chloride, $BiOCl$. Bismuth nitrate when added to water is hydrolyzed to form basic bismuth subnitrate, a compound used medicinally in treatment of certain digestive disturbances:

$$Bi(NO_3)_3 + H_2O \rightleftharpoons BiONO_3 \downarrow + 2 HNO_3$$

OTHER ELEMENTS OF GROUP V

$$_{23}V \quad^{50.95}_{2\ 8\ 11\ 2} \qquad _{41}Nb \quad^{92.91}_{2\ 8\ 18\ 12\ 1} \qquad _{73}Ta \quad^{180.9}_{2\ 8\ 18\ 32\ 11\ 2}$$

ELEMENT	SYMBOL	SP. GR.	MELTING POINT	VALENCE
Vanadium	V	5.96	1710°	2, 3, 4, 5
Niobium	Nb	8.4	1950°	5
Tantalum	Ta	16.6	2850°	5

Vanadium, niobium,[1] and tantalum. These elements have a predominant valence of five and constitute a subgroup of the nitrogen-phosphorus family. Their occurrence is comparatively rare. Two of the better known minerals containing vanadium are *vanadinite*, $Pb_5(VO_4)_3Cl$, and *carnotite*, $K_2(UO_2)_2(VO_4)_2 \cdot 3 H_2O$. *Columbite*, $FeO \cdot Nb_2O_5$, and *tantalite*, $FeO \cdot Ta_2O_5$, have been sources of compounds of niobium and tantalum.

The most stable of the compounds of these elements are those in which the element exhibits a valence of five.

The above elements combine directly with oxygen, chlorine, and nitrogen to form oxides, chlorides, and nitrides, respectively. A small

[1] Formerly called columbium.

percentage of vanadium alloyed with steel gives a high tensile strength product which is very tough and resistant to shock and vibration. For this reason vanadium alloy steels are used in the manufacture of high-speed tools and heavy machinery. Vanadium oxide is employed as a catalyst in the "contact process" of manufacturing sulfuric acid. Niobium is a very rare element and has no important uses. Tantalum is a steel-gray metal which may be rolled or hammered with difficulty. It has a very high melting point (2850°) and is resistant to corrosion by most acids and alkalies; thus, it may be used as a platinum substitute for certain laboratory utensils. Tantalum carbide is almost as hard as diamond and is a component of some abrasive and cutting mixtures. A marked improvement in rock drilling results from the use of tantalum carbide bits on the end of drill steel.

EXERCISES

1. Approximately how many pounds of As_2O_3 are used in making 1 ton of $Pb_3(AsO_4)_2$? Ans. 440.
2. Write names and formulas of two acids containing antimony.
3. Write formulas for:

   (a) ortho and meta arsenic acids
   (b) lead ortho and meta arsenites
   (c) stibine
   (d) bismuthyl nitrate (also known as bismuth oxynitrate)

4. Write equations for:

   (a) calcium phosphide + dilute HCl
   (b) hydrolysis of antimony trichloride
   (c) preparation of copper arsenite from the raw materials, As_2O_3, H_2O, $CuSO_4$

5. Given As_2S_3, limestone, air, and water; write equations for a practical way of preparing calcium arsenite.
6. A Seattle concern prepares a garden ground rock mixture composed of $(NH_4)_3PO_4$, $CaCO_3$, and granite. It is desired to have the mixture analyze 0.2 per cent phosphorus. What weight of ammonium phosphate should be in each 100 pounds of the mix? Ans. 1 lb. approx.
7. A ton of rock contains 5 per cent carnotite. On treatment, 90 per cent of the vanadium and uranium is recovered from the ore. What weights of the respective metals are obtained from the rock?
8. An alloy containing one gram atom each of Pb, Cd, Sn, and Bi would have what percentage of bismuth? Ans. 32.3.
9. Discuss the relative merits of superphosphate, ammonium phosphate, and phosphoric acid as fertilizers. Name some of the advantages of triple phosphate, which is made:

$$Ca_3(PO_4)_2 + 4\,H_3PO_4 \longrightarrow 3\,Ca(H_2PO_4)_2$$

10. White phosphorus from a bursting shell burns to an oxide, which by hydration forms a white smoke of H_3PO_4 particles. What weight of white smoke can form from burning 1 lb. of phosphorus? Ans. 3.1.

11. Arsenic (at. no. 33, at. wt. 75) occurs in Group V *A* of the periodic table. How many electrons are there in each consecutive orbit? How many protons in the nucleus? What are the valences of As as indicated by its structure?

REFERENCES

"Matches," *J. Chem. Ed.* **6,** 1359 (1929).

L. F. Audrieth and O. F. Hill, "Recent Developments in the Chemistry of Phosphorus," *ibid.* **24,** 80 (1948).

W. H. Waggaman, "Phosphate Rock Industry of the United States," *ibid.* **10,** 391 (1933).

—— and H. W. Easterwood, *Phosphoric Acid, Phosphates, and Phosphatic Fertilizers,* Reinhold.

A. J. Mee, "Phosphorescence and Phosphorus," *Science Progress,* **30,** 635 (1936).

Vincent Sauchelli, "Evolution in Fertilizer Phosphate Industry," *Ind. & Eng. Chem.* **41,** 1314 (1949).

T. L. Wilkerson, "Processing Phosphate Rock for Use in Agriculture," *ibid.* **41,** 1316 (1949).

H. W. Davis, "Vanadium," U. S. Dept. of Interior *Minerals Yearbook* (1949), 1262–1265.

XXIV

The Sulfur Family

$$_{16}S^{32.06} \quad {}_{2\ 8\ 6} \qquad _{34}Se^{78.96} \quad {}_{2\ 8\ 18\ 6} \qquad _{52}Te^{127.6} \quad {}_{2\ 8\ 18\ 18\ 6}$$

ELEMENT	SYMBOL	COLOR	SP. GR.	MELTING POINT	BOILING POINT	VALENCE
Sulfur . . .	S	pale yellow	2.07	113° C.	445° C.	2, 4, 6
Selenium . .	Se	steel gray	4.8	220° C.	688° C.	2, 4, 6
Tellurium .	Te	metallic	6.24	452° C.	1390° C.	2, 4, 6

The sulfur family includes the elements oxygen, sulfur, selenium, and tellurium which appear in Group VI of the periodic table. Although there appears to be little in common between the yellow solid, sulfur, and the colorless gas, oxygen, nevertheless we shall find that these elements form many similar compounds.

SULFUR

Occurrence of sulfur. Sulfur was known to the ancients as brimstone, which means "burning stone." It is often referred to in the Bible; ancient priests taught of hell as a place not only of fire but of burning brimstone (choking odor of SO_2). The Greek philosophers considered sulfur to be an elementary substance, although their concept of an element was different from the view held today. It was extensively used in the treatment of disease and as a fumigant.[1]

In the free state, the element is found rather extensively, especially in volcanic regions. Large deposits of sulfur are found in Sicily and in Louisiana and Texas. Up to the year 1900, most of the sulfur came

---

[1] In the *Odyssey*, it is related that Penelope ordered brimstone burned in the marble halls of her home after her long-absent husband Ulysses came home and slew and scattered about bodies of men who had sought to marry his wife and wasted his flocks. It is interesting to know that the rudiments of fumigation were known in this early time.

from Sicily, but the United States now furnishes about 80 per cent of the world's supply.

In the combined state, sulfur occurs in the form of metallic sulfides, such as *sphalerite*, ZnS; *galena*, PbS; *chalcocite*, Cu_2S; *chalcopyrite*, $CuFeS_2$; *iron pyrites*, FeS_2; *cinnabar*, HgS; and several other minerals. These compounds are of economic importance, as they are the sources of the metals Zn, Cu, Pb, Hg, etc. Some combined sulfur exists as sulfates of calcium (*gypsum*, $CaSO_4 \cdot 2\,H_2O$) and barium (*barite*, $BaSO_4$). Many organic compounds contain sulfur; proteins in the body contain small amounts, as do certain vegetable compounds in onion, garlic, horseradish, and mustard. Sulfur appears to be one of the elements essential to vital life processes.

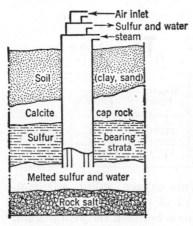

Fig. 90. Frasch process.

The extraction of sulfur. In volcanic regions, the sulfur is mixed with soil and rocks, from which it can be separated by heat. Heat melts the sulfur, leaving the impurities in a solid condition. In Louisiana and Texas the sulfur deposits are found several hundred feet below the surface of the ground. Because these deposits are covered with a layer of quicksand, the sulfur cannot be mined by ordinary means. Herman Frasch, a German-American chemist and engineer, has devised an ingenious method for obtaining the sulfur from its underground deposits (Fig. 90). His method is based on the relatively low melting point of sulfur (113°). A hole is bored into the bed of sulfur and the well is then lined with a series of three concentric pipes, *i.e.*, one fitted inside another. Superheated steam and air are forced down the well under pressure through two of the pipes. The steam melts the sulfur, which is then forced to the surface in a frothy liquid state by compressed air. The sulfur is allowed to solidify in large blocks at the surface. Each well may produce several hundred tons daily and the product is about 99.5 per cent pure.

Different forms of sulfur. Free sulfur may exist in several forms. The form of sulfur found in nature is known as the *rhombic* variety, so called from the shape of the crystals. If these crystals are heated to a temperature of 96°, they slowly change into another more needle-like crystalline variety, which is called *monoclinic* sulfur. The temperature at which a given solid will change its crystalline form is known as the *transition point* or *transition temperature*. Thus, 96° is a transition point of sulfur. This property of a substance of existing in more than one physical form in the same physical state is termed *allotropy*, and the different forms are referred to as *allotropes*. Other elements, such as phosphorus and carbon, may exist in allotropic forms.

When rhombic sulfur is heated, it melts at a temperature of 113° to a straw-colored liquid. This liquid variety of pale yellow or amber colored sulfur is called *mobile* sulfur because it flows freely. When allowed to cool and solidify, crystals of monoclinic sulfur are obtained. If the heating of mobile sulfur be continued, the liquid darkens and becomes thick and sticky, like molasses. This form of sulfur is called *viscous* sulfur. Continued heating changes the liquid sulfur to vapor at a temperature of about 445°. If viscous sulfur be cooled rapidly by immersion in cold water, a rubbery, plastic mass of solid sulfur is obtained, which is called *plastic* or amorphous sulfur. Amorphous means noncrystalline. Under ordinary conditions, this variety of sulfur will gradually change into rhombic sulfur, the stable form at ordinary temperatures. The relationship between the various forms of sulfur may be represented by the diagram:

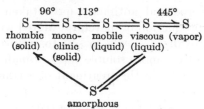

The transformations are reversible except that of amorphous to rhombic, all forms finally reverting to the stable rhombic form under ordinary conditions.

Chemical properties. Sulfur combines directly with most of the metals to form sulfides. When iron is heated with sulfur a great deal of heat is evolved, and a vigorous reaction ensues, with the formation of ferrous sulfide. Other metals combine similarly. In some cases, the combination may take place at ordinary temperature. Thus when mercury and sulfur are ground together in a mortar, black mercuric sulfide is formed:

$$Hg + S \longrightarrow HgS$$

Sulfur will combine directly with certain of the nonmetals, although the combination does not take place as readily as with metals. Sulfur burns with a blue flame in air or oxygen to form sulfur dioxide:

$$S + O_2 \longrightarrow SO_2$$

Other compounds of sulfur with nonmetals are carbon disulfide, CS_2, phosphorus sesquisulfide, P_4S_3, and sulfur chloride, S_2Cl_2.

Sulfur exhibits a variable valence from -2 to $+6$. The sulfur atom has six electrons in its outer orbit and tends to acquire two more electrons to complete a stable configuration. Usually these electrons are acquired by sharing. If the electrons are obtained from a more positive element, such as hydrogen, the valence is regarded as negative, while if the source of electrons is an element more negative than the sulfur atom, such as oxygen, then the valence of sulfur is regarded as positive. The valence of sulfur in sulfides is -2, in sulfites $+4$, and in sulfates $+6$.

Uses of sulfur. Most of the sulfur produced is used in the preparation of sulfuric acid and other compounds of sulfur. Another extremely important use is in the *vulcanization* of rubber. Pure rubber tends to become sticky when slightly warmed and brittle when cold. In the vulcanization process, sulfur is incorporated into the rubber and a product is obtained which extends the temperature at which rubber has the desirable properties of resiliency and toughness. Heated with lime, sulfur forms "lime sulfur spray" which is used as an insecticide. Black gunpowder is a mixture of carbon, sulfur, and saltpeter (KNO_3). Sulfides of phosphorus and antimony have taken the place of free phosphorus in the production of matches. Mixed with rock phosphate fertilizer, sulfur is oxidized slowly in soil to sulfuric acid which converts the fertilizer into a more soluble form. Small amounts of sulfur are employed medicinally in the treatment of certain skin diseases.

HYDROGEN SULFIDE

Hydrogen sulfide is produced during the destructive distillation of proteins and other sulfur-containing compounds. It is a constituent of coal gas and sewer gas. The offensive odor of rotten eggs is largely due to the presence of this substance.

Preparation of hydrogen sulfide. Sulfur does not combine appreciably with hydrogen at ordinary temperatures, but at an elevated temperature combination takes place readily to form hydrogen sulfide:

$$H_2 + S \rightleftharpoons H_2S$$

The reaction, however, is reversible, and since hydrogen sulfide itself is quite unstable toward heat, the yield is small.

In the laboratory it is most conveniently prepared by the action of a nonoxidizing acid on certain metallic sulfides:

$$FeS + \text{(dilute)} H_2SO_4 \longrightarrow FeSO_4 + H_2S$$
$$ZnS + 2\,HCl \longrightarrow ZnCl_2 + H_2S$$

These equations are further examples of the general method of preparing an acid, that is, by treating a salt of the desired acid with a less volatile acid. While hydrochloric acid is a volatile acid, it is less volatile from water solution than hydrogen sulfide and consequently may be used.

Properties. Hydrogen sulfide is a colorless gas at ordinary temperatures and is characterized by its foul odor — that of rotten eggs. It may be condensed to a liquid at $-59.6°$ and converted to a solid at $-83°$. It is not very soluble in water, one liter of water dissolving about three liters of the gas at ordinary temperatures. The gas is very poisonous, and if the concentration exceeds one-half of one per cent in the air, breathing of this air may be fatal to humans and animals. The physiological effect of hydrogen sulfide is paralysis of the nerve centers of the heart and lungs. Fortunately, hydrogen sulfide in small quantities is easily detected by its characteristic odor.

Hydrogen sulfide reacts with water to form a solution with acidic properties:

$$H_2S + 2 H_2O \rightleftharpoons 2 H_3O^+ + S^{--}$$

The ionization is very slight; consequently hydrosulfuric acid is classed as a weak acid. It exhibits typical weak acid reactions, reacting with bases to form salts, *e.g.*

$$2 NaOH + H_2S \longrightarrow Na_2S + 2 H_2O$$

Hydrogen sulfide burns in the air with a blue flame, producing sulfur dioxide and water:

$$2 H_2S + 3 O_2 \longrightarrow 2 H_2O + 2 SO_2$$

If combustion takes place in a limited supply of air (as for example in an open bottle) free sulfur is deposited:

$$2 H_2S + O_2 \longrightarrow 2 H_2O + 2 S$$

Hydrogen sulfide is a good reducing agent as may be shown by the reactions:

$$3 H_2S + (dilute) 2 HNO_3 \longrightarrow 3 S + 2 NO + 4 H_2O$$
$$H_2S + I_2 \longrightarrow S + 2 HI$$
$$H_2SO_4 + H_2S \longrightarrow S + SO_2 + 2 H_2O$$
$$2 H_2S + SO_2 \longrightarrow 3 S + 2 H_2O$$

Certain metallic ions produce colored sulfides with hydrogen sulfide, such as lead sulfide (black), copper sulfide (black), cadmium sulfide (yellow), antimony sulfide (orange), manganese sulfide (pink). The formation of a colored sulfide may be used as a basis for a test for the presence of hydrogen sulfide. If a piece of filter paper which has been saturated with lead nitrate solution is placed in a stream of hydrogen sulfide gas, a black deposit of lead sulfide is formed on the paper:

$$Pb^{++} + H_2S \longrightarrow PbS \downarrow + 2 H^+$$

This test is useful in locating breaks in sewer lines, as well as in pipes carrying coal gas or natural gas, which usually contain a little hydrogen sulfide.

Uses of hydrogen sulfide. The use of hydrogen sulfide is confined largely to the chemical laboratory where it is employed in the separation and identification of metallic ions. Its use as an analytical reagent is very important. Let us consider for a moment the way in which it functions as a qualitative reagent.

The equilibrium

$$H_2S \rightleftharpoons 2 H^+ + S^{--}$$

may be shifted by the addition of an acid or base. If acid is added, repression of ionization occurs resulting in a decrease of the sulfide ion concentration. The addition of hydroxyl ions from a base causes a shift in equilibrium to the right because of the formation of unionized water by the combination of hydrogen and hydroxyl ions. This results in an increase of the sulfide ion concentration. It is evident, then, that the sulfide ion concentration can be controlled by proper adjustment of the acidity or basicity of the solution. Since the metallic sulfides have different solubility product constants, we could theoretically successively precipitate the metallic ions as sulfides by proper control of the acidity of the solution. Actually in qualitative analysis, the concentration of hydrogen ion is adjusted to 0.3 molar, in which solution the sulfides of arsenic, antimony, mercury, tin, lead, copper, bismuth, and cadmium are precipitated. Other metallic sulfides are not precipitated because the sulfide ion concentration in the solution is not sufficient to exceed the solubility product of these other sulfides. By making the solution basic the sulfide ion concentration is increased to the point where another group of sulfides precipitate. By means of hydrogen sulfide, the metallic ions may be readily separated into three groups: (1) those whose sulfides are insoluble in dilute acid; (2) those sulfides which are insoluble in basic solution; and (3) those sulfides which are soluble in both acidic and basic solutions.

OXIDES AND ACIDS OF SULFUR

Sulfur forms several oxides, only two of which will be considered here. Sulfur dioxide and sulfur trioxide are the acid anhydrides of the acids, sulfurous and sulfuric, respectively.

Preparation of sulfur dioxide. (a) *By burning sulfur.* Sulfur burns with a blue flame in air:

$$S + O_2 \longrightarrow SO_2$$

(b) *By roasting sulfides.* Roasting consists in heating a metallic sulfide in the presence of air or oxygen. The metal is converted to an oxide. This process is very important in the metallurgy of ores, since it represents one step in the production of a metal from its sulfide ore:

$$2\,PbS + 3\,O_2 \longrightarrow 2\,PbO + 2\,SO_2$$
$$2\,ZnS + 3\,O_2 \longrightarrow 2\,ZnO + 2\,SO_2$$
$$4\,FeS_2 + 11\,O_2 \longrightarrow 2\,Fe_2O_3 + 8\,SO_2$$

(c) *Reduction of sulfuric acid.* Metals react with hot concentrated sulfuric acid to form sulfur dioxide:

$$Cu + 2\,H_2SO_4 \longrightarrow CuSO_4 + SO_2 + 2\,H_2O$$

(d) *Action of acids on sulfites.* Sulfur dioxide is conveniently prepared in small quantities by treatment of a sulfite or bisulfite salt with an acid, *e.g.*

$$Na_2SO_3 + 2\,HCl \longrightarrow 2\,NaCl + H_2SO_3 \longrightarrow SO_2 + H_2O$$

or

$$NaHSO_3 + HCl \longrightarrow NaCl + H_2SO_3 \longrightarrow SO_2 + H_2O$$

The sulfurous acid is unstable and decomposes into sulfur dioxide and water. As a result of this unstable character of sulfurous acid, sulfite salts effervesce on addition of acids.

Properties of sulfur dioxide. Sulfur dioxide is a gas at ordinary temperatures and has a disagreeable, penetrating odor. The gas is about twice as heavy as air and may be liquefied easily by cooling in a salt-ice mixture. The boiling point of the liquid is $-10°$. The gas is quite soluble in water, 1 liter of water dissolving about 80 liters at $0°$. It reacts with water, forming a solution of weakly acidic properties:

$$SO_2 + H_2O \rightleftharpoons 2\,H^+ + SO_3^{--}$$

Sulfurous acid has not been isolated, but its salts (sulfites) are well known. A solution of sulfurous acid gives typical acid reactions, reacting with metals above hydrogen in the activity series and with bases:

$$Zn + H_2SO_3 \longrightarrow ZnSO_3 + H_2$$
$$2\,NaOH + H_2SO_3 \longrightarrow Na_2SO_3 + 2\,H_2O$$

Sulfurous acid slowly absorbs oxygen from the air, forming sulfuric acid:

$$2\,H_2SO_3 + O_2 \longrightarrow 2\,H_2SO_4$$

Sulfur dioxide is a good reducing agent, as illustrated by the following reactions:

$$5\,SO_2 + 2\,KMnO_4 + 3\,H_2SO_4 \longrightarrow K_2SO_4 + 2\,MnSO_4 + 5\,SO_3 + 3\,H_2O$$
$$2\,H_2O + 3\,SO_2 + 2\,HNO_3 \longrightarrow 2\,NO + 3\,H_2SO_4$$

Use of sulfur dioxide and sulfites. The most important use of SO_2 is in the preparation of sulfuric acid. A solution of sulfurous acid is a mild bleaching agent and may be used for bleaching straw, silk, or wool. The bleaching action is probably due to the reducing property of the acid. Sulfur dioxide is also used as a refrigerant. *Calcium bisulfite*, $Ca(HSO_3)_2$, and *magnesium bisulfite*, $Mg(HSO_3)_2$, are used extensively in the paper and pulp industry for dissolving lignin, a resinous substance which holds the wood fibers together.

Sulfur trioxide and sulfuric acid. The preparation of sulfuric acid involves first the preparation of its anhydride, sulfur trioxide. The solution of the anhydride in water forms H_2SO_4. Two methods are now employed for the commercial preparation of H_2SO_4.

Fig. 91. Stock pile of sulfur outside a sulfuric acid plant.

(a) *Contact process.* Sulfur dioxide does not combine with oxygen appreciably at room temperature, but at a temperature of about 400° in the presence of a catalyst, the reaction is about 98 per cent complete:

$$2\,SO_2 + O_2 \rightleftharpoons 2\,SO_3$$

At one time platinum was used as a catalyst, but owing to the ease with which the platinum became poisoned (rendered inactive), this metal has been largely replaced by a mixture of various metallic oxides with vanadium pentoxide, V_2O_5. The sulfur trioxide is absorbed in concentrated sulfuric acid, in which it is readily soluble, forming pyrosulfuric acid:

$$SO_3 + H_2SO_4 \longrightarrow H_2S_2O_7$$

pyrosulfuric acid
(fuming sulfuric acid)

Pyrosulfuric acid is then converted into sulfuric acid by adding water:

$$H_2S_2O_7 + H_2O \longrightarrow 2\ H_2SO_4$$

The acid produced by this process is 100 per cent.

(b) *Lead chamber process.* In this process a mixture of sulfur dioxide, air, and oxides of nitrogen (NO and NO_2) and steam are allowed to react in lead-lined chambers. The reactions taking place are somewhat complex; the ultimate changes may be represented by the reactions:

$$SO_2 + NO_2 \longrightarrow SO_3 + NO$$
$$SO_3 + H_2O \longrightarrow H_2SO_4$$
$$2\ NO + O_2 \longrightarrow 2\ NO_2$$

Intermediate in the formation of H_2SO_4 there is formed a compound with the formula

$$H \underset{\cdot\cdot}{\overset{\cdot\cdot}{O}} \overset{xx}{\underset{xx}{S}} \underset{x}{\overset{\cdot\cdot}{O}} \underset{xx}{\overset{x}{N}} \overset{\cdot\cdot}{O} :$$

called *nitrosyl sulfuric acid.* It forms as white crystals in the lead chambers especially when insufficient steam is being used.

The oxides of nitrogen are not destroyed in the reactions and may be used over and over again. A solution containing 60 to 70 per cent sulfuric acid is obtained by this process. Although the chamber process is the older of the methods for making sulfuric acid, the contact process now produces most of the supply of commercial acid. The contact process has the advantage of making 100 per cent acid and requiring less investment in equipment. The chamber process has the advantage that impure sulfur dioxide can be used; the sulfur dioxide used in the contact process must be relatively pure.

Properties of sulfuric acid. Pure sulfuric acid is a heavy, viscous liquid (sometimes called "oil of vitriol"), with a density of 1.84. Sulfuric acid exhibits three distinct sets of chemical properties.

(a) *Acid properties.* Dilute sulfuric acid exhibits typical acid reactions. It reacts with metals above hydrogen

$$Fe + H_2SO_4 \longrightarrow FeSO_4 + H_2$$

and neutralizes bases to form salts:

$$2 \, NaOH + H_2SO_4 \longrightarrow Na_2SO_4 + 2 \, H_2O$$
$$Ca(OH)_2 + H_2SO_4 \longrightarrow CaSO_4 + 2 \, H_2O$$

Concentrated sulfuric acid reacts with salts by double decomposition to produce salts and acids (general method of preparing volatile acids):

$$2 \, NaCl + H_2SO_4 \longrightarrow Na_2SO_4 + 2 \, HCl \uparrow$$
$$2 \, NaNO_3 + H_2SO_4 \longrightarrow Na_2SO_4 + 2 \, HNO_3 \uparrow$$

(b) *Oxidizing agent.* Hot concentrated sulfuric acid acts as an oxidizing agent, reacting with some metals below hydrogen in the activity series:

$$Cu + 2 \, H_2SO_4 \longrightarrow CuSO_4 + SO_2 + 2 \, H_2O$$
$$2 \, Ag + 2 \, H_2SO_4 \longrightarrow Ag_2SO_4 + SO_2 + 2 \, H_2O$$

Some metals above hydrogen act in the same manner with the concentrated acid:

$$Zn + 2 \, H_2SO_4 \longrightarrow ZnSO_4 + SO_2 + 2 \, H_2O$$

Sulfuric acid reacts with metals below hydrogen in the activity series, not because of its acid property but because of its oxidizing action.

(c) *Dehydrating agent.* Concentrated sulfuric acid has a great affinity for water. If an open container nearly full of the acid is allowed to stand in contact with the air for some time, the liquid in the container increases in volume and may even flow over the top. Water is absorbed from the air and the acid diluted. Advantage is taken of this property in producing a dry atmosphere. Concentrated sulfuric acid placed in a closed space absorbs moisture, leaving a virtually dry atmosphere.

When concentrated sulfuric acid is added to sugar, a charred mass, consisting of carbon is formed. Sugar is a compound in which the ratio of hydrogen to oxygen is the same as in water, that is, two atoms of hydrogen to one atom of oxygen:

$$C_{12}H_{22}O_{11} \longrightarrow 12 \, C + 11 \, H_2O$$

The hydrogen and oxygen are removed from the sugar molecule in the form of water because of the affinity of the sulfuric acid for water. The acid probably is not changed chemically in the reaction but is diluted by the water formed. Wood is blackened in contact with sulfuric acid because of a similar reaction:

$$C_6H_{10}O_5 \longrightarrow 6 \, C + 5 \, H_2O$$

The manufacture of explosives (discussed in chap. XXII) involves the use of concentrated sulfuric acid. The action of concentrated nitric acid on such compounds as glycerin seems to be markedly hastened by concentrated sulfuric acid as water is removed from the interaction of the two compounds:

$$C_3H_5(OH)_3 + 3\ HNO_3 \xrightarrow{H_2SO_4} C_3H_5(NO_3)_3 + 3\ H_2O$$

$$\underset{\text{glycerin}}{} \qquad\qquad \underset{\text{nitroglycerin}}{}$$

Uses of sulfuric acid. There is hardly an industry which is not directly or indirectly dependent upon the use of sulfuric acid. Annual consumption in tons of 100 per cent acid in the various industries of the United States is shown in Table 24.

TABLE 24

USE OF SULFURIC ACID IN THE UNITED STATES[1]

INDUSTRY	TONS (100% acid)	USE
1. Fertilizer	3,470,000	The acid is used in producing ammonium sulfate and superphosphate.
2. Petroleum refining	1,210,000	Sulfuric acid acts as a purifier of petroleum by removing dark-colored products, especially sulfur compounds.
3. Chemicals	2,060,000	Preparation of hydrochloric and nitric acids, metal sulfates, ether, etc.
4. Coal products	620,000	Preparation of dyes and drugs from coal products.
5. Iron and steel	520,000	Removal of rust on iron and steel before galvanizing or enameling.
6. Metallurgical	325,000	Refining of metals by electrolysis.
7. Paints and pigments	670,000	
8. Explosives	123,000	Used as a dehydrating agent in the nitration of organic compounds.
9. Rayon and cellulose film	650,000	
10. Textiles	75,000	
11. Miscellaneous	377,000	
Total	10,100,000	

[1] From *Minerals Yearbook*, 1949, United States Department of the Interior, Bureau of Mines.

SELENIUM AND TELLURIUM

Selenium and tellurium closely resemble sulfur although tellurium exhibits more metallic properties than other members of the group. This is in accord with the general tendency of nonmetallic elements to show increasing metallic properties as the atomic weight increases.

Selenium is obtained as a by-product of the roasting of pyrites.

Selenium, along with tellurium, is also obtained as a by-product from the electrolytic refining of copper, lead, and other metals. A minor use of selenium is in the production of red glass and in certain electrical devices, since selenium strangely becomes an increasingly better conductor of an electric current according to the strength of light impinging on it. Tellurium has no major use at present. Some use is made of the relatively insoluble selenates and tellurates by incorporating them into paints for ship bottoms. Barnacles and other organisms are somewhat discouraged from growing. Uses for these elements are being sought, since at present they are mainly waste products.

EXERCISES

1. How could you demonstrate experimentally that a given yellow solid is sulfur?
2. Point out chemical similarities and differences of the elements sulfur and oxygen.
3. What physical properties of sulfur are taken advantage of in the separation of sulfur from other substances with which it is associated in nature?
4. Summarize the different kinds of evidence upon which is based the classification of sulfur as a nonmetal.
5. Write equations for the combustion of hydrogen sulfide in (a) excess oxygen; (b) a limited supply of oxygen. Calculate the volume of air (20 per cent oxygen) necessary for the combustion of 10 liters of hydrogen sulfide.

    Ans. 75 l.

6. How would you demonstrate experimentally that H_2S

    (a) is an acid   (c) has a molecular weight of 34
    (b) contains sulfur   (d) is a reducing agent

7. Write equations for four different methods of preparing SO_2. Which of these methods are commercially important?
8. Calculate the weight of SO_2 obtainable by the roasting of 100 pounds of an ore, 60 per cent of which is zinc sulfide. Calculate also the volume of this weight of SO_2 at standard conditions. (22.4 cu. ft., ounce molecular volume)

    Ans. 39.5 lb.; 220 cu. ft.

9. What conditions of temperature and pressure would be most favorable to the production of SO_3 by the reaction:

$$2\,SO_2 + O_2 \rightleftharpoons 2\,SO_3 + 44,000 \text{ calories}$$

10. Even though silver is a metal below hydrogen in the activity series, silverware is tarnished on coming in contact with H_2S. Explain.
11. Calculate the number of milliliters of H_2S gas measured at standard conditions necessary to precipitate PbS from 100 ml. of a 2 molar solution of lead nitrate.

    Ans. 4480.

12. Given the following chemicals in the laboratory and no others: water, ferrous sulfide, concentrated H_2SO_4, barium chloride, air. Write equations to show reactions you might carry out to prepare (a) H_2S; (b) $BaSO_4$; (c) SO_2.

13. Write the equations and state conditions of the reactions for the manufacture of H_2SO_4 by the contact process.
14. Why is H_2SO_4 not prepared from a sulfate of a metal treated with an acid?
15. Describe briefly an experiment, writing equations and telling of the phenomena observed, to show (a) that a certain gas is hydrogen sulfide and not sulfur dioxide; (b) that a certain solution contains sodium sulfate and not sodium chloride.
16. In the burning of sulfur, how many liters of oxygen would be required to produce 150 liters of SO_2?
17. Write balanced chemical equations illustrating the use of H_2SO_4 in the fertilizer industry; making bulk chemicals; iron and steel industry; explosive industry.
18. Explain how you would proceed in the laboratory to prove a face remedy paste contained some elemental powdered sulfur in it.
19. In preparation of fuel gas in a western city, the gas is passed through a bed of wood chips impregnated with $FeSO_4$. What volume of H_2S would theoretically be taken from the gas by 648 pounds of $FeSO_4$?
20. A match mixture is made of 20 pounds of Sb_2S_3, 70 pounds of $KClO_3$, 10 pounds of starch. What is the per cent of sulfur in the mixture?
21. Acid that has been used to dry Cl_2 gas has a density of 1.6 and is 60 per cent H_2SO_4. What volume in liters of the acid contains 2000 pounds of H_2SO_4?
22. Ten cubic centimeters of battery acid (density 1.21) was diluted to 100 cc. Thirty cubic centimeters of the dilute solution was neutralized by 45 cc. of 0.5 N base. What was the normality of the diluted acid? its strength in terms of grams per liter? What was the strength of the undiluted 1.21 density acid in terms of grams per liter? its percentage strength?
23. A sulfuric acid plant burns 300 tons of sulfur a day. If the plant is 80 per cent efficient, what tonnage of 95 per cent sulfuric acid is its daily output?

REFERENCES

W. A. Cunningham, "Sulfur, Pt. 1," *J. Chem. Ed.* **12**, 17 (1935).

C. W. Johnston, "Sulfur Dioxide as a Refrigerant," *Ind. and Eng. Chem.* **24**, 626 (1932).

D. B. Mason, "The Sulfur Industry, History and Development," *ibid.* **30**, 740 (1938).

W. F. Lurdy, "Known and Potential Sulfur Resources of the World," *ibid.* **42**, 2199 (1950).

R. A. King, "Economic Utilization of Sulfur Dioxide from Metallurgical Gases," *ibid.* **42**, 2241 (1950).

G. H. Reid, "Producing Sulfur at New Gulf," *Chem. and Met. Eng.* **37**, 688 (1930).

A. P. Thompson, "Platinum, Vanadium Pentoxide as Catalysts for Sulfuric Acid Manufacture," *Trans. Amer. Inst. Chem. Eng.* **27**, 264 (1931).

XXV

Carbon and Its Oxides

$$_6\mathrm{C}^{12.01}\ {\scriptstyle 1\ 1 \atop 2\ 4 \atop 1\ 1}$$

Carbon appears in Group IV of the periodic table and is thus centrally located between those elements which act distinctly as metals and those elements which act distinctly as nonmetals. We shall see that carbon in some forms possesses certain properties characteristic of metals and in others exhibits properties usually associated with nonmetals.

Occurrence. Carbon stands nineteenth in abundance among the chemical elements but even so its percentage in the earth's crust is only .027. It is widely distributed in both the free and combined states. Elementary carbon is found as diamond, graphite, and in the various forms of coal. Its compounds are practically innumerable; every living cell, plant or animal, contains carbon compounds; petroleum is a mixture of compounds of carbon and hydrogen (hydrocarbons); most of our food and clothing consist of mixtures of compounds of this vital element. In addition, many carbonate minerals occur on the earth's surface.

Carbon forms compounds only by sharing electrons; in other words all of its compounds are covalent. Not only does it share electrons with other elements but possesses a great ability to share electrons with itself, that is, many carbon atoms may condense together to form molecules of great complexity. The chemistry of these compounds is so extensive that it comprises a special field in itself — organic chemistry. More compounds of carbon are known than of any other element except oxygen and hydrogen with which carbon itself forms numerous compounds. Later chapters of this book introduce the various classes of organic compounds.

It is estimated that there is 30,000 times as much carbon in rocks of the earth's crust and as carboniferous deposits as there is carbon in the air as carbon dioxide. We can infer from this that the percentage of carbon dioxide in the air in earlier geologic times was much higher than the 0.034 per cent now present.

Allotropic forms. Carbon exists in three allotropic forms, two of which are definitely crystalline. The crystalline forms are *graphite* and *diamond*, which will be considered in more detail later. The third allotropic form, *amorphous* carbon, has a number of common names as we encounter it with various impurities, *e.g.*, coke, charcoal, soot, lampblack, sugar charcoal, and boneblack. These forms of carbon have been shown by X-ray analysis to be minutely crystalline, but the crystals are too small to give to the substance any apparent crystalline properties.

Destructive distillation of wood and coal. Charcoal is obtained from wood, and its properties will depend to a large extent upon the kind of wood from which it is derived. Wood may be covered with sand to exclude air, and heated. Volatile material is given off and charcoal remains. In a more modern treatment, wood is heated in airtight ovens, whence it is decomposed to charcoal, water vapor, and a poor-burning gas. From this gas there may be condensed wood alcohol, acetic acid, and acetone. Such a process of heating a substance in absence of air to form nonvolatile and volatile products is termed *destructive distillation*.

The biggest industrial application of destructive distillation is heating suitable coal in ovens to yield coke and volatile products. The coke retains the nonvolatile mineral matter of the coal, but it also contains a high percentage of carbon and thus is much used in metallurgical operations, in making gas, and in home furnaces. The volatile products from the destructive distillation of coal are coal gas, benzene, coal tar, and ammonia. The benzene and coal tar are raw materials for chemical industries which produce medicinals, dyes, photographic developers, explosives, certain kinds of plastics, and in general, many organic compounds.

Formation of coal. Coal is the result of change of fossil plant material which has been protected from complete decay by overlying water-washed earthy deposits. Since at one time in the earth's history, during the so-called Carboniferous era, the air had a much higher carbon dioxide content than at the present time, the average earth surface temperature was higher, and vegetative material grew in profusion. The carbon dioxide content of the air in generations of time was lessened as it was used in growing plants and by conversion into carbonate rocks. Today plants make use of the 0.034 per cent CO_2 in the air.

During the time that the carboniferous material was beneath earthy cover, changes were effected by pressure, heat, and other factors. The original plant material probably had a composition somewhat like that of wood. Preliminary decomposition of such material gives a product called *peat*. Peat may be dug from its deposits and burned. It constitutes a rather poor fuel. In its formation, carbon dioxide and methane are the principal gases evolved. The methane is known as marsh gas, since it occurs in the bubbles coming up through the water in boggy regions where organic decomposition takes place. Further loss of carbon dioxide, water, and minor amounts of other gases from the underground organic mass brings about an increase of the percentage of carbon with the resultant formation of coal. Various grades of coal differ, according to the amount of metamorphosis the carboniferous deposit underwent during geological time.

Fuels. Wood, coal, and oil are man's most useful fuels. They are mixtures, composed largely of carbon or carbon-containing compounds. Burning them gives usable heat energy. Carbon dioxide and water are the main products of their combustion. Results of chemical analysis on a number of varieties of fuels are given in Table 25.

TABLE 25

FUELS

FUEL	ULTIMATE ANALYSIS (per cent)						PROXIMATE ANALYSIS (per cent)				Cal. per Gram
	C	H	N	O	S	Si, Fe, Mg Oxides	Moisture	Volatile Matter	Fixed C	Ash	
Anthracite . . .	82.	0.5	0.1	1.8	0.9	14.7	4.5	3.0	78.7	13.8	7100
Pa. Bituminous . .	71.5	5.3	1.3	9.1	3.1	9.7	1.8	32.8	47.3	18.2	7200
Ore. Subbituminous	51.1	5.5	1.2	28.2	0.8	—	16.1	31.1	39.6	13.2	5500
N. D. Lignite . .	37.4	6.4	0.6	45.0	0.2	—	36.9	24.9	27.7	10.4	5000
Coke	—	—	—	—	—	—	—	—	89.0	10.2	7200
Charcoal	—	—	—	—	—	—	—	—	97.0	3.0	7700
Wood	40.0	7.2	0.8	50.7	—	1.3	—	—	—	—	4500
Petroleum . . .	84.0	13.	—	—	—	—	—	—	—	—	10400

Ultimate analysis aims at ascertaining the percentages of the elements in a mixture, such as wood or coal. *Proximate analysis*, which is much more rapid, is a practical means of evaluating the coal for its different uses. A bituminous coal with a high percentage of volatile matter gives a higher yield of coal gas and coal tar than an anthracite coal. The lignite coals with high percentage of moisture and a low percentage of carbon make mediocre fuels.

Petroleum is a naturally occurring mixture of compounds of carbon and hydrogen (chap. XXXIX). Wood is largely composed of cellulose and lignin which are compounds containing carbon, hydrogen, and oxygen.

In general the higher the hydrogen content of a fuel the greater the heat liberated per unit of it burned, and the higher the oxygen content of fuel the lower the heating value of it. *Calorific value* is the measured amount of heat liberated per unit quantity of a substance burned, and may be measured in calories or British thermal units.[1]

Gaseous fuels find marked demand because of their convenience in pipe delivery. *Natural gas* is obtained from bore holes in many parts of the country, and chemically is composed of the lighter hydrocarbon molecules. Methane, CH_4, is a high percentage constituent of natural gas.

Coal gas from the destructive distillation of coal may heat homes in cities or be used as industrial fuel. Coal gas is carefully treated to remove hydrogen sulfide, ammonia, and small particles of solid or liquid matter; and as distributed for use is about 50 per cent hydrogen, 30–35 per cent methane, 8 per cent carbon monoxide, about 2 per cent other hydrocarbons, and the remainder mainly nitrogen.

A gas called "water gas" is produced in some communities by passing steam over red hot coke:

$$C + H_2O \longrightarrow CO + H_2$$

This gas burns with a high heat and with an almost colorless flame. It is usual to add a little hydrocarbon gas to it to give a little color to the almost invisible flame.

Properties and uses of carbon. Charcoal as prepared from various substances is quite porous. Since a small weight of charcoal has a large surface area due to its high porosity, it is widely used as an adsorbent. *Adsorption* is the tendency exhibited by all solids to condense selectively upon their surfaces a layer of gas or liquid with which they are in contact. It has long been a practice by farmers to suspend a gunnysack of charcoal in a cistern to adsorb smelly gases. Similarly, gas mask cannisters for wartime use contain specially prepared charcoal of high adsorptive capacity. A brownish impure sugar solution is rendered colorless by filtering it through charcoal. While considering this phenomenon of adsorption, it should be stressed that adsorption by a given solid is selective; charcoal adsorbs coloring matter but not sugar from solution; charcoal adsorbs a high percentage of

---

[1] A British thermal unit (B.T.U.) is the amount of heat required to raise the temperature of one pound of water one degree Fahrenheit.

hydrogen sulfide gas from an atmosphere containing it but adsorbs only a small percentage of nitrogen.

Other uses of various kinds of amorphous carbon are printer's ink, filler for rubber, shoe polish, paints, and enamels.

Fig. 92. Emergency breathing tubes.

Chemical properties. At ordinary temperatures carbon does not readily unite with other elements, but at higher temperatures it enters into chemical combination with many metals and nonmetals.

When carbon is heated in air it burns to form CO_2 with an evolution of about 7900 calories per gram of carbon. Carbon is thus a good fuel material. If it is heated in a limited amount of air, or at a very high temperature, carbon monoxide is produced rather than CO_2 according to the equation

$$2\,C + O_2 \longrightarrow 2\,CO$$

Carbon monoxide is a dangerous product resulting from incomplete oxidation of carbon or its compounds. When carbon or its compounds are burning in the open air, where a large volume of oxygen is available, the carbon monoxide, if first formed, readily burns to carbon dioxide.

Carbon disulfide is a compound readily formed by sulfur vapor in contact with hot carbon. It is a liquid in demand in increasing tonnage to make "viscose," an intermediary substance in rayon production. It is also used to kill rodents. Since it is a readily volatile and inflammable liquid, care must be exercised to keep it away from open flames.

Carbon tetrachloride is a noninflammable liquid used as a solvent for oils and greases. Carbon does not form this compound, however, by direct union with chlorine. It may be made by chlorination of carbon disulfide:

$$CS_2 + 3\,Cl_2 \longrightarrow CCl_4 + S_2Cl_2$$

Carbon tetrachloride is used as a solvent in dry cleaning and as a filler in certain fire extinguishers with the trade name Pyrene.

Reducing action. Carbon and carbon monoxide are the cheapest reducing agents available and thus are extensively used in obtaining metals from metal oxide ores in metallurgical industry, *e.g.*

$$ZnO + C \longrightarrow Zn + CO$$
$$Fe_2O_3 + 3\,CO \longrightarrow 2\,Fe + 3\,CO_2$$

Carbides. The more active metals cannot be prepared from their oxides in the above manner because of their tendency to unite with hot carbon to form carbides. Aluminum would be a much cheaper metal if it could be obtained by heating aluminum oxide with carbon. The chemical change which does take place is

$$2\,Al_2O_3 + 9\,C \longrightarrow 6\,CO + Al_4C_3$$

Certain other metals in union with carbon form similar carbides. Carbides of this nature when acted on by water yield the gas methane, CH_4:

$$Al_4C_3 + 12\,H_2O \longrightarrow 4\,Al(OH)_3 + 3\,CH_4 \uparrow$$

In a similar manner by heating sand and coke in an electric furnace, silicon carbide, called Carborundum, may be made:

$$SiO_2 + 3\,C \longrightarrow SiC + 2\,CO$$

The impure blue-black, iridescent, crystalline Carborundum is almost as hard as diamond and is used extensively as an abrasive, in the form of powder, whetstones, or grinding wheels.

Carbon and lime heated together in an electric furnace form calcium carbide, which will react with water to produce acetylene gas, the basis of an important industry:

$$CaO + 3\,C \longrightarrow CO + CaC_2$$
$$CaC_2 + 2\,H_2O \longrightarrow Ca(OH)_2 + C_2H_2 \uparrow$$

From its formula, CaC_2, we can deduce a structural formula:

The triple valence bond between carbon atoms is typical of the compound acetylene, $H—C{\equiv}C—H$, and, accordingly, CaC_2 may be called calcium acetylide.

In the iron and steel industry other carbides are encountered. Steels may contain some Fe_3C or Mn_3C. Fe_3C is called *cementite* and being a hard crystalline substance is accountable for much of the hardness and brittleness of a high carbon steel.

Graphite. This shining black, soft, slippery feeling, flaky, crystalline form of carbon occurs in widely separated deposits. It is mined in Ceylon, Siberia, and to a lesser extent on the North American continent. Naturally occurring graphite has the mineral name *plumbago*. Plumbago deposits have probably resulted from heating of carbonaceous material to high temperature underneath a covering of rock. Simulating nature, man produces graphite by heating hard coal in an electric furnace, under cover of sand, to a temperature of 3500°. At this temperature carbon seems to vaporize quite readily and the condensing carbon vapor molecules form hexagonal crystals of graphite.

Figure 54 (p. 160) shows the hexagonal structure of carbon atoms of graphite in one plane as compared to the less closely interbonded third dimension. This structure helps to account for the flaky nature of graphite and the fact that it can be oxidized to various six-carbon organic compounds. The interplanar bonding electrons allow graphite to exhibit a relative softness and some degree of electrical conductivity.

Since graphite is a better conductor of the electric current than other forms of carbon and is resistant to heat and chemical change, it has numerous uses. Electrodes and crucibles are made of it. The scalelike crystals readily slip over each other and graphite thus makes a good lubricant. A suspension of graphite powder in water for lubricating purposes is known as "aquadag." Stove polish contains graphite to inhibit oxidation of the iron. Lead pencils contain as a core a mixture of graphite and clay, the hardness being determined by the percentage of clay and the texture of the mix.

Diamond. Duke Cosmo of Tuscany in 1694 supplied a small diamond to two Florentine academicians, Averani and Targioni. The diamond, on being heated in air by focusing sunlight through a powerful magnifying lens, glowed like a red-hot coal and disappeared. Lavoisier in 1772 heated a diamond in the absence of air and found it unchanged, but when he heated it in air, reported carbonous acid as being formed. Smithson Tennant in 1797 wrote of the definite chemical identity of diamond and carbon. Diamond is, then, a crystalline form of carbon. Carbon atoms tend to share four electron pairs with other carbons, which results in the special construction unit called the tetrahedron (see Fig. 53, p. 160). Tetrahedrons may pack into other isometric crystal forms such as the octahedron or the cube. In any event, the symmetrical close-packed electron-pair sharing produces a very hard, nonconducting, chemically inactive substance.

Many of the naturally occurring rough looking pebble diamonds are black throughout due to flakes of carbon. Since diamond is the hardest known material, the black diamonds (also called borts or carbonades) are used in cutting and grinding other gems. They are also inset in the grinding bit of a diamond drill for drilling holes through rocks. The clearer or water-white stones are subjected to expert cutting and fashioned into prized gems. The rough and superficially stained gems are cut in such form that light is most effectively refracted.

Some diamonds have traces of color due to small amounts of impurities. The Hope diamond is of light blue color; the Tiffany diamond is amber colored.

The weight of a diamond is expressed in carats. A carat is about 0.2 gram and has an average value of about $500. Diamonds are found

Fig. 92x. Headframe at diamond mine, Kimberley, South Africa.

in several localities; the principal deposits are in South Africa, the East Indies, and Brazil. South African diamonds occur embedded in hard blue clay. Masses of this blue clay are blasted out and allowed to crumble by weathering. Since the diamonds are so brittle, the clay cannot be put through crushers. The clay is washed away to leave the heavier diamond-containing residue. The largest diamond, the Cullinan, was mined in 1905 from the Transvaal mines and weighed 3025 carats, about $1\frac{1}{3}$ pounds. It was cut into two brilliants of 516.5 and 309 carats and various other smaller sized stones.

The first successful attempt to make artificial diamonds was made by the French chemist, Moissan, in 1893. Liquid iron will dissolve considerable carbon. As a mass of liquid iron containing dissolved carbon is suddenly cooled, as by plunging it in cold water, a solid crust of iron is formed enclosing molten iron in the interior. Iron containing dissolved carbon expands on cooling, hence tremendous interior pressures are set up. The carbon, being less soluble in cold solid iron, crystallizes from solution at the high pressure as diamond. The iron mass may be dissolved by hydrochloric acid from the very small diamonds thus formed.

Accurate determinations of the melting and boiling points of carbon have never been made since carbon melts near 3500°, which is a difficult temperature to attain, and since solid carbon has a high vapor pressure near its melting point. If one could attain this high temperature under considerable pressure so as to keep the liquid carbon from vaporizing, the liquid carbon on slow solidification would probably form diamond.

CARBON DIOXIDE

Carbon dioxide is present in the air to the extent of 3.4 parts in 10,000. This amount is constantly being added to by burning carbon compounds, decay, fermentation, respiration, and volcanic gases. In turn, some of the carbon dioxide of the air is being absorbed by plants, dissolved by water, and fixed into such minerals as calcium or magnesium carbonate. There are some gas wells in the central United States and Mexico from which carbon dioxide issues at considerable pressure. Companies freeze the carbon dioxide to solid carbon dioxide (dry ice), and this product is used for refrigeration. Escaping carbon dioxide from ground waters in a cave near Naples, Italy, builds up a cave atmosphere such that a small dog walking into the quiet air of the cave will keel over of suffocation. A man walking upright will have little discomfort. The explanation is based on the fact that carbon dioxide is about 1.4 times as heavy as air and the cave floor concentration is markedly higher than at the five-foot level. Carbon dioxide is not a poison, but a person suffers from lack of oxygen and inability to get rid of carbon dioxide from the body when in a moderately high concentration of it.

Preparation. (*a*) Carbon dioxide is the product of the complete burning of carbon or its compounds. Most vaporizable or gaseous carbon compounds when mixed with air form an explosive mixture. Occasionally serious explosions occur when a suspension of finely divided solid carbon compounds in air (coal dust, flour dust, etc.) is subjected to a spark or flame. Precautions must be taken in mills that are grinding organic material so that sparks or flame do not contact the organic dust-laden air. The slow oxidation processes of rotting and respiration form carbon dioxide as a product.

(*b*) Fermentation of carbohydrate compounds results in the formation of alcohol and carbon dioxide. Yeast cells secrete an organic compound called "zymase" which hastens the fermentation process. Such an organic substance which is produced by living cells and which catalyzes specific chemical changes is called an *enzyme:*

$$\underset{\text{glucose}}{C_6H_{12}O_6} \overset{\text{zymase}}{\longrightarrow} \underset{\text{alcohol}}{2\ C_2H_5OH} + 2\ CO_2 \uparrow$$

(*c*) Carbon dioxide is a product of heating metal carbonates except those of the alkali metals (as Na_2CO_3, K_2CO_3). The process of heating limestone to produce lime constitutes a large industry:

$$CaCO_3 \longrightarrow CaO + CO_2$$

This chemical change requires a temperature of about 800° and since the reaction is reversible, a draft is used to keep removing the carbon dioxide.

(*d*) The most convenient laboratory method of preparing carbon dioxide is by action of an acid on a carbonate:

$$CaCO_3 + 2\ H^+ \longrightarrow Ca^{++} + H_2O + CO_2$$
$$Na_2CO_3 + 2\ H^+ \longrightarrow 2\ Na^+ + H_2O + CO_2$$

Physical properties.

Molecular weight	44
Solubility at 15° and 1 atm. pressure	1 vol. in 1 H_2O
Solubility at 15° and 4 atm. pressure	4 vol. in 1 H_2O
Critical pressure	72 atm.
Critical temperature	31.4°
Melting point	−56°
Sublimes at	−79°

Carbon dioxide gas is $1\frac{1}{2}$ times as heavy as air and being noninflammable may be used to blanket a flame and extinguish it. A 4 per cent carbon dioxide atmosphere over burning wood, even if 17 per cent oxygen be present, will smother the flame. It is moderately soluble in water under ordinary conditions and markedly more soluble under pressure. Its solubility is enhanced by the combination:

$$CO_2 + H_2O \rightleftharpoons H_2CO_3$$

Carbonic acid has a slightly sour or biting taste which accounts for the use of carbonated or soda water.

Carbon dioxide may be liquefied by pressure and as a liquid is transported in steel cylinders. If the nozzle of such a cylinder is opened, with the nozzle end lower than the rest of the cylinder, liquid carbon dioxide is ejected into the air. The liquid under the reduced pressure immediately boils. Since a boiling liquid absorbs its heat of vaporization from the surroundings, a marked cooling takes place. If the liquid is allowed to squirt into a cloth bag so that the cooling is confined, some of the carbon dioxide liquid will cool to the solid state. Solid carbon dioxide, which is commercially called "dry ice," is so made. The solid carbon dioxide gasifies in air at a temperature of about $-79°$.

A convenient low-temperature mixture may be prepared by making a mush of solid carbon dioxide and ether. Unlike the familiar salt-ice mixture, this one does not give a temperature lower than that of either ingredient, but it provides better contact than dry ice alone. Its use may be demonstrated as follows:

Into a crystallizing dish containing a mush of ether and carbon dioxide, place a small matchbox or pillbox. Fill the box with mercury. As the mercury begins to solidify, insert a small wooden stick so that the mercury freezes around it. The box mold may then be torn from the solid mercury. One now has a mercury hammer with which nails may be driven.

Chemical properties. Carbon dioxide is a very stable substance except at exceedingly high temperatures where it decomposes:

$$2\,CO_2 \longrightarrow 2\,CO + O_2$$

Carbon dioxide from the atmosphere is constantly dissolving in water over the earth's surface and thus natural water is really a dilute solution of carbonic acid. This dilute acid has much to do with the disintegration of rocks. Minerals are acted on by the dilute acid and today there are enormous deposits of limestone, $CaCO_3$, and dolomitic limestone, $CaCO_3 \cdot MgCO_3$.

Carbon dioxide is tested for on the basis of the chemical change:

$$Ca(OH)_2 + CO_2 \longrightarrow CaCO_3 \downarrow + H_2O$$

A calcium hydroxide solution (lime water) when subjected to carbon dioxide becomes milky as calcium carbonate precipitates. If to a fine suspension of calcium carbonate, carbon dioxide is added, the milkiness will clear up since calcium acid carbonate, which is water soluble, is formed:

$$CaCO_3 + H_2CO_3 \longrightarrow Ca(HCO_3)_2$$

This chemical change is a most important one in the problem of water softening. Naturally occurring limestone is constantly being slowly dissolved by carbonic acid in ground water to form soluble calcium acid carbonate (also called calcium bicarbonate). As water containing this compound is heated, the reverse of the above reaction takes place and a calcium carbonate precipitate forms. Kettles or boiler tubes receiving a feed of water containing calcium bicarbonate become coated with a cake of calcium carbonate. Natural waters often also contain the bicarbonates of iron and magnesium. The brown color of boiler or kettle cake is largely due to iron compounds. Since mineral bicarbonate compounds $Ca(HCO_3)_2$ and $Mg(HCO_3)_2$ are decomposed by heat and thus precipitate the metal carbonate from water, these minerals are said to cause "temporary hardness" in water (chap. XXX).

The formation of stalactites and stalagmites in caves is due to decomposition of calcium bicarbonate from percolating ground waters. As such water encounters a pressure reduction on coming into the cave, the chemical change takes place:

$$Ca(HCO_3)_2 \longrightarrow CaCO_3 \downarrow + H_2O + CO_2$$

Plants take into their leaves carbon dioxide from the air and water from the soil, and with sunshine for energy and in the presence of chlorophyll synthesize carbohydrates:

$$6\,CO_2 + 5\,H_2O \longrightarrow C_6H_{10}O_5 + 6\,O_2$$

This *photosynthesis* process is not as simple as inferred, since this equation is a summation of intermediate chemical changes. The unit $C_6H_{10}O_5$ seems to unite with other like molecules to form successively larger molecules to which we assign the formula $(C_6H_{10}O_5)_x$. It is to be assumed that this photosynthesis would be much faster if plants had available a higher concentration of carbon dioxide than the 0.034 per cent in air. Increased temperature and increase of sunlight would also hasten the plant process. By subjecting growing corn in a hothouse to an atmosphere containing more carbon dioxide than is present in ordinary air, some phenomenally rapid rates of plant growth are obtained.

Carbonates. Reference has been made to the bulk deposits of carbonate rocks, chief minerals of which are limestone, $CaCO_3$, and dolomite, $CaCO_3 \cdot MgCO_3$. "Desert alkali" that occurs in arid regions is mainly sodium carbonate, Na_2CO_3. This substance may be mined for use or made industrially:

$$CO_2 + 2\,NaOH \longrightarrow Na_2CO_3 + H_2O$$

From a cold solution of sodium carbonate, the decahydrate, $Na_2CO_3 \cdot 10\,H_2O$, crystallizes. It is known as washing soda. Excess carbon dioxide bubbled into a solution of washing soda forms sodium bicarbonate ($NaHCO_3$, baking soda):

$$Na_2CO_3 + CO_2 + H_2O \longrightarrow 2\,NaHCO_3$$

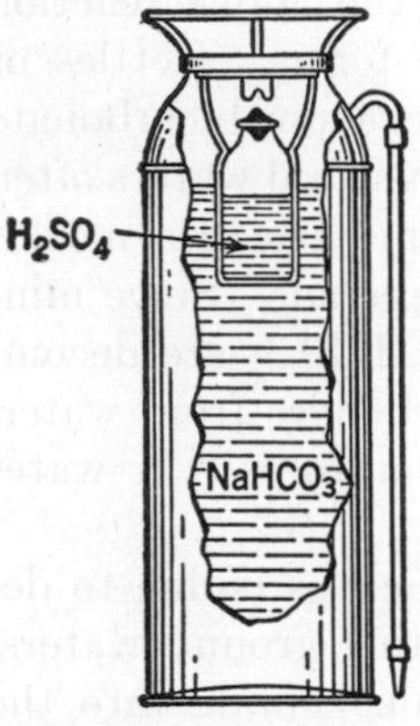

Fig. 93. Fire extinguisher.

A commonly used fire extinguisher is one nearly filled with a sodium bicarbonate solution. When such an extinguisher is tipped upside down a bottle of acid loses its stopper and acid begins acting on the solution:

$$NaHCO_3 + H^+ \longrightarrow Na^+ + H_2CO_3 \overset{\displaystyle \rightarrow H_2O + CO_2}{}$$

Gas pressure develops as CO_2 is formed and forces a stream of liquid with dissolved CO_2 from the cylinder; this stream may be directed upon a fire. Figure 93 shows a diagram of this type of fire extinguisher. If to the soda solution is added some alum and oil of licorice, a more frothy stream of liquid, the bubbles being filled with carbon dioxide, is given which better covers a fire. The latter type mix, called Foamite, has had some use in putting out oil and gasoline fires.

CARBON MONOXIDE

We most commonly hear of carbon monoxide as a product of the incomplete burning of gasoline:

$$2\,C_8H_{18} + 25\,O_2 \longrightarrow 16\,CO_2 + 18\,H_2O \text{ (complete combustion)}$$
$$2\,C_8H_{18} + 17\,O_2 \longrightarrow 16\,CO + 18\,H_2O \text{ (incomplete combustion)}$$

With insufficient oxygen, a gasoline compound such as octane, C_8H_{18}, will give off a large quantity of carbon monoxide.

Pure carbon monoxide may be prepared by heating oxalic acid in the presence of concentrated sulfuric acid:

$$H_2C_2O_4 \longrightarrow H_2O + CO_2 + CO$$

The carbon dioxide can be dissolved from the carbon monoxide by solution in potassium hydroxide solution.

Carbon monoxide is a light gas, very slightly soluble in water. It is an insidious poison since it has no odor to warn of its presence. Whereas oxygen combines with hemoglobin to form a compound that readily decomposes again to yield oxygen to body tissue, carbon monoxide unites with hemoglobin to form a stable compound. Since hemoglobin becomes used up on combination with carbon monoxide as one breathes in an atmosphere containing it, an insufficient amount of hemoglobin remains to function in its oxygen-carrying capacity. A person suffocates for lack of enough body oxygen when about one-third of his hemoglobin has been combined with carbon monoxide.

As carbon burns, carbon monoxide is almost always an intermediate oxidation product:

$$2\,C + O_2 \longrightarrow 2\,CO$$

The blue flame surrounding burning carbon is due to the oxidation of carbon monoxide:

$$2\,CO + O_2 \longrightarrow 2\,CO_2$$

Good draft in a furnace allows for complete burning of carbon; a dampered furnace may yield considerable carbon monoxide, which escapes up the chimney.

Knowing that carbon monoxide is formed by incomplete combustion of carbon or its compounds, and that it is a cumulative poison, some means should be employed to warn of its presence. Canaries are sometimes kept in garages as they are more sensitive to suffocation than man. Rather than a garageman relying on a canary, it is better to ensure sufficient ventilation of the building and to minimize the running of automobile motors indoors.

CYANIDES

Hydrogen cyanide, called *prussic acid*, is very poisonous and is the gas used in the lethal chambers for capital punishment in some states. It may be prepared by adding an acid to a cyanide salt:

$$2\,NaCN + H_2SO_4 \longrightarrow Na_2SO_4 + 2\,HCN \uparrow$$

The gas is also used in fumigation. Since HCN has the rather pleasant smell of bitter almonds or crushed peach leaves, it is customary in fumigation to add to it some cyanogen chloride, CNCl, which is likewise toxic but because of its irritating odor gives warning of the presence of poison. Historical writings tell of ancient Egyptians boiling peach leaves and seeds to obtain a poisonous solution, which was dilute HCN. Certain tropical trees emit small concentrations of HCN into the air.

Sodium and potassium cyanides may be prepared in several ways on a commercial scale:

$$2\,NH_3 + 2\,Na \longrightarrow 2\,NaNH_2 + H_2 \qquad (1)$$
$$2\,NaNH_2 + 2\,C \text{ at red heat} \longrightarrow 2\,H_2 + 2\,NaCN$$

$$CaCN_2 + C + Na_2CO_3 \overset{heat}{\longrightarrow} CaCO_3 \downarrow + 2\,NaCN \qquad (2)$$

Cyanides are used in dissolving gold and silver from ores, in cleaning silverware, as insecticides or rodenticides, in electroplating, and in casehardening steel.

Alkali cyanides have a marked tendency to unite with cyanides of metals of higher valence:

$$4\,KCN + Fe(CN)_2 \longrightarrow 4\,KCN \cdot Fe(CN)_2 \quad \text{or} \quad K_4Fe(CN)_6$$
$$\text{potassium}$$
$$\text{ferrocyanide}$$

An antidote for a cyanide, if taken soon enough, is a solution of a ferrous compound:

$$FeSO_4 + 2\,KCN \longrightarrow Fe(CN)_2 + K_2SO_4$$
$$Fe(CN)_2 + 4\,KCN \longrightarrow K_4Fe(CN)_6$$

From an ionic standpoint:

$$Fe^{++} + 6\,CN^- \longrightarrow Fe(CN)_6^{----}$$

The latter ion does not have the poisonous qualities of CN^-.

Salts such as potassium ferrocyanide, $K_4Fe(CN)_6$, and potassium ferricyanide, $K_3Fe(CN)_6$, are important in analytical chemistry. If finely divided scrap iron, nitrogenous animal refuse, and K_2CO_3 are heated together, $K_4Fe(CN)_6$ may be dissolved from the residue. This constitutes a method for its preparation.

South American natives throw NaCN into a stream above a deep pool — fish are poisoned and float downstream to be scooped from the water. Any cyanide residual in the fish is probably converted to harmless cyanate

$$2\,NaCN + O_2 \longrightarrow 2\,NaCNO$$

during the cooking. When it is necessary to kill out undesired fish life from a lake or pond, prior to restocking, cyanide may be used. In running streams cyanides are oxidized to cyanates, as shown by the above equation.

A cyanide will similarly unite with finely divided sulfur when heated to yield thiocyanates:

$$KCN + S \longrightarrow KCNS$$

A few metal cyanides tend to decompose, yielding a lower valence cyanide of the metal:

$$2\,Cu(CN)_2 \longrightarrow 2\,CuCN + (CN)_2\uparrow$$

Cyanogen is the name for $(CN)_2$ gas, which is poisonous, water soluble, and in chemical behavior resembles Cl_2:

$$(CN)_2 + H_2O \rightleftharpoons HCN + HCNO$$

When cyanogen gas is heated to 400° C., it polymerizes to form para-cyanogen, $(CN)_x$, a white solid.

FLAMES

Flame is produced whenever gases burn. As wood or coal is heated, gases are evolved, which, mixed with air, burn with a flame. Charcoal and coke, since they do not form an appreciable amount of vapor on being heated, do not burn with a flame. Flames are commonly colorless unless some solid particles are present to be heated to luminosity. Hydrogen gas burns with a color-less flame, but if some hydrocarbon gas is added, a yellow flame is obtained, as carbon particles formed by incomplete combustion are heated to above redness:

$$CH_4 + O_2 \longrightarrow C + 2\,H_2O$$

Various mineral salts of copper, strontium, potassium, calcium, barium, and sodium when vaporized give distinctive colors to a flame.

When a mixture of combustible gases and oxygen is ignited, an explosive instantaneous flash or flame results. If a combustible gas is allowed to jet into air or oxygen and ignited,

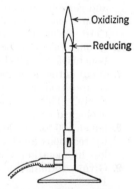

Fig. 94. Bunsen flame.

a flame of discernible cones is obtained (Fig. 94). The inner cone is of cool gas, surrounded by a zone of combustion where gas and oxygen are being mixed and burned. Further, there may be an intermediate cone due to progressive combustion of the gas. For example, CO may be formed just outside of the pure gas cone as partial oxidation occurs, and thence a somewhat blue outer cone of flame as the CO is further oxidized to CO_2. Parts of a flame may be referred to as an oxidizing zone or a reducing zone dependent on the chemical content of the gases involved. Just outside of the inner pure gas cone where the gas is being partially oxidized there will be hot CO and H_2 and thus a reducing atmosphere. Nearer the outside of the flame where O_2 is being heated by the flame an oxidizing atmosphere exists. This can be verified by holding a clean copper wire in the oxidizing zone and noticing that it acquires a black CuO coating. As this blackened wire is immersed into the reducing zone it again acquires a copper color.

EXERCISES

1. What weight of 90 per cent pure calcium carbide, CaC_2, is needed to prepare 896 liters of acetylene, C_2H_2? Ans. 2840 g.
2. Will an atmosphere containing 5 per cent carbon dioxide, 15 per cent oxygen, and 80 per cent nitrogen support the combustion of wood?
3. Explain how certain physical properties of carbon dioxide make it useful as a refrigerant.
4. Complete and balance the equations:
    (a) $CO_2 + OH^- \longrightarrow$
    (b) $Na_2C_2 + H_2O \longrightarrow$
    (c) $CO_2 + C \longrightarrow$
    (d) $NaHCO_3 + heat \longrightarrow$
    (e) $Ca(OH)_2 + CO_2 + H_2O \longrightarrow$
5. Since it is estimated that there is 30,000 times as much carbon in earth rocks and carboniferous matter as in air, about what would be the per cent CO_2 in air if one thousandth of earthbound carbon were converted to atmospheric CO_2? What effect would this have on plant life? on animal life?
6. If one wishes to be exact in statement, why cannot charcoal, coke, and boneblack be called amorphous carbon?
7. What is the percentage composition of $(C_6H_{10}O_5)_x$? What is the percentage composition of the product as it loses 2 and 4 molecules of water, respectively? This is somewhat analogous to woody material becoming coal in geological time.
8. Given 100 tons of 20 per cent ZnS, 80 per cent siliceous ore. Write equations for reactions involved in obtaining zinc metal. Assuming 5 per cent metal loss in operation what weight of zinc may be obtained? Ans. 12.7 t.
9. Give a formula for a metal acetylide and for a metal carbide. What is Fe_3C?
10. The density of liquid CO_2 is 0.81, as it exists under pressure in a cylinder. A liter of this CO_2 liquid will expand to what volume of CO_2 gas measured at standard conditions? Ans. 412 l.

REFERENCES

W. A. Bone and G. W. Himus, *Coal and Its Scientific Uses*, Longmans.
H. E. Howe, "The Manufacture of Carbon Dioxide," *Ind. and Eng. Chem.* **20,** 1091 (1928).
C. L. Jones, "Carbon Dioxide in Industry," *Chem. and Met. Eng.* **40,** 76 (1933).
J. M. Weiss, "The Distillation of Coal Tar," *Jour. Soc. Chem. Ind.* **51,** 219 (1932); **51,** 246 (1932).
"Diamonds," *Life* **32,** 11, 67 (1952).

XXVI

Silicon and Glass

$$_{14}Si \bullet {}^{28.06} \begin{matrix} | & | & | \\ 2 & 8 & 4 \\ | & | & | \end{matrix}$$

Silicon appears with carbon in Group IV of the periodic table and like carbon has four valence electrons in its outer orbit. Silicon is nonmetallic and acid forming like carbon, and many silicon analogs of carbon compounds are known. Unlike carbon the element is not found in the free state. Silicon is found in nearly all rocks and minerals and appears to be the central element of the mineral kingdom in the same way that carbon is the central element of the animal kingdom.

Occurrence of silicon. Silicon is second only to oxygen in abundance, constituting approximately 26 per cent of the earth's crust. Since practically all the silicon occurs combined with oxygen as SiO_2 (or as compounds of SiO_2 with metal oxides) this compound comprises over 50 per cent of the weight of all matter available to us.

Inasmuch as a combination of silicon and oxygen composes so high a percentage of the earth's crust, it is appropriate to digress for a moment and consider what little is known of the composition of this planet. The density of the earth as a whole approaches the density of iron; half of the meteors found are mostly iron with a little nickel; seismographic waves travel through the core of the earth with the same speed that they travel through iron. These facts strongly indicate that the earth possesses a core of iron thousands of miles in diameter. A zone above this core exists but little is conjectured as to its composition. The outer zone of the earth is composed largely of what is called *siliceous rocks*. Rocks that have probably resulted from solidification of liquid on or near the earth's surface are known as *igneous* rocks. The weathering of these rocks, erosion, and deposition by water have resulted in vast deposits of *sedimentary* rocks. Examples of sedimentary rocks are sandstone, shale, and limestone. As new intrusions of hot liquid rock have penetrated the earth's crust, heat and marked pressure effects have caused alteration of igneous and sedimentary rocks to *metamorphic* rocks. When a sandstone is subjected to marked heat and pressure effects, it crystallizes to a more compact rock called quartzite; limestone by heat and pressure is altered to the metamorphic rock, marble.

The chemistry of igneous rocks is the chemistry of many complex silicates. Liquid, glassy masses which originally covered all or part of the earth (some lavas still exist in the earth) are metal oxides dissolved in or combined with silicon dioxide. When a water solution of many salts freezes, one finds many different salt crystals throughout the ice. Similarly a magma (molten rock) on solidifying contains crystalline compounds throughout the quartz, SiO_2.

Granite is a good example of an igneous rock. A molten mass of SiO_2, Al_2O_3, K_2O, Na_2O, Fe_2O_3, and H_2O solidifies to the minerals, *feldspar*, $K_2O \cdot Al_2O_3 \cdot 6\,SiO_2$ or $Na_2O \cdot Al_2O_3 \cdot 6\,SiO_2$; *mica*, $K_2O \cdot 2\,Al_2O_3 \cdot Fe_2O_3 \cdot 6\,SiO_2 \cdot 2\,H_2O$; and *quartz*, SiO_2. On close examination of a good granite building stone, one can see the cream-colored feldspar, the black flaky mica, and white quartz. Hundreds of different minerals may form as varying compositions of molten magmas solidify or are altered chemically by weathering. A few more of the common silicates are *wollastonite*, $CaSiO_3$; *asbestos*, $Mg_3Ca(SiO_3)_4$; *talc*, $H_2Mg_3(SiO_3)_4$; *zircon*, $ZrSiO_4$; *clay*, $2\,H_2O \cdot Al_2O_3 \cdot 2\,SiO_2$. These types of siliceous rock comprise most of our surface rock and soil particles.

Preparation. Silicon may be prepared by the reduction of silicon dioxide with an active metal like magnesium or aluminum at an elevated temperature:

$$SiO_2 + 2\,Mg \longrightarrow Si + 2\,MgO$$

More commonly the element is prepared by reducing the oxide with carbon in an electric furnace:

$$SiO_2 + 2\,C \longrightarrow Si + 2\,CO\uparrow$$

The proportions of reactants must be carefully regulated to prevent the formation of silicon carbide.

Properties and uses. Silicon as ordinarily prepared is a brownish powder but may exist also as hard gray crystals with a metallic luster. The element is relatively inactive at ordinary temperatures. When heated with oxygen, it combines readily to form the dioxide; however, the action soon stops as a tightly adhering protective coating forms on the surface and prevents further action. The element readily reacts with the halogens at elevated temperatures to form volatile halides, *e.g.*

$$Si + 2\,Cl_2 \longrightarrow SiCl_4\uparrow$$

Silicon by itself has no major uses, but alloyed with iron as *ferrosilicon* it finds extensive application in the manufacture of steel as a deoxidizing agent for dissolved gases. The alloy is prepared by heating together ferric oxide, silicon dioxide, and carbon. Silicon in small amounts in steel gives a softer steel which is easily magnetized and hence is used in magnets and transformers. Alloyed with iron in larger amounts, a product is obtained which is highly resistant to the action of acids and chemicals. *Duriron* (15 per cent Si, 85 per cent Fe) is used for laboratory drain pipes and sinks.

Silicon is not attacked by acids, but does react as a nonmetal with strong bases to liberate hydrogen:

$$\text{Si} + 4\,\text{OH}^- \longrightarrow \text{SiO}_4^{----} + 2\,\text{H}_2\uparrow$$

A small amount of hydrogen is produced industrially in this manner.

Silicon dioxide. Of silicon compounds, silicon dioxide or *silica* is by far the most abundant. Sand and sandstone are very high in silica. A crystalline form, *quartz*, is widely disseminated through other rock minerals and even makes up whole mountains in Scotland and Ireland as well as in several other localities. Several varieties of quartz are known; a clear transparent form is *rock crystal;* colored varieties include *amethyst, rose quartz, onyx,* and a hydrated form called *opal.* The color of the latter varieties is probably due to the presence of traces of certain metallic oxides. *Flint* is an opaque quartz.

Silica appears to be important in certain biological processes. The ashes of certain grains, *e.g.,* oats and barley, have been found to contain silica; feathers of certain birds contain appreciable quantities. The supporting structure of the *diatom,* a tiny organism which thrives in sea water, is largely composed of silica. In certain areas the accumulation of the skeletons of these diatoms has resulted in deposits several hundred feet deep. This silica in a finely divided form is called *diatomaceous earth* or *infusorial earth* and finds application as a filtering medium for certain dye products. It is also used as a mild abrasive in scouring powders.

Silica has a melting point of approximately 1700° C. When the fused compound is allowed to cool, it solidifies to a clear colorless glass. Since it has the lowest coefficient of expansion of any known substance, it finds considerable application in the preparation of beakers, flasks, and other chemical apparatus. A quartz beaker or flask may be heated red hot and plunged into cold water without breakage. Quartz window glass is finding use in hospitals since it transmits beneficial ultraviolet rays, a property not possessed by ordinary glass.

Articles made of fused silica or quartz are relatively expensive as compared with similar articles made from ordinary glass.

Silicic acids and silicates. Many silicates, some simple and some complex, are known. While silicon dioxide is insoluble in water and does not react with water to form a silicic acid, nevertheless it may be considered as the anhydride of the many possible silicic acids.

Although free silicic acids (except possibly H_4SiO_4) have not been isolated, many salts of the hypothetical acids are known. In the following section a theory of the formation of the acids, from which the salts are presumably derived, is given.

The combination of one molecule of water with one molecule of silica would produce H_2SiO_3; two molecules of water would yield H_4SiO_4. Two or more molecules of the latter acid may condense together and subsequently lose one or more molecules of water, giving rise to a large number of *polysilicic acids*. For example, the loss of a molecule of water from two molecules of H_4SiO_4 will yield $H_6Si_2O_7$, a disilicic acid:

$$Si\begin{matrix}OH\\OH\\OH\\OH\end{matrix} + \begin{matrix}HO\\HO\\HO\\HO\end{matrix}Si - H_2O \longrightarrow \begin{matrix}HO\\HO\end{matrix}Si-O-Si\begin{matrix}OH\\OH\\OH\end{matrix}$$

or
$$2\,H_4SiO_4 - H_2O \longrightarrow H_6Si_2O_7$$

Loss of a second molecule of water would yield $H_4Si_2O_6$:

$$H_6Si_2O_7 - H_2O \longrightarrow H_4Si_2O_6$$

Condensation of three molecules of silicic acid and successive losses of a molecule of water would yield a series of trisilicic acids, etc.:

$$3\,H_4SiO_4 - 2\,H_2O \longrightarrow H_8Si_3O_{10}$$
$$H_8Si_3O_{10} - H_2O \longrightarrow H_6Si_3O_9$$
$$H_6Si_3O_9 - H_2O \longrightarrow H_4Si_3O_8$$

Many salts of the latter acid are found in nature, such as *orthoclase*, $KAlSi_3O_8$, and *albite*, $NaAlSi_3O_8$.

Silica possesses very definite acidic properties, reacting with bases and metallic oxides to form silicate salts. If silica is fused with sodium carbonate the equation for the reaction may be written:

$$Na_2CO_3 + SiO_2 \longrightarrow Na_2SiO_3 + CO_2$$

Carbon dioxide escapes as a gas and the product remaining is easily soluble in water. The solution of sodium silicate, called *water glass*, is used as a cement or adhesive for fibrous materials such as wood and asbestos, as a fireproofing agent for stage scenery, and as a preservative for eggs. The commercial substance represented by the formula Na_2SiO_3 is probably a mixture of various hydrated sodium silicate compounds.

When an acid is added to a solution of sodium silicate, a jellylike colloidal suspension of hydrated SiO_2 is obtained, which gradually loses water when warmed or allowed to stand in the open air. The acid, H_2SiO_3, does not appear to exist, and the formula for the jellylike mass should be written as x $SiO_2 \cdot y$ H_2O. When this product is dehydrated to five per cent water or less, a granular, porous solid remains. This solid, termed *silica gel*, is widely used as an adsorbent for gases and as a carrier for platinum and other catalysts in certain contact catalytic reactions.

X-ray examination of silicate minerals reveals that the basis of their structure is the silicate ion, SiO_4^{--}. Metal ions are interspaced with the negative silicate ions. The SiO_4^{--} ion has a tetrahedronal structure with an atom of silicon at the center of the tetrahedron and an oxygen atom at each of the four corners. By sharing oxygen atoms with one another, these tetrahedra appear to be able to condense together in two-dimensional or three-dimensional patterns by which many of the characteristic properties of some of the more complex silicates may be explained. For example, these tetrahedra may arrange themselves in two-dimensional sheets which would explain the cleavage of mica and talc into thin sheets. The arrangement of these units in long chains explains the fibrous nature of asbestos. Three-dimensional structures may also be produced, giving rise to large and complex molecules.

Other silicon compounds. Silica, while resistant to the action of the strong mineral acids, HCl, H_2SO_4, HNO_3, is rapidly attacked by hydrofluoric acid with the formation of gaseous SiF_4:

$$SiO_2 + 4 \, HF \longrightarrow SiF_4 \uparrow + 2 \, H_2O$$

SiF_4 is readily hydrolyzed with water to form fluosilicic acid, H_2SiF_6:

$$3 \, SiF_4 + 4 \, H_2O \longrightarrow H_4SiO_4 + 2 \, H_2SiF_6$$

The latter acid is used as an analytical reagent in the determination of sodium and potassium, since Na_2SiF_6 and K_2SiF_6 are among the few water insoluble salts of these elements. *Sodium fluosilicide* may be used as a germicide and *lead fluosilicide* as an electrolyte in the electrolytic refining of lead.

Silicon tetrachloride, which may be formed by the direct action of chlorine on silicon, is a volatile liquid which fumes strongly in moist air with the formation of a smoke or cloud of finely divided ortho silicic acid:

$$SiCl_4 + 4\,H_2O \longrightarrow H_4SiO_4 + 4\,HCl$$

If ammonia gas is added, the density of the smoke is increased by the formation of ammonium chloride.

GLASS

When a mixture of limestone, sodium carbonate, and sand is fused, a clear homogeneous mixture of sodium and calcium silicates is produced. When the fused liquid is cooled it becomes more and more

Courtesy The Linde Air Products Company

Fig. 95. Some of the "glass plumbing" required in a large research laboratory.

viscous and finally hardens to a transparent rigid mass called *glass*. During the cooling process the transition from liquid to solid does not take place at any definite temperature, and likewise in the reverse process, when the glass is warmed it gradually softens and shows no definite transition temperature which is characteristic of the change from the solid state. X-ray examination reveals no definite pattern or orientation of atoms which is a characteristic of the solid state. Glass then is really a solid solution.

The proportions of raw materials in glass may be varied within wide limits, and by the substitution of other metal oxides a great variety of glasses may be obtained. Common glass is a soda-lime glass consisting of a mixture of sodium and calcium silicates with an excess of dissolved silica. It is often termed soft glass as it melts at a relatively low temperature. The substitution of potassium for sodium results in a harder glass with a higher melting point and one more insoluble in water and alkalies. The substitution of lead oxide for calcium oxide yields *flint* glass, which has a high refractive index. It is used in the production of lenses and other optical glass. If a part of the silica is replaced by boric oxide and the metal oxide content reduced, a product with a low coefficient of heat expansion is obtained. *Pyrex* is one variety of the borosilicate glasses. Colored glasses may be obtained by incorporating small amounts of certain substances either in true solution or as a colloidal suspension. A colloidal dispersion of gold or selenium produces a red glass; cobalt oxide gives a blue glass; chromium or ferrous oxide produces a greenish colored glass.

The general procedure for the manufacture of glass is as follows: A properly proportioned mixture of the ingredients is heated in a furnace until a homogeneous solution is obtained. The glass is removed from the furnace as a semifluid mass and fashioned into various shapes by molding, rolling into sheets, blowing, or pressing. While many of these operations were formerly carried out by hand, nearly all glass shapes are now turned out by machinery. To relieve strains set up by rapid cooling, the glass must be *annealed*. This is accomplished by a very slow and gradual cooling of the glass object over a period of hours or days. Annealing of the huge 200-inch reflecting telescope lens on Mount Palomar in California required nearly a year.

Safety glass is produced by cementing together two thin sheets of ordinary glass with a transparent resinous plastic. When the glass breaks, it does not shatter, as the broken pieces stick to the plastic binding.

EXERCISES

1. Discuss the similarities and differences in properties of carbon and silicon.
2. Contrast the differences in composition and properties of the following types of glasses: ordinary soft glass; pyrex; optical glass; safety glass; colored glasses; quartz.
3. List several varieties of silicon dioxide.
4. Chemically how does SiO_2 behave? Explain the action of limestone as a flux to remove SiO_2 in various smelting operations.
5. How is ferrosilicon prepared? For what is it used?

6. Give the formula for the acid formed when three molecules of water are liberated as three molecules of silicic acid condense. Substitute symbols of metal atoms for the hydrogen atoms of this acid to represent a complex silicate.

7. Write the formula for calcium orthosilicate; zinc metasilicate.

8. Write equations for the reactions:

   (a) $Mg_2SiO_4 + HF \longrightarrow$

   (b) Fusion of K_2CO_3, $CaCO_3$, and SiO_2

9. Germanium (at. no. 32, at. wt. 72.6) is in the same family of the periodic table as carbon and silicon. How many electrons in its outer orbit? Write formulas for three possible compounds of the element. Write formula for orthogermanic acid; for sodium metagermanate.

REFERENCES

E. C. Eckel, *Cements, Limes, and Plasters*, Wiley.

Minerals Year Book, United States Department of the Interior, Bureau of Mines.

A. F. Rogers, *Introduction to the Study of Minerals and Rocks*, McGraw-Hill.

J. W. Howard, "Agates," *J. Chem. Ed.* **10,** 67 (1933); "Garnets," *ibid.* 713 (1933); "Emeralds," *ibid.* **11,** 323 (1934).

G. W. Morey, "Glass, Its Composition and Properties," *ibid.* **8,** 421 (1931).

R. C. Merrill, "Chemistry of the Soluble Silicotes," *ibid.* **24,** 262 (1947).

J. A. Upper, "The Manufacture of Abrasives," *ibid.* **26,** 676 (1949).

XXVII

The Colloidal State of Matter

What is a colloid? When sugar is dissolved in water, the crystals of sugar are reduced to molecular size. Individual molecules of sugar are dispersed or scattered throughout the water, the distances between the sugar molecules being relatively large. Such a mixture of two or more substances molecularly or ionically dispersed is termed a *true solution.*

If finely ground clay is mixed with water, a *suspension* results, in which the clay will slowly settle out. The larger the particles of clay, the faster the settling will occur. It is impossible to reduce the size of the clay particles to molecular size, and we say that the clay is insoluble. The mixture of sugar and water is said to be homogeneous, while the mixture of clay and water, since the clay particles are not of molecular dimensions, is said to be heterogeneous.

Between true solutions and ordinary suspensions, there may exist mixtures of two substances, the particles of which are so finely divided that they do not settle and cannot be filtered by ordinary means. The particles in such a mixture are smaller than those in a suspension, but larger than those in true solutions. These mixtures are referred to as colloidal dispersions or *colloidal solutions.*

Size of colloidal particles. In discussing the size of colloidal particles, we should introduce a smaller unit of linear measurement than was studied in the metric system. This is desirable because of the "smallness" of these particles. This unit is the millimicron, designated $m\mu$ and defined as one millionth of a millimeter. If we assume that molecules are spherical in shape, the diameter of an average size molecule would be about $\frac{1}{10}$ $m\mu$. Particles of clay dispersed in water would have an average size of 1000 $m\mu$ or more in diameter. Dispersed particles of a diameter ranging between 1 $m\mu$ and 100 $m\mu$ have properties characteristic of the "colloidal state." Differences between true solutions, colloidal solutions, and suspensions are largely a matter of size of the dispersed particles. It should be pointed out that there is no sharp dividing line between the three kinds of mixtures. The molecules of certain compounds are large enough to come within the size of colloidal particles, and indeed these large molecules exhibit properties characteristic of the colloidal state.

The colloidal state is not peculiar to any particular class of substances; rather, any material may be brought into a colloidal state under the proper conditions. It is true that some substances tend to assume the colloidal state. One limitation must be imposed for the formation of a colloidal solution; the *dispersed phase* (the substance which is suspended) and the *dispersion medium* (the substance in which another substance is suspended) *must be mutually insoluble*. A colloidal solution of sugar in water is impossible, since when sugar and water are mixed, the sugar is dissolved; that is, the particles are reduced to molecular size. However, sugar may be brought into colloidal solution in some liquid in which the sugar does not dissolve.

The particles in a colloidal solution are made up of aggregates or clusters of molecules. A single particle may be made up of a hundred or a thousand molecules of a substance. Even the smallest of colloidal particles will consist of many molecules.

Kinds of colloidal solutions. In chapter XV the various kinds of solutions were listed, such as gas, liquid, or solid dissolved in a liquid, gas in a gas, solid in a solid, etc. Similarly, colloidal solutions may be of several kinds. The most familiar type of colloidal solution is one in which the dispersion medium is a liquid. We may list the possible types of colloidal solutions with examples of each:

1. *Gas dispersed in gas.* Gases mix in all proportions, forming a homogeneous mixture or solution; consequently there are *no* colloids of this type.

2. *Gas dispersed in a liquid.* Foams and whipped cream are examples.

3. *Gas dispersed in a solid.* Gases adsorbed by charcoal are colloidally dispersed. White flowers and white hair contain air which is colloidally dispersed.

4. *Liquid dispersed in a gas.* Fog is composed of liquid water particles dispersed in air.

5. *Liquid dispersed in a liquid.* This type of dispersion is called an *emulsion*. Milk contains butterfat in water. Mayonnaise salad dressing consists of oil dispersed in vinegar.

6. *Liquid dispersed in a solid.* Cheese contains a dispersion of butterfat in casein. Pearl consists of calcium carbonate in which sea water is colloidally dispersed.

7. *Solid dispersed in a gas.* Smoke and dust particles dispersed in the air may be of colloidal size.

8. *Solid dispersed in a liquid.* This is the most common type. Examples are coffee, tea, and paints.

9. *Solid dispersed in a solid.* Certain colored glasses and porcelain are examples.

Of the above types, we shall consider in detail only (5) and (8). A liquid colloidal solution is called a *sol;* if the liquid is water, it is called a *hydrosol.* A dispersion of a liquid in a liquid is called an *emulsion.*

Preparation of colloidal solutions. Two general methods are available for the preparation of colloidal solutions: (1) *dispersion* and (2) *condensation.* Dispersion methods involve the breaking up of large particles into particles of a colloidal size. Condensation refers to the condensing of molecules (which are smaller than colloidal particles) to particles of colloidal size.

$$\text{Molecules} \xrightarrow{\text{condensation}} \text{Colloids} \xleftarrow{\text{dispersion}} \text{Precipitates and Large Particles}$$

1. *Dispersion.* Certain devices, called colloid mills, are available for reducing the size of coarse particles to colloidal size. These are essentially pulverizing devices. Certain chemicals aid in attaining dispersion of the particles to the colloidal state. Such substances are called *peptizing agents.* Clay particles may be peptized with an alkaline solution.

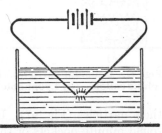

2. *Condensation.* Certain metals may be brought into colloidal form by the "Bredig arc process" (Fig. 96). This consists in producing an electric arc between two electrodes of the metal beneath the surface of the dispersion medium. Small quantities of the metal may be vaporized, subsequently condensed to solid, and dispersed in the liquid.

Fig. 96. Bredig arc method for preparation of colloidal solutions.

Condensation methods may employ chemical reactions, in which the starting materials are in true solution. The chemical reaction forms an insoluble substance which may be dispersed colloidally. If a solution of ferric chloride is allowed to drip slowly into boiling water, a reddish colored dispersion of iron hydroxide is obtained:

$$FeCl_3 + 3\,H_2O \longrightarrow Fe(OH)_3 \downarrow + 3\,HCl$$

Arsenic sulfide is insoluble in water and may be produced in a colloidal condition by passing hydrogen sulfide gas into a saturated solution of arsenic oxide in water:

$$As_2O_3 + 3\,H_2S \longrightarrow As_2S_3 \downarrow + 3\,H_2O$$

Gold and silver colloids may be prepared by the action of certain reducing agents upon solutions of salts of these metals.

The importance of colloids. A few typical examples may illustrate the importance of colloids in everyday life. Our bodies are largely colloidal in nature. The protoplasm of living cells and tissue is a colloidal substance. Most of the body fluids, glandular secretions, and blood are colloidal. Many foods are colloidal. Thus the essential vital processes, nutrition, digestion, and secretion are concerned with colloidal solutions.

Jellies of all kinds are colloidal dispersions. The color of the sky is due to a colloidal dispersion of dust. The action of soap in removing dirt and grease is due to a colloidal phenomenon.

Dispersions of solids in liquids. If a small amount of gelatin is dissolved in hot water and the solution cooled, the whole changes to

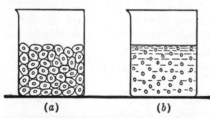

(a)   (b)

Fig. 97. Colloidal particles. (a) Lyophilic colloid. (b) Lyophobic colloid.

a semisolid jellylike mass; pectin added to sugared fruit juices causes the solution to jell. The dispersed particles in these two instances seem to have an attraction for the dispersion medium. A large shell of the dispersion medium may be formed about each colloidal particle and this prevents the free movement of these particles (Fig. 97). In some cases the dispersed phase may surround minute pockets of the liquid. Much as beeswax encases honey, a colloidal substance in film form may enclose small droplets of the liquid dispersion medium. As a result the colloidal system assumes a semisolid state. Colloids in which the dispersed phase has an attraction for the dispersion medium are called *lyophilic* colloids. If the liquid is water, the colloid is said to be *hydrophilic*. Lyophilic colloids are usually of an organic nature; examples are starches, soaps, glues, and gums.

Substances of an inorganic character usually form *lyophobic* colloidal solutions — a dispersion in which there is no attraction between the two phases. If arsenic sulfide is dispersed in water, there is little attraction of the arsenic sulfide for the water, and the solution has almost exactly the same properties as the dispersion medium.

Lyophilic colloids are reversible, lyophobic colloids are not. By reversible we mean that if the colloid is precipitated, the solid may again be dispersed in a colloidal condition when the dispersion medium is added. If albumen be precipitated without heat coagulation by means of a salt solution, and then washed free of the salt and water added, the albumen becomes dispersed again in the colloidal state.

Characteristics of colloidal solutions. Colloidal systems exhibit certain properties which enable us to differentiate them from true solutions.

(a) *Tyndall effect.* If a beam of light is passed through a colloidal solution, a very definite path of the light is visible through the solution (Fig. 98). The light ray is made visible by the scattering of light by the suspended particles. This phenomenon is not observed in true solutions as the molecules present are too small to scatter the light. This property of colloidal solutions was first called to attention by Tyndall, an English physicist. If such a beam of

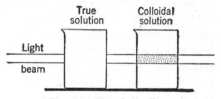

Fig. 98. Tyndall effect.

light is observed at right angles by means of a high power microscope, the refraction of light from the individual particles in suspension can be seen. Such a device is called an *ultramicroscope*. Although the particles in suspension cannot actually be seen, a study of the tiny specks of light leads to many interesting conclusions as to the size and properties of the particles. The Tyndall effect is analogous to the scattering of light entering a darkened room in which dust particles are suspended in the air. A well-defined path of light is visible because of the scattering of light by the suspended dust particles. The observation of light flashes from colloidal particles in the ultra-microscope is analogous to the transmission of signals from a considerable distance by sunlight flashes from a pocket mirror — even though the mirror itself is too small to be seen.

(b) *The Brownian movement.* When a colloidal solution is viewed under an ultramicroscope, the suspended particles are seen as tiny specks of light dancing about in the solution. They appear to move at random, first one way, then another. This zigzag motion was first observed by the botanist, Brown, in a suspension of pollen dust. It is believed that this motion is due to a bombardment of the suspended particles by molecules in the solution. The molecules in a liquid move at relatively high speeds, and when they collide with a larger particle (of colloidal size), the larger particle is moved in one direction or another. Since, on the average, a particle will not receive the same number of hits on all sides at the same time, the net result is a zigzag

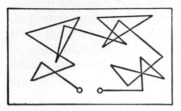

motion. The Brownian movement appears to be a stability factor of colloidal solutions; the particles are kept from settling out because of this ceaseless molecular bombardment.

(c) *Colloidal particles are electrically charged.* Colloidal solutions act as fair conductors of the electric current. If a current is passed through a solution be-

Fig. 99. Brownian movement.

tween a pair of electrodes (as in electrolysis), the colloidal particles will all move toward either the positive or the negative pole. This indicates that the particles in suspension carry an electric charge. The particles are discharged at one of the electrodes and as a result the colloid is precipitated. This movement of the colloidal particles toward one of the electrodes is termed *cataphoresis*. The charge carried by the colloidal particles depends upon the nature of the colloid itself. Most of the metals and their sulfides form negatively charged colloids, while metallic hydroxides in general are positive.

The charge on a colloidal particle is probably due to the adsorption of ions from the dispersion medium. *Adsorption* means an adhering to the surface. It is usually considered to embody a layer of adsorbed substance of but one molecule or ion thickness on the adsorption media. Adsorption differs, then, from absorption. An example of the latter is a sponge taking up water by capillary action. The columns of liquid in the pores of the solid absorbent are many molecular diameters in size. A single colloidal particle probably adsorbs many ions. Certain dispersed substances adsorb positive ions and as a result become positively charged; others adsorb negative ions and become negatively charged. The adsorbed ions cause the colloidal particle to move through the solution during electrolysis.

The charge on the colloidal particle is another important reason why the solutions are stable and do not settle out. Since like charges repel, the force of repulsion will prevent the particles from coalescing to form larger particles and precipitating.

The precipitation of colloidal particles. It is reasonable to assume that if the charge on the colloidal particle could be removed or neutralized, this would allow the particles to come together and form larger particles. Eventually the particles would be large enough to settle out in the form of a precipitate; neutralization of the charge should result in coagulation of the colloid. This appears to be the case, since the addition of electrolytes (substances which ionize) causes the colloid to precipitate. Ions of opposite charge to those borne by the colloidal particle are probably adsorbed, thereby neutralizing the charge on the particle. The higher the valence of the ion adsorbed, the more effective the precipitating electrolyte.

Coagulation may also be effected by the addition of a colloid of opposite charge. Thus iron hydroxide colloid, which is positive, added to arsenic sulfide colloid, which is negative, results in coagulation of both colloidal solutions. This process is termed *mutual coagulation*.

Dialysis. In order to prepare a stable colloidal system it is necessary to remove substances in the ionic state which would tend to precipitate the colloid. This separation may be effected by a process called *dialysis*. This process is based on the fact that colloidal particles are much larger than ions. If an animal membrane bag containing the colloidal solution which is contaminated with electrolytes is immersed in a bath of distilled water, the ions will diffuse through the membrane until the concentration of the ions is the same inside and outside the membrane; colloidal particles are retained within the bag. By renewing the water on the outside frequently, practically all the electrolyte may be removed from the colloidal solution. Dialysis is really a kind of filtration, since one kind of substance is retained on one side of the membrane, while the other passes through. Membranes used for this purpose include certain animal membranes, parchment paper, and collodion film.

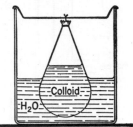

Fig. 100. Purification of a colloid by dialysis.

Protective colloids. In many cases a colloidal system may be stabilized by the addition of a second colloid. The second colloid probably forms a protective film around the particles and adsorbed ions of the first colloid, thereby preventing the particles from coming together and coalescing. These protective colloids are of the lyophilic type. Gelatin may be added to an ice cream mixture to prevent the formation of large crystals. Gelatin is also employed in the photographic industry to form a film about the silver bromide particles which are dispersed on the photographic plates. Protective colloids find application also in the preparation of inks.

Emulsions. If two mutually insoluble liquids be vigorously shaken together, small droplets of one will be dispersed in the other. Thus when kerosene and water are shaken together, the kerosene is dispersed as small droplets throughout the water medium. The kerosene particles soon coalesce, and finally separation of the oil and water into two distinct layers takes place. Such a temporary emulsion may be made more permanent by the addition of an *emulsifying agent* such as soap. An emulsifying agent is a protective colloid which forms a film about each oil particle, preventing coalescence. Milk is an emulsion of drops of butterfat in water, casein acting as an emulsifying agent. The yolk of eggs acts as an emulsifying agent in an emulsion of olive oil in dilute vinegar (mayonnaise dressing).

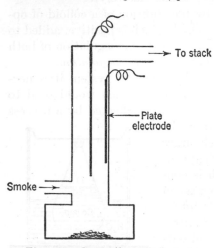

Fig. 101. Cottrell precipitator.

Applications of colloids. Most ores contain large percentages of worthless or gangue material admixed with the desired metal minerals. A step toward obtaining a metal from its ore is known as concentration, removal of much of the unwanted earthy matter from the metal minerals. A flotation process which involves colloidal sized particles proves invaluable for the concentration of certain ores. The ores are finely ground and suspended in water. Air bubbles are beaten or blown into the water and the bubbles are stabilized by use of a small quantity of oil and soda. Metal sulfide mineral particles or free gold or silver selectively adhere to the oil coated air bubbles and are floated to the surface of the water and skimmed off as an ore concentrate. The unwanted siliceous minerals do not adhere to the rising air bubbles but settle out at the bottom of the tank (see chap. XXVIII).

Smoke, which is a colloidal dispersion of solid particles in air, constitutes a nuisance around manufacturing centers. The smoke from smelters and certain other industrial plants is particularly undesirable. Such smoke may be treated by a Cottrell precipitator (Fig. 101), which makes use of the fact that colloidal smoke particles in general have like adsorbed electrical charges and may be precipitated as a powder by passing the smoke between highly charged plates or electrodes. In addition to eliminating the smoke nuisance, valuable materials may be recovered as by-products from the precipitated smoke powder. For example, one of our main sources of industrial arsenic oxide is the dust that is recovered from smelter smoke by a Cottrell precipitator.

Colloids as mixtures of minute particles of one substance insoluble but dispersed throughout another, are finding innumerable applications; to mention a few: preparation of paints, salad dressings, glass and chinaware, oils and lubricants, photographic emulsions, and drugs.

EXERCISES

1. Give an example of (general name or specific example): a lyophilic colloid; a liquid-in-gas colloid; a solid-in-gas colloid; a liquid-in-liquid colloid; a gas-in-solid colloid; cataphoresis; adsorption.
2. List and describe four ways in which you could distinguish between a yellow arsenic sulfide colloid and a yellow K_2CrO_4 solution. Tell how both the colloid and K_2CrO_4 would act in each case.
3. What are the two general methods for the preparation of colloidal solutions?
4. What do you understand by the terms: colloidal solution; dialysis; adsorption; cataphoresis; emulsifying agent; lyophobic; lyophilic; emulsion; true solution?
5. List a number of common substances which have colloidal characteristics.
6. Differentiate between: smoke and mist; hydrophilic colloid and hydrophobic colloid; dialysis and electrolysis; adsorption and absorption; microscope and ultramicroscope; cataphoresis and osmosis.
7. Would 342 g. of colloidal gold in 10 l. of water have as much effect on boiling point and freezing point as 342 g. of sugar ($C_{12}H_{22}O_{11}$)? Explain.
8. Colloidal gold in water gives a purple sol. $KMnO_4$ in water gives a purple solution. Aside from the slight difference in colors, list tests in which the colloidal gold and $KMnO_4$ solution will act differently.
9. A 1 cc. cube has a surface area of 6 cm². If it were cut into cubes 1 mm. on an edge, what would be the total surface area of the resulting cubes? What general inference can be drawn as to the surface area of a colloid as compared to the same amount of material in solid form?

REFERENCES

J. Alexander, *Colloid Chemistry*, Van Nostrand.
S. A. Arrhenius, *Chemistry in Modern Life*, Van Nostrand.
W. D. Bancroft, *Applied Colloid Chemistry*, McGraw-Hill.
E. O. Kramer, *Advances in Colloid Science*, Interscience.

XXVIII

Metals, Metallurgy

In previous chapters of this book nonmetals and their compounds have been more specifically discussed than metals and metallic compounds. During the discussion of salts and bases (chap. X), metals were briefly considered since salts and bases are respectively metal-nonmetal and metal-hydroxyl type compounds.

From an atomic structure standpoint, metals are those elements having few electrons in their outer orbit, which electrons are comparatively readily given up to form ions, *e.g.*:

$$\underset{\text{atom}}{\text{Na}} \longrightarrow \underset{\text{ion}}{\text{Na}^+} + e$$

$$\text{Zn} \longrightarrow \text{Zn}^{++} + 2\,e$$

$$\text{Al} \longrightarrow \text{Al}^{+++} + 3\,e$$

The activity series of metals (p. 93), also called the electromotive series (p. 441), lists the metals in order of their comparative tendencies to give up electrons to form ions. As nonmetallic or negative radical ions associate themselves with these positive metallic ions, salts result; with the OH^- ions, a base results.

In this chapter we shall concern ourselves particularly with the physical and chemical properties of metals as a class of substances. The properties of specific metallic elements will be covered in following chapters. The periodic classification of the elements (chap. IV) groups the elements into families having similar chemical characteristics and to a certain extent similar physical properties. In subsequent chapters it will be convenient to study these groups of similar metallic elements rather than devote a chapter to each single element.

Metallic properties and atomic structure. The physical and chemical properties of metals must be basically a manifestation of the atomic structure of the respective metals. The outer electron structure of metals is a dominant factor in determining many physical properties of atoms as well as chemical properties. In a given periodic family group, however, there is a somewhat progressive change from the lightest to the heaviest element; *e.g.*, lithium to cesium or beryllium to radium. Consult periodic table inside back cover.

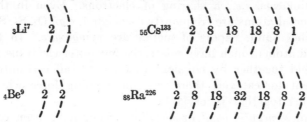

The valence or outer electron of cesium is much further removed from the positive nucleus than the valence electron of lithium. Accordingly, the outer electron of cesium is less tightly held; this manifests itself in the fact that cesium has the lowest *ionization potential* for gaseous atoms (ionization potential is a measure of the ease with which electrons may be removed from gaseous atoms). It follows that many *physical and chemical properties are related to atomic size and the lability of outer electrons.* This is not a definite rule, however, as other factors are involved when dealing with a bulk metal rather than with single atoms. For example, one would expect cesium to be an excellent conductor of electricity and better than lithium in this respect. The fact is that lithium is a considerably better conductor than cesium. Apparently the nature of the *interatomic bonding between atoms of a given metal is also a basic factor in the comparative physical and chemical properties of metals.*

Although beryllium and radium have the same valence, radium is a more chemically active metal than beryllium and, although both exhibit similar physical properties, size and comparative valence electron mobility can account for degrees of difference in these properties

In the case of families III to VI of the periodic table, the lighter elements possess more nonmetallic properties and progress toward distinctly metallic properties in the heavier atoms. This is readily related to the fact that the smaller, lighter atoms of these families, with outer electrons in an orbit not distant from the positive nucleus, hold on to their electrons and even tend to acquire more to become negative ions; whereas the heavier, larger atoms of these families, from a comparative standpoint, tend to lose outer electrons which are quite distant from the nucleus and thus act as metals. Family VII elements, because of need of only one electron to fill the outermost orbit of 8, almost always act as nonmetals.

Bonding forces of metals and nonmetals. Nonmetals have several electrons in the outer orbit of their atoms. As a result, nonmetal atoms are probably held together in the solid state by covalent linkages, *i.e.*, a sharing of electrons. Even in the vapor state nonmetal atoms are frequently associated, *e.g.*, O_2, S_2, S_4, S_8, C_x. On the other hand, vapors of metals are *monatomic*. In the solid state metal atoms which have relatively few outer electrons probably are not held together by covalent linkages — and certainly not by electrovalent forces; yet, there is some binding force which holds metal atoms together in crystals.

The names *metallic bond* or *metallic valency* have been coined for use in considering intermetallic bonding tendency. A marked feature of metallic bonding is the fact that bonding remains or is instantaneously renewed on mechanical deformation of the metal. For example, a crystal of copper may be drawn into a long wire. This may in part be explained by the tendency of metals to assume a very close packed cubic crystalline structure in which a large number of planes of flow or slippage allow for deformation, but with instantaneous renewal of metallic bonding, without detracting from the strength of the interatomic attraction.

The exact nature of the interatomic attraction between metallic atoms has not yet been ascertained. This is a good example of the sort of problem that arises to challenge the scientist. Until he had learned something of the structure of the atom, he did not realize that the problem even existed. Almost certainly the successful solution of this problem will raise others equally difficult.

Physical properties of metals. Various physical properties of metals are basically dependent on the mobility of the outer electrons. Metals are good *electrical conductors* as compared to nonmetals. An electrical current in a metal wire is presumed to be a movement of the outer electrons from one atom to another down the wire. Such elements as silver, sodium, and copper, having but one or two valence electrons are among the best of conductors. On the other hand, sulfur, with six outer electrons (as an example of a nonmetal), tends to hold its outer electrons and even capture electrons, and thereby acts as an *insulator* material.

Heat conductivity of elements closely parallels electrical conductivity; metals are good heat conductors, and this may be because of the capacity of the outside electrons to absorb energy and readily move from atom to atom in the solid metal.

The ease with which metals may be deformed or pounded into shape, termed *malleability*, is related to the weakness or mobility of bonding between metallic atoms. Gold, for example, is very malleable; it can be pounded into gold leaf as thin as $\frac{1}{300,000}$ inch. Lead is also very malleable. A *ductile* element is one that can be easily pulled into wire; copper and aluminum are very ductile. The two general properties of metals of malleability and ductility determine the usefulness of metals for various purposes. The opposite of malleability and ductility is *brittleness*. Diamond, which is typical of nonmetals in that the atoms are held together by covalent linkages, is the *hardest* element and is very brittle.

An allied property of metals as far as usefulness is concerned is their *elasticity*. They may be deformed to a considerable extent after which they spring back to their original state; or they may be deformed to such an extent that the *elastic limit* or *yield point* is exceeded, so that the piece will no longer spring back to its original dimensions but undergoes permanent deformation, yet remains as one piece. Whatever the binding force between the metal atoms, within limits it remains after deformation. There is a sort of *plastic flow* as metals undergo stretching or pounding. Contrast the fact that a crystal of a nonmetal or of a salt fractures when slightly distorted; their elastic limit is soon reached. This fracturing of salts and crystalline nonmetals is experienced as these brittle substances are ground with a mortar and pestle. One cannot readily grind a metal. Plastic flow of metals accounts for the capacity to fashion them into various shapes by pounding, rolling, pulling, or drawing through a die, extruding or squirting under high pressure through an orifice, pressing, or bending. If the force pulling on a piece of metal is increased sufficiently, it will rupture the metal, and the magnitude of the force necessary to pull apart a piece of known cross-sectional area is a measure of the *tensile strength*. The yield points and tensile strength of a number of metals are shown in Table 26.

TABLE 26

YIELD POINT AND TENSILE STRENGTH OF METALS

Material	Yield Point Lb. per Sq. In.	Ultimate Tensile Strength Lb. per Sq. In.
Aluminum (cold rolled)	18,700	20,900
Lead (cast)	——	1,780
Nickel (cast)	25,000	60,000
Nickel (cold rolled)	120,000	160,000
Iron (wrought)	25,000	48,000
Steel	36,000–170,000	50,000–200,000
Alloy steel	39,000–276,000	60,000–340,000
Zinc	12,800	17,000–42,000

Heat treatment and mechanical working, such as rolling or drawing, in general, increase the strength of a metal.

Metals, in general, are capable of giving a polished surface which reflects a high percentage of impinging light. Since smooth metal surfaces reflect light, metals are said to have *metallic lustre;* whereas, nonmetals are not lustrous and at times are even transparent.

Metals are, of course, selectively used according to such desired physical properties as tensile strength, malleability, ductility, electrical and heat conductivity, melting temperature, hardness, resistance to corrosion, density, etc. There are marked differences in properties in the various metals. This statement is exemplified in the variation in density from the metal lithium which is little more than one-half as heavy as water (density .534) to osmium which has a density of 22.48. Table 27 lists some common physical properties of some of the important metals.

TABLE 27

PHYSICAL PROPERTIES OF SOME IMPORTANT METALS

METAL	MELTING POINT ° C.	BOILING POINT ° C.	DENSITY AT 20° C.	RADIUS [1] OF METAL ION IN CRYSTALS cm.	ELECTRICAL RESISTANCE AT 20° ohm-cm.	SPECIFIC HEAT cal./gram
Lithium	179	1372	0.534	0.6×10^{-8}	9.3×10^{-6}	0.80
Sodium	97.5	892	0.97	0.95	4.6	0.25
Potassium . . .	63.5	774	0.86	1.33	7.0	0.18
Cesium	28.4	690	1.90	1.69	20.	0.05
Beryllium . . .	1300	1530	1.73	0.31	18.5	0.42
Magnesium . .	650	1107	1.75	0.65	4.46	0.25
Calcium	851	1487	1.55	0.99	4.6	0.145
Strontium . . .	757	1384	2.6	1.13		
Barium	850	1640	3.75	1.35		0.07
Radium	960	1140	6.0			
Copper	1083	2310	8.92	0.96	1.69	0.09
Silver	960	1950	10.5	1.26	1.62	0.055
Gold	1063	2600	19.3	1.37	2.4	0.031
Zinc	420	907	7.14	0.74	6.	0.092
Mercury . . .	− 38.9	357	13.6	1.1	95.8	0.033
Aluminum . . .	659	2057	2.71		2.62	0.22
Tin	231.8	2260	7.3	0.71	11.4	0.054
Lead	327.5	1620	11.3	0.84	21.9	0.032
Bismuth . . .	271	1420	9.8	0.74	119.	0.03
Chromium . . .	1550	2470	7.1	0.52	2.6	0.11
Manganese . . .	1220	2150	7.2		5.	0.11
Iron	1530	2730	7.8	0.75	10.	0.11
Nickel	1452	2730	8.9	0.69	6.9	0.10
Platinum . . .	1770	4400	21.45		10.5	0.032

[1] The radius of a metal ion in a crystal will in general be considerably smaller than the radius of the metal atom.

A more comprehensive listing of the various physical properties of metals is given in various handbooks of chemistry and physics.

Periodicity of properties. Many properties of the elements are periodic functions of their atomic numbers. For example, atomic radii and, hence, volumes of the atoms show a definite periodicity as the atomic number increases. Atomic volumes, which are obtained by dividing atomic weights by densities, are plotted in Figure 102 against atomic numbers. It is evident that the alkali group, except Li, occupy maxima while members of other families occupy lower but similar relative positions on the curve.

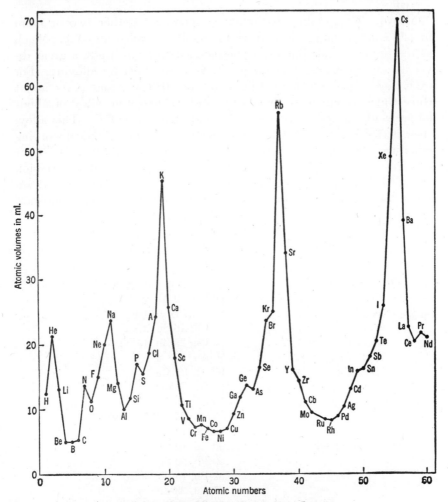

Fig. 102. Periodicity of atomic volumes.

The alkali metals which have comparatively large atomic volumes have comparatively low melting points. Elements such as the covalent bonded nonmetals carbon and silicon have very high melting points. The general statement may be made that melting point decreases as atomic size increases. This is as would be expected, as melting means disruption of the bonds holding the atoms together and atomic bonding between large metallic atoms is generally weaker.

Periodicity of such properties as heat expansivity, heat and electrical conductivity, magnetic susceptibility, melting point, compressibility, hardness, and distribution of spectral lines has also been observed.

Alloys. The product obtained by melting together two or more metals and allowing the mixture to solidify is called an *alloy*. Much as the fundamental colors may be blended to many tints, a great diversity of properties of metal products is obtained by alloying. For example, copper has a melting point of 1083° C., and costs about three times as much as zinc per pound. *Brass* is an alloy of about 66 per cent Cu and 34 per cent Zn, and melts at 900° C. This alloy, then, is easier to remelt than copper, and has good mechanical working qualities. An alloy of approximately 14 per cent silicon and 86 per cent iron, known as *ferrosilicon* or *duriron*, is very resistant to corrosion and to the action of acids. Accordingly, it is used in laboratory drain pipes. Several of the more common alloys and their compositions are shown in Table 28.

TABLE 28

COMMON ALLOYS

Trade Name	Per Cent Composition
Aluminum bronze	90 Cu, 10 Al
Babbitt	90 Sn, 7 Sb, 3 Cu
Bearing bronze	82 Cu, 16 Sn, 2 Zn
German silver	60 Cu, 25 Zn, 15 Ni
Gold coinage	90 Au, 10 Cu
Magnalium	90 Al, 10 Mg
Manganese bronze	95 Cu, 5 Mn
Nickel coinage	75 Cu, 25 Ni
Pewter	85 Sn, 6 Bi, 7 Cu, 2 Sb
Red brass	90 Cu, 10 Zn
Silver coinage	90 Ag, 10 Cu
Solder	50 Pb, 50 Sn
Type metal	82 Pb, 15 Sb, 3 Sn
Yellow brass	67 Cu, 33 Zn
Wood's metal	50 Bi, 25 Pb, 12.5 Sn, 12.5 Cd

Binary alloys (of two metals) may be of several types depending on the following factors: complete solubility, partial solubility, or insolubility of the given metals in the solid state; possible compound formation between the metals. Intermetallic compounds in alloys are fairly numerous, for example, Al_2Mg_3, Ag_3Sb, $CuMg$, $CuMg_2$.

Courtesy The International Nickel Company, Inc.

Fig. 103. Tricky alloys are made in the high-frequency induction furnace.

If two metals completely soluble in the melted state are also completely soluble in the solid state a homogeneous alloy is obtained. A homogeneous alloy may also be prepared if the melt of two metals has the exact composition of a compound of the two. For various purposes a homogeneous alloy is best, but most alloys are heterogeneous and for many uses this is an advantage. The desired surface hardness and thus wearing quality of some steel is due to hard needlelike crystals of Fe_3C throughout an iron matrix. The bearing metal called babbitt (90 Sn, 7 Sb, 3 Cu) has a hard antimony-containing needlelike component embedded in a softer tin component. On wear the soft component smears the surface so there is little bearing friction, while the harder component gives rigidity. Babbitt is an example of a ternary alloy.

Alloys are frequently analyzed by etching a polished metal surface with weak acid followed by microscopic examination. The different components of a smooth alloy surface react at different rates with weak acids and thus a new irregular surface is formed. Acid resistant sections will be microscopic plateaus as compared to degrees of depression of the more acid soluble components (see Fig. 104).

Fig. 104. Polished and acid-etched surface of manganese steel.

Eutectics. Much as a dissolved substance lowers the freezing point of water, one metal dissolved in the liquid of a second metal lowers the freezing point of the latter. This is evident from Figure 105.

As silver is dissolved in liquid copper, the freezing point or melting temperature of the alloys formed is progressively lower as the percentage of silver increases; as copper is dissolved in liquid silver, the freezing point or melting temperature of the alloy progressively decreases. Necessarily a mixture exists which is the *alloy of lowest melting point*. It is called the *eutectic* alloy and is represented in the diagram by *E*, which shows a composition of 28 per cent copper and 72 per cent silver. If a solution of composition *A* is cooled, copper begins to crystallize out, and the composition of the solution alters along the curve toward *E*. At *E* the entire mass which consists of copper and the eutectic mixture (28 per cent Cu, 72 per cent Ag) solidifies. Similarly if a solution of composition *B* is cooled, silver crystallizes out with concomitant change in composition of the liquid until *E* is reached, when the entire mass solidifies.

Occurrence of metals. Only those metals that have little affinity for oxygen or other nonmetals occur in the elemental state in nature. Gold and platinum are found as nuggets or specks in rock or in alluvial gravel. Silver, copper, and mercury are occasionally found in the free (not chemically combined) state, but the principal occurrence of the latter metals is in the combined state. The more active metals always occur in nature as compounds.

Since oxygen is the most abundant nonmetal, metals usually occur in nature as oxides. Metal oxides act basic toward the very abundant acidic compound silica, SiO_2, and the result is that

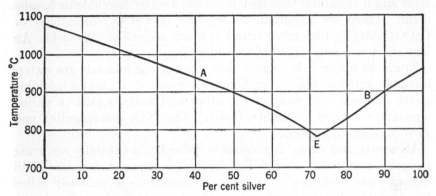

Fig. 105. Freezing-point curve for solutions of copper and silver.

silicate rocks (which may be considered as made up of various metal oxide-silica compounds) comprise the bulk of earth material. Thus the main occurrence of the metal elements is as silicates, *e.g.*, sodium feldspar, $Na_2O \cdot Al_2O_3 \cdot 6\ SiO_2$; potassium feldspar, $K_2O \cdot Al_2O_3 \cdot 6\ SiO_2$; wollastonite, $CaSiO_3$, ferrous silicate, $FeSiO_3$; mica, $K_2O \cdot 2\ Al_2O_3 \cdot Fe_2O_3 \cdot 6\ SiO_2 \cdot 2\ H_2O$. Silicates are not usually satisfactory sources of the metals because of the cost of extracting the metal. Weathering of rocks in geological time has effected decomposition of much rock silicate and there are resultant metal oxide deposits. Bauxite, $Al_2O_3 \cdot 2\ H_2O$, is an example of a natural metal oxide mineral resulting from silicate weathering. Much of the reds or browns in soil is due to iron oxide or hydrated iron oxide that was once part of a silicate rock.

In long periods of geological time, ground waters containing dilute acids have selectively dissolved salts from the silicate minerals and these salts have found their way into the sea or been deposited in arid regions. Large deposits of the salts $NaCl$, Na_2CO_3, $NaNO_3$, K_2SO_4, $MgSO_4$, $Na_2B_4O_7$ are found on the earth's surface.

Rock deposits of metal compounds may also result from precipitations as diverse ground water solutions flow together. Suppose a mineral water containing H_2S joined a ground water solution containing Cu^{++}:

$$Cu^{++} + S^{--} \longrightarrow CuS \downarrow$$

Deposits of copper sulfide mineral would accrue as these diverse waters over thousands of years continued to meet. *Sulfide* minerals such as ZnS (sphalerite), PbS (galena), Cu_2S (chalcocite), As_2S_3 (orpiment), HgS (cinnabar) constitute some of the principal minerals from which metals are obtained.

Carbonic acid is among the most important of the ground water acids and it is natural that rock deposits of water-insoluble *carbonates* occur. There are mountainous deposits of $CaCO_3$ (limestone) or $CaCO_3 \cdot MgCO_3$ (dolomite) found in many regions of the world. An important iron mineral is $FeCO_3$ (siderite).

From the above it is evident that most of our minerals are water-insoluble sulfides, oxides, carbonates, or silicates. Water-insoluble metal compounds of most of the other acid radicals exist in varied amounts; examples are $BaSO_4$ (barite), $Ca_3(PO_4)_2$ (phosphorite), and $PbWO_4$ (lead tungstate).

Minerals and ores. A *mineral* is defined as a naturally occurring inorganic compound. Silicon dioxide, SiO_2, is the most abundant of all minerals and according to its form of occurrence is variously called silica, quartz, diatomaceous earth, and other names. According to our definition, naturally occurring water is a mineral. Usually when one refers to a mineral, he has in mind some naturally occurring metal-nonmetal compound. Metal minerals are commonly classed according to the nonmetal with which they are united. Metal oxides, sulfides, carbonates, and silicates are examples of important classes of minerals.

An *ore* is a naturally occurring mineral mixture from which a metal may be extracted economically. While both clay and bauxite are minerals of aluminum, only the latter is termed an ore, since aluminum on a commercial basis is extracted from bauxite but not clay.

Metallurgy. The science which considers the extraction of metals from ores is called *metallurgy*. All those processes of breaking, grinding, pulverizing, and sizing of ore particles, and of concentrating the desired mineral from the unwanted rock mass in which it occurs, comprise what is known in metallurgical industry as *ore dressing*. Having obtained a mineral concentrate, it remains to carry on appropriate chemical changes to obtain the desired metal or metals. Processes of *pyrometallurgy*, *hydrometallurgy*, or *electrometallurgy* may be involved. The names are in themselves explanatory, as heat, water, or electric current are used in obtaining the metal from its ore.

Suppose a company has an ore which is 5 per cent galena, PbS, and 95 per cent quartz, SiO_2. After mining, breaking, crushing, and grinding of the rock, it might be subjected to *gravity* concentration. Taking advantage of the difference in specific gravity between the heavy PbS particles and the lighter SiO_2 particles, the use of running water in suitable concentration machines could effect a considerable separation of the ore and silica. A product of such concentration machines from the raw ore might assay 50 per cent PbS and 50 per cent SiO_2. Most of the silica in the original rock could be discarded with only a small loss of PbS. This is evident from the following:

$$
\begin{array}{l}
\text{500 lb. PbS} \\
\text{9,500 lb. } SiO_2 \\
\text{10,000 lb. ore}
\end{array}
\xrightarrow[\text{machines}]{\text{concentration}}
\begin{array}{l}
\text{475 lb. PbS} \quad + \quad \text{25 lb. PbS} \\
\text{475 lb. } SiO_2 \quad + \quad \text{9,025 lb. } SiO_2 \\
\text{950 lb. concentrate} \quad \text{9,050 lb. reject}
\end{array}
$$

It may be noted that most of the PbS is now concentrated in less than one-tenth the original amount of rock material. If this ore concentration is effected in a mill at the mine much haulage and transportation of waste material is saved. At the smelter to which the concentrated ore is shipped less heat is thus required in the subsequent pyrometallurgy.

To obtain metallic lead from the above, the concentrate may now be heated in suitable furnaces in the presence of air, in which case the following chemical changes take place:

$$2\,PbS + 3\,O_2 \longrightarrow 2\,PbO + 2\,SO_2$$
$$2\,PbO + PbS \longrightarrow 3\,Pb + SO_2$$

The process above of heating an ore in contact with air is called *roasting*. This is one of the more important pyrometallurgical processes of treating metallic sulfide ores.

Carbon is commonly used to obtain a metal from its oxide. When the oxide is heated with carbon, it is reduced, *e.g.*:

$$ZnO + C \longrightarrow Zn + CO$$
$$PbO + C \longrightarrow Pb + CO$$
$$Fe_2O_3 + 3\,C \longrightarrow 2\,Fe + 3\,CO$$

Carbon monoxide is also an effective reducing agent for a metallic oxide:

$$Fe_2O_3 + 3\,CO \longrightarrow 2\,Fe + 3\,CO_2$$

Smelters, also called reduction plants, get their name from the fact that melted metal is usually the product of their pyrometallurgical operations.

An example of hydrometallurgical treatment would be as follows: Suppose an ore contained about 2 per cent of a copper-oxide–copper-carbonate mineral intermixed with 98 per cent of worthless silica or silicate rock. Worthless mineral is referred to as *gangue*. The crushed ore could be put into large vats and treated with dilute sulfuric acid.

The dilute acid would act on the copper minerals to give water-soluble $CuSO_4$, the solution of which could be drained from the gangue. This particular use of a water solution (thus a hydrometallurgical process) may be called *leaching*. Leaching consists essentially of a selective dissolving of one mineral or group of minerals from an ore.

The copper sulfate solution obtained above could be electrolyzed in a cell to obtain metallic copper. This would be an example of electrometallurgy. In the ultimate refining of metals, electrometallurgy is commonly used, the impure metal of the anode being deposited electrolytically as pure metal on the cathode.

Most of our metals may be obtained from their ores by some appropriate selection of processes of ore dressing, pyrometallurgy, hydrometallurgy, or electrometallurgy.

Flotation concentration. Gravity concentration has been mentioned as an early step in the quest of metals from low percentage ores.

Fig. 106. Behavior of water and mercury on glass.

Many modern ore dressing mills use a so-called *flotation* process for the elimination of gangue. The process is based on the selective wetting of surfaces by various liquids or selective attraction or repulsion between liquids and solids. To illustrate, consider the liquids water and mercury in contact with a solid such as glass. Water spreads out on a clean surface and wets the glass. Mercury, on the other hand, does not spread out but forms a globule which does not wet the glass. Certain organic liquids such as pine oil or various organic sulfur compounds have a marked tendency to wet and cling to metal or metal sulfide surfaces but do not cling to siliceous matter. Powdered ore suspended in water is fed into a vat into which impinges a mechanism to beat or blow air bubbles into the suspension. A chemical such as cresylic acid is added to produce a froth and to stabilize the bubbles. Next, an organic chemical such as ethyl xanthate is added in amount as little as 0.1 pound per ton of ore. The xanthate adheres to metal and metal sulfide mineral as well as to the air bubbles. Accordingly, the powdery metal-containing particles are floated to the surface as the air bubbles to which they cling rise, whence they are scraped off in a froth, which

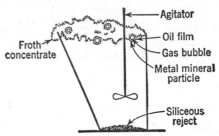

Fig. 107. Apparatus for flotation concentration.

when dried, gives a metal mineral concentrate. The siliceous particles do not collect against the air bubbles but drop to the bottom of the vat (Fig. 108).

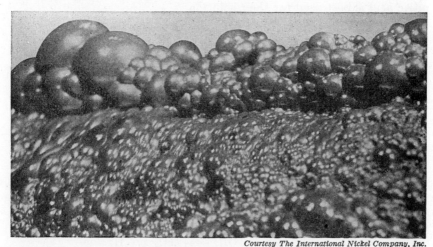

Fig. 108. In the flotation process the metal sulfides are carried to the surface by these oily bubbles.

Nonaqueous electrometallurgy. Electrometallurgy for such active metals as sodium or aluminum is carried out with nonaqueous electrolytes. Sodium or aluminum if freed as cathode products in the presence of water would react with it. Sodium is obtained by electrolysis of fused NaOH. Aluminum is produced by electrolysis of aluminum oxide dissolved in hot molten cryolite, Na_3AlF_6.

Chemical properties of metals. Metals unite with nonmetals under appropriate conditions of temperature and contact to form binary compounds called salts, $viz.$, FeS, Zn_3P_2, $AuCl_3$.

Contingent upon their position in the electromotive series, metals may take part in replacement chemical changes. Action of dilute acids on metals above hydrogen in the activity series are examples of replacement. One of the best ways to get a metal or alloy into solution is by use of an acid. Hydrochloric acid is satisfactory for most metals above hydrogen in the activity series. Metals below hydrogen require the use of an oxidizing acid for solution; nitric acid is most commonly used. Gold and platinum metals do not react with nitric acid; aqua regia is the common solvent.

Alloys are commonly classified as *ferrous* and *nonferrous*. In dissolving an alloy for analysis, filings or cuttings from a specimen are taken rather than putting the bulk piece in acid. Hydrochloric acid is the appropriate solvent to use in dissolving *ferrous alloys* (alloys of iron or ironlike metals). Since *nonferrous alloys* often contain copper, lead, mercury, silver, etc., which are insoluble in hydrochloric acid, nitric acid is best used for their solution:

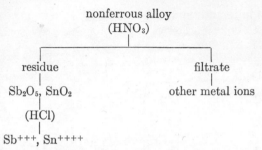

In this treatment with nitric acid, tin and antimony are converted to white oxides, or hydrated oxides, which are insoluble in the solution; however, the latter may be dissolved in hydrochloric acid.

Certain metals react with strong bases, *e.g.*:

$$Zn + 2\,OH^- \longrightarrow ZnO_2^{--} + H_2$$
$$2\,Al + 2\,OH^- + 2\,H_2O \longrightarrow 2\,AlO_2^- + 3\,H_2$$

A mixture of powdered aluminum and solid sodium hydroxide has been put into bore holes in frozen ground of Alaska placer gold mines and the heat of reaction has thawed out the surrounding area. Similarly, some use of this mix has been made in thawing frozen water pipes.

Metal ions (cations). A fundamental property of metals is their ability to release electrons, resulting in the formation of positively charged ions, termed *cations*. Therefore, metals act as *electron donors*. This release of electrons may be accomplished in various ways. If a metal atom reacts with water or an acid, *electrons are transferred from the metal to* H^+, producing free hydrogen, *e.g.*:

$$2\,Na + 2\,H^+ \longrightarrow 2\,Na^+ + H_2$$
$$Zn + 2\,H^+ \longrightarrow Zn^{++} + H_2$$

A metal may combine directly with certain nonmetals, in which case *electrons are transferred from the metal to the nonmetal atom, e.g.*:

$$2\,Au + 3\,Cl_2 \longrightarrow 2\,Au^{+++} + 6\,Cl^-$$

An active metal will displace a less active metal from its solution, a process in which *electrons are transferred from the more active metal to the less active metal ion* (cation), *e.g.*:

$$2\,Al + 3\,Cu^{++} \longrightarrow 3\,Cu + 2\,Al^{+++}$$
$$Zn + 2\,Ag^+ \longrightarrow 2\,Ag + Zn^{++}$$

Electron interchange may result from certain *intermetallic ion reactions,* *e.g.:*

$$2\ Fe^{++} + Sn^{++++} \longrightarrow 2\ Fe^{+++} + Sn^{++}$$
$$2\ Hg^{++} + Sn^{++} \longrightarrow Hg_2^{++} + Sn^{++++}$$

A salt is a compound composed of positive and negative ions and is formed when a solution containing cations and anions is evaporated sufficiently. By *ionic union* the oppositely charged ions form a crystal lattice and hence the ions are present in the solid state. Where a salt is quite insoluble, addition of a dilute solution of the positive ions of the salt to a dilute solution of negative ions of the salt results in the formation of a precipitate, *e.g.:*

$$Ag^+ + Cl^- \longrightarrow Ag^+Cl^- \downarrow$$
or $$3\ Cu^{++} + 2\ PO_4^{---} \longrightarrow Cu_3^{++}(PO_4)_2^{---} \downarrow$$

Salts are usually classed according to the anion with which the cation combines, *e.g.*, chlorides, sulfates, phosphates, chromates, etc. The solubility rules (p. 180) are helpful in predicting the precipitation of salts from solution.

In those cases where an element exhibits several positive valences, *e.g.*, Mn, metallic characteristics are more pronounced in the lower states of valence; indeed in the higher valences the element may appear as part of an anion, in which case it may be said that the element is acting in the capacity of a nonmetal rather than a metal. While manganese exhibits many metallic properties, it also forms manganates and permanganates in which the Mn appears as part of the anion. *These changes in valence,* of course, *involve an electron transfer; e.g.,* when permanganate ion is reduced with Fe^{++}, the oxidation-reduction reaction may be written:

$$5\ Fe^{++} \longrightarrow 5\ Fe^{+++} + 5\ e\ \text{(oxidation)}$$
$$5\ e + MnO_4^- + 8\ H^+ \longrightarrow Mn^{++} + 4\ H_2O\ \text{(reduction)}$$

A further example is the reduction of ferrate ion (FeO_4^{--}) with stannite ion (SnO_2^{--}):

$$6\ OH^- + 3\ SnO_2^{--} \longrightarrow 3\ SnO_3^{--} + 3\ H_2O + 6\ e\ \text{(oxidation)}$$
$$6\ e + 2\ FeO_4^{--} + 5\ H_2O \longrightarrow Fe_2O_3 + 10\ OH^-\ \text{(reduction)}$$

Metal oxides and hydroxides. Most metallic oxides and hydroxides are quite water-insoluble. (See solubility rules, p. 180.) The alkali (Na, K) oxides and hydroxides are very soluble and produce strong alkaline solutions. Alkaline earth (Mg, Ca, Sr, Ba) oxides and hydroxides are sparingly soluble.

EXERCISES

1. Write a brief summary of what might be done to obtain pure copper from a mine ore that contains about 20 pounds Cu as Cu_2S per ton. The gangue is mainly granite and quartz.

2. Discuss how galena (PbS) ore, containing 2 per cent PbS and 98 per cent siliceous matter, could be concentrated. How would metallic lead be obtained from the concentrate?

3. Explain the meaning of: eutectic, ternary alloy, elastic limit, yield point.

4. What factors enter into the question of whether a two-foot thick ledge of quartz assaying $20 per ton in gold is an ore or not?

5. Calculate the atomic volume for potassium and for silicon.

6. Compare physical properties such as melting point, boiling point, atomic volume for a family of elements such as the alkali metals or a Group III family.

7. Complete and balance:

$$Ag + HNO_3 \longrightarrow$$
$$Pb + HNO_3 \longrightarrow$$
$$Sn + HNO_3 \longrightarrow$$

8. From the later chapters of this book pick two examples of pyrometallurgy; two of electrometallurgy; one of hydrometallurgy.

9. Write ionic equations illustrating: a metal as an electron donor to hydrogen ion; a metal as electron donor to a nonmetal; a metal as an electron donor to a metal ion; metal ion union with a divalent anion.

10. A siliceous rock assays 4 per cent copper, 3 per cent zinc, and 0.3 oz. gold per ton. 100 tons of this ore is shipped to a concentration mill. After gravity and flotation concentration there remains 10 tons of concentrate, assaying 35 per cent copper, 20 per cent zinc, and 2.5 oz. gold per ton. Some metal values were lost in the discarded 90 tons. What percentage of each metal was recovered in the concentrate?

REFERENCES

L. S. Auston, *Metallurgy of the Common Metals*, Wiley.

G. E. Doan, *The Principles of Physical Metallurgy*, McGraw-Hill.

W. Gowland, *Metallurgy of Nonferrous Metals*, Lippincott.

C. R. Hayward, *An Outline of Metallurgical Practice*, Van Nostrand.

D. M. Liddell and G. E. Doan, *The Principles of Metallurgy*, McGraw-Hill.

Minerals Year Book, U. S. Bureau of Mines.

G. A. Rousch (ed.), *Minerals Industry*, McGraw-Hill.

Lange, *Handbook of Chemistry*, Handbook Publishers.

C. D. Hodgman, *Handbook of Chemistry and Physics*, Chemical Rubber Publishing Co.

D. Olsen, *Van Nostrand's Chemical Annual*, Van Nostrand.

Bruce A. Rogers, "The Nature of Metals," Iowa State College Press (Am. Soc. of Metals), 1951.

XXIX

The Alkali Metals

$$_{3}\text{Li}^{\cdot 6.94}\quad _{11}\text{Na}^{23}\quad _{19}\text{K}^{39.1}$$

$$_{37}\text{Rb}^{85.5}\quad _{55}\text{Cs}^{132.9}$$

METAL	SYMBOL	SP. GR.	MELTING POINT	BOILING POINT	VALENCE
Lithium	Li	0.53	186	1200	1
Sodium	Na	0.97	97.5	880	1
Potassium	K	0.87	62.3	760	1
Rubidium	Rb	1.53	38.5	700	1
Cesium	Cs	1.87	26.5	670	1

The above elements constitute a closely related family of metals in Division A of Group I of the periodic table. The metals are all very active, the activity (except for Li which is nearly as active as Cs) gradually increasing as the atomic weight increases. Cesium, the most active of the group, is the most active metal known. The elements are called *alkalies* since their hydroxides give strongly alkaline solutions. All exhibit an electrovalence of 1, which indicates one valence electron in the outermost orbit of the atom. The densities of the metals are relatively low, a property not usually associated with metals; yet from a chemical standpoint these elements are the most metallic of all. Because of their extreme activity the elements are never found in the free state, and liberation from their compounds is accomplished with some difficulty. All may be prepared by electrolysis of the fused chlorides or hydroxides. The metals themselves are relatively unimportant as they are too active for most purposes, but their compounds are exceedingly important, particularly those of sodium and potassium, the most abundant of the alkali metals.

SODIUM

History and occurrence. The element sodium was first prepared in 1807 by Davy by the electrolysis of fused sodium hydroxide. Davy's experiments involving the preparation of sodium and other alkali metals by means of electrolysis was the beginning of a new field in chemistry — electrochemistry.

Sodium is one of the more abundant of the chemical elements and comprises 2.36 per cent of the earth's crust. While never found in the free state because of its extreme activity, its compounds are nevertheless widely distributed. Most silicate rock masses contain sodium minerals; *soda feldspar* or *albite*, $Na_2Al_2Si_6O_{16}$, is an abundant mineral. Enormous deposits of *rock salt*, $NaCl$, are found in various parts of the world. Sea water contains about 3 per cent of mineral matter, most of which is sodium chloride. Because of the solubility of most sodium salts, they are leached out by streams and ground waters and eventually find their way to the sea. Alkaline lakes in Nevada and California contain large quantities of sodium carbonate which may be obtained by evaporation.

Preparation of metallic sodium. Although some sodium is still produced by Davy's original process, this method has been largely supplanted at the present time by the electrolysis of fused sodium chloride. The electrolysis is carried out in a Downs electrolytic cell, a cross section of which is shown in Figure 109. The anode, which is placed at the center of the cell, is composed of carbon. The cathode consists of an iron cylinder, which surrounds the anode and is separated from it by an iron gauze, which keeps the products of electrolysis separated. The electrolyte is fused sodium chloride to which sodium carbonate has been added to lower the melting point from 800° to about 600°. The cell is so arranged that chlorine which is formed at the anode may be drawn away into a compartment just above the carbon anode. Meanwhile, metallic sodium which is formed at the cathode rises to the surface of the cell since its density is less than that of the fused electrolyte. Here it is collected in a special receptacle.

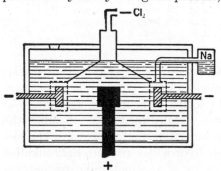

Fig. 109. **Downs cell.**

Properties. Sodium is a soft metal and may be easily molded into any desired form. When cut with a knife, it reveals a silver-white surface. It is very light, having a density of 0.97. The property of lightness is usually not associated with metallic properties, yet here is a metal which is lighter than water. Sodium melts at 97° and boils at 880°.

Chemically, sodium is one of the most active metals; it reacts vigorously with water, displacing hydrogen:

$$2\,Na + 2\,H_2O \longrightarrow 2\,Na^+ + 2\,OH^- + H_2$$

The metal combines readily with oxygen and if heated will burn in the air. With the halogens and other nonmetals it combines readily to form salts. The metal amalgamates quickly with mercury to form a liquid alloy; the latter is useful as a reducing agent as the action is less vigorous than with pure sodium. Sodium imparts a characteristic yellow coloration to a flame, a property which serves as a delicate test for the presence of sodium or its compounds.

Uses. Most of the sodium prepared commercially is used in the preparation of certain salts which are more easily prepared from the free metal than from its compounds. Sodium peroxide is prepared by passing oxygen over aluminum trays containing metallic sodium. Sodium cyanide and tetraethyl lead are other compounds which are prepared from sodium metal. Sodium is an effective reducing agent in the synthesis of indigo and certain other dyes and drugs.

COMPOUNDS OF SODIUM

Sodium chloride. Sodium chloride is one of the most abundant minerals of the earth. The compound is widely distributed and vast deposits have been found in many localities. These large deposits have probably been formed as a result of evaporation of inland bodies of water in desert or arid regions. Reference to the high salt content of the Great Salt Lake in Utah has been made previously (chap. XVI). One of the largest deposits in the United States is a layer several hundred feet deep and covering an area of many thousand square miles in Kansas, Oklahoma, and Texas. These deposits lie below the surface and the salt is obtained by pumping water into the salt bed where a saturated solution of the salt is formed. This saturated solution then is pumped to the surface and evaporated.

Sodium chloride may be recovered from sea water by evaporation. This is not practicable except in certain localities because of the cost involved in evaporating the relatively dilute solution. Of course, the plan is feasible if the solution can be evaporated by the sun's rays. Solar evaporation of sea water is practical in certain areas where the evaporation exceeds the total rainfall. Sodium chloride obtained by this method is usually impure and contains other salts in small percentages. The impurities in general are more soluble than sodium chloride and remain in the mother liquor during the crystallization of the common salt. One of the most troublesome impurities in salt is magnesium chloride, which is deliquescent and causes the salt to "cake" in a moist atmosphere. This situation can be alleviated somewhat by the addition of starch which coats the salt particles and prevents their sticking together.

Sodium chloride serves as the source for its constituent elements, sodium and chlorine, and is the starting material in the preparation of most of the compounds of sodium. It is believed to be an essential constituent of animal food; its use as a seasoning agent dates back to ancient times. It has been estimated that the human body requires about 29 pounds of salt per year in a direct or indirect form. "Salt torture" in which the victim was given plenty of food but deprived of salt was one of the ancient methods of torture. Sodium chloride plays an important role in the proper functioning of the human body. It is a source material from which the body prepares hydrochloric acid in the gastric juices of the stomach for the digestion of food. It is also present in the blood and in case of severe shock and loss of blood a physiological salt solution (0.8 per cent aqueous solution of sodium chloride) may be introduced into the blood stream. The United States produces more than nine million tons of sodium chloride per year, valued at about $3 per ton.

Sodium carbonate. As an industrial chemical, sodium carbonate is second only to sulfuric acid in importance and use. Some natural-occurring sodium carbonate is found with other salts in certain desert regions. The oldest known deposits are in Egypt. Near Death Valley in California, deposits of *trona*, $Na_2CO_3 \cdot NaHCO_3 \cdot 2 H_2O$, have been found associated with borax and other salts. While some sodium carbonate is obtained from natural sources, by far the greater portion is manufactured from sodium chloride as a starting material. The commercial product is known as "soda" or "soda ash." Two methods are now used for the production of soda on a commercial scale: (1) Solvay process; (2) electrolytic process.

Solvay process. This process was developed about 1860 by Ernest Solvay, a Belgian manufacturer, and since that time has provided most of the world's supply of soda. The process takes place in several distinct steps as follows:

1. Limestone is heated to furnish carbon dioxide and lime:

$$CaCO_3 \longrightarrow CaO + CO_2 \uparrow$$

2. Carbon dioxide and ammonia gases are bubbled into a saturated solution of sodium chloride, with the resultant formation of ammonium bicarbonate:

$$NH_3 + CO_2 + H_2O \longrightarrow NH_4HCO_3$$

3. Ammonium bicarbonate reacts with the salt in solution to form sodium bicarbonate:

$$NH_4HCO_3 + NaCl \longrightarrow NaHCO_3 \downarrow + NH_4Cl$$

The reaction proceeds to the right since sodium bicarbonate is sparingly soluble and precipitates in a finely divided form.

4. Sodium bicarbonate is heated to convert it to sodium carbonate:

$$2\,NaHCO_3 \xrightarrow{\text{heat}} Na_2CO_3 + CO_2 \uparrow + H_2O$$

5. Ammonia is recovered from the ammonium chloride by treatment with lime, CaO, from step 1:

$$2\,NH_4Cl + CaO \longrightarrow CaCl_2 + 2\,NH_3 \uparrow + H_2O$$

A careful study of the reactions involved in this process proves the economic feasibility of the method. The raw materials are limestone and salt, both very cheap materials. While ammonia is used in the process and is relatively costly, nearly all of the ammonia is recovered from the operation. The limestone functions not only as a source for carbon dioxide but provides the base for the liberation and recovery of ammonia in step 5. One disadvantage of the process is the production of calcium chloride, a compound for which there is little demand at the present time.

The *electrolytic* process for the manufacture of soda is becoming increasingly popular in this country as the result of development of large quantities of hydroelectric power. It will be recalled that the electrolysis of an aqueous solution of sodium chloride produces chlorine at the anode and hydrogen gas and sodium hydroxide solution at the cathode. Treatment of sodium hydroxide with CO_2 results in the formation of sodium carbonate or sodium bicarbonate depending on the amount of carbon dioxide added:

$$2\,NaOH + CO_2 \longrightarrow Na_2CO_3 + H_2O$$
$$NaOH + CO_2 \longrightarrow NaHCO_3 \text{ (excess } CO_2)$$

Carbon dioxide is obtained in the same manner as in the Solvay process, namely, by heating limestone. Principal disadvantage of the process is the cost of electric power. At the present time about one-third of the soda in this country is produced by the electrolytic method.

Uses of sodium carbonate. As a result of the hydrolysis of *sodium carbonate* hydroxyl ions are formed; consequently sodium carbonate exhibits a distinctly basic reaction in aqueous solution.

$$2 \, Na^+ + CO_3^{--} + H_2O \rightleftharpoons 2 \, Na^+ + OH^- + HCO_3^-$$

The salt neutralizes strong acids, liberating carbon dioxide. When crystallized from aqueous solution the decahydrate is obtained, $Na_2CO_3 \cdot 10 \, H_2O$. This compound is commonly known as *washing soda*. It is an efflorescent salt decomposing slowly into the mono-hydrate, $Na_2CO_3 \cdot H_2O$.

The estimated consumption of soda ash in the United States in 1949 by industries, in short tons, is recorded in Table 29.

Sodium bicarbonate. Sodium bicarbonate, or *baking soda* as it is commonly called, is produced as an intermediate substance in the Solvay process or may be produced in the electrolytic soda process by treating sodium hydroxide with an excess of carbon dioxide (see above). Its reaction with acids is similar to that of soda, liberating carbon dioxide and forming a sodium salt of the acid added. An aqueous solution is mildly alkaline, as the bicarbonate ion reacts with water (hydrolysis) to form weak carbonic acid and hydroxyl ions:

$$HCO_3^- + H_2O \rightleftharpoons H_2CO_3 + OH^-$$

TABLE 29

ESTIMATED U. S. CONSUMPTION OF SODA ASH

Consuming Industry	Short Tons	Per Cent of Total
Glass	1,190,000	29.00
Soap	125,000	3.05
Caustic and bicarbonate	850,000	20.72
Other chemicals	950,000	23.20
Cleansers and modified sodas	130,000	3.17
Pulp and paper	200,000	4.88
Water softeners	110,000	2.68
Petroleum refining	24,000	.59
Textiles	55,000	1.34
Nonferrous metallurgy	210,000	5.12
Exports	77,000	1.88
Miscellaneous	179,000	4.37
Total	4,100,000	100.00

Baking soda as the name implies is often used in cooking. Its function is to furnish carbon dioxide, which acts as a leavening agent. A weak acid, such as lemon juice, vinegar, or sour milk, added to sodium bicarbonate, liberates carbon dioxide.

Baking powders. Baking powders are mixtures of three essential ingredients:

1. Sodium bicarbonate, which furnishes carbon dioxide.

2. Some substance which will furnish hydrogen ions to react with the sodium bicarbonate and liberate carbon dioxide when water is added to the baking powder.

$$HCO_3^- + H^+ \longrightarrow CO_2 \uparrow + H_2O$$

3. A substance such as starch to prevent intimate contact and reaction between ingredients 1 and 2.

All baking powders are alike in ingredients 1 and 3 but the second ingredient is variable. *Cream of tartar*, $KHC_4H_4O_6$, an acid salt, is a constituent of certain baking powders. In water solution this reaction takes place:

$$NaHCO_3 + KHC_4H_4O_6 \longrightarrow NaKC_4H_4O_6 + H_2O + CO_2 \uparrow$$

Phosphate baking powders contain primary calcium acid phosphate which acts on sodium bicarbonate:

$$2\,NaHCO_3 + Ca(H_2PO_4)_2 \longrightarrow CaHPO_4 + Na_2HPO_4 + 2\,CO_2 \uparrow + 2\,H_2O$$

Alum baking powders contain potash alum. Due to hydrolysis of the aluminum sulfate contained in the alum, hydrogen ions are produced which react with the bicarbonate to liberate carbon dioxide. Certain baking powders may contain mixtures of alum and calcium acid phosphate.

Sodium hydroxide. Sodium hydroxide, commonly called *caustic soda* or *lye*, is a compound of major importance in industry. Its strongly basic properties are familiar. Two methods of manufacture are employed at the present time:

1. The electrolytic method is the more modern method and has already been discussed (p. 196).

2. The older method consists in treating a suspension of slaked lime with sodium carbonate:

$$Ca(OH)_2 + Na_2CO_3 \longrightarrow CaCO_3 \downarrow + 2\,NaOH$$

Calcium carbonate precipitates and may be filtered off; the filtrate is evaporated to dryness to remove water. The solid sodium hydroxide is easily melted and is cast into sticks, in which form it is usually marketed.

Major uses include the manufacture of artificial silk, soap, and other chemicals. Annual production of the United States is about 1,500,000 tons.

Sodium sulfate. Considerable amounts of this salt are used in the production of glass and soap. There is some natural occurrence of it in certain mineral waters. The largest source of the compound, however, is the production of hydrogen chloride from sodium chloride and nitric acid from sodium nitrate. When these salts are treated with sulfuric acid they yield sodium sulfate as a by-product, which is usually referred to as *salt cake*. When crystallized from water, below a temperature of 32.38°, the hydrate $Na_2SO_4 \cdot 10 H_2O$, called *Glauber's salt*, is obtained, while if the crystallization is carried out above 32.38°, the anhydrous salt is obtained. The temperature 32.38° is termed the transition temperature of the hydrate to the anhydrous salt. This temperature is so easily reproduced that it is often used as a fixed point for the standardization of thermometers.

Other salts of sodium. Other important compounds of sodium with their sources and uses are shown in Table 30.

TABLE 30

COMPOUNDS OF SODIUM

Compound	Source	Use
$NaNO_3$ (Chile saltpeter)	Natural deposits in Chile	Preparation of HNO_3 and KNO_3
NaCN	Synthetically produced from soda, C, and N_2	Extraction of gold and silver from ores; electroplating
$Na_2B_4O_7$	Occurs native	Washing powder and water softener
$Na_2S_2O_3$ (thiosulfate, "hypo")	Made from Na_2SO_3	Photography (fixing agent)
Na_2O_2	$Na + O_2$	Oxidizing agent

POTASSIUM

History and occurrence. Potassium is only slightly less abundant than sodium; its percentage in the earth's crust is 2.28. Although the element itself was not isolated until 1807, many of its compounds have been known and used for a very long time. The cleansing properties of extracts from the ashes of wood and plant matter appears to have been known at an early date; and also their value as a fertilizer. Compounds of potassium are widely distributed in rocks, two of the more important ones being *orthoclase*, $KAlSi_3O_8$, and *leucite*, $KAlSi_2O_6$. Gradual ground water leaching of these silicates and similar compounds results in soluble potassium salts in the soil. Potassium appears to be necessary for the growth of plants, and soils which have been depleted in this element must be furnished with artificial fertilizer in the form of potassium salts. In soils containing both sodium and potassium salts, the latter are selectively absorbed by the plant, leaving the sodium salts to be leached out and carried away in ground waters. Consequently potassium compounds concentrate in land plants, while sodium compounds find their way to the sea and are utilized by sea plants. When wood or plant material is burned, the potassium salts of the organic acids present in the plant fiber are converted to potassium carbonate, or *potash*. Thus the extraction of wood ashes was the first important source of potash.

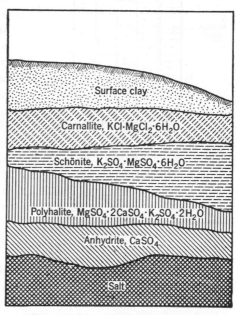

Fig. 110. Stassfurt salt deposits.

Stassfurt deposits. The Stassfurt salt deposits in Germany provide the chief source of potash and other potassium compounds. These deposits consist of layers of minerals which were probably formed by the evaporation of a large inland body of water. Principal constituents of these deposits are shown in Figure 110. *Sylvite*, KCl, and *carnallite*, $KCl \cdot MgCl_2 \cdot 6\,H_2O$, are the most important potassium bearing salts. Because of these deposits, Germany is the leading producer of potassium compounds, followed by France and the United States. Some potassium has been successfully recovered from *greensand* and *alunite*, complex minerals. In addition, salt deposits have been found at Searles Lake in California which contains considerable quantities of potassium salts. Some potassium is recovered as a by-product from the fermentation of molasses, from cement kilns, and from blast furnaces. The United States annually consumes about 600,000 tons of potassium compounds calculated in terms of K_2O, of which nearly 400,000 tons are imported.

Separation of potassium salts from the minerals in the Stassfurt deposits is largely one of a complex series of fractional crystallizations.

Preparation of metallic potassium. Potassium may be obtained by the electrolysis of either the fused hydroxide or chloride. The preparation is similar to that of sodium; the Castner cell (Fig. 111) is usually employed. The cathode consists of an iron bar which projects through the middle of the base of the cell. An iron cylinder surrounding the cathode serves as the anode. The resistance to the passage of the current during electrolysis is usually sufficient to keep the hydroxide or chloride in a molten condition; however, heat may be supplied by a ring of burners on the outside if necessary. Metallic potassium collects in the compartment above the cathode and may be drawn off from time to time. There is little demand for the metal since sodium which is produced much more cheaply will usually serve the same purpose.

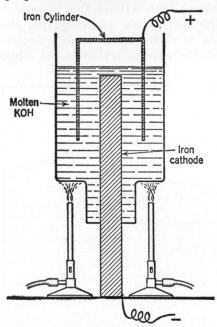

Fig. 111. Castner cell for the preparation of potassium.

Properties. Potassium is very similar to sodium in properties and what has been said about sodium will in general apply to potassium. Like sodium, potassium is soft and may be cut with a knife or molded into shape. A freshly cut surface is bluish, but contact with the air tarnishes it rapidly. Potassium is above sodium in the activity series and is the most active of the common metals. Water is decomposed violently with the evolution of hydrogen; sufficient heat is produced to ignite the hydrogen gas. Potassium and its compounds impart a violet color to a flame.

COMPOUNDS OF POTASSIUM

Potassium halides. Potassium chloride is the starting material in the preparation of most of the compounds of potassium. In addition the salt is used as such for fertilizers. Potassium chloride, *sylvite*, is obtained from the Stassfurt deposits or may be obtained from carnallite, $MgCl_2 \cdot KCl \cdot 6 H_2O$, which is also found in these deposits.

To separate it from the magnesium chloride, the carnallite is dissolved in water and the solution evaporated. Since potassium chloride is less soluble than magnesium chloride, it crystallizes from solution leaving the more soluble magnesium chloride in the mother liquor. Recrystallization of potassium minerals found in New Mexico and Texas also yields considerable potassium chloride.

Potassium bromide and potassium iodide are prepared by treating potassium hydroxide with free halogen; with iodine the reaction is

$$6 \, KOH + 3 \, I_2 \longrightarrow KIO_3 + 5 \, KI + 3 \, H_2O$$

The mixture of iodate and iodide is heated with carbon which reduces the iodate to iodide. The salt is purified by recrystallization. Both potassium bromide and iodide find use in photography and as medicinals.

Potassium carbonate. Potassium carbonate, or *potash*, cannot be prepared by the Solvay process since potassium bicarbonate is much more soluble than the corresponding sodium bicarbonate and does not separate from solution. The salt is usually prepared by heating magnesium carbonate, water, carbon dioxide, and potassium chloride under pressure:

$$2 \, KCl + 3 \, MgCO_3 + CO_2 + 5 \, H_2O \longrightarrow 2 \, KHMg(CO_3)_2 \cdot 4 \, H_2O \downarrow + MgCl_2$$

The double salt of potassium and magnesium precipitates from solution and may be separated from the magnesium chloride which remains in solution. When a suspension of the double salt in water is heated, decomposition takes place according to the reaction

$$2 \, KHMg(CO_3)_2 \cdot 4 \, H_2O \overset{\text{heat}}{\longrightarrow} 2 \, MgCO_3 \downarrow + K_2CO_3 + CO_2 \uparrow + 5 \, H_2O$$

After filtering off the insoluble magnesium carbonate, the potash is recovered by crystallization from the solution. Principal uses of potash are in the preparation of glass and soft soaps.

Potassium bicarbonate may be prepared from potassium carbonate by saturating a solution of the latter with carbon dioxide:

$$K_2CO_3 + H_2O + CO_2 \longrightarrow 2 \, KHCO_3$$

Potassium hydroxide. Potassium hydroxide may be obtained by the electrolysis of an aqueous solution of potassium chloride (similar to the preparation of sodium hydroxide) or by the treatment of slaked lime with potassium carbonate. The solid is prepared by evaporating the solution to dryness, after which the solid is melted and cast into sticks. In contrast to sticks of sodium hydroxide, which are practically anhydrous, the sticks of potassium hydroxide may contain several per cent of water. Potassium hydroxide is very hygroscopic and may be used as a drying agent. Its chemical properties are very much like those of sodium hydroxide. There is relatively little demand for potassium hydroxide since the cheaper product, sodium hydroxide, will serve as well for most purposes. Its principal use is in the preparation of soft soaps.

Potassium nitrate. Potassium nitrate, or *saltpeter*, is first referred to in literature in connection with the preparation of gunpowder. It is probable that it was used in early times as references to its use in gunpowder are numerous after the twelfth or thirteenth century. Deposits of the salt have been found in dry and arid countries of the East, particularly in the neighborhood of villages where organic matter and refuse had been allowed to accumulate. The action of bacteria on this organic matter resulted in the formation of the salt. The salt is usually prepared from *Chile saltpeter*, $NaNO_3$, and potassium chloride:

$$NaNO_3 + KCl \longrightarrow NaCl + KNO_3$$

The preparation is based upon the fact that the solubilities of the three salts, KCl, KNO_3, and $NaNO_3$, increase rapidly as the temperature is raised, while the solubility of sodium chloride is very little greater in hot water than in cold water. Thus if sodium nitrate and potassium chloride are brought into contact in a relatively small amount of hot water they will dissolve. Double decomposition takes place since the sodium chloride which is formed crystallizes from solution, thus shifting the equilibrium to the right. The precipitated sodium chloride is filtered from the hot solution and the solution cooled. Very little more sodium chloride crystallizes from solution as cooling proceeds (since the solubility of the salt changes only slightly); however, crystallization of nitrate takes place because it is much less soluble in the cold solution. Thus a product is obtained which contains a small amount of sodium chloride. Recrystallization of this product results in potassium nitrate of a high degree of purity. Reference to the solubility curves (p. 181) will clarify this procedure.

Until the beginning of the twentieth century large amounts of saltpeter were used in the preparation of black gunpowder. This powder was prepared by mixing powdered saltpeter, carbon, and sulfur intimately. When ignited, sulfur and carbon are very rapidly oxidized by the potassium nitrate, producing several gaseous products. The rapid change in volume (due to gases and also to expansion of these gases with heat) results in an explosion. In recent years black gunpowder has been largely replaced by smokeless powders prepared from organic nitrogen compounds. Some black powder is still employed as a blasting agent in soft rock mining operations.

Potassium nitrate is a particularly effective fertilizer as it contains both potassium and nitrogen. It is also used in preserving meats.

Potassium tartrates. As noted on page 387, potassium acid tartrate, $KHC_4H_4O_6$, commonly called *cream of tartar*, is used in some baking powders. The main source of cream of tartar is the crystalline crusts deposited by grape juice during fermentation. This salt of potassium is sparingly soluble. Potassium antimonyl tartrate, $KSbOC_4H_4O_6$, called *tartar emetic*, is used medicinally.

OTHER ALKALI METALS

Lithium. Lithium is a relatively rare element although its compounds are rather widely distributed. It is found in certain mineral waters and some soils. Chief naturally occurring compounds are *lepidolite*, a complex silicate, and *amblygonite*, $LiAlFPO_4$. Certain plants such as tobacco and sugar beets seem to absorb lithium compounds from soil as the element is found in the ashes of these plants.

Chemically the element is very similar to sodium and may be prepared by electrolysis of the fused chloride. It is the lightest metal known, with a specific gravity of about 0.5. The metal is of about the same activity as cesium and is thus one of the most active of the alkali family of elements. It decomposes water vigorously to form hydrogen. In certain respects lithium resembles magnesium in the alkaline earth family. Lithium hydroxide, $LiOH$, lithium phosphate, Li_3PO_4, and lithium carbonate, Li_2CO_3, in contrast to corresponding compounds of the other alkali metals, are relatively insoluble, similar to corresponding compounds of magnesium. Lithium compounds yield a crimson color when heated in a flame. Lithium compounds are used in the preparation of special glasses and in fireworks.

Rubidium and cesium. Small amounts of these elements are found in certain mineral waters, and in ashes from tobacco, tea, and coffee. Both elements were discovered by Bunsen; cesium in 1860 and rubidium in 1861. The names of the elements refer to the lines in the spectrum which they emit when heated. Rubidium produces dark red lines and cesium blue lines. Both elements are very much like sodium and potassium but are more active. Cesium is the most active metal known and in contact with the air it oxidizes with almost explosive violence. A small amount of cesium is used in the manufacture of radio tubes and photoelectric cells.

SPECTRA AND THE SPECTROSCOPE

Much as sunlight is refracted by raindrops into a rainbow, which exhibits all colors, a beam of sunlight when allowed to pass through a glass prism is separated into its various color components (Fig. 112).

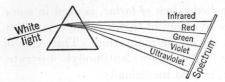

Fig. 112. Refraction of sunlight.

In passing through the prism the light is bent or refracted according to its wave length; the reds are bent the least and the violets the most. This array of colors is termed the visible spectrum; from the red to violet the wave lengths of light range from 6500 to 4000 angstrom units. An angstrom unit is equal to 1×10^{-8} cm.

Certain elements produce characteristic colors when heated in a flame. The emission of light of characteristic wave lengths is due to a displacement of electrons in the various electron orbits in the atom. An instrument called the *spectroscope* was invented by Bunsen and Kirchhoff in 1859 to analyze light emitted from heated substances. It consists of an enclosed central prism with three telescopic arms arranged as shown in Figure 113. Light from the heated object is allowed to enter a rectangular slit in a collimator, after which it strikes the prism, is refracted and projected onto a scale which has been calibrated. Images of the slit will appear on the scale corresponding to certain wave lengths of light characteristic of that particular element. The spectrum will appear as a parallel group of vertical lines or bands. By

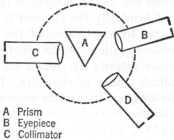

A   Prism
B   Eyepiece
C   Collimator
D   Scale

Fig. 113. Fundamental parts of the spectroscope.

making scale readings and comparing with standard or known readings for the various elements, the element may readily be identified from its emission spectrum.

Since the spectrum of each element is so distinctive, several of the rarer elements were discovered by discriminating use of the spectroscope. Rubidium and cesium were the first elements to be discovered by its use. Heated compounds each give a characteristic banded spectrum so that the compound nature of some substances may be ascertained. Small quantities of a substance in a mixture can be approximated by the relative intensity of spectral lines.

All of the alkali metals are readily detected by means of a spectroscope; as a matter of fact a simple flame test (holding a volatile compound of the element in a flame) will suffice in many instances to identify the element.

Courtesy The International Nickel Company, Inc.

Fig. 114. With the spectrograph one can determine the chemical composition of a mere speck of metal.

EXERCISES

1. Summarize the general properties of the alkali metals. Point out differences between members of the alkali group.
2. List various products which chemical industry manufactures from NaCl as a raw material.
3. By equations show how you might prepare a sample of K_2CO_3, starting with KCl; $NaNO_3$, starting with NaCl.
4. From a consideration of properties of the alkali metals, predict the properties of element No. 87.
5. 10.6 g. of Na_2CO_3 are dissolved in water and the solution diluted to 1 liter. What is the normality of the solution? 25 ml. of this solution required 20 ml. of H_2SO_4 solution for complete neutralization. Calculate the normality of the sulfuric acid solution. Ans. 0.2; 0.25.
6. Suggest a method of recovering pure NaCl from sea water.

7. Why cannot K_2CO_3 be prepared by a series of reactions similar to those of the Solvay process?

8. Calculate the volume of CO_2 measured at standard conditions which would be obtained by heating 42 g. $NaHCO_3$. Ans. 5. 6 l.

9. A cleaner is known to be a mixture of NaOH and SiO_2. A 1 g. sample of the cleaner required 50 cc. of 0.3 N H_2SO_4 to neutralize it. What weight of NaOH is in the gram sample, and thus what percentage of NaOH?

REFERENCES

H. L. Bailey, *Development and Use of Baking Powder and Baking Chemicals,* U. S. Department of Agriculture, Circular 138, 1930.

T. B. Brighton and C. M. Dice, "Increasing the Purity of Common Salt," *Ind. and Eng. Chem.* **23,** 336 (1931).

H. N. Gilbert, *et al.,* "Sodium," *ibid.* **25,** 735 (1933).

H. L. Tiger, *et al.,* "Desalting Sea Water," *ibid.* **38,** 1130 (1946).

Sir Humphry Davy, "The Decomposition of the Fixed Alkalies and Alkaline Earths," *Alembic Club Reprints,* No. 6.

G. R. Mansfield, "Potash in the U. S.," *J. Chem. Ed.* **7,** 737 (1930).

W. H. Schechter and Jacob Kleinberg, "Oxides of the Alkali and Alkaline Earth Metals," *ibid.* **24,** 302 (1947).

J. R. Partington, *The Alkali Industry,* Van Nostrand.

XXX

The Alkaline Earth Family

$_4\text{Be}^{9.0}\,{}^{|\,|}_{2\,2}\,{}_{|\,|}$ $_{12}\text{Mg}^{24.3}\,{}^{|\,|\,|}_{2\,8\,2}\,{}_{|\,|\,|}$ $_{20}\text{Ca}^{40.1}\,{}^{|\,|\,|\,|}_{2\,8\,8\,2}\,{}_{|\,|\,|\,|}$

$_{38}\text{Sr}^{87.6}\,{}^{|\,|\,|\,|\,|}_{2\,8\,18\,8\,2}\,{}_{|\,|\,|\,|\,|}$ $_{56}\text{Ba}^{137.4}\,{}^{|\,|\,|\,|\,|\,|}_{2\,8\,18\,18\,8\,2}\,{}_{|\,|\,|\,|\,|\,|}$ $_{88}\text{Ra}^{226}\,{}^{|\,|\,|\,|\,|\,|\,|}_{2\,8\,18\,32\,18\,8\,2}\,{}_{|\,|\,|\,|\,|\,|\,|}$

Metals	Symbol	Sp. Gr.	Melting Point	Boiling Point	Valence
Beryllium	Be	1.84	1280	1500	2
Magnesium	Mg	1.70	651	1110	2
Calcium	Ca	1.55	810	1240	2
Strontium	Sr	2.54	800	1150	2
Barium	Ba	3.75	850	1140	2
Radium	Ra	5.00	960	1140	2

The term "earth" was originally applied to those substances which are relatively insoluble in water and which do not undergo change when heated. Typical "earths" were alumina (aluminum oxide) and ferric oxide. A few other "earths" were slightly soluble in water and gave an alkaline solution; accordingly they were called the alkaline earths, and inasmuch as they resisted all efforts of the early chemists to decompose them, were thought to be elements. We now know the "alkaline earths" to be oxides of the metals listed in the above table. Because of certain unusual properties of radium, this element is considered in a separate chapter (chap. XXXI).

The metals of this group are quite active, the activity increasing with increasing atomic weight. The only valence exhibited by members of the group is two, indicating two electrons in the outermost orbit of their atoms. In general, compounds of these elements are more important from a practical standpoint than the free metals, although the exception to this statement is magnesium, which is an extremely important metal in the free state.

Beryllium, the first member of the group, resembles aluminum (third group) in some respects. Although its valence is two, the hydroxide of beryllium is amphoteric like aluminum hydroxide.

CALCIUM

History and occurrence. Compounds of calcium were known and used for a long time before the element itself was isolated. Davy first prepared it in 1808 by electrolysis.

Calcium is the fifth most abundant of the chemical elements and the third most abundant metal; the earth's crust contains 3.22 per cent. The metal is too active to exist in the free state, but its compounds are numerous and widely distributed. Of these calcium carbonate, $CaCO_3$, is the most abundant. Many forms of the carbonate are known: *limestone, chalk, pearl, calcite, coral, marble,* and others. Other important naturally occurring compounds are *gypsum*, $CaSO_4 \cdot 2 H_2O$; *anhydrite*, $CaSO_4$; *dolomite*, $CaCO_3 \cdot MgCO_3$; *fluorite*, CaF_2; *apatite*, $(CaF)Ca_4(PO_4)_3$ or $(CaCl)Ca_4(PO_4)_3$; and *phosphorite* or *phosphate rock*, $Ca_3(PO_4)_2$. Sea water contains some calcium salts, usually the sulfate, chloride, or bicarbonate, and these salts are the source of calcium utilized by marine animals in building up their shells, which are mainly calcium carbonate. A certain amount of calcium is required for human and animal nutrition, as the bones and teeth are composed largely of calcium phosphate. Rich food sources of calcium are milk, leafy and root vegetables, egg yolk, potatoes, and peas.

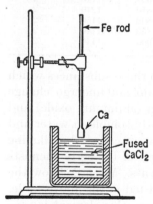

Fig. 115. Preparation of metallic calcium. As the metal is deposited, the iron cathode is slowly raised so that only metallic calcium dips into the bath.

Preparation. Calcium metal is prepared by the electrolysis of fused calcium chloride in a graphite crucible which serves as the anode (Fig. 115). The cathode consists of an iron rod which dips just below the surface of the fused salt and is situated near the center of the crucible. As calcium is deposited on the iron cathode, the latter is slowly raised from the bath and a continuous rod of calcium metal is formed. The calcium itself acts as the cathode for the cell after the initial deposition. Calcium fluoride is sometimes added to the electrolyte to lower the melting point of the latter.

Properties and uses. Calcium is a silver-white metal, harder than lead, with a density of 1.55. It is malleable and ductile, for it may be hammered into plates or drawn into wire. The metal is stable in dry air but oxidizes in moist air. Calcium is one of the more active metals and will react with cold water slowly:

$$Ca + 2\,H_2O \longrightarrow Ca(OH)_2 + H_2$$

At high temperatures, the metal burns vigorously in the air to form both calcium oxide and calcium nitride, Ca_3N_2. The metal reacts rapidly with dilute mineral acids to produce hydrogen.

Calcium is not extensively used industrially because of the difficulty and cost of producing it. The metal is an active reducing agent and may be employed in the reduction of certain metallic oxides, such as those of chromium and tungsten. An alloy with lead containing about 0.1 per cent calcium is used in the manufacture of storage battery plates and as a bearing metal. Calcium may also be used to remove traces of nitrogen and oxygen in producing high vacua.

COMPOUNDS OF CALCIUM

Calcium carbonate. Calcium carbonate is by far the most abundant and most widely used compound of calcium. Two crystalline forms are known: (1) *aragonite*, which crystallizes in the rhombic system, and (2) *calcite*, or *Iceland spar*, which forms rhombohedral crystals. *Limestone* is a more or less impure form of the carbonate, usually containing iron and magnesium carbonates and other impurities. *Marble* consists of a compact and coherent mass of small crystals of nearly pure calcium carbonate. *Dolomite* is a natural-occurring compound of equal molecular proportions of calcium and magnesium carbonates, $CaCO_3 \cdot MgCO_3$. Marine shells, pearls, and coral, as well as eggshells, are composed largely of calcium carbonate. *Stalactites*, which form on the roofs of certain caves, and *stalagmites*, which form on the floors beneath, are composed of calcium carbonate. Calcium carbonate is soluble in water containing carbon dioxide to form calcium bicarbonate. The pressure is reduced when the bicarbonate solutions enter the caves, carbon dioxide escapes, and calcium carbonate is precipitated and deposited.

Calcium carbonate finds extensive application in many industrial processes. Certain forms of limestone and marble are used as building materials. Limestone in large quantities is used in the production of cement (p. 401) and soda ash (p. 385). It serves as a basic flux in the smelting of certain metals, notably iron (p. 507).

Calcium oxide. When limestone is heated (technically called *burning*), carbon dioxide and calcium oxide are formed. The latter is commonly called *lime* or *quicklime:*

$$CaCO_3 \rightleftharpoons CaO + CO_2$$

The above reaction is an equilibrium system and proceeds to the right only when the carbon dioxide is removed. At any given temperature, the carbon dioxide being liberated exerts a certain pressure. If this pressure can be increased to a value which exceeds the atmospheric pressure, carbon dioxide will escape and the reaction becomes complete to the right. Since this required pressure is attained only at a temperature above 900°, limestone must be heated to this point to make the process practical. The heating is usually carried out in large furnaces or *kilns.* The process is continuous; fresh limestone is introduced at the top, and lime removed at the bottom. Both vertical and rotary kilns are employed.

The product, if pure, is white in color and extremely porous. It is very stable toward heat (melting point 2572°). Its principal use is in the manufacture of slaked lime (see next section). It is also used in the preparation of bleaching powder and as a base in the neutralization of acid soils.

Calcium hydroxide. When calcium oxide is added to water, a vigorous reaction ensues with the liberation of a considerable quantity of heat — enough to convert part of the water to steam. The white product is calcium hydroxide, commonly termed *slaked lime.*

$$CaO + H_2O \longrightarrow Ca(OH)_2$$

Calcium hydroxide is the cheapest of the bases. It is only slightly soluble in water. Because of its basic characteristics, it absorbs carbon dioxide from the atmosphere and is converted into calcium carbonate. Thus, slaked lime which is exposed to the atmosphere for some time contains a considerable amount of calcium carbonate.

Although not very soluble in water, an aqueous solution of the hydroxide (lime water) may be used in testing for the presence of carbon dioxide gas. When carbon dioxide gas is passed into lime water, the latter becomes turbid due to the precipitation of calcium carbonate:

$$Ca(OH)_2 + CO_2 \longrightarrow CaCO_3 \downarrow + H_2O$$

If an excess of carbon dioxide is added, the precipitate dissolves to form calcium bicarbonate, which is soluble:

$$CaCO_3 + CO_2 + H_2O \longrightarrow Ca(HCO_3)_2$$

Slaked lime has many uses, of which the chief ones are the preparation of mortar and plaster. *Mortar* consists of a mixture of sand and slaked lime to which enough water has been added to form a paste. As mortar sets, some water evaporates and the $Ca(OH)_2 \cdot xH_2O$ solidifies to a firm gel with included sand particles. After years of time, the outer one-eighth inch or so of mortar is converted to a calcium carbonate-sand mixture as CO_2 from the air is slowly absorbed. *Plaster* is identical with mortar except that hair may be added to help hold the mass together. Sometimes plaster of Paris, $CaSO_4 \cdot \frac{1}{2} H_2O$, is added to give a smoother plaster as in the finishing coat.

Other uses of slaked lime include *milk of lime*, which is a suspension of calcium hydroxide in water; preparation of bleaching powder; and whitewash.

Cement. More than a century ago one Joseph Aspdin found that if he highly heated some rock occurring naturally near his home in Portland, England, and pulverized the product, he had a powder that, with water, would set to a strong mass. The rock became known as Portland stone, and thus the origin of the name "Portland cement." Portland cement is now prepared from a properly proportioned mixture of limestone and clay. In some cases natural rock formations contain these ingredients in suitable proportions and may be used directly for cement manufacture. The mixture after being ground to a fine powder is heated in rotary kilns until the mass just begins to fuse. During the heating, carbon dioxide is lost from the limestone which then combines with silica and alumina from the clay to form calcium silicates and calcium aluminate. The resulting sintered mass is known as "clinker." The clinker is ground finely and a small amount of gypsum is added to retard the rate of setting. When a paste is made of cement with water and allowed to stand, the material sets to a hard, durable, rocklike mass. This process will take place even though the material is under water, due to the insolubility of the constituents. While the mechanism of the setting process is somewhat obscure, it has been established that hydration of the constituents takes place so that the mass is securely bound together by interlacing crystals of the hydrates formed.

Cement is never used alone, but is mixed with sand and gravel and the resulting set mixture is called *concrete*. If the concrete is to be used where it will be subject to considerable strain, it may be reinforced with steel rods or wire netting.

Other calcium compounds. Another naturally occurring compound of calcium is *gypsum*, $CaSO_4 \cdot 2 H_2O$, which has been formed as the result of the evaporation of sea water or ground waters containing calcium and sulfate ions. Since calcium sulfate is relatively insoluble, the salt is one of the first to crystallize from solution. In some instances the anhydrous salt, $CaSO_4$, may deposit; it is known as "anhydrite."

When gypsum is heated carefully below 125°, it loses three-fourths of its water of hydration and forms the hemihydrate of calcium sulfate, sometimes written $CaSO_4 \cdot \frac{1}{2} H_2O$, and commonly known as *plaster of Paris:*

$$2 CaSO_4 \cdot 2 H_2O \longrightarrow (CaSO_4)_2 \cdot H_2O + 3 H_2O$$

On mixing the hemihydrate with water to form a paste, the above reaction is reversed and on setting, a hard mass of interlacing crystals of gypsum is formed. It is used in making plaster casts for holding broken bones and also in making statuary casts.

Gypsum is used for many purposes; a good deal is used as fireproofing for building materials; about 2 per cent gypsum is added to Portland cement to retard and regulate the setting process; some is used as a soil fertilizer.

In an important process of manufacturing pulp from wood, a water solution of calcium acid sulfite, $Ca(HSO_3)_2$, is used. Wood chips are largely composed of cellulose, lignin, and resins. $Ca(HSO_3)_2$ solution dissolves lignin and resin from the cellulose pulp. The solution of lignin and resins issuing from pulp mills is called industrial "waste sulfite liquor." The calcium bisulfite solution is made as follows:

$$S + O_2 \longrightarrow SO_2$$
$$SO_2 + H_2O \longrightarrow H_2SO_3$$
$$CaCO_3 + H_2SO_3 \longrightarrow CaSO_3 + CO_2 + H_2O$$
$$CaSO_3 + H_2SO_3 \longrightarrow Ca(HSO_3)_2$$

In some mills $Mg(HSO_3)_2$ or NH_4HSO_3 is used instead of $Ca(HSO_3)_2$. Other important compounds of calcium are given in Table 31.

Hard waters. Most natural waters with the exception of rain water contain dissolved mineral matter. This mineral matter is derived from the rocks and soil and contains calcium, magnesium, or iron salts as chlorides, sulfates, or bicarbonates. Waters containing any of these salts are objectionable for certain household and industrial uses and are termed *hard waters.* When soap is added to a hard water, a precipitate forms before a lather can be obtained. This residue may stain the cloth with which it comes in contact, and of course the soap used in forming the precipitate is wasted. Soap is a sodium or potassium salt of complex organic acids, namely, stearic, palmitic, or oleic acids. For convenience we may represent its formula as NaSt, where St stands for the stearate acid radical. If calcium ions were present in water, the following reaction would take place with soap:

$$Ca^{++} + 2 NaSt \longrightarrow Ca(St)_2\downarrow + 2 Na^+$$

TABLE 31

OTHER COMPOUNDS OF CALCIUM

SALT	FORMULA	SOURCE	USES
Calcium chloride . . .	$CaCl_2$	By-product of Solvay soda process	Drying agent; lay dust on roads
Calcium cyanamide . .	$CaNCN$	Calcium carbide + nitrogen	Prep. of ammonia; fertilizer
Bleaching powder . . .	$CaOCl_2$	Lime and chlorine	Bleaching
Calcium carbide . . .	CaC_2	Lime and carbon	Source of acetylene
Calcium phosphate . .	$Ca_3(PO_4)_2$	Occurs as phosphate rock	Making fertilizer
Superphosphate . . .	$Ca(H_2PO_4)_2 + 2\ CaSO_4$	Rock phosphate + H_2SO_4	Fertilizer
Calcium silicate . . .	$CaSiO_3$	Limestone, sand	In glass along with Na_2SiO_3

Temporary water hardness. Waters containing bicarbonates of calcium, magnesium, or iron are said to possess *temporary hardness*, since the hardness may be removed simply by boiling the water. Thus when calcium bicarbonate is heated, the following reaction takes place:

$$Ca(HCO_3)_2 \longrightarrow CaCO_3 \downarrow + H_2O + CO_2$$

Calcium carbonate precipitates and since the calcium ions are removed, the water will no longer act with soap. Such a water from which the ions responsible for the precipitation of soap are removed is termed *soft* water. The decomposition of bicarbonates is responsible for the scale formed in tea kettles in which considerable water has been boiled. Water containing bicarbonates is also objectionable from an industrial standpoint, as it will form boiler scale (carbonates of calcium or magnesium). This scale deposits on the inside of boiler pipes and since it is a poor conductor of heat, the efficiency of the boiler is reduced.

Temporary hardness may be removed by adding the proper amount of slaked lime, $Ca(OH)_2$, or household ammonia, NH_4OH:

$$Ca(HCO_3)_2 + Ca(OH)_2 \longrightarrow 2\ CaCO_3 \downarrow + 2\ H_2O$$
$$Ca(HCO_3)_2 + 2\ NH_4OH \longrightarrow CaCO_3 \downarrow + (NH_4)_2CO_3 + 2\ H_2O$$

Permanent hardness. Permanent hardness in water is due to the presence of chlorides or sulfates of such metals as calcium or magnesium. Boiling does not remove these salts and a substance must be added to such a water to form a precipitate with these salts. Such a substance is called a *water softener*. The more common water softeners are soda, Na_2CO_3, and borax, $Na_2B_4O_7$. With either of these salts, calcium or magnesium carbonate or borate is precipitated from solution as an insoluble substance. Typical reactions of the above water softeners are:

$$Ca^{++} + CO_3^{--} \longrightarrow CaCO_3 \downarrow$$
$$Mg^{++} + B_4O_7^{--} \longrightarrow MgB_4O_7 \downarrow$$

In some cases both soda and slaked lime are used to soften water, the slaked lime to remove temporary hardness and the soda to remove permanent hardness.

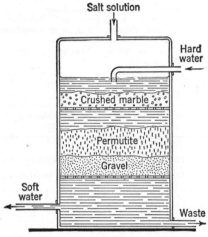

Permutite. Another method of softening water utilizes an artificial sodium aluminum silicate called *permutite* or *zeolite*. If water is allowed to filter through this coarse grained material, sodium ions are displaced by calcium and magnesium ions:

$$Na_2 \text{ Zeolite} + Ca^{++} \longrightarrow$$
$$Ca \text{ Zeolite} \downarrow + 2 Na^+$$

Sodium ions left in solution are not objectionable as they do not render the water hard. In this process, the sodium zeolite may be regenerated by treatment with a concentrated sodium chloride solution. By mass action the above action is reversed and the original permutite is re-formed:

$$Ca \text{ Zeolite} + 2 NaCl \longrightarrow CaCl_2 + Na_2 \text{ Zeolite}$$

Fig. 116. Permutite water softener.

STRONTIUM AND BARIUM

Strontium and barium resemble calcium very closely in both chemical and physical properties; hence little discussion of these elements is necessary. Both metals are somewhat more active than calcium, barium being the most active of the alkaline earth family except the rare element radium. Barium oxidizes readily in moist air and reacts vigorously with water. Both elements are much less abundant than calcium; strontium is less abundant than barium. Because of their activity, they are not found in the free state. Both strontium and barium are found in nature in the form of carbonates and sulfates;

strontium as *strontianite*, $SrCO_3$, found near Strontian, Scotland, hence its name, and *celestite*, $SrSO_4$; barium as *witherite*, $BaCO_3$, and *barite* or *heavy spar*, $BaSO_4$. In the United States, strontium deposits are found in Arizona, Washington, and Texas, and barium deposits are located in Tennessee and Georgia.

Both strontium and barium metals may be prepared by electrolysis of the fused chlorides; however, there is very little demand for the metals. Barium is employed to a limited extent to remove the last traces of gases from vacuum tubes and as a constituent of certain bearing metals.

Strontium compounds heated in the flame give a deep carmine color to the flame. These compounds find some application in the manufacture of "red fire" for flares, fireworks, and signal lights. For this purpose the carbonate is usually converted to the nitrate before use. Some strontium salts have been employed to facilitate crystallization of sugar from molasses residues, and in removal of iron from commercial caustic soda.

Barium sulfate is the most insoluble sulfate of the group. It is used as a filler for rubber goods and as an ingredient of lithopone, a paint pigment. Barium salts are prepared from the sulfate — the sulfate is first reduced with carbon to barium sulfide:

$$BaSO_4 + 4\ C \longrightarrow BaS + 4\ CO$$

Barium sulfide treated with the appropriate acid forms soluble barium salts which may be crystallized from solution. Barium salts produce a light green color when heated in the flame and like strontium salts may be used in the manufacture of flares and signal lights.

MAGNESIUM

History and occurrence. Like other members of the alkaline earth group, compounds of magnesium have been known and used for some time, although the metal itself was not isolated until 1808 by Davy. Magnesium sulfate was extracted from mineral water in Epsom, England, in 1695 by Grew, and since that time has been known as *Epsom salts*.

Since magnesium is a very active metal, it is not found free in nature. Its compounds are widely distributed, however, and in abundance magnesium stands eighth among the elements present in the earth's crust. Many complex silicates, some of which are important commercially, are found in nature. Some of the more important are *asbestos*, $Mg_3Ca(SiO_3)_4$; *meerschaum*, $Mg_2Si_3O_8 \cdot 2\ H_2O$; *talc*,

$H_2Mg_3(SiO_3)_4$; *olivine*, Mg_2SiO_4. From the standpoint of source of metallic magnesium, the more important naturally occurring compounds are *magnesite*, $MgCO_3$, large deposits of which are found in Washington and California, and *magnesium chloride*, $MgCl_2 \cdot 6 H_2O$, which is obtained from salt brines and sea water. The most abundant mineral of magnesium is *dolomite*, $CaCO_3 \cdot MgCO_3$.

Preparation. Magnesium metal may be produced by electrolysis of the fused chloride. The chloride is obtained from salt brines by a complex series of recrystallizations. The cell for the electrolysis consists of an iron container which acts as the cathode and carbon rods as anodes. Some other chloride, such as sodium or calcium chloride is added to lower the melting point of the magnesium chloride. Magnesium metal is less dense than the bath and collects on the surface of the electrolyte; a salt covering prevents its oxidation. Heat for the cell to keep the electrolyte molten is supplied from the outside.

A second method for the preparation of the metal used extensively in Germany is similar in principle to the Hall electrolytic process for making aluminum. Magnesium oxide is dissolved in a molten mixture of fluorides of magnesium, barium, and sodium. An iron cathode and carbon anode are used.

Properties and uses. Magnesium is silvery white, tough and strong, and the lightest of the rigid metals. It is malleable and ductile and may be rolled into sheets or drawn into wire. Magnesium is high in the activity series, somewhat less active than calcium which appears just above it in the series, reacts with hot water slowly to liberate hydrogen, and reacts readily with acids (except hydrofluoric) to produce hydrogen. It is stable in dry air but corrodes slowly in moist air to form a basic carbonate. In a finely divided state or in the form of a thin ribbon, the metal burns vigorously in air to form both magnesium oxide and magnesium nitride. During combustion, a bright white light is produced which is rich in short wave lengths of light; consequently the metal mixed with an oxidizing agent such as potassium chlorate is used in flash powders for photographic purposes. It also finds application in military pyrotechnics as signals, flares, incendiaries, etc. In large pieces, the metal does not ignite readily and may thus be forged and worked at high temperatures.

At the present time magnesium has high strategic importance because of its use in military aircraft, incendiary bombs, and flares. Alloyed with aluminum, magnesium forms a light, strong, and durable metal for aircraft construction. These alloys with aluminum are easily machined and worked, and are resistant to corrosion. Because of its **many advantages** for aircraft construction, production of the metal has increased tremendously in the past few years; in the United States alone production for the year 1939 was more than double that of the previous year. Estimates of production for the years 1940–1949 are shown in Table 32.

TABLE 32

MAGNESIUM PRODUCTION

(Short tons)

Year	U. S.	World	Year	U. S.	World
1940	6,261	49,500	1945	32,792	54,900
1941	16,295	85,500	1946	5,317	12,900
1942	48,963	141,600	1947	12,344	21,400
1943	183,584	297,400	1948	10,003	21,300
1944	157,100	259,700	1949	11,598	23,700

The principal use of magnesium is the preparation of alloys. *Magnalium*, an alloy of aluminum containing 5–30 per cent magnesium, and *duralumin* (Mg 5, Cu 3–5, and Al) are the more important alloys used in airplane construction.

Due to greater and cheaper production of the metal, the price has dropped from several dollars a pound in 1915 to 25 cents per pound, the 1953 price.

COMPOUNDS OF MAGNESIUM

Magnesium chloride. $MgCl_2 \cdot 6 H_2O$, the principal direct source of magnesium metal, is obtained from salt brines in Michigan, from sea water, and the Stassfurt salt deposits in Germany. It may be obtained also from solution of magnesium metal or the carbonate in hydrochloric acid and subsequent crystallization. Magnesium chloride is frequently a constituent of impure table salt and is responsible for caking in moist weather. A type of cement is made by mixing magnesium oxide and a solution of magnesium chloride. The mass hardens on drying probably because of the formation of a complex addition compound.

Magnesite. $MgCO_3$, in a nearly pure form, is found in large amounts in the northeastern part of the state of Washington. When the carbonate is heated, it breaks down to form the oxide and carbon dioxide. The action takes place at a somewhat lower temperature than does the decomposition of limestone. MgO thus produced may be used in the electrothermal production of Mg. A basic carbonate, $MgCO_3 \cdot Mg(OH)_2$, formed by the addition of a soluble carbonate to a solution of magnesium ions, is used as a filler and as a component of certain toothpastes and polishing powders. Like $CaCO_3$, magnesium carbonate is soluble in water containing dissolved carbon dioxide, because of the soluble bicarbonate formation, $Mg(HCO_3)_2$.

Magnesium oxide. A product of the heating of magnesite, magnesium oxide is slightly soluble in water to form *magnesium hydroxide*. Since only a few hydroxyl ions are formed in solution, a suspension of magnesium hydroxide, known as *milk of magnesia*, is used as a mildly alkaline substance for treatment of hyperacidity. It also acts as a mild laxative. The oxide is very resistant to the action of heat and consequently is much used as a refractory for lining furnaces.

Magnesium sulfate. $MgSO_4 \cdot 7 H_2O$, or Epsom salts, is a constituent of many springs and mineral waters. The salt is very soluble in water, and has a very bitter and unpleasant taste. In veterinary medicine it is used as a purgative; it is also used as a fireproofing agent and in weighting cotton.

Magnesium ammonium phosphate. This white crystalline insoluble salt is precipitated from solutions of magnesium ion by the addition of disodium phosphate and ammonium hydroxide:

$$Mg^{++} + NH_4OH + Na_2HPO_4 \longrightarrow MgNH_4PO_4 \downarrow + 2 Na^+ + H_2O$$

It is the final identifying substance for magnesium in most qualitative analysis procedures and is the substance formed in the estimation of magnesium content of a sample quantitatively. When ignited, the compound is converted to *magnesium pyrophosphate*, $Mg_2P_2O_7$, which is weighed as such.

BERYLLIUM

The element beryllium is present in many natural silicates, most important of which is *beryl*, an aluminum silicate of the composition $(BeO)_3 \cdot Al_2O_3 \cdot 6 SiO_2$. A green transparent form of this mineral containing traces of chromium is called *emerald*. Beryllium may be obtained by electrolytic methods, but due to the high melting point, 1280°, considerable difficulty is encountered in the process. As a result the price of the element has remained high (several dollars a pound), and there is little demand for it. It alloys readily with aluminum to which it adds strength and resistance to corrosion; these alloys offer considerable promise in the construction of aircraft. The element is but slightly more dense than magnesium, and hence it would seem that if the element could be prepared cheaply, it might find considerable application as an alloy for airplane structural purposes.

EXERCISES

1. Point out similarities and differences in properties of members of the alkaline earth family. Contrast the general properties of the group with those of the alkali group.
2. What difficulties are encountered in attempting to prepare the elements by reduction of their oxides with carbon?
3. Calculate the quantity of soda ash necessary to soften 1000 gallons of water (sp. gr. = 1) containing 10 mg. $Ca(HCO_3)_2$ and 15 mg. $MgSO_4$ per liter.

   Ans. 75 g.
4. In exercise 3 above, if $Ca(OH)_2$ is added to remove the temporary hardness and Na_2CO_3 the permanent hardness, calculate the quantities of $Ca(OH)_2$ and Na_2CO_3 required.
5. A rock is 74 per cent $SrCO_3$; the rest of the rock is not acted on by acid. What weight of 40 per cent HNO_3 is needed to act on 1 ton of the rock to convert the $SrCO_3$ to $Sr(NO_3)_2$?   Ans. 3160 lb.
6. A seller of superphosphate fertilizer $Ca(H_2PO_4)_2 + 2\ CaSO_4$ was suspected of diluting his product with fine sand. Analysis of a one-gram sample of the product yielded 0.4 g. $Mg_2P_2O_7$. This weight of $Mg_2P_2O_7$ represents what per cent phosphorus in the sample? Had the dealer markedly diluted his product?   Ans. No, product is more than 90 per cent superphosphate.
7. By equations show how you would prepare:

   (a) $Ba(NO_3)_2$ from $BaCl_2$ (c) $Ca(HCO_3)_2$ from $Ca(OH)_2$

   (b) $MgSO_4$ from metallic Mg   (d) $MgNH_4PO_4$ from $MgCO_3$
8. How could you distinguish between the four white solids: $CaCO_3$; $BaSO_4$; $MgCl_2$; $Sr(NO_3)_2$?
9. From Table 27 (p. 368) we obtain the following ionic radii of the paired alkali–alkaline earth metals: Na 0.95, Mg 0.65; K 1.33, Ca 0.99; Cs 1.69, Ba 1.35. What does this suggest in regard to the greater activity of the alkali metal in each pair?
10. List the raw materials used in the production of each of the following: cement, mortar, glass, superphosphate.
11. List as many industrial operations as you can which use limestone as a raw material.
12. An egg weighing 32 g. was oxidized so that all the sulfur was converted to Na_2SO_4. Addition of $BaCl_2$ precipitated 0.466 g. of $BaSO_4$. What was the percentage of sulfur in the egg?

REFERENCES

E. R. Riegel, *Industrial Chemistry*, Reinhold.

C. B. Sawyer and B. R. Kjellgren, "New Developments in Beryllium," *Ind. and Eng. Chem.* **30**, 501 (1938).

C. R. Payne, "Cements," *ibid.* **41**, 2100 (1949).

W. Tranton, "The Barium Industry," *Jour. Soc. Chem. Ind.* **51**, 5 (1932).

W. E. Caldwell and G. Waterman, "A Northwest Strontium Mineral Deposit," *Scientific Monthly* **70**, Apr. (1950).

XXXI

Radioactivity and Nuclear Changes

Ancient scientists philosophized that all matter is made up of minute particles called atoms. This theory is today accepted as fact, and the number of atoms that make up a given weight of an element is known with a percentage of accuracy equal to that for the population of New York City. A constant number (Avogadro's number) of the atoms of any element gives its gram atomic weight, thus

$$6.02 \times 10^{23} \text{ atoms of hydrogen weigh} \quad 1.008 \text{ g.}$$
$$6.02 \times 10^{23} \text{ atoms of copper weigh} \quad 63.57 \text{ g.}$$
$$6.02 \times 10^{23} \text{ atoms of silver weigh} \quad 107.88 \text{ g.}$$

The reason for listing silver here is that 4 silver dollars (8 fifty-cent pieces) weigh about 108 grams and are thus composed of about 6.02×10^{23} atoms of Ag. Suppose you had 4 silver dollars, were philanthropically inclined, and had the capability of a genii to distribute these atoms of silver equally to everyone on this earth; yes, even to the estimated 45,000,000,000 people who had lived on this earth in the past 35,000 years. By dividing 6.02×10^{23} by 45,000,000,000 one obtains the number of 13,000,000,000,000, or the number of silver atoms that would be the share of each individual, alive or dead, from the atoms in 4 silver dollars. This calculation must impress a reader as to the minute size of an atom.

Small as are the atoms, there are several reasons for knowing that atoms are not the ultimate division of matter and that atoms are themselves composed of smaller particles. Among the reasons for believing atoms complex rather than indivisible unit particles are the following: (1) The discovery of cathode rays (electron beams) and of positive rays (pp. 30, 32) gave definite evidence of subatomic particles. (2) It is a fact that 43 of 90 elements have an atomic weight within 0.1 of being a whole number. Is this a random happening? If a person at the seashore at random picked up 90 pebbles of varying size and then weighed the lightest one, what chance is there that 43 of the 90 pebbles would have a weight within 0.1 of a whole number of times as great as the lightest one? The chance of this happening is but 1 in 131 million. It is logical, then, since 43 of 90 elements are nearly whole numbers, as compared to $\frac{1}{16}$ the atomic weight of oxygen, that this is not a random relationship. This logic supported Prout's hypothesis of 1815 that all atoms were composed of hydrogen atoms. This thinking is now modified to the belief that all atoms are composed of the same units. (3) The most conclusive evidence of atomic complexity is the phenomenon of radioactivity, which is herewith developed.

Radioactivity. In 1896, Henry Becquerel discovered that a photographic plate was sensitive to the presence of uranium minerals, even though the plate was wrapped in black paper which is opaque to ordinary light. This unknown radiation was similar in action to X-rays, which had been discovered nearly a year earlier by Roentgen. Furthermore, uranium salts rendered the air a good conductor of electricity as was evidenced by the discharge of an electroscope. This new phenomenon, the spontaneous emission of radiation by an element, was termed *radioactivity*, and those elements responsible for the radiation were termed *radioactive elements*.

Madame Curie and her husband, Pierre, began the investigation of the new phenomenon and found that *pitchblende*, an ore of uranium, consisting largely of U_3O_8, exhibited an activity greater than could be accounted for on the basis of the uranium present. Then began a long series of tedious and painstaking experiments in the separation and analysis of this uranium mineral. After several months of work, Madame Curie announced the separation of an element more active than uranium, which she named *polonium* after her native country, Poland. The work continued, and in 1898 the Curies announced the discovery of *radium* which showed an activity a million times as great as uranium itself.

Radium is an element similar to barium, and like $BaSO_4$, the compound $RaSO_4$ is very insoluble even in acid solution. Use is made of this fact in concentrating radium from other metals with which it occurs. Actually radium is present in high grade uranium ore only in the amount of 0.2 gram per ton. The element itself was isolated by Madame Curie in 1910 by the electrolysis of radium chloride.

During the studies with uranium minerals, Madame Curie found that all uranium minerals are radioactive, and that the activity of a sample depends upon the amount of uranium present. As a result of her studies, Madame Curie concluded that radioactivity is a specific property of the atom, and is not affected by the nature of the chemical combination in which the atom exists; nor is it affected by physical conditions.

Radioactive rays. By means of an electric field, Rutherford was able to identify three types of radiation from radioactive substances.

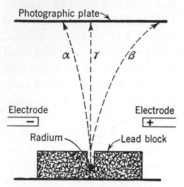

Fig. 117. Three kinds of rays produced from the radioactive disintegration of radium.

A bit of radioactive substance was placed in a depression in a block of lead (Fig. 117). All rays except those moving directly upward were absorbed by the lead. Electrodes and a photographic plate to record the emitted radiation were placed above the block of lead. This experiment shows that the radiation may be resolved into three kinds: one kind being unaffected by the electrode, the other two kinds showing opposite charges as evidenced by the bending of the rays in opposite directions. From the extent and the direction of bending, it is possible to calculate the masses and charge of the radiations. The three types of radiation were named *alpha* (α), *beta* (β), and *gamma* (γ) rays.

Alpha rays are positively charged particles with a mass four times that of the hydrogen atom, and through spectral studies have been shown to be nuclei of helium atoms, each particle consisting of 2 neutrons and 2 protons. These particles are expelled from radioactive substances at moderate velocities (10,000–12,000 miles per second) and have a low penetrating power since they may be stopped by thin sheets of paper. Air through which alpha particles pass becomes ionized due to electrons knocked out of molecules in the air on impact with these relatively heavy particles. If this ionized air is saturated with water vapor and suddenly cooled, the ionized particles in the air act as nuclei for the condensation of small droplets of water, and these particles are rendered visible as a fog. C. T. R. Wilson was able to follow the path of an alpha particle by photographing the fog tracks thus produced.

The expulsion of alpha particles from radioactive material

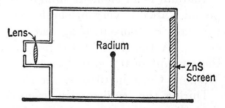

Fig. 118. Spinthariscope.

may also be observed with the aid of a *spinthariscope*, a device consisting of a narrow tube which is fitted at one end with a lens and with a screen coated with zinc sulfide at the other end (Fig. 118). If a piece of radium is placed in front of the screen and the latter observed through the lens, flashes of light may be seen as a result of alpha particles colliding with zinc sulfide particles.

Beta rays are negatively charged particles and are identical with electrons. They are sometimes referred to as "high speed electrons" since their speed sometimes approaches that of light (186,000 miles per second). These rays are somewhat more penetrating than alpha particles, passing through thin layers of metals.

Gamma rays are of high frequency and are identical with X rays of very short wave length. They possess relatively high penetrating power and like alpha and beta rays affect a photographic plate. They carry no charge. Gamma rays constitute the portion of radioactive emission which affected the photographic plate of Becquerel even though the plate had been wrapped in several layers of black paper.

Disintegration of atoms. In 1902, Rutherford suggested that elements may spontaneously change into other elements or break down into simpler elements. This idea was revolutionary since elements were supposed to be permanent; however this theory has been completely confirmed by experimental evidence, and today there is no doubt that elements may be broken down into simpler elements. When radium disintegrates, an alpha particle is expelled from the nucleus of the radium atom, leaving an atom of atomic weight 4 units less than radium. The change may be represented thus (only the nucleus is shown):

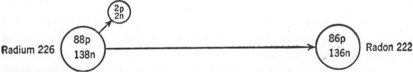

Rutherford was able to collect an inert gas from the disintegration of radium and named it niton, now called *radon*. Ramsey studied this "radium emanation," and found its atomic weight to be 222, which is what we should expect from theoretical considerations.

During the disintegration of radioactive substances, not all three types of rays are emitted at the same time. A pure sample of uranium emits only α rays at first, but after a time β rays are also emitted. The explanation of the fact that both α and β rays are obtained after a time is the formation of other radioactive substances, during the disintegration process, which do emit β particles. Uranium itself emits only α particles; but uranium X_1 which is formed in the first step gives off β particles. Gamma rays are light rays and not discrete particles and accompany all types of radioactive decay, but do not necessarily appear in every particular case. An entire series of disintegration products of uranium has been discovered and the successive changes are represented in Table 33.

TABLE 33

DISINTEGRATION OF URANIUM [1]

Element	At. Wt.	At. No.	Half-Life Time	Kind of Ray Emitted	Periodic Family
Uranium I	238	92	4.67×10^9 years	alpha	VI A
Uranium X_1	234	90	24.5 days	beta	IV A
Uranium X_2	234	91	68.4 seconds	beta	V A
Uranium II	234	92	$3. \times 10^5$ years	alpha	VI A
Ionium	230	90	$8. \times 10^4$ years	alpha	IV A
Radium	226	88	1690 years	alpha	II A
Radon	222	86	3.82 days	alpha	VIII A
Radium A	218	84	2.05 minutes	alpha	VI A
Radium B	214	82	26.8 minutes	beta	IV A
Radium C	214	83	19.7 minutes	beta	V A
Radium C′	214	84	10^{-6} second	alpha	VI A
Radium D	210	82	22 years	beta	IV A
Radium E	210	83	5 days	beta	V A
Radium F	210	84	140 days	alpha	VI A
End product . . . . Pb	206	82	stable	none	IV A

[1] This table is somewhat historical in character as it lists names of elements of some years ago rather than as isotopes of currently known elements. There is also question whether the Uranium I, X_1, X_2, II elements belong to the periodic family designated or to a "rare rare earth" or otherwise called "actinide series."

It is to be noted that the expulsion of an alpha particle results in a decrease of 2 in atomic number (loss of 2 protons) and a decrease of 4 in atomic weight (2 protons and 2 neutrons), while the emission of a β particle[2] results in no change in atomic weight (electrons have negligible weight) but an increase of 1 in atomic number. A part of the uranium disintegration series is shown below.

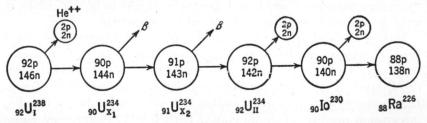

[2] We should differentiate very carefully between the loss of electrons from the nucleus of an atom (radioactivity) and the loss of electrons from the valence orbits of an atom (ionization).

Half-life periods. The time required for the decomposition of one-half of any given amount of radioactive element is termed its half-life period. The half-life period of radium is 1690 years, which means that during this time one-half of any given sample of radium will decompose; during the next 1690 years half of that remaining (one-fourth of the original) will decompose, etc. Half-life periods vary greatly from .000001 second for radium C' to 4,670,000,000 years for uranium.

Properties of radium. Radium appears in Group II A of the periodic table, and except for its radioactive properties is not unlike the other elements in this group, calcium, strontium, and barium. Although not as active as members of the alkali group, it is the most chemically active member of Group II and will decompose water with the formation of hydrogen. Radium has distinct metallic properties and forms the strong base, radium hydroxide. Its compounds are very similar to those of the other alkaline earth elements.

Radioactivity is the distinctive property of radium. Radium atoms are spontaneously and continuously disintegrating at a constant rate whether the element is free or combined with other elements. Furthermore, there seems to be nothing that the chemist can do to accelerate or retard this rate.

Rays from radium have a powerful effect on living tissues and produce severe and painful sores if allowed to come in contact with the skin for any length of time. Fortunately the effect is greater on diseased than on healthy tissue and if very carefully controlled, radium may be used in the treatment of cancerous tissue and other malignant growths. Its principal application is in the treatment of surface cancer. Radon is used also as a therapeutic agent by sealing the gas in tiny glass tubes and inserting the tubes in cancerous flesh. Since the rays of radium are so penetrating, it is stored in heavy lead containers to prevent injury to those working around it.

One of the principal sources of radium is *pitchblende*, U_3O_8, a mineral found in the Belgian Congo and northern Canada. Purest deposits of pitchblende yield about .2 gram of radium per ton of ore. Deposits of *carnotite*, a low-grade ore of uranium, are found in Utah and Colorado. The current price of radium is approximately $20,000 per gram.

Radioactive and stable atomic nuclei. The nuclear structure of atoms was briefly discussed in chapter III, where it was pointed out that the nuclei of all atoms contain protons and neutrons. The nuclei of the *lighter stable atoms contain about an equal number of neutrons and protons;* in fact, many contain an equal number of neutrons and protons, for example, $_2He^4$, $_6C^{12}$, $_7N^{14}$, $_8O^{16}$, $_{16}S^{32}$, $_{20}Ca^{40}$. The subscripts to the left and below these symbols designate atomic number, while the superscripts to the right and above are isotopic weights. Atoms heavier than calcium lose the tendency to have about an equal proton-neutron ratio — there is a tendency for the *excess of neutrons over protons to increase with atomic weight;* for example, $_{24}Cr^{52}$, $_{42}Mo^{96}$, $_{92}U^{238}$. However, for each element there is apparently a *narrow range of stability insofar as the proton-neutron ratio is concerned.* This range of stability for a given element is an index of the number of stable isotopes for that element. As long as the proton-neutron ratio is within this range for a particular element, the isotopes will be stable, but if this ratio falls outside this range an unstable isotope results which would be subject to radioactive disintegration. To illustrate, three stable isotopes of oxygen are known, $_8O^{16}$, $_8O^{17}$, $_8O^{18}$, which indicates that the range of stability in proton-neutron ratio is 8 : 8 to 8 : 10. Atoms of oxygen such as $_8O^{13}$ or $_8O^{20}$ must be too unstable to exist. The range of stability for most of the heavier elements appears to be wider than for the lighter elements, hence more stable isotopes are possible (see Table 5).

The heaviest naturally occurring atoms are characterized by radioactivity; the nuclei of these heaviest atoms are subject to alpha or beta particle emission. When an atom loses an alpha particle, which means 2 protons and 2 neutrons from the nucleus, the residual atom will be two less in atomic number and four less in atomic weight. When an atom loses a beta particle (an electron) from the nucleus there must be some disintegration of a nuclear neutron into a proton and the ejected electron. At any rate the residual atom gains in atomic number while the atomic weight remains practically the same. The newly formed nucleus may be stable or itself radioactive.

The displacement law. The displacement law of radioactive change states that the expulsion of an α particle from a radioactive element results in the formation of an element two places to the left in the periodic table, while the expulsion of a β particle results in an element one place to the right. This law at once becomes evident when we consider that loss of an alpha particle decreases the atomic number by two, whereas loss of a beta particle increases the atomic number by one. See the diagram on page 414 in studying the above relationship.

Isotopes of lead. Radioactivity ceases with the formation of radium G with an atomic weight of 206. In the series of changes between uranium and radium G, a total of 8 α particles have been lost per atom, which means a decrease of 32 (8 × 4) units of mass. Since the atomic weight of uranium is 238, we should expect an atomic weight of 206 for radium G (238 − 32). Radium G has been shown to be an isotope of lead. Although the atomic weight of lead is given as 207.2, this value is for lead not associated with radioactive changes. Careful determinations of the atomic weight of lead from radioactive sources by T. W. Richards yield a value of 206, confirming that radium G is an isotope of lead.

As uranium minerals disintegrate, this isotope of lead accumulates, since it is not radioactive. From half-life periods it is possible to calculate the amount of lead which will be formed in a given time from a given amount of uranium. From the ratio of lead to uranium in minerals found today, it is possible to determine the time necessary for the establishment of this ratio and thus to calculate the age of the mineral and a minimum age of the earth. This "radioactive clock" shows that some of these minerals were formed more than a billion years ago.

Radioactivity and atomic structure. Radioactivity has contributed immeasurably to the modern concept of atomic structure. The spontaneous disintegration of atoms at once explodes Dalton's theory that atoms are compact, indivisible particles. Since definite particles of matter are expelled during radioactive changes, it is natural to assume that very probably these same particles were units in the structure of the atom from which they were expelled. These considerations have led to the present ideas regarding atomic structure in which the fundamental units of which an atom is composed, namely, protons, electrons, and neutrons, are regarded as common to the atoms of all the chemical elements.

The positron is a further well-known particle and names such as neutrino and mesotron are given to some of the less well-known particles. Mesotrons of at least two different weights, a π mesotron, and a μ mesotron are known. Just what part these particles play in nuclear make-up is not completely understood. The source or place of cosmic ray particles in the structure of matter is also unknown.

Artificial transmutation of elements. The facts of radioactivity immediately bring to mind the questions: Can the atoms of those elements which are not radioactive be broken down by artificial means into atoms of simpler elements, and can atoms of the simpler elements be built up into more complex atoms? In either case a transmutation of the element would result, a problem at which the alchemists worked vainly for centuries. Radioactivity proves to us that if we can alter the nucleus of atoms, new elements must result. Some success in transmutation has been achieved by bombarding atoms with high speed particles such as protons or neutrons. Since atoms resemble solar systems in that their volume is largely open space, with a nucleus of exceedingly small diameter as compared to the diameter of the atom, the problem of hitting the minute positively charged nucleus to effect nuclear change is difficult. Necessarily a particle for nuclear bombardment must be smaller than the atom to penetrate the electron atmosphere. If a properly directed positive particle is to hit the positive nucleus, it must have sufficient speed to overcome the repelling force of the positively charged nucleus. Rutherford reasoned correctly that alpha particles from naturally radioactive elements would have sufficient speed and mass to disrupt an atomic nucleus.

In 1919 Rutherford allowed a beam of alpha particles from a radioactive substance to pass through nitrogen gas. Some of the high speed alpha particles, on collision with the nuclei of nitrogen atoms, effected a change as represented by the equation (α particles are helium nuclei)

$$_7N^{14} + {}_2He^4 \longrightarrow {}_8O^{17} + {}_1H^1$$

where the superscripts represent the masses of the various particles and the subscripts atomic numbers. In this particular case an isotope of oxygen (atomic weight 17, atomic number 8) was obtained from the nitrogen and helium. Only a few alpha particles were effective in bringing about a change since atoms are very porous and hence only a few of the alpha particles actually collided with a nucleus. In fact only about one alpha particle in 50,000 made an effective collision, but this marked the first accomplishment of artificial transmutation.

Many further experiments in bombarding atoms with alpha particles resulted in small scale transmutations. Examples are:

$$_{13}Al^{27} + {}_2He^4 \longrightarrow {}_{14}Si^{30} + {}_1H^1$$
$$_5B^{11} + {}_2He^4 \longrightarrow {}_7N^{14} + {}_0n^1$$
$$_4Be^9 + {}_2He^4 \longrightarrow {}_6C^{12} + {}_0n^1$$

This last equation in brief denotes the way in which Chadwick discovered the neutron, $_0n^1$ (p. 32). Because of their neutral character neutrons should make good nuclear bombardment particles, but manmade electrical machines cannot accelerate neutrons. Slow neutrons have, however, been shown effective in instigating certain nuclear changes. To accelerate a beam of any nuclear particle, such as helium ion, proton, or deuteron (heavy hydrogen nucleus), E. O. Lawrence of the University of California invented the *cyclotron*, which gives a nuclear beam of considerably greater concentration than that produced by any natural radioactive source. In this machine the particles are accelerated in a strong magnetic field between electrodes, which change in charge at intervals equal to the time of half a revolution of the particles. These accelerated particles have been effective in many transmutations. A second accelerating machine is the *betatron*. The betatron throws off high energy electrons, which are used to produce high energy gamma rays, and these in turn instigate many nuclear changes. The *synchrotron* is a third and newer type electrical machine to give increased kinetic energy to electrons. The *cosmotron* and *bevatron* are very high energy producing machines related to the cyclotron. The bevatron is so named because it can produce billion-electron-volt protons.

Further examples of artificial transmutation are:

$$_3Li^6 + _0n^1 \longrightarrow _2He^4 + _1T^3$$
$$_7N^{14} + _0n^1 \longrightarrow _6C^{14} + _1H^1$$
$$_{14}Si^{28} + _1D^2 \longrightarrow _{15}P^{29} + _0n^1$$
$$_{19}K^{39} + _1H^1 \longrightarrow _{20}Ca^{39} + _0n^1$$
$$_{77}Ir^{191} + _2He^4 \longrightarrow _{79}Au^{194} + _0n^1$$

The above five examples of nuclear changes may be designated respectively as (n, t), (n, p) (d, n), (p, n), (α, n) as the bombardment nuclear particle and emission one are listed. These pairs are often referred to as the "in" and "out" particles. Nuclear changes of the (d, n), (d, p), (p, n), (n, γ), $(n, 2n)$, (α, n) and (α, p) are among the most common.

Note that the sum of the subscripts on the left side of the equation is equal to the sum on the right. Likewise, the superscripts, which represent atomic weights, must give the same total on both sides of the equation.

Artificial radioactivity. Recently it has been found that the bombardment of nuclei of several of the lighter elements results in the formation of isotopes of elements which disintegrate spontaneously, very similar to the action of the heavier radioactive elements. For example, when aluminum is bombarded with alpha particles, an isotope of phosphorus is formed, thus

$$_{13}Al^{27} + _2He^4 \longrightarrow _{15}P^{30} + _0n^1$$

This isotope of phosphorus is radioactive and decomposes spontaneously, thus

$$_{15}P^{30} \longrightarrow _{14}Si^{30} + e^+$$

where e^+ is a *positron*, a unit of matter shown to possess the same mass as an electron but a positive charge. This isotope of phosphorus of half-life 2.5 minutes is said to be artificially radioactive since it has been produced by artificial means. Other artificially radioactive elements have been produced and they offer promise as therapeutic agents to share the place of naturally radioactive elements like radium. In general, these radioactive isotopes have short half-life periods and this offers certain advantages in treatment of disease. An additional example is

$$_{53}I^{127} + _{0}n^1 \longrightarrow _{53}I^{128} \longrightarrow _{54}Xe^{128} + \text{electron}$$
$$\text{Half-life} = 25 \text{ min.}$$

The discovery of these light radioactive elements may lead to very significant new discoveries in the metabolism of plants and animals. For example, the passage of radioactive phosphorus and calcium may be followed through the body of an animal by means of a very sensitive instrument called a Geiger counter.

As a result of research in the past twenty years radioactive isotopes of every known element have been artificially prepared. The elements 43, 61, 85, and 87 were for years blank spaces in the periodic table. After much unsuccessful research to find them was carried on, it began to be realized that if they existed in nature at all it was in exceedingly small amount. They have now been prepared in small or trace amounts by nuclear reactions or identified as branch elements in radioactive decay series.

Experiments with small scale artificial transmutations resulting in stable or radioactive new atoms gave rise to the idea that atoms heavier than uranium might be produced. Research on the small scale production of transuranium atoms was successful, and in the work the phenomenon of nuclear fission was discovered. Since nuclear fission takes place in a so-called atomic bomb, the next section is devoted to these topics.

ATOMIC ENERGY AND THE ATOMIC BOMB

In early August of 1945 came the startling announcement that an atomic bomb of unprecedented explosive violence had been dropped on the Japanese city of Hiroshima. The war with Japan came to an end a few days later. It was then revealed that scientists since early in the war had been concentrating their attentions on the release of atomic energy — an atomic bomb was the result. Preliminary experiments had been carried out with the bomb near Los Alamos, New Mexico. Four huge plants for the manufacture of the essential ingredients of the bomb had been erected, three in Tennessee, and one on the Columbia River in the state of Washington.

Although the details of the construction of the atomic bomb are still secret, the underlying scientific principles have been fairly well known for some time. The reader of this book is referred to the several references at the end of this chapter. It is beyond the purpose of this text to delve at length into said topics. A brief presentation of some of the principles follows.

Chemical energy and atomic energy. In ordinary chemical changes, atoms of the elements may undergo rearrangement, but the identity of the atom is retained. In terms of the structure of the atom, electrons in the valence orbit may be transferred or shared but the remainder of the atom is unchanged. If carbon is burned in oxygen, the carbon atom is not changed basically but appears as such in the product of combustion, carbon dioxide. Likewise the oxygen atoms entering into the combination appear as such in the carbon dioxide. The combination takes place as a result of the sharing of outer electrons between the two kinds of atoms:

$$C + O_2 \longrightarrow CO_2$$

This reaction provides the basis of most of the energy developed for industrial uses; coal is essentially carbon; various fuel oils are carbon-containing compounds. In their combustion, carbon dioxide is produced. These reactions are exothermic, *i.e.*, energy is evolved in the form of heat. The heat energy is said to be derived from the chemical or potential energy of the reacting substances.

Atomic energy is associated with *changes in the nuclei* of atoms; as a result, the basic nature of the atom is changed, the product atoms are not the same as the reacting atoms. For example, lithium and hydrogen may combine to form helium:

$$_3Li^7 + _1H^1 \longrightarrow 2\ _2He^4$$

This reaction is also exothermic, but in contrast to the 4.1 electron volts (ev) of energy produced from the combustion of one atom of carbon, 17,000,000 electron volts are produced from the reaction of one atom of lithium with one atom of hydrogen. It is evident then that the energy produced in nuclear reactions is many million times greater than that produced as a result of ordinary chemical change.

What is the source of this tremendous amount of energy? In the reaction of lithium with hydrogen, the mass of the lithium atom is 7.01818, that of the hydrogen atom 1.00813, or a total of 8.02631 units of mass of reacting substances. The two atoms of helium weigh 8.00778[1] so that the mass of products is not equal to the mass of reactants. A

---

[1] Weights used in this paragraph are physical atomic weights based on the main oxygen isotope as 16 rather than chemical atomic weights based on the weight of natural oxygen (mixture of O^{16}, O^{17}, O^{18}) as 16.

mass loss of 8.02631 − 8.00778 or .01853 unit occurs. Einstein, in 1905, stated the law of the equivalence of mass and energy, which says in effect that matter may be converted into energy or vice versa. By using the Einstein equation, it may be shown that the loss of .01853 units of mass would yield about 17 million electron volts (mev) of energy.[1] We should try to appreciate the tremendous amounts of energy associated with small amounts of matter — one kilogram of matter, if converted completely into energy, would give 25 billion kilowatt-hours of energy — equal to the energy that would be generated by the total electric power industry in the United States (1939) running for two months. Only 8.5 kilowatt hours would be obtained from burning an equivalent amount of coal.

In summary, we may say that chemical energy is derived from ordinary chemical changes which affect only the outer configuration of atoms, while atomic energy is derived from changes in the nuclei of atoms, where most of the mass is concentrated.

Chain reactions. The question might arise, why are not nuclear reactions with the evolution of these tremendous amounts of energy taking place about us in everyday life much the same as ordinary chemical changes are taking place. The answer seems to be that whereas most chemical changes are self-maintaining, nuclear changes are not. In a chemical reaction, once the action is started, it proceeds until the reactants are used up. A piece of wood or coal ignited in the air continues to burn until used up. However, in nuclear changes the nuclear "fire" usually goes out soon after it is started. If some way were available to keep a nuclear fire burning, nuclear changes would proceed as easily as ordinary chemical changes; a so-called *chain re-*

---

[1] An electron volt is the energy necessary to raise an electron through a potential difference of one volt. It is related to the erg as follows:

$$6.24 \times 10^5 \text{ mev} = 1 \text{ erg}$$

The relation between the atomic mass unit (amu) and the gram (cf. p. 410) is

$$6.02 \times 10^{23} \text{ amu} = 1 \text{ gram}$$

According to Einstein $e = mc^2$, where e is the number of ergs, m is the number of grams, and c is the velocity of light (3×10^{10} cm/sec). As a corollary to this

$$1 \text{ gram} = 9 \times 10^{20} \text{ ergs}$$

By substituting their equivalents for the gram and erg in the last equation, we get

$$6.02 \times 10^{23} \text{ amu} = 9 \times 10^{20} \times 6.24 \times 10^5 \text{ mev}$$

But the mass loss in the lithium + hydrogen ⟶ helium reaction is 0.01853 amu.

Therefore $0.01853 \text{ amu} = \dfrac{9 \times 10^{20} \times 6.24 \times 10^5 \times 1.853 \times 10^{-2}}{6.02 \times 10^{23}} \text{ mev} = 17 \text{ mev}$

action in which the action once started would pass from one atom to another as in the links of a chain appears to be necessary for a self-maintaining nuclear reaction. Before 1939, many nuclear reactions were known and had been carried out on a very small scale, but in so doing more energy was used in maintaining the reaction than was obtained as a result of it.

Atomic fission. The transmutation of many elements has already been described (pp. 417–419). In general, in these atom smashing experiments, only small fragments of matter such as protons, electrons, helium ions, etc., were knocked out of the nucleus or added to it. As a result, the product atom had an atomic number very near that of the bombarded atom.

Researchers in Germany, in 1939, discovered a new and potentially most important type of nuclear change. By bombarding uranium with neutrons traveling at moderate speeds, they split the atom into two fragments of approximately equal size. Actually it was only the U^{235} isotope in natural uranium that was subject to this change. This process now referred to as *fission* was accompanied by the evolution of a tremendous amount of energy. Furthermore, in the fission process, in addition to the relatively large fragments produced, several neutrons were released in the fission of each atom. The implications of the latter were at once clear — these product neutrons might be used to bombard another parent atom, the fission of which in turn would produce more neutrons; thus a self-maintaining or chain reaction seemed to be a definite possibility. A chain reaction would be self-maintaining only if a neutron from each fission produced fission in at least one other atom and so on. We may illustrate a nuclear fission by the following equation and diagram:

$$_{92}U^{235} + {_0}n^1 \longrightarrow {_{38}}Sr^{94} + {_{54}}Xe^{139} + 3\ {_0}n^1 + \text{energy}$$
$$\text{(about 200 mev)}$$

In the above illustration, strontium and xenon are shown as the two large fragments produced in the fission; however, it should not be assumed that these two elements always constitute the major fragments of a fission, since many other elements near the middle of the periodic table have been identified as products (see Fig. 120). The mass of all the products of the fission is not quite equal to the mass of the reactants; the loss in mass is responsible for the very large amounts of energy evolved in these nuclear fissions, *i.e.*, mass is converted into energy.

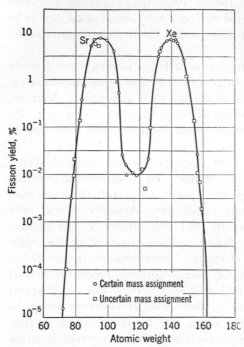

Fig. 120. Yields of U^{235} fission-product chains as a function of mass.

No whole units of mass are lost in a fission, and it may be noted in the fission equation above that the sum of atomic numbers on the left equals that on the right, and that whole number atomic weight sums on left and right are equal. The energy is derived from but a fractional part of one unit of mass. Note also that the $_{38}Sr^{94}$ and $_{54}Xe^{139}$ are isotopes of these elements of high neutron-proton ratio. It is the radioactive decomposition of such atoms that accounts for the intense radiation associated with fission, radiation mostly of beta and gamma rays.

U^{235} is not the only atom subject to fission. Slow neutrons also produce fission of U^{233} and Pu^{239}; in addition, fast neutrons produce fission of Th^{232}, Pa^{231}, U^{238}, and Np^{237}. The substances U^{233} and Pu^{239}, not occurring in nature, are obtained from the relatively abundant isotopes Th^{232} and U^{238} respectively by interaction with intermediate energy neutrons. For example:

$$_{90}Th^{232} + _{0}n^1 \longrightarrow {}_{90}Th^{233} + \gamma$$
$$_{90}Th^{233} \longrightarrow {}_{91}Pa^{233} + \beta \longrightarrow {}_{92}U^{233} + \beta$$

Other elements of fissionable importance will probably be developed. There is much experimentation with bombardment particles other than neutrons for producing fission of fissionable elements. Among such particles are protons, deuterons, and alpha particles. Similar experiments have been made with gamma rays.

Controlled fissions. It is evident that if the neutrons liberated in the fission of uranium were utilized in producing more fissions, a rapid and violent reaction might take place; *i.e.*, a piece of uranium, once the reaction was started, would explode. Although a violently explosive substance was the immediate objective in producing an atomic bomb, many problems had to be solved before this objective was achieved. One of the first problems to confront scientists working on the atomic energy project was to find a means of controlling these atomic fissions. We may indicate in a general way how this was accomplished in the following section.

Ordinary uranium is composed of three isotopes, which occur in the following proportions: U^{238}, 99.276 per cent, U^{235}, 0.719 per cent, U^{234}, 0.005 per cent. Thus in ordinary uranium the ratio of the U^{235} isotope, which is the one fissionable by slow neutrons, to U^{238} is about 1 to 140. For a fission chain to be set up, neutrons liberated by the fission of one U^{235} atom must hit another U^{235} atom, and so on. But neutrons resulting from fission are fast enough so that many of them are captured by U^{238} atoms, though not in a fission-yielding process. Also, if the piece of uranium is small, many or most of the fast neutrons may escape through the surface of the metal before being absorbed by other nuclei. The uranium isotope U^{238} is particularly effective in capturing neutrons and although this absorption lessens the chance for absorption of neutrons to produce fission in U^{235} atoms, it is of utmost importance in other considerations as will be pointed out later.

It is evident that at least one neutron from each fission must be effective in bringing about another fission; otherwise the chain is broken and reaction ceases. U^{235} atoms seem able to capture slow neutrons in competition with the more numerous U^{238} atoms, but U^{238} atoms capture most of the high energy neutrons. In order to increase the probability of capture of neutrons by U^{235} and hence fission, it is necessary to slow down the liberated neutrons. This may be accomplished with a "moderator," graphite for example, which absorbs a part of the energy of the neutron and slows it down. With a latticework arrangement of uranium lumps imbedded in graphite, called a "pile" and larger than a so-called "critical size," neutrons which might ordinarily be lost from the surface will diffuse back and forth through the latticework until they have lost sufficient energy to be captured by a U^{235} nucleus. The capture results in fission with liberation of more neutrons and the chain reaction is set up. The first pile was constructed at the University of Chicago in 1942 with about six tons of ordinary uranium and many tons of graphite. Since the fission process is exothermic, it is obvious that the pile would heat up as the fission process continues to take place more and more rapidly and would eventually reach a temperature high enough to cause an explosion. However, the pile may be controlled by providing passageways through which rods of neutron absorbing material such as cadmium metal may be inserted. Neutrons are absorbed by the cadmium and the chain reaction is broken. Proper adjustment of the cadmium rods will allow the reaction to proceed at only a given rate or power level. To raise the power level the rods would be partially withdrawn; to lower it the rods would be pushed in farther. Thus such a controlled pile provides a means for producing low temperature heat energy from atomic energy.

Separation of uranium isotopes. Since U^{235} undergoes fission by slow-moving neutrons, whereas U^{238} does not, an important wartime project was to separate the two isotopes from the naturally occurring mixture of 0.7 per cent U^{235} and 99.3 per cent U^{238}. Experimental research on the separation of isotopes had been reported in scientific literature, but separation in quantity was indeed a big problem. Three methods of separation of the uranium isotopes will be briefly described.

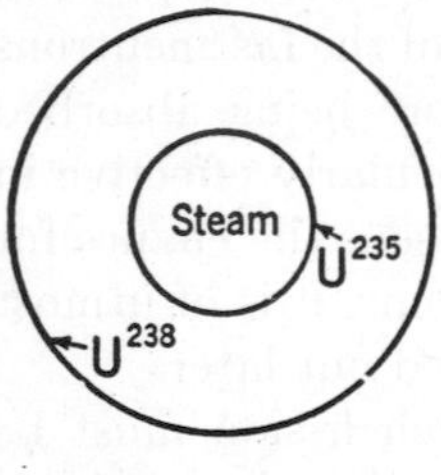

Small scale testing of the separation of uranium isotopes by *thermal diffusion* was promising enough so that a massive plant for this purpose was built at Oak Ridge, Tennessee. In actual operation, a compound of uranium, containing both isotopes, is fed into a thermal diffusion plant which consists essentially of thousands of units of concentric pipes (Fig. 121). Steam passes through the innermost pipe and the uranium compounds in liquid form are in the outer pipe. The lighter isotope tends to travel to the hot inner wall of the unit and to rise. The heavier isotope is to some extent left in more concentrated form at the outer cold wall. By draining solution from near the center and top and also from the outside and bottom of the pipe and repeating the cycle over and over again, thousands of times, a product much higher in percentage of U^{235} is obtained.

Fig. 121. Cross section of concentric pipes.

The thermal diffusion plant had such large and costly steam requirements that a *gaseous diffusion* method for separation of the isotopes soon took its place. You will recall Graham's law of diffusion which states that the comparative rates of diffusion of two gases vary inversely as the square roots of their densities. If naturally occurring uranium is converted to gaseous UF_6, the compound containing the lighter isotope will diffuse a little faster through a porous barrier.

One passage of the isotopic gas mixture, of course, does not effect complete separation, so an enormous amount of gas recycling is necessary. Much as in fractional distillation, an eventual concentration of U^{235} is effected by fractional gas diffusion.

The *electromagnetic separation* process is based upon the use of the mass spectrograph (p. 48). A uranium compound in vapor form is ionized by an electron beam. The ions produced are accelerated and pass through a narrow slit into a large evacuated region where electromagnetic forces act on them. Since the lighter isotopic ions have less weight although of the same charge, they are deflected into a smaller semicircular path than the heavier ions. Slits are placed at the termini of the semicircular ionic beams, such that the respective isotopic ions are separately collected.

Separation of the two principal isotopes of uranium by any of the above methods is very costly and requires large plant installations.

Plutonium. It has been stated that ordinary uranium tends to absorb neutrons and thus to slow down the chain reaction if not to actually break it. This absorption of neutrons by U^{238} turned out to be extremely important, since the absorption leads to the formation of a new element, plutonium, Pu, atomic number 94, which like U^{235} may undergo fission with the release of more neutrons. The changes taking place in the formation of Pu from U^{238} may be represented diagrammatically:

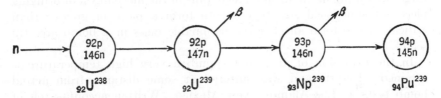

U^{238} absorbs a neutron to form U^{239} which then emits a beta particle, resulting in the formation of *neptunium*, Np, a new element of atomic number 93. Neptunium then emits a beta particle which results in the formation of *plutonium*, Pu.

The "piles" referred to previously were actually constructed for the purpose of manufacturing plutonium. The large amounts of heat energy evolved in the operation of the piles were not used. A large plant for plutonium manufacture was constructed at Hanford, Washington, in 1943. Several piles were set in operation, the heat from the reactions was dissipated into the Columbia River by pumping river water through the piles to absorb the heat.

The atomic bomb. With the discovery of Pu, two substances,

U^{235} and Pu^{239}, were available for the manufacture of atomic bombs. Plutonium manufacture possesses certain definite advantages over the recovery of U^{235} from ordinary uranium. The separation of U^{235} from U^{238} is exceedingly difficult since *physical means* which take advantage of the relatively small differences in the mass of the two isotopes must be employed. Thermal diffusion, gaseous diffusion, and electromagnetic methods have been listed as used to effect the separation but many stages of purification are necessary. Plutonium, when produced in an uranium pile, can be separated from unconverted uranium by *chemical means*, since Pu is a different element and as such exhibits a different set of chemical properties.

Relatively little information has been released regarding the construction of the bomb itself. It was known early in the studies of this project, however, that a certain critical size of material was necessary for a chain reaction to be self-perpetuating and for an explosion to take place. In a small piece of U^{235} or Pu^{239}, where the ratio of surface area to volume is large, too many neutrons escape through the surface and consequently a chain reaction is not maintained. As the size of the piece is increased, the ratio of surface area to volume decreases and there is more chance that neutrons will be captured before escaping through the surface. In producing an atomic bomb it seems logical that pieces of subcritical size might be brought together rapidly, possibly by using one or more pieces as projectiles and another as a target in a firing mechanism. The details of the mechanism of bringing pieces of subcritical size together to form a piece of greater than critical size to form an effective fissionable mass in a bomb are still secret.

In the explosion of an atomic bomb a very high temperature is attained. Desert sand was sintered at some distance from actual bomb tests at Los Alamos, New Mexico. Written accounts tell of vaporization of the metal of the tower holding the test bomb. Just how high a temperature is reached is difficult to estimate, as man on this earth has not heretofore attained temperatures above about 4000° C. It does recall the calculation of Jeans that an object the size of a pea, but at a temperature of 40,000,000° C. (estimated internal temperature of the sun) would be liberating so much heat that it would shrivel up a man a thousand miles away in the flick of an eye. This excessively high temperature consideration leads us to some understanding as to the nature of possible temperature effects in an atomic bomb explosion. Probably no large mass of material in an atomic bomb blast is heated as high as the internal part of the sun. Certainly some very high temperature is reached locally, whence the atomic bomb explodes and causes such air expansion, and later contraction on cooling, as to produce a cyclonic wind or blast effect. The radioactive fragments that may vary in size down to minute particles clinging to dust are very dangerous.

Atomic fusion and the hydrogen bomb. It has been seen that the splitting of uranium or plutonium, in a fission process, into elements having atomic weights and atomic numbers roughly half as great results in the liberation of tremendous amounts of energy. To say that this energy derives from a considerable decrease in mass, does not, of course, explain why there is a mass decrease. The explanation for this fact lies in an understanding of the relationship between nuclear size and nuclear stability.

If one considers all nuclei occurring in nature as arranged in order of increasing mass, *i.e.*, increasing number of nuclear constituent particles, one finds at first a general stability increase up to an atomic weight of about 55. A decrease in the mass *per nuclear particle* accompanies the stability increase. With further increase in atomic weight, however, there occurs a steady *decrease* in nuclear stability (and an accompanying increase in mass per nuclear particle) as a result of the mutual repulsion of the positively charged nuclear protons for each other (important only where this number is fairly large). Thus we see why the very heavy nuclei of uranium and plutonium are unstable with respect to fission into lighter atoms.

It is evident from the foregoing that there exists another potential source of nuclear energy in a *fusion* process, in which the very lightest nuclei might be made to combine to give somewhat heavier, more stable nuclei, with an attendant release of energy. Fundamentally, this is the idea behind the much discussed hydrogen bomb. The most obviously energetically favorable, though probably not practical, reaction to use for such a purpose would involve the direct conversion of hydrogen to helium, with the release of vast amounts of energy:

$$4\,_1H^1 \longrightarrow {}_2He^4 + energy$$

A number of more practical alternatives to this process have been discussed, such, for example, as the reaction between $_3Li^7$ and $_1H^1$ to give $2\,_2He^4$, shown on page 421. Tritium, $_1H^3$, and its possible union with hydrogen, $_1H^1$, also figures prominently in these discussions.

Peacetime uses of atomic energy. Vast new fields have been opened by the advent of atomic energy, which are only just beginning to be explored. The heat released by an atomic pile constitutes a potent source of energy. Already at Harwell, England, an eighty office building is being heated by a nearby pile. An atomic powered submarine, currently under construction, is expected to be completed this year. Other obvious applications would include the propulsion of large airplanes or the generation of electricity in areas of the country isolated from other power sources. In all such installations, the use of considerable heavy and bulky shielding is required to protect personnel from radiation. Such small-scale applications as atomic-powered automobiles do not, therefore, look very promising at present.

The use of atomic piles has made possible the preparation of artificial radioactive isotopes in amounts hitherto unimagined. A pile at the Oak Ridge National Laboratory is now given over to this exclusive purpose. The isotopes are derived from two sources: (1) direct uranium fission products, separated and chemically purified, and (2) neutron irradiation in the pile of various target materials. The latter source is by far the most important at present. Since the war, over twenty thousand isotope shipments have been made from Oak Ridge and the rate of use is constantly increasing.

These isotopes are finding application as "tracers" in medicine, scientific research, industrial research, and industrial control. The isotope, I^{131}, is being very extensively used in the medical treatment of hyperthyroidism. Radioactive iodine administered to the patient tends to concentrate in the thyroid gland and provide radiation therapy right at the location of the trouble by virtue of its high energy gamma rays. Cobalt-60, also a gamma emitter, of 5.3 year half-life, is currently being much used as a very, very much cheaper substitute for radium, both in medicine and industry. Cobalt sources equivalent to many grams of radium may be used for radiation therapy or in-dustrially, for "X-raying" metal castings to check for flaws.

Representative of the extensive use of tracers in scientific research, is the application of the 5000 year half-life isotope of carbon, C^{14}, to the study of photosynthesis. Photosynthesis is the process in which green plants utilize the energy of sunlight to convert CO_2 (from the air) and H_2O into living material. Its mechanism has long baffled scientists. By allowing plants to photosynthesize for a time in an atmosphere containing $C^{14}O_2$, and then carrying out chemical separations on the plant material, it is possible to find which compounds contain radio-carbon, to ascertain the chemical nature of the various initial com-pounds formed, and thus to block out the individual chemical steps in the photosynthetic process. In experiments of this sort, for example, it was early shown that no radioactive formaldehyde, HCHO, was formed, and therefore that this is not a primary photosynthetic product as was once thought. Biochemists are using C^{14} and P^{32} in the study of body chemistry.

The use of isotopes in industry is only just getting started, but will unquestionably increase tremendously in the years ahead.

TRANSURANIUM ELEMENTS

Neptunium, $_{93}Np^{239}$, and plutonium, $_{94}Pu^{239}$, are artificially produced elements above uranium in atomic number. Several isotopes of each of these elements have now been prepared. These elements were discovered in connection with neutron capture by uranium and subsequent beta emissions (see diagram, p. 427):

$$_{92}U^{238} + _{0}n^1 \longrightarrow _{92}U^{239}$$
$$\downarrow$$
$$_{93}Np^{239} + \text{electron}$$
$$\downarrow$$
$$_{94}Pu^{239} + \text{electron}$$

$_{93}Np^{239}$ has a half-life of but 2.3 days and on its beta particle ejection forms $_{94}Pu^{239}$, which is quite stable with a half-life of 2.4×10^4 years. An isotope of neptunium of much longer half-life may be prepared.

$$_{92}U^{238} + _{1}d^2 \longrightarrow _{93}Np^{237} + 3 _{0}n^1$$

Neptunium shows valences of 6, 5, 4, and 3.

The chemical properties of plutonium were originally studied by *tracer technique*. To explain the nature of tracer technique assume that a very small quantity of plutonium ions is mixed with several other metal ions in solution. A quantitative scheme of analysis involving precipitations and separations is carried out. The minute amount of plutonium may be followed through the various chemical separations due to its radioactivity, and its chemistry is then likened to that of the metal ions it follows. Solutions of plutonium ion as dilute as $10^{-8}M$ may be treated by such tracer technique, and in this manner much of the chemistry of the element has been worked out. Plutonium is now available in pound quantities for current investigations of it and its compounds, and tracer technique or microchemistry is not as important for it as for some other scarce elements or isotopes. Plutonium may exhibit valences of 6, 5, 4, and 3 in various compounds.

Experimental endeavor to make still higher atomic number atoms has met with some success. Bombardment of U^{238} and Pu^{239} with very high-energy helium ions in the cyclotron has produced isotopes of elements of atomic numbers 95 and 96. Names for these new elements, respectively, are *americium*, symbol Am, and *curium*, symbol Cm.

$$_{92}U^{238} + _{2}He^4 \longrightarrow _{94}Pu^{241} + _{0}n^1$$
$$_{94}Pu^{241} \longrightarrow e + _{95}Am^{241} \text{ (500 year half-life)}$$
$$_{94}Pu^{239} + _{2}He^4 \longrightarrow _{0}n^1 + _{96}Cm^{242} \text{ (5 mo. half-life)}$$

Recently, researchers at the University of California by somewhat similar nuclear reactions have made trace quantities of elements *berkelium*, $_{97}Bk^{245}$, and *californium*, $_{98}Cf^{246}$. The properties of the elements and their compounds are being studied. They are, of course, in the realm of very radioactive elements.

The chemistry of all these transuranium elements is being studied by tracer technique and is subject to the following speculation. In considering atomic structure and periodic table placement of elements it is to be noted that the "rare earths" which follow lanthanum, atomic number 57, are a peculiar part of a transition group of elements, in which the 4th orbit is building up from 18 to 32 electrons (p. 35). It follows, by analogy, that beginning with actinium, atomic number 89, a second instance of a group of elements filling up (in whole or part) an inner orbit may occur, namely orbit 5. There is definite experimental evidence that transuranium elements have a characteristic valence of 3 and thus are a part of what may be called a "rare rare-earth" group, or "actinide" series.

ENERGY OF THE SUN

The source of the energy that the sun has dissipated over many many millions of years, and of the heat to maintain its estimated millions of degrees of internal temperature has long been the subject of conjecture. Chemical changes, involving mere electron interchange, cannot account for solar energy. It has been postulated that some hydrogen to helium nuclear reaction produces the sun's energy. Much as the mechanism of catalysis is sometimes explained by intermediate compound formation and step chemical changes, it has been theorized that the following chain of nuclear changes may be involved in hydrogen to helium formation in which C^{12} acts as a catalyst.

$$_6C^{12} + _1H^1 \longrightarrow _7N^{13} + \text{energy}$$
$$_7N^{13} \longrightarrow _6C^{13} + e^+ + \text{neutrino}$$
$$_6C^{13} + _1H^1 \longrightarrow _7N^{14} + \text{radiation}$$
$$_7N^{14} + _1H^1 \longrightarrow _8O^{15} + \text{radiation}$$
$$_8O^{15} \longrightarrow _7N^{15} + e^+ + \text{neutrino}$$
$$_7N^{15} + _1H^1 \longrightarrow _6C^{12} + _2He^4$$

Summing and canceling leaves

$$4\,H^1 \longrightarrow _2He^4 + \text{energy equal to 29 mev.}$$

The matter of possible stepwise nuclear changes may have significance in man's endeavor to increase his energy sources.

Astronomical evidence indicates that protons are much more abundant than any other nuclear particle in stars. A part of the energy of the sun is ascribed to proton union to form deuterons:

$$_1H^1 + {_1H^1} \longrightarrow {_1D^2} + e^+$$

EXERCISES

1. What is the essential difference between the loss of an electron from a radioactive substance and loss of an electron by ionization?
2. Diagram the changes taking place in the nucleus of the uranium atom in its series of disintegrations to finally produce radium G.
3. How does artificial radioactivity differ from natural radioactivity?
4. With reference to the discovery of the fission of U^{235} discuss:
   (a) Implications of the discovery.
   (b) Difference between "fission" and "atom smashing experiments before 1939."
   (c) The basic principle involved in the release of atomic energy.
   (d) Subsequent discovery of fissionable materials.
   (e) Possible peacetime applications.
5. Discuss as briefly as you can the structural design of the uranium pile. Include necessary components and function of each. Explain briefly how the pile operates.

In questions 6 to 12 select the true statement (one or more may be correct).

6. (a) RaB is not radioactive.
   (b) RaB and RaD are isotopes.
   (c) RaD and RaE are isotopes.
   (d) U_{x_1} and Io are isotopes.
   (e) RaB and RaG are isotopes.
7. (a) The atomic number of U_I and U_{II} is 92.
   (b) U_I and U_{II} are isotopes.
   (c) RaG is radioactive.
   (d) Chemically, Rn is a very active element.
   (e) Ra forms the compound RaCl.
8. (a) RaA and Ra B have the same atomic weights.
   (b) RaA and Ra B have the same atomic numbers.
   (c) RaG has an atomic weight of 206.
   (d) RaD has an atomic weight of 212.
   (e) RaC' has an atomic weight of 238.
9. (a) The expulsion of an alpha particle from a nucleus results in a decrease in atomic weight but not in atomic number.
   (b) The expulsion of a beta particle results in an increase of atomic weight.
   (c) Radioactive disintegration is accompanied by evolution of rays of very short wave length.
   (d) Increase of temperature speeds up the rate of disintegration.
   (e) Speed of radioactive disintegration is not affected by changes in temperature or pressure.
10. (a) Rn would be similar in properties to neon.
    (b) Atomic weight of Io is 230.

(c) Atomic weight of U_{z_1} is 230.

(d) Ra F is produced by expulsion of a beta particle from Ra G.

(e) Ra is similar in properties to Al.

11. Fission of U^{235} takes place when:

(a) ordinary uranium loses an alpha particle.

(b) U^{235} loses an electron from the nucleus.

(c) U^{235} ionizes.

(d) U^{235} is bombarded by neutrons.

(e) U^{235} absorbs a neutron.

12. The absorption of a neutron by U^{238} and subsequent expulsion of a beta particle results in:

(a) formation of Np.

(b) fission.

(c) formation of Pu.

(d) formation of an isotope of U.

(e) ionization.

13. Consider the radioactive decay of $_{90}Th^{234}$. This isotope loses a β particle to produce element X, which in turn loses a β particle to produce element Y, which then loses an α particle to produce element Z. Complete the table.

Element	At. Wt. (Isotopic Weight)	Atomic Number
Th	234	90
$\downarrow \beta$		
X	——	——
$\downarrow \beta$		
Y	——	——
$\downarrow \alpha$		
Z	——	——

14. An isotope has a half life of 1 year. Starting with 96 grams, 3 grams will be present after 5 years. How much will be present at the end of the 6th year?

Ans. 1.5 g.

15. Considering the neutron-proton ratio, for each of the following pairs of isotopes, select the member of each pair you would expect to be stable; (a) $_{10}A^{20}$, $_{10}A^{30}$; (b) $_4B^9$, $_4B^5$; (c) $_{80}Hg^{200}$, $_{80}Hg^{160}$.

16. A radioactive isotope has a half life of 1 day. Starting with 6400 atoms, how many atoms of the original would be left after 1 week (7 days)?

Ans. 50.

17. Suppose a man had stored away 4.52 g. of radium in the year 1900. Assuming the half life of radium to be 1700 years, what weight of radium would be left in the year 3600? Approximately what weight of lead would be left? of other products?

18. Calculate in mev (million electron volts) the energy which would be released in the following process:

$$4_1H^1 \longrightarrow {}_2He^4 + energy$$

A decrease in mass of 1.0000 atomic mass unit corresponds to an energy release of 931 million electron volts. Take the masses involved as $_1H^1 = 1.008123$ and $_2He^4 = 4.00390$.

19. Complete the following equations for radioactive decay processes:

(a) $_6C^{11} \longrightarrow {}_5B^{11} + \underline{\hspace{1cm}}$

(b) $_{11}Na^{24} \longrightarrow \underline{\hspace{1cm}} + \beta^-$

(c) $_{90}Th^{232} \longrightarrow {}_{88}Ra^{228} + \underline{\hspace{1cm}}$

(d) $_{16}S^{35} \longrightarrow {}_{17}Cl^{35} + \underline{\hspace{1cm}}$

(e) $_8O^{15} \longrightarrow \underline{\hspace{1cm}} + \beta^+$

(f) $_{94}Pu^{239} \longrightarrow \underline{\hspace{1cm}} + \alpha$

20. Complete the following equations for nuclear bombardment reactions:

(a) $_7N^{14} + {}_0n^1 \longrightarrow {}_6C^{14} + \underline{\hspace{1cm}}$

(b) $_{17}Cl^{37} + {}_0n^1 \longrightarrow \underline{\hspace{1cm}} + \gamma$

(c) $_{15}P^{31} + {}_1H^2 \longrightarrow {}_{15}P^{32} + \underline{\hspace{1cm}}$

(d) $_{24}Cr^{50} + {}_1H^2 \longrightarrow \underline{\hspace{1cm}} + {}_0n^1$

(e) $_{25}Mn^{55} + {}_0n^1 \longrightarrow \underline{\hspace{1cm}} + 2\,{}_0n^1$

(f) $_{29}Cu^{63} + {}_2He^4 \longrightarrow {}_{31}Ga^{66} + \underline{\hspace{1cm}}$

(g) $_{94}Pu^{239} + {}_2He^4 \longrightarrow {}_{96}Cm^{241} + \underline{\hspace{1cm}}$

(h) $_{92}U^{233} + {}_0n^1 \longrightarrow {}_{57}La^{144} + \underline{\hspace{1cm}} + 3\,{}_0n^1$

REFERENCES

"Plutonium Project, Nuclei Formed in Fission," *J. Am. Chem. Soc.* **49**, 2411–42 (1946).

E. R. Rutherford, James Chadwick, and C. D. Ellis, *Radiations from Radioactive Substances*, Macmillan.

Wm. Q. Hull, "The Transuranium Elements," *Chem. & Eng. News* **30**, 232 (1952).

G. T. Seaborg, "The Impact of Nuclear Chemistry," "The Heavy Elements" *ibid.* **24**, 1192 (1946).

H. D. Smyth, *Atomic Energy for Military Purposes*, Princeton, 1945.

G. Friedlander and J. W. Kennedy, *Introduction to Radiochemistry*, Wiley, 1949.

E. C. Pollard and W. L. Davidson, *Applied Nuclear Physics*, 2d ed., Wiley.

A. C. Wahl and N. A. Bonner, *Radioactivity Applied to Chemistry*, Wiley, 1951.

O. Hahn, *New Atoms*, Elsevier Publishing Company, 1950.

S. Glasstone, *Sourcebook of Atomic Energy*, Van Nostrand, 1951.

E. V. Condon, "Physics Gives Us — Nuclear Engineering," *Westinghouse Engineer*, Nov. (1945).

W. E. Shoupp, "The Structure of the Nucleus," *ibid.* July (1946).

—— and Hugh Odishaw, "Nuclear Reactions," *ibid.* Nov. (1946).

—— and J. W. Coltman, "The Big Guns of Nuclear Physics," *ibid.* May (1947).

Frederick Seitz, Jr., "The Relation Between Energy and Mass," *ibid.* March (1946).

C. F. Wagner and J. A. Hutcheson, "Nuclear Energy Potentialities," *ibid.* July (1946).

K. K. Darrow, "Nuclear Chemistry," *J. Chem. Ed.* **12**, 76 (1935).

Maxwell L. Eidinoff, "Uranium Fission," *ibid.* **23**, 60 (1946).

——, "The Search for Tritium — The Hydrogen Isotope of Mass Three," *ibid.* **25**, 31 (1948).

George A. Scherer, "A General Chemistry Experiment in Radioactivity," *ibid.* **26**, 111 (1949).

I. Perlman, "Atomic Energy in Industry," *ibid.* **24**, 115 (1947).

——, "The Transuranium Elements and Nuclear Chemistry," *ibid.* **25**, 273 (1948).

S. K. Love, "Natural Radioactivity of Water," *Ind. & Eng. Chem.* **43**, 1541 (1951).

XXXII

Electrochemistry

Electrochemistry is that division of chemistry which deals with (1) the use of the electric current in bringing about chemical changes and (2) the generation of an electric current by means of a chemical change. In recent years applied electrochemistry has played an increasingly important role in the manufacture of many industrial products. To cite just a few — hydrogen and oxygen may be produced by electrolysis of water; electrolysis of an aqueous solution of sodium chloride yields hydrogen, sodium hydroxide, and chlorine; many metals are purified by electrodeposition; aluminum and the alkaline earth metals are produced by electrolysis of nonaqueous solutions of their respective compounds.

Conduction of the electric current. The electric current may be carried by either of two types of conductors: (1) a metallic conductor such as a piece of copper wire, or (2) a solution of an electrolyte, *e.g.*, a solution of sodium chloride in water. (1) is called a conductor of the *first class*, and (2) a conductor of the *second class*. In a conductor of the first class, electricity is carried simply by a movement of electrons through the metal, while in a conductor of the second class, the current is carried by the ions in solution moving toward the electrodes of opposite charge. In the latter case since an ion is a charged particle of matter, the passage of current involves the transport of matter, which is an essential difference from conduction in metals.

Electrolysis. This process consists of passing a direct current through a solution of an electrolyte between two electrodes where chemical changes take place. Consider the electrolysis of aqueous hydrogen chloride (hydrochloric acid). Principal ions in the solution are H_3O^+ and Cl^-. Chloride ions (anions) move toward the anode where they give up their electrons. These electrons move through the metallic conductor and through the battery or generator of the electric current to the cathode where hydronium ions (cations) are discharged by taking up these electrons. The battery or generator may be considered as simply a device for moving electrons from one electrode to the other. Since the above process involves the transfer of electrons the chemical change occurring must be one of oxidation-reduction. At the anode electrons are given up by anions; hence *oxidation takes place at the anode;* at the cathode electrons are taken up by cations; hence *reduction takes place at the cathode.*

Electrical units. When an electric current passes through a conductor (first or second class), a certain *resistance* to the passage of the

Fig. 122. Tank room in an electrolytic refinery.

current is offered, which depends upon the nature of the conductor. The greater the resistance of a conductor, the poorer the conductance, *e.g.*, water offers a high resistance to the passage of current and is therefore classed as a poor conductor; hydrochloric acid has a low resistance and is classed as a good conductor. The unit of electrical resistance is the *ohm*, which is defined as the resistance of a column of mercury 106.3 cm. long, weighing 14.4521 g. and of uniform cross section. The unit of current is the *ampere* defined as that current necessary to deposit .001118 g. of silver in one second from a solution containing silver ions. The unit quantity of electricity is the *coulomb*, defined as a current of one ampere flowing for one second, *i.e.*, ampere-second.

In order that a current may pass from one point to another through a conductor, a *difference of potential* or *electromotive force* must exist.

Just as water will flow only from a higher to a lower level, so the electrical current will pass only from a region of high potential to one of lower potential. The unit of electrical potential or electromotive force is the *volt*, defined as that potential which will drive a current of one ampere through a resistance of one ohm.

Faraday's laws. In 1833, Michael Faraday, an English scientist, discovered that during electrolysis (1) *the quantities of substances produced at the electrodes are directly proportional to the quantity of electricity passing through the solution,* and (2) when a given quantity of electricity is passed through solutions of several electrolytes, *the weights of substances formed at the electrodes are directly proportional to their equivalent weights* (atomic weight divided by valence). The quantity of elec-

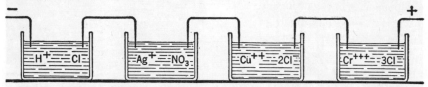

Fig. 123. One equivalent of an element is deposited for each faraday of electricity passed through the solution.

tricity required to liberate one equivalent of an element was found to be 96,500 coulombs, and in honor of Faraday, has been termed a *faraday*. If one faraday is passed through a series of solutions such as shown in Figure 123, one equivalent of substance is liberated at each electrode, *i.e.*, 1 g. of hydrogen, 107.88 g. of silver, $\frac{63.57}{2} = 31.78$ g. of copper, and $\frac{52.01}{3} = 17.34$ g. of chromium.

Voltaic cells. The fact that the electric current may bring about a chemical change might well lead to the question: Can the process be reversed — can the electric current be generated from a chemical reaction? We shall find that the answer is yes, providing certain conditions are fulfilled in carrying out the reaction.

Chemical changes are always attended by energy changes. Usually this energy is manifest in the form of heat and light. In order to produce an electrical current, chemical energy must be transformed not to heat and light energy, but to electrical energy. As is the case in electrolysis, electrons must be transferred, and therefore the reaction must be one of oxidation-reduction. Consider the reaction occurring when a strip of metallic zinc is dipped into a solution of cupric sulfate; zinc goes into solution as zinc ion (since zinc is more active than copper), and metallic copper is formed. The process may be represented by the equation

$$Cu^{++} + Zn \longrightarrow Cu + Zn^{++}$$

or by the two reactions

$$Zn \longrightarrow Zn^{++} + 2\ e \text{ (oxidation)}$$
$$Cu^{++} + 2\ e \longrightarrow Cu \text{ (reduction)}$$

Electrons are transferred directly from zinc to copper ions. This reaction is exothermic and heat energy is released which is absorbed by the solution and container. No electric current has been generated in this case, but if the oxidation and reduction reactions above could be made to take place at *different points* in the solution, and the transfer of electrons were made through a metallic conductor, then at least a part of the chemical energy would be transformed into electrical energy. Thus, if we set up an arrangement as shown in Figure 124 in which metallic zinc is in contact with its ions, and at another point a strip of copper is in contact with

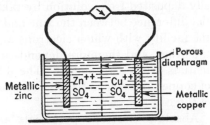

Fig. 124. **The Daniell cell. Electrons flow from the Zn electrode to the Cu electrode, thus generating an electric current.**

copper ions, an electric current is generated by the flow of electrons through the wire which connects the two metals outside the solution. This will be indicated by a deflection of the needle of the voltmeter connected in series between the two electrodes. A porous diaphragm serves to prevent mixing of the solutions of zinc and copper ions but allows the passage of the SO_4^{--} under the influence of the current.

In order to generate an electric current, it is necessary, then, that the reaction be one of *oxidation-reduction*, and furthermore, *these two processes must be made to take place at different points in a solution.*

Electrode potentials. When a metal is placed in contact with water, the metal shows a tendency to pass into solution to produce ions of the metal and consequent liberation of electrons to the metal surface. This tendency of a metal to lose electrons sets up an electrical potential difference between the metal and the solution, and the resulting voltage is termed the *electrode potential* for that particular metal. As ions of the metal are formed, the reverse of the above process, that is, the deposition of metal from ions occurs, and eventually an equilibrium exists between the metal and its ions.

If a metal is placed in contact with its ions and the tendency of the ions to deposit out is greater than the tendency of the metal to pass into solution, then the former process takes place until equilibrium between metal and ions has been established. The potential difference between a metal and a solution of its ions at a concentration of 1 molar is termed the *standard electrode potential* and is designated as E^0. The tendency for different metals to form ions and give electrons varies widely, and therefore the electrode potentials of metals vary greatly. In the cell described above, if the concentrations of Zn^{++} and Cu^{++} are fixed at 1 molar, zinc shows a much greater tendency than copper to produce ions in solution; thus electrons flow through the wire from the zinc electrode to the copper electrode. There, copper ions are actually deposited from solution by taking up these electrons. The potential difference between the zinc and copper electrodes will depend upon the facility with which electrons are transferred from one electrode to the other, and therefore depends upon the difference in electrode potentials of the two metals. The difference in the electrode potentials of copper and zinc is 1.1068 volts, and consequently that is the voltage of the cell.

Absolute electrode potentials are not readily determined as the potential difference between a metal and a solution of its ions cannot be recorded on a voltmeter directly. However, if the metal and its solution are made one half of a cell in which the other half is likewise made up of a metal and a solution of its ions, then the potential difference of the two half cells can be measured and a relative value or relative potential may be assigned. Thus in the zinc and copper cell above, while we do not know the absolute potential difference of either of the half cells, or *couples* i.e., $Zn \longrightarrow Zn^{++}$ and $Cu \longrightarrow Cu^{++}$, the relative potential of one to the other can be said to be 1.1068 volts.

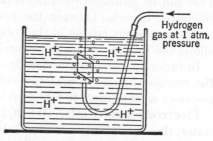

Fig. 125. The hydrogen electrode.

In order to arrive at a working system of electrode potentials, all values are referred to a standard electrode — the hydrogen electrode, which has been assigned the arbitrary value of zero potential. The electrode (Fig. 125) consists of a piece of platinum foil which has been coated with a spongy deposit of platinum black in contact with a solution containing hydrogen ions of a concentration of 1 molar. Hydrogen gas at one atmosphere pressure is bubbled over the platinum electrode, setting up the equilibrium:

$$H_2 \rightleftharpoons 2H^+ + 2e \qquad E^0 = 0$$

By setting up a cell using this hydrogen half cell in conjunction with a half cell composed of a metal and its ions at a concentration of 1 molar, the relative potential of the latter referred to the standard can be directly measured. Thus if the cell indicated in Figure 126 is set up, the voltage is 0.762, and since zinc gives up electrons more easily than does hydrogen, the standard potential of the Zn–Zn^{++} electrode is recorded as +.762. The electrode potential of Cu–Cu^{++} may be determined in a similar manner. Since in the cell reaction, hydrogen gives up electrons to form H$^+$, and Cu^{++} takes up these electorns, copper gives up electrons less readily than hydrogen and the voltage of the Cu–Cu^{++} couple is recorded as −.3448.

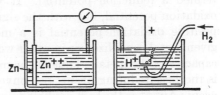

Fig. 126. The voltage of the cell is .762 volt. Since E^0 for the hydrogen electrode is arbitrarily taken as 0, the E^0 for the zinc electrode must be +.762.

By combining the two half cells Zn–Zn^{++} and Cu–Cu^{++}, it is evident that the potential difference of such a cell should be .762 − (−.3448) = 1.1068 volts.

Standard electrode potentials of several of the common metals are given in Table 34.

TABLE 34

STANDARD ELECTRODE POTENTIALS

HALF-CELL RECTION	E^0
K $\rightleftharpoons$ K$^+$ + e	+2.92
Na $\rightleftharpoons$ Na$^+$ + e	+2.71
Mg $\rightleftharpoons$ Mg^{++} + 2 e	+2.34
Al $\rightleftharpoons$ Al^{+++} + 3 e	+1.67
Zn $\rightleftharpoons$ Zn^{++} + 2 e	+0.762
Fe $\rightleftharpoons$ Fe^{++} + 2 e	+0.44
Sn $\rightleftharpoons$ Sn^{++} + 2 e	+0.25
Pb $\rightleftharpoons$ Pb^{++} + 2 e	+0.126
H$_2$ $\rightleftharpoons$ 2 H$^+$ + 2 e	0.0
Cu $\rightleftharpoons$ Cu^{++} + 2 e	−0.3448
Ag $\rightleftharpoons$ Ag$^+$ + e	−0.7995
Pt $\rightleftharpoons$ Pt^{++} + 2 e	−1.2
Au $\rightleftharpoons$ Au^{+++} + 3 e	−1.42

It may be noted that the metals in this electromotive series are in the same order as in the activity series (see p. 93). It is evident, then, that the activity of a metal is a measure of its ability to lose electrons. We may note also from Table 34 that the half reactions as written to give up electrons are oxidation reactions. The electrode potentials are sometimes referred to as *oxidation potentials*. If the half reaction is written as a reduction (electrons taken up) then the potential may be termed a reduction potential. It will have the same value as the oxidation potential, but with the sign reversed. The magnitude of the positive oxidation potential is a measure of the ease with which a given metal is oxidized or in other words it is a measure of the reducing capacity of the metal. Thus of the metals listed in Table 34, potassium is the best reducing agent, or conversely K^+ is the poorest oxidizing agent; Au^{+++} is the best oxidizing agent and Au is the poorest reducing agent. Reducing ability decreases on the left side and oxidizing ability increases on the right side (for the ions) in going from top to bottom of the table. It follows that any metallic ion in the table should oxidize any of the metals appearing above it in the series, thus Zn^{++} should oxidize Mg but not Cu; Cu^{++} will oxidize Zn but not Ag.

This same information can be derived in another way by combining couples, writing down the cell reaction and considering the voltage of the cell. If the potential of the cell is positive, then the reaction (cell reaction) will proceed as written. Consider the reaction

$$Pb^{++} + Zn \longrightarrow Pb + Zn^{++}$$

involving the couples $Zn \longrightarrow Zn^{++}$ and $Pb^{++} \longrightarrow Pb$. The potential of the first couple is .762, that of the second is .126. Since in the above reaction Pb^{++} will accept electrons rather than Pb giving up electrons (reduction), the sign of the potential will be reversed and given the value $-.126$

$$Zn \longrightarrow Zn^{++} + 2e \quad E^0 = \quad .762 \text{ (oxidation)}$$
$$2e + Pb^{++} \longrightarrow Pb \quad E^0 = -.126 \text{ (reduction)}$$

Adding the two steps to obtain the cell reaction:

$$Zn + Pb^{++} \longrightarrow Zn^{++} + Pb \quad E_{cell} = +.636$$

Since the potential for the cell is positive, the reaction will proceed as written, that is, Pb^{++} will oxidize Zn.

Consider a second example: Will Ag^+ oxidize Au? In other words will the following reaction occur?

$$Au + 3 Ag^+ \longrightarrow Au^{+++} + 3 Ag$$

Setting up the two half reactions, one the oxidation, the other reduction:

$$Au \longrightarrow Au^{+++} + 3e \quad E^0 = -1.42 \quad \text{(oxidation)}$$
$$3e + 3 Ag^+ \longrightarrow 3 Ag \quad E^0 = \quad .7995 \text{ (reduction)}$$

The latter potential is positive because the step is reduction (the table gives oxidation potentials). The fact that 3 electrons are involved in balancing does not change the potential. Adding the two steps, we obtain

$$Au + 3\,Ag^+ \longrightarrow Au^{+++} + 3\,Ag \quad E_{cell} = -.6305$$

The negative value for the voltage of the cell indicates that the reaction will *not* proceed as written. The reverse change will take place.

While a further discussion of oxidation potentials is beyond the scope of this book, the student will be interested to learn that oxidation potentials may be determined for most oxidation processes. This information proves invaluable in predicting whether or not a given reaction is possible. Exactly the same process as outlined above may be employed: if the potential of a cell (which may be a hypothetical one) is positive, then the reaction may proceed as written. Of course, concentration effects are important factors in determination of oxidation potentials and in some cases where the oxidation potentials are nearly the same, these effects may serve to reverse the effect which one might predict on the basis of the standard electrode potentials (which are for 1 molar solutions of the ions).

The dry cell. For small intermittent currents (flashlights, door bells, etc.) the dry cell is convenient and effective (see Fig. 127). The cell consists of a zinc container which acts as the negative electrode; a graphite rod as the positive electrode, and a paste of ammonium chloride, zinc chloride, manganese dioxide, with water as the electrolyte. To prevent evaporation of water, the top of the cell is sealed with wax. The cell is not really dry although the substances are present in a semisolid (paste) state. At the negative electrode, Zn passes into solution as Zn^{++}, giving up electrons to the electrode:

$$Zn \longrightarrow Zn^{++} + 2\,e$$

At the carbon electrode (positive pole) ammonium ion is converted into ammonia and hydrogen by taking up electrons:

$$2\,e + 2\,NH_4^+ \longrightarrow 2\,NH_3 + H_2$$

The products of the latter reaction are gases and it is necessary that these gases be removed since their accumulation would result in a swelling and eventual bursting of the cell. Ammonia gas is absorbed by the zinc ions present, forming the complex $Zn(NH_3)_4^{++}$ ion:

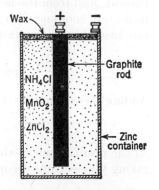

Fig. 127. The dry cell.

$$Zn^{++} + 4\,NH_3 \longrightarrow Zn(NH_3)_4{}^{++}$$

Hydrogen gas formed at the carbon electrode tends to remain in contact with the electrode. An accumulation of the gas forms an insulating layer which increases the resistance of the cell, thereby reducing the voltage of the cell. Such a cell is said to be *polarized*. The function of the manganese dioxide is as a *depolarizer* since it oxidizes the hydrogen to water by the reaction:

$$MnO_2 + H_2 \longrightarrow MnO + H_2O$$

In the event that current is drawn from a dry cell continuously, the voltage soon drops to zero because of the accumulation of hydrogen gas on the carbon electrode. When allowed to stand for a brief period, the hydrogen is slowly oxidized by the manganese dioxide and the voltage of the cell rises to the normal value, which for the dry cell is 1.5 volts.

The storage battery. The storage battery is a cell which after discharge can be restored to its original state by passage of a direct electric current from an outside source through the cell. Theoretically the reaction which takes place in any cell producing an electric current may be reversed by passing an electric current through the cell in the opposite direction. Practically, this cannot be done with most cells; a storage cell is one in which a cell reaction may be carried out *reversibly*.

The lead storage battery is the most common of this type. The electrodes consist of plates or grids arranged in pairs; the negative electrode is a sheet of pure lead and the positive pole a framework of lead in which lead dioxide has been deposited. The electrolyte is sulfuric acid. When the cell is discharging, *i.e.*, producing an electric current, lead from the negative electrode produces lead ions which immediately combine with sulfate ions from the sulfuric acid to precipitate insoluble lead sulfate:

$$Pb \longrightarrow Pb^{++} + 2\,e$$
$$Pb^{++} + SO_4{}^{--} \longrightarrow PbSO_4 \downarrow$$

Adding these reactions, the net reaction at the negative pole would be

$$Pb + SO_4{}^{--} \longrightarrow PbSO_4 \downarrow + 2\,e$$

At the positive pole of the battery, lead dioxide is reduced to Pb^{++} by taking up electrons according to the equation

$$2\,e + PbO_2 + 4\,H^+ \longrightarrow Pb^{++} + 2\,H_2O$$

Lead ion immediately combines with sulfate ion to precipitate lead sulfate:

$$Pb^{++} + SO_4^{--} \longrightarrow PbSO_4 \downarrow$$

The net reaction at the positive pole would then be

$$2\,e + PbO_2 + 4\,H^+ + SO_4^{--} \longrightarrow PbSO_4 \downarrow + 2\,H_2O$$

Now the sum of the reactions taking place at the two electrodes would give as the over-all reaction taking place during *discharge* of the battery:

$$Pb + PbO_2 + 2\,H_2SO_4 \longrightarrow 2\,PbSO_4 \downarrow + 2\,H_2O$$

During *charge* of the battery this reaction is reversed:

$$2\,PbSO_4 + 2\,H_2O \longrightarrow Pb + PbO_2 + 2\,H_2SO_4$$

It should be evident from the above reactions that during discharge the concentration of sulfuric acid in the cell decreases, while during charge the sulfuric acid is regenerated and its concentration in the cell thereby increased. The state of charge of a battery may be approximately determined by means of a hydrometer which gives the specific gravity of the acid. In a fully charged battery the specific gravity of the acid is about 1.20. The voltage of the lead storage cell is about two volts. For automobile batteries, usually three of these cells are used in series which gives a total potential of six volts.

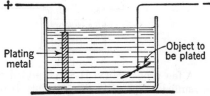

Fig. 128. **A spoon may be silver plated by making it the cathode in a cell in which a bar of pure silver acts as anode. A NaAg(CN)$_2$ solution makes a good electrolyte.**

Electroplating. Very often, in order to prevent a metal from corroding or to give it a more pleasing appearance, a second metal may be coated over it. This is most effectively accomplished electrolytically. The metal object which is to be coated or plated is made the cathode in an electrolytic cell (Fig. 128). The anode usually consists of a strip of the plating metal dipping into the electrolyte. As the current is passed through the cell, the plating metal dissolves at the anode and the ions thus produced migrate to the cathode where they are discharged and plated out upon the object. Any desired thickness of deposit may be obtained. If one metal does not adhere well to another, a series of platings may be necessary. Thus, an auto bumper may be first plated with copper, then with nickel, and finally with chromium.

EXERCISES

1. What is the difference between conductors of the first and second classes?

2. Calculate the quantity of electricity in coulombs necessary to deposit 15.89 g. of copper from a solution of $CuSO_4$.   Ans. 48,250 coulombs.

3. What are the necessary conditions which must be fulfilled to obtain electrical energy from chemical energy?

4. From the table of standard electrode potentials (p. 441) determine the electromotive force of the following cells:

    (a) Zn, Zn^{++} and Pb^{++}, Pb   (c) Al, Al^{+++} and Fe^{++}, Fe

    (b) Cu, Cu^{++} and Ag^+, Ag   (d) H_2, H^+ and Mg^{++}, Mg

5. Define the terms: ohm, volt, coulomb, ampere, faraday, depolarizer.

6. Write equations for reactions taking place at the electrodes during

    (a) Electrolysis of a solution of copper sulfate with copper electrodes.

    (b) Discharge of a dry cell.

    (c) Discharge of a lead storage cell.

    (d) Electrolysis of aqueous sodium bromide solution.

7. What weight of copper would be deposited from a solution of $CuSO_4$ by the passage of a current of 0.5 ampere for two hours?   Ans. 1.19 g.

8. The two electrolytic cells below are connected in series:

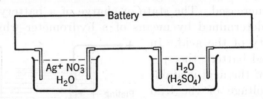

A few drops only of H_2SO_4 is added to the water in the second cell. When a sufficient quantity of electricity is passed through the solutions to deposit 107.9 g. of silver on the cathode of the first cell, what volumes of hydrogen and oxygen at standard conditions would be produced in the second cell?   Ans. 11.2 l.; 5.6 l.

9. According to Faraday's laws, 96,500 coulombs of electricity if passed through suitably constructed electrolytic cells would produce what weight of each of the following: atomic weights are in parenthesis. (a) hydrogen (1), (b) silver (107.9), (c) copper (63.5), (d) aluminum (27)?

10. The same amount of electricity which deposits 0.415 g. of silver will deposit 0.254 g. of gold from a solution. What is the equivalent weight of gold?   Ans. 65.7.

REFERENCES

H. J. Creighton and W. A. Koehler, *Electrochemistry*, Wiley.

Colin G. Fink, "Fundamentals in Applied Electrochemistry," *J. Chem. Ed.* **25,** 219 (1948).

Arthur W. Davidson, "A Modern Approach to the Teaching of Electrochemistry," *ibid.* **25,** 533 (1948).

James E. Cassidy, "Storage Batteries," *ibid.* **27,** 63 (1950).

XXXIII

Copper, Silver, Gold

$_{29}$Cu $^{63.6}$ | | | | $^{2\ 8\ 18}$ | | | | | $_{47}$Ag $^{107.9}$ | | | | | $^{2\ 8\ 18\ 18}$ | | | | | | $_{79}$Au $^{197.2}$ | | | | | | $^{2\ 8\ 18\ 32\ 18}$ | | | | | |

METAL	SYMBOL	SP. GR.	MELTING POINT	BOILING POINT	VALENCE
Copper	Cu	8.9	1083	2340	1, 2
Silver	Ag	10.5	961	1950	1
Gold	Au	19.3	1063	2600	1, 3

These three metals appear in division *B* of Group I of the periodic table. A marked contrast in properties is to be observed between the members of divisions *A* and *B* in this group. Metals of division *A* (alkali metals) are very active chemically, while the metals of division *B* are very resistant to chemical action and are near the bottom of the activity series. However, copper, silver, and gold have one electron in the outer structure of their atoms and therefore exhibit a characteristic valence of positive one. Copper and gold also exhibit higher valences, which may be attributed to the transfer of one or more electrons from an inner to the valence orbit.

Copper, silver, and gold were among the first of the chemical elements discovered and used by man, while the alkali metals in division *A* were only recently isolated from their compounds. The occurrence of these elements in the free state accounts for their early use.

COPPER

The use of copper is older than written history. References to it are made in early writings, and objects of copper and bronze have been found dating back to three or four thousand years before the Christian era.

447

Because of its relative inactivity and resistance to corrosion, copper is used extensively in the preparation of a wide variety of articles. The United States is the leading producer, furnishing one-third of the world's supply (Table 35).

TABLE 35

WORLD PRODUCTION OF COPPER IN METRIC TONS

	1945	1949
Canada	198,604	239,149
United States	784,173	682,880
Chile	462,588	367,036
Germany	20,000	—
U.S.S.R.	140,000	200,000
Japan	—	32,741
Belgian Congo	160,200	141,399
Rhodesia	195,600	259,084
Estimated Total Production . .	2,200,000	2,235,000

Occurrence. Copper ores are widely distributed over the earth's surface. Large deposits of native copper are found in the Lake Superior region of Michigan, on the island of Cyprus, and in Bolivia. However, the metal usually occurs in the combined state as sulfides, oxides, or carbonates. Most of the metal produced in this country comes from sulfide minerals, chief of which is *chalcopyrite*, $CuFeS_2$. Another important sulfide mineral is *chalcocite*, Cu_2S. In general, sulfide ores are of low grade, the copper content usually running from 1 to 10 per cent. Oxide and carbonate ores have been formed as a result of the action of dissolved oxygen and carbon dioxide in ground water. *Cuprite*, Cu_2O, a reddish mineral, is found in South America, and *malachite*, $CuCO_3 \cdot Cu(OH)_2$, a green mineral, is found in Arizona. Principal copper-producing localities in the United States are Montana, Arizona, and Utah.

Copper in fairly high percentage has been found in the feathers of certain birds of brilliant plumage. It is interesting that the touraco bird of Africa has quite a high copper content in its feathers, which feathers have the red color of cuprite and the green color of malachite. Traces of copper are found in several sea plants and marine animals. In oysters, it appears that a copper compound is substituted for an iron compound as an oxygen carrier in the hemoglobin of the blood. There is some evidence to indicate that copper in minute amounts may play a vital role in the health and well-being of man and animals. For example, a healthy cow's liver contains between 40 and 200 parts per million of copper.

Metallurgy. In general the metallurgy of copper is quite complex, and the method of treatment depends upon several factors including the type of ore and the facilities for treatment. We shall outline here only the principal types of treatment. Native copper ores require the simplest of the metallurgical processes. The ore, which consists of copper pellets dispersed in silica and rock, is crushed and heated to a temperature sufficient to melt the metal. The metal is heavier than the rock or gangue with which it is associated and settles to the bottom and may be separated. In some cases separation is effected by mechanical means; the lighter particles of silicate rock are floated away by washing the ore with large quantities of water.

Oxide and carbonate ores may be reduced with carbon or mixed with sulfide ores and smelted with the latter. Low grade oxide ores are often leached with sulfuric acid after which the copper sulfate solution is electrolyzed and the copper plated out.

Eighty per cent of the copper produced in this country comes from sulfide ores, most of which are low grade and associated with large quantities of iron pyrites and silica. After the ore is crushed, it is concentrated by gravity and flotation processes (see p. 376). The ore concentrate contains 20 to 50 per cent copper. The ore is next roasted to remove some of the sulfur. Following the roasting process, the ore is smelted in special type reverberatory furnaces with arching roofs to reflect the heat down onto the charge. Limestone is added as a flux to combine with the silica to form a slag of calcium silicate. Some ferrous oxide also combines with silica to form ferrous silicate. A heavy molten layer of a mixture of iron and copper sulfides called "copper matte" remains under the liquid slag. After drawing off the slag, the liquid copper matte is charged into a converter made of steel plates and lined with magnesia. The converter is quite similar to the Bessemer converter used for the production of steel. It is equipped in such a way that a blast of air may be blown through the charge from small holes in the bottom of the converter. The blast of air oxidizes the iron sulfide to the oxide:

$$2\,FeS + 3\,O_2 \longrightarrow 2\,FeO + 2\,SO_2 \uparrow$$

This action takes place before the sulfides of copper are converted to oxide, since iron sulfide is more easily oxidized than copper sulfide. The oxidation process produces enough heat to keep the mass molten and no fuel is necessary. Silica is added to form a slag of ferrous silicate with the iron oxide:

$$FeO + SiO_2 \longrightarrow FeSiO_3$$

The charge in the converter is approximately 65 tons. Removal of the iron requires approximately three hours. The slag is removed at intervals by tilting the converter until oxidation of iron sulfide is complete. The air blast is continued for approximately two hours more and the sulfide of copper is slowly oxidized:

$$2\,Cu_2S + 3\,O_2 \longrightarrow 2\,Cu_2O + 2\,SO_2 \uparrow$$

The oxide thus formed reacts with the sulfide present to form metallic copper:

$$2\,Cu_2O + Cu_2S \longrightarrow 6\,Cu + SO_2$$

In order completely to remove the slag, the metal is treated in a small reverberatory furnace which permits a careful control and skimming off of slag. Traces of copper oxide are removed by stirring the charge with poles made from green saplings. The latter evolve gases which act as reducing agents to change oxide to metallic copper. The product, called "blister copper" because of blisters formed on the surface by the escape of gas, is cast into large blocks or plates for electrolytic refining.

Electrolytic refining of copper. Blister copper is approximately 99 per cent copper, the remaining 1 per cent being made up of gold, silver, arsenic, bismuth, iron, and zinc. Nearly all of the gold and silver present in the original ore is retained by the blister copper, and their recovery from the refining process furnishes approximately one-fourth of the silver and about one-seventh of the gold used for commercial purposes. Arsenic is a particularly objectionable element in copper as it very appreciably lowers the conductivity of the metal. Since large quantities of copper wire are used in the transmission of electric power, it is necessary to remove arsenic from the finished product. Bismuth and iron in the copper make for brittleness.

Blister copper is refined electrolytically by making impure copper the anode in an electrolytic bath with pure copper as the cathode. Reference to Figure 129 will make the operation of the process clear. The copper anode consists of a block of blister copper approximately three feet square and two inches thick. A thin sheet of pure copper is used as the cathode. The electrolyte consists of an aqueous solution of copper

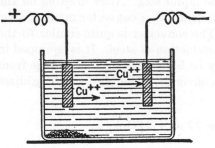

Fig. 129. Electrolytic refining of copper.

sulfate, sulfuric acid, and sodium chloride. On passage of the current, copper dissolves at the anode by giving up two electrons per atom. The resulting copper ions migrate toward the cathode where they are deposited; as a result the copper cathode gradually increases in size as the anode decreases in size. Iron and zinc ions also pass into solution along with the copper at the anode, but by proper regulation of the voltage, these ions are not deposited at the cathode. Silver ions, which are also produced at the anode, are immediately precipitated by chloride ions from the sodium chloride, and the precipitated silver chloride settles to the bottom of the electrolytic tank. Gold, platinum, and arsenic do not go into solution and drop to the bottom of the tank in the form of a sludge called "anode mud." This mud is later refined and the valuable metals recovered. The value of the gold and silver obtained from this sludge is sufficient to pay for the entire cost of the electrolytic refining. The copper plated out on the cathode is 99.95 per cent pure. The cathode copper is remelted and cast into bars for wire rolling mills.

Properties. Copper is a soft metal with a melting point of 1083° and a boiling point of about 2300°. By reflected light it appears red in color, while by transmitted light in thin sheets its color is green. The metal is very ductile and malleable, and while not as tough as iron, it may be used for many structural purposes. It does not respond to heat treatment as does steel, but the addition of small quantities of alloying elements such as manganese and silicon yields a product which may be hardened by heating.

Copper lies low in the activity series and thus is quite resistant to corrosion. Dry air, water, and nonoxidizing acids do not attack the metal. However, long exposure to air and moisture gradually forms a tightly adhering coating of a green basic carbonate on the surface. Corrosion then ceases, in direct contrast to the rusting of iron which in time changes the metal over completely to iron oxide. Hydrochloric acid does not act on copper unless oxygen is present, in which case it gradually dissolves according to the equation:

$$2\,Cu + 4\,HCl + O_2 \longrightarrow 2\,CuCl_2 + 2\,H_2O$$

Nitric acid acts readily on the metal to form copper nitrate, but hydrogen is *not* liberated; instead the other products are oxides of nitrogen and water. Hot concentrated sulfuric acid dissolves the metal to form copper sulfate, sulfur dioxide, and water:

$$Cu + 2\,H_2SO_4 \longrightarrow CuSO_4 + SO_2 + 2\,H_2O$$

Copper is an excellent conductor of heat and is second only to silver as a conductor of electricity.

Uses. Large quantities of copper are used for the fabrication of wire, cables, and bars for transmission of the electric current. The construction of motors, generators, and other electrical devices requires smaller amounts of the metal. Because of its resistance to corrosion, copper may be used as a roofing material and for covering ships' bottoms. Cooking vessels used for cooking food in large quantities may

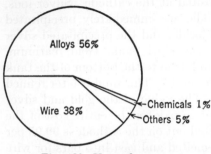

Fig. 130. Uses of copper.

be made of copper. Since copper salts are poisonous, it is necessary to clean the latter frequently to prevent contamination of foods.

One of the principal uses for the metal is in the preparation of alloys. The two most common and important alloys are *brass*, which contains copper and zinc, and *bronze*, which contains copper and tin. Bronze or brass does not refer to alloys of a definite composition but rather to all alloys of copper with zinc and tin in varying percentages. Hundreds of brasses, for example, are listed, all varying somewhat in percentage of zinc and other elements present. A small amount of copper is frequently alloyed with steel as the resistance of the latter to corrosion is greatly increased by as little as 0.25 per cent copper. Copper is also alloyed with gold, silver, and nickel for coinage purposes.

The metal is also used in electrotyping. A wax impression of the type is covered with a layer of graphite to make it an electrical conductor. The carbon coated wax impression is then made the cathode in an electrolytic cell which contains a copper salt as the electrolyte. Passage of the current deposits copper on the impression as a thin layer. This layer of copper is separated from the wax and reinforced by pouring lead or type metal over the back of the plate. Such copper plates may be used for printing a hundred thousand copies.

Compounds of copper. Copper forms two series of compounds, *cuprous* in which the valence of copper is 1, and *cupric* compounds in which the valence is 2. In general the cupric compounds are the more stable and hence the more commonly used.

Cuprous oxide, Cu_2O, occurs naturally as the mineral, *cuprite*. The red oxide may also be obtained by careful oxidation of copper in air or by precipitation of cuprous ions from solutions with sodium or potassium hydroxide. Cuprous hydroxide is not known. Cuprous oxide is also obtained as a reduction product of *Fehling's solution*, a reagent used to test for the presence of reducing sugars in the urine in the diagnosis for diabetes. Fehling's solution consists of an aqueous solution of copper sulfate, sodium hydroxide, and sodium potassium tartrate (Rochelle salt). The tartrate forms a complex with cupric ion and as a result so few free cupric ions are left in solution that no precipitate of copper hydroxide is obtained when the sodium hydroxide is added. Reducing sugars reduce cupric ions to cuprous, and cuprous oxide separates as a reddish precipitate.

Black *cupric oxide* may be obtained by heating copper in air to a fairly high temperature, or by heating cupric hydroxide. The compound is used as an oxidizing agent in the analysis of organic compounds and is also a starting material in the preparation of many copper salts.

The addition of sodium hydroxide to a solution of cupric ions produces a light blue gelatinous precipitate of *cupric hydroxide*. The latter compound is very unstable toward heat, breaking down to cupric oxide. *Bordeaux mixture* consists of copper sulfate and calcium hydroxide. The mixture produces cupric hydroxide and is widely used as a spray and insecticide.

Copper sulfate, or *blue vitriol*, $CuSO_4 \cdot 5 H_2O$, is the most important and widely used salt of copper. On heating, the salt slowly loses water to form first the trihydrate, $CuSO_4 \cdot 3 H_2O$, then the monohydrate, $CuSO_4 \cdot H_2O$, and finally the anhydrous salt. The latter is white in color. The anhydrous salt is often used to test for the presence of water in organic liquids. For example, some of the white salt added to alcohol which contains water will turn blue because of the hydration of the salt.

One use of copper sulfate is in electroplating. The object to be plated with copper is made the cathode in a bath containing copper sulfate as the electrolyte. The salt also serves as the electrolyte in the refining of blister copper. Copper sulfate is sometimes used in lakes or other bodies of water to kill algae and other fungus growths. Fishermen dip their nets into copper sulfate solution to inhibit growth of organisms which play an important part in rotting the fabric.

Cupric sulfide, CuS, a black salt, is precipitated when hydrogen sulfide is added to solutions of cupric ion. It is one of the most insoluble of the compounds of copper; hydrochloric acid and sulfuric acid have little effect, but the compound is readily soluble in nitric acid, since the latter oxidizes the sulfide to free sulfur, cupric ions meanwhile passing into solution.

When ammonium hydroxide is added to a solution of cupric ions, a greenish precipitate of cupric hydroxide or a basic cupric salt is formed which dissolves as more ammonium hydroxide is added. The excess ammonia forms an ammoniated complex with the cupric ion of the composition, $Cu(NH_3)_4^{++}$:

$$Cu^{++} + 4\,NH_3 \longrightarrow Cu(NH_3)_4^{++}$$

This ion is only slightly dissociated, and hence in an ammoniacal solution very few cupric ions are present. Most insoluble copper compounds are dissolved by ammonium hydroxide; cupric sulfide is an exception. The formation of the cupric ammonia ion is often used as a test for cupric ion because of its deep and intense blue color.

Cupric ion is reduced by the addition of either sodium or potassium cyanide, forming cuprous cyanide and poisonous cyanogen gas:

$$2\,Cu^{++} + 4\,CN^- \longrightarrow 2\,CuCN\downarrow + (CN)_2\uparrow$$

Cuprous cyanide is soluble in an excess of the cyanide, since it forms a complex cyanide ion, $Cu(CN)_2^-$:

$$CuCN + CN^- \longrightarrow Cu(CN)_2^-$$

The latter ion is even less dissociated than the ammoniated complex and consequently nearly all insoluble copper salts are soluble in excess alkali cyanides.

Cupric ferrocyanide, $Cu_2Fe(CN)_6$, is obtained as a reddish brown precipitate on the addition of a soluble ferrocyanide to a solution of cupric ions. The formation of this salt is sometimes used as a test for the presence of cupric ions. It is more delicate than the blue color formed with excess ammonia.

SILVER

History and occurrence. Metallic silver has been known since prehistoric times. The symbol for silver, Ag, comes from the Latin, *argentum*, which means white. The alchemist associated silver with the moon and used a crescent as the symbol for the element.

Silver occurs in nature both free and combined. In the native state it is sometimes found as nuggets but usually occurs in veins in rock masses alloyed with copper and gold. Principal minerals of silver are *argentite*, Ag_2S, and *argyrite*, $AgCl$, also called *horn silver*. The element is nearly always present in copper and lead ores and follows these metals through the various metallurgical processes. The refining of copper and lead in which the silver is recovered constitutes one of the principal sources of silver produced. In the United States approximately 80 per cent of the silver is obtained this way. About 70 per cent of the world's production comes from the western hemisphere.

Mexico is the leading producer followed by the United States, Canada, and Peru. World production is about 300,000 fine ounces per year.

Metallurgy. Since most of the silver produced in this country is a by-product of the refining of copper and lead, the treatment of these latter metals for recovery of silver is of primary interest. In the electrolytic refining of copper, the silver finds its way into the anode sludge or mud along with gold, platinum, bismuth, and arsenic. This sludge after treatment with dilute sulfuric acid, which removes most of the base metals, is dried and mixed with sodium carbonate, sodium nitrate, and silica. The mixture is highly heated to oxidize and flux away the remainder of the base metals. Silver remains along with any gold or platinum originally present.

Silver is recovered from lead by the Parkes process. This process depends upon the greater solubility of silver in zinc. About one per cent of zinc is added to molten lead and the mixture thoroughly stirred. The silver concentrates in the layer of zinc which is skimmed off. The zinc and silver are separated by distillation; zinc being more volatile passes into the distillate and may be used in treating subsequent batches of lead. The silver remaining usually contains gold and some lead. The metal is refined by heating in a shallow hearth made of bone ash or other absorbent material. An oxidizing atmosphere is maintained which oxidizes and volatilizes some of the lead as oxide; the remainder of the liquid lead oxide is absorbed by the bone ash, leaving a silver-gold alloy. The process is called *cupellation*. The silver and gold are separated or *parted* by means of sulfuric or nitric acid which dissolves silver and other metals present but has no effect on the gold. The silver which passes into solution may be further refined by electrolysis.

Silver ores after being crushed finely may be leached with a dilute sodium or potassium cyanide solution in the presence of air. Metallic silver or its compounds are soluble because of the formation of a complex cyanide:

$$4 \, Ag + 8 \, CN^- + O_2 + 2 \, H_2O \longrightarrow 4 \, Ag(CN)_2^- + 4 \, OH^-$$

The metal is precipitated from the cyanide solution by the addition of zinc shavings:

$$2 \, Ag(CN)_2^- + Zn \longrightarrow Zn(CN)_4^{--} + 2 \, Ag$$

Properties. Silver is a white metal intermediate in hardness between copper and gold. It is ductile and malleable and the best conductor of heat and electricity known. Silver lies low in the activity series and is classed as an inactive metal. It is resistant to the action of air, water, alkalies, and the nonoxidizing acids. Sulfur and sulfur compounds attack silver, readily producing a black deposit of silver sulfide. The action is responsible for the tarnishing of the metal. Silver is also attacked by the halogens to form an adhering layer of halide salt which soon stops the action.

Uses. Silver is used principally for ornaments, coins, jewelry, and various articles of silverware. Pure silver is too soft for these purposes and is usually alloyed with copper to increase its hardness and durability. *Sterling* is 92.5 per cent silver and 7.5 per cent copper; it is said to be 925 fine. American silver coinage is 900 fine or 90 per cent silver and 10 per cent copper. Silver is often plated onto cheaper metals. Copper may be readily plated on iron and this in turn may be plated with silver — silver adheres much more readily to the copper than to iron. The plating bath is usually a solution of a complex silver cyanide. Silver may be precipitated on mirrors by reducing a silver salt with an organic reducing agent, after which the surface may be highly polished.

Compounds of silver. *Silver nitrate*, sometimes called *lunar caustic* is the most important salt of silver. It melts readily and may be cast into sticks for use by surgeons in cauterizing wounds. The salt is prepared by dissolving silver in nitric acid and evaporation of the solution. The salt is the starting material for most of the compounds of silver, including the halides which are used in photography. The salt is readily reduced by organic reducing agents with the formation of a black deposit of finely divided silver. This action is responsible for black spots left on the fingers from the handling of the salt. Indelible marking inks and pencils take advantage of this property of silver nitrate.

The *halides* of silver except the fluoride are very insoluble compounds and may be precipitated by the addition of a solution of silver salt to a solution containing chloride, bromide, or iodide ions. Of the three halides, silver iodide is the most insoluble. The latter compound is yellow in color, while silver bromide is pale yellow and silver chloride is white. All three salts are darkened on exposure to light, a fact which is taken advantage of in photography.

The addition of a strong base to a solution of a silver salt precipitates brown *silver oxide*, Ag_2O. Normally one might expect the hydroxide of silver to precipitate, but it seems likely that silver hydroxide is very unstable and breaks down into the oxide and water if, indeed, it is ever formed at all. However, a solution of silver oxide is definitely basic which would indicate the presence of hydroxyl ions in solution.

Photography. Photography is based upon the sensitivity of the silver halides to light. Of these silver bromide is most commonly used.

The salt is precipitated from silver nitrate and potassium bromide in the presence of gelatin, which acts as a protective colloid (p. 361) to prevent the particles of silver bromide from becoming too coarse. The gelatin solution is spread as a thin coating onto glass or film made from cellulose nitrate. The fundamental operations in the preparation of a photograph are described below.

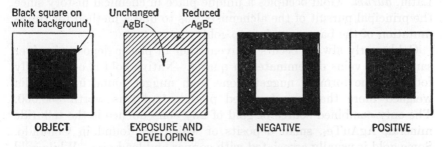

Fig. 131. Steps in making a photograph.

The film is *exposed* by opening the shutter of a camera for a moment. The image of the object being photographed is projected onto the film through the lens, and the light reflected from the object brings about a change in the silver bromide emulsion in direct proportion to the intensity of the light. Light parts of the object will reflect more light than the darker portions and thus effect a greater change on the film. The change which takes place is somewhat obscure, but it seems likely that some free silver is produced by reduction of the silver bromide. The film is next *developed* by washing it in a solution of a mild reducing agent such as hydroquinone or ferrous oxalate. The ease of reduction is a direct function of the intensity of light falling on the film during exposure. The light parts of the object appear as dark patches on the plate because of the reduction of the salt probably to finely divided silver. The film is next *fixed* by washing in a solution of sodium thiosulfate (hypo) which dissolves away the unchanged silver bromide that has not been affected in the exposure stage. After being washed thoroughly with water this "negative" is dried. *Printing* consists of allowing light to pass through the negative onto paper which is coated with silver bromide. The light and dark portions of the negative are again reversed, and the object now appears as a "positive." The process of developing and fixing the positive is essentially a repetition of the treatment of the negative. The photo may be toned by use of a solution of gold or platinum chloride. Silver is replaced in part by the latter metals which impart characteristic colors.

GOLD

History and occurrence. Without question, gold was one of the first metals known to man. History records the use of the metal for jewelry and ornamental purposes in very early times. The fact that the metal occurs free, is pleasing in appearance, and is easily worked would account for its early use. The symbol, Au, is derived from the Latin, *aurum*. Gold occupies a unique place in chemical history since the principal pursuit of the alchemists was to find a method for transmutation of the baser metals into gold.

Gold nearly always occurs native, either in placer deposits in river sands or in veins disseminated in quartz. Native gold is occasionally found in the form of nuggets; one such nugget found in Australia weighed more than one hundred pounds and was worth $50,000. The only combined source of gold of any consequence is the telluride mineral, $AgAuTe_2$, small deposits of which are found in Colorado. Some gold is usually associated with copper and lead ores. While gold is widely distributed over the earth, relatively few deposits pay to work. A very small amount of gold is present in sea water — less than 0.00005 gram per ton of water. More than 50 per cent of the world's supply of gold comes from South Africa. The United States, Canada, and Australia follow in order of production.

Gold production. The era of gold production that followed the discovery of America was in all probability the greatest the world had witnessed up to that time. The exploitation of mines by slave labor and the looting of palaces, temples, and graves in Central and South America resulted in an influx of gold that unbalanced the economic structure of Europe and disturbed its political structure. The history and romance of Spanish galleons carrying Inca gold as treasure, leads to thought as to the bulk and value of said gold. From the discovery of America by Columbus in 1492 to 1600, over 8,000,000 ounces of gold came from South America, which was 35 per cent of the world production during this time. This amount of gold would have a bulk of an eight-foot cube and a value of $280,000,000. Contrary to usual belief it did not take many galleons to carry this bulk of gold — there were no large rooms filled with golden treasure. This amount of gold, which seemed of fabulous value to people of the fourteenth century, is small as compared to money values involved in twentieth century world finance. South American mines (especially Colombian mines) continued in the fifteenth and sixteenth centuries to furnish 61 and 80 per cent respectively of world gold production; 48,000,000 ounces were mined between 1700 and 1800. During the second era of intensive gold production, the 25 years following 1850, more gold was produced in the world than in the 358 years immediately previous, chiefly because of discoveries of gold in California and Australia. A third marked increase in world gold recovery was in the period from 1890 to 1915, when gold discoveries in Alaska, in the Yukon, and on the Rand in the Transvaal were made. A big factor was the introduction of the cyanide process for recovery of gold from low grade ores and ores containing minute particle size gold.

Throughout the years gold production has increased until just prior to World War II the average yearly gold production was greater than production during 1493–1600 or 1600–1700. The 1936 world production, for example, was 32,960,158 ounces, having a value of $1,153,605,530 (at $35 an ounce). This amount of gold stacked as gold bricks would make a 13-foot cube. Postwar gold production has not quite reached the prewar level. Since most mined gold goes through counting houses and mints, a fairly accurate account of all gold mined since 1493 is recorded. The world production from 1493 to 1940 closely approximates 1,222,000,000 ounces, with a value (at $35 an ounce) of $42,770,000,000. Said gold would have the bulk of a 41-foot cube; which is indeed a small volume of matter to have so influenced the toil and destiny of so many people.

Metallurgy. Placer mining is based upon the high specific gravity of gold. The gold occurs usually as small particles mixed with sand and gravel. The sand may be washed in pans or long troughs called *sluices*, the particles of gold being heavier settle to the bottom and are retained behind cleats or riffles, while the lighter sand particles are washed away.

Gold ore obtained from hard rock vein deposits is crushed to a powdery condition, after which a water suspension of the ore is passed over copper plates covered with a coating of mercury. Mercury amalgamates (p. 470) with the gold and at intervals the copper plates are scraped. The amalgam (Hg-Au) is heated and the mercury distilled away from the gold, which remains as a residue. The recovered mercury is used over and over again. The tailings from this treatment may be leached with cyanide solution, which removes more of the gold.

If a gold ore is "free milling" (gold not intimately associated with other metal sulfides) and if the gold is in the ore in a quite finely divided state, it may be treated with sodium cyanide solution after having first been ground to a porous granular mass. Like silver, gold is quite soluble in NaCN or KCN solution:

$$4\,Au + 8\,CN^- + O_2 + 2\,H_2O \longrightarrow 4\,Au(CN)_2^- + 4\,OH^-$$

The gold may be recovered from the cyanide solution by adding zinc dust or allowing the solution to flow over zinc shavings; the zinc replaces and precipitates the gold.

The recovery of gold and silver as by-products of the smelting of copper and lead ores has already been discussed.

An alloy of gold and silver may be treated with nitric acid and the silver dissolved away from the gold, provided the content of the gold in the alloy is not greater than 25 per cent. An alloy of greater gold content is not soluble in the acid. More silver may be added to lower the gold content below 25 per cent or the alloy may be refined by electrolysis. The impure gold is made the anode in a cell with gold chloride and hydrochloric acid as the electrolyte and a sheet of pure gold as the cathode. Passage of the current causes gold to pass into solution at the anode and pure gold is deposited on the cathode.

Properties. Gold is a soft yellow metal with a specific gravity of 19.3. It is a good conductor of heat and electricity and is the most malleable and ductile of metals. The metal may be hammered into sheets only 0.00001 inch in thickness, and 1 gram of the metal may be drawn into a wire 3 kilometers in length (about 1.8 miles). Gold is resistant to the action of most chemicals. Air, oxygen, and water have no effect, nor do the common acids attack the metal. However, a mixture of hydrochloric and nitric acids (aqua regia) dissolves the metal to form auric chloride or chloroauric acid. The action is probably due to free chlorine present in the aqua regia:

$$3 \text{ HCl} + \text{HNO}_3 \longrightarrow \text{NOCl} + \text{Cl}_2 + 2 \text{ H}_2\text{O}$$
$$2 \text{ Au} + 3 \text{ Cl}_2 \longrightarrow 2 \text{ AuCl}_3$$
$$\text{AuCl}_3 + \text{HCl} \longrightarrow \text{HAuCl}_4$$

Chlorine and bromine attack the metal readily and it dissolves slowly in selenic acid.

Uses. Principal uses of gold are for coinage and jewelry. Pure gold is too soft for these purposes and is usually alloyed with copper to increase its hardness. The purity or fineness of gold is measured in terms of "carats," 24 carat gold is 100 per cent gold. Thus 18 carat gold would be $\frac{18}{24}$ or 75 per cent gold, 12 carat gold would be 50 per cent, etc. American gold coinage is 21.6 carats or 90 per cent; British coinage is 22 carats or 91.7 per cent. Many alloys of gold are on the market containing varying percentages of gold, such as white gold (gold and silver) and green gold (gold and cadmium or silver). Various articles are electrolytically plated with a thin coating of gold.

Compounds of gold. Because of its inactivity, gold forms relatively few compounds. Two series of compounds are known, monovalent and trivalent. Monovalent(aurous) compounds resemble silver compounds, aurous chloride being water insoluble and light sensitive, while the higher valence (auric) compounds tend to form complexes or nonmetallic ions. If gold is dissolved in aqua regia and the solution is evaporated, yellow crystals of *chloroauric* acid, $HAuCl_4 \cdot 4 H_2O$, are obtained. On controlled heating of the latter, red crystals of *auric chloride* are formed. Further heating results in the decomposition of auric chloride into *aurous chloride* and finally into free gold. The complex cyanide, $KAu(CN)_2$, is obtained by dissolving the metal in potassium cyanide solution in the presence of air. This compound is the chief form in which gold is used for plating purposes.

EXERCISES

1. Contrast the differences in physical and chemical properties between the members of divisions A and B of Group I of the periodic table.
2. List formulas and mineral names of the more important ores of Cu, Ag, Au.
3. What is the principal property of members of this group which makes them useful for ornaments and jewelry?
4. List the principal steps in the recovery of pure copper from low-grade sulfide ores. What is the purpose of each step?
5. What weight of silver would be displaced from solution by 31.8 grams of copper.   Ans. 107.8 g.
6. By means of chemical changes, how could you distinguish between:
   (*a*) gold, silver, copper?
   (*b*) silver, magnesium, aluminum?
   (*c*) chlorides of silver, lead, and copper?
   (*d*) sulfates of copper, silver, and magnesium?
7. Diagram an electrolytic cell by which a copper spoon could be plated with silver.
8. What is the weight in grams of a gold brick $5 \times 10 \times 20$ cm.? (The specific gravity of gold is 19.3.) What is its weight in kilograms? in pounds?
9. Outline the chemistry involved in the various steps from exposure to development of a photographic plate.
10. Complete and balance the equations:
    (*a*) $Ag + HNO_3 \longrightarrow NO_2 +$
    (*b*) $Cu^{++} + NH_3 \longrightarrow$
    (*c*) $Cu(OH)_2 + H^+ \longrightarrow$
    (*d*) $Au + HNO_3 + HCl \longrightarrow NOCl +$
    (*e*) $Cu^{++} + Fe(CN)_6^{----} \longrightarrow$
11. Diagram an electrolytic cell in which an object might be gold plated. Indicate the nature of the electrodes and the electrolyte.
12. Write equations for steps you would take in preparing reasonably pure samples of the following (reactions must be complete): AgCl from Ag; $Cu(NO_3)_2$ from $CuSO_4$; Ag_2SO_4 from $AgNO_3$; Cu from CuO; $CuCl_2$ from Cu.

13. A U. S. dollar weighs 26.5 g. With silver worth $77\frac{1}{2}$¢ per troy ounce, what is a dollar really worth? (A troy ounce is 31.1 g.)
14. A counterfeit coin weighing 10 g. was dissolved in HNO_3. The addition of HCl precipitated 5.95 g. of AgCl. What was the percentage of silver in the coin?
15. A 16 carat gold ring weighs 4.5 g. At the legal rate of $35 a troy ounce, what is the value of the gold in the ring? (A troy ounce is 31.1 g.)
16. Write equations to indicate the manner of preparing copper arsenate from solid As_2O_5, solid $CuSO_4$, and water.
17. An insecticide mixture consists of $Ca_3(AsO_4)_2$ and powdered sand as filler. A 1 g. sample contains 0.1 g. arsenic. What is the percentage of $Ca_3(AsO_4)_2$ and of filler in the sample?

REFERENCES

Bulletins of Anaconda Copper Co., Butte, Montana.
J. V. Dorr, *Cyanidation and Concentration of Gold and Silver Ores*, McGraw-Hill.
W. H. Emmons, *Gold Deposits of the World*, McGraw-Hill.
William S. Wise, *et al.*, "Brass and Copper Industry," *Ind. & Eng. Chem.* **39,** 632 (1947).
Philip Miller, "Production of Copper Arsenite," *ibid.* **39,** 1521 (1947).
C. L. Bulow, "Wrought Copper and Copper Base Alloys," *ibid.* **43,** 2218 (1951).
William C. Root, "Gold-Copper Alloys in Ancient America," *J. Chem. Ed.* **28,** 76 (1951).
W. E. Caldwell, "Gold," *Encyclopædia Britannica*, 1953.

XXXIV

Zinc, Cadmium, and Mercury

$$_{30}Zn^{65.4} \quad {}_{2\;8\;18\;2} \qquad _{48}Cd^{112.4} \quad {}_{2\;8\;18\;18\;2} \qquad _{80}Hg^{200.6} \quad {}_{2\;8\;18\;32\;18\;2}$$

METAL	SYMBOL	SP. GR.	MELTING POINT	BOILING POINT	VALENCE
Zinc	Zn	7.14	419	907	2
Cadmium	Cd	8.65	321	770	2
Mercury	Hg	13.60	− 39	357	1, 2

Beryllium and magnesium are sometimes included with the above three metals in division *B* of Group II of the periodic table. While the former two elements vary quite widely in properties from other members of division *A* (calcium, strontium, and barium), similarities in atomic structures would place them in division *A* rather than in division *B*. Zinc, cadmium, and mercury show greater differences in properties than the members of division *B* of Group I (copper, silver, and gold). Zinc and cadmium lie relatively high in the activity series, while mercury is near the bottom of the series. Zinc and cadmium react with steam to form hydrogen; mercury does not react with water at any temperature. The characteristic valence for members of this group is two although mercury in some of its compounds also exhibits a valence of one.

ZINC

Brass, an alloy of zinc and copper, has been known since very early times. The term *brass* appears many times in the Old Testament. The alloy was doubtless obtained by the smelting of ores containing both copper and zinc. The pure metal itself was probably not obtained until a good deal later, and its identity as an element was not established until the latter part of the seventeenth century.

463

Occurrence. Zinc does not occur in the free state, but its compounds are widely scattered over the earth's crust. Principal naturally occurring compounds are ZnS, *zinc blende* or *sphalerite;* Zn_2SiO_4, *calamine;* $ZnCO_3$, *smithsonite;* and a complex mixture of the oxide with oxides of manganese and iron called *franklinite*. The United States is the principal producer of the metal, annually producing about 700,000 tons or about 90 per cent of the world production. In the United States, principal states smelting the ore are Oklahoma, Missouri, Montana, Kansas, and New Jersey.

Metallurgy. Sulfide ores are ground and concentrated by the flotation process, after which they may be roasted to convert the sulfide to oxide:

$$2\,ZnS + 3\,O_2 \longrightarrow 2\,ZnO + 2\,SO_2 \uparrow$$

Carbonate ores are heated to convert to the oxide:

$$ZnCO_3 \longrightarrow ZnO + CO_2 \uparrow$$

The oxide is next heated with carbon in a retort approximately five feet in length, where reduction to the metal takes place:

$$ZnO + C \longrightarrow Zn + CO \uparrow$$

As the metal is produced it is distilled off at a temperature of about 1200° and condensed in a receiver which is maintained at a temperature high enough to keep the zinc in a molten condition. If the temperature of the receiver drops below the melting point of zinc, 420°, the metal condenses as zinc dust. The metal cast into bars is called "spelter" and contains small amounts of iron, cadmium, and arsenic. The latter elements may be removed by redistillation of the spelter. However, most of the spelter is used for galvanizing purposes where the impurities present are not objectionable.

In a second metallurgical procedure, sulfide ores are roasted at a lower temperature which converts most of the sulfide to sulfate:

$$ZnS + 2\,O_2 \longrightarrow ZnSO_4$$

The product is then leached with dilute sulfuric acid which dissolves any zinc oxide and also oxides of other metals as well as the zinc sulfate. The addition of zinc dust to this solution causes the precipitation of the heavier metals and electrolysis of the filtered solution produces zinc of 99.9 per cent purity.

Properties of zinc. Zinc is a crystalline, silver-white metal which is brittle at ordinary temperatures but may be rolled into sheets at a temperature of 120° to 150°. Above 200° it again becomes brittle.

On contact with air an adherent film of basic carbonate forms on the surface of the metal which prevents further corrosion.

Zinc is fairly high in the activity series and therefore quite an active metal. It reacts readily with acids to produce hydrogen and displaces less active metals from their salts. The action of acids on impure zinc

Fig. 132. Horizontal retort zinc furnace.

is much more rapid than on very pure zinc, since in the latter case bubbles of hydrogen gas collect on the surface of the metal and slow down the action. If another metal is present as an impurity, the hydrogen is liberated from the surface of the contaminating metal rather than from the zinc. An electric couple is probably set up between the two metals, which facilitates the action.

Zinc is soluble in a strongly basic solution, forming zincate ions and free hydrogen gas:

$$Zn + 2\ OH^- \longrightarrow ZnO_2^{--} + H_2$$

The reaction illustrates the amphoteric nature of zinc, as in this particular case the zinc is present in the acid radical and is therefore functioning as a nonmetal.

Uses of zinc. Principal uses and distribution of the metal are shown in the accompanying diagram (Fig. 133). By far the chief use is in the manufacture of *galvanized iron*. An iron sheet which has been thoroughly cleaned is dipped into molten zinc and a thin layer of the latter is formed on the surface of the iron. The galvanized iron thus produced is much more resistant to corrosion than the iron alone, since the zinc forms a basic carbonate coating on its surface which prevents further action. In another process of coating iron with zinc, called *sherardizing*, zinc dust and zinc oxide are sprinkled on the surface of the iron sheet and heated. A tightly adhering layer is thus formed.

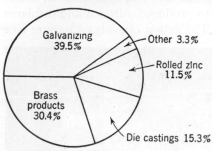

Fig. 133. Uses of metallic zinc.

Electrogalvanizing of iron objects has been performed successfully. In this process the iron article to be coated is made the cathode in a cell and drawn slowly through the bath containing zinc ions. Although the latter method is somewhat more expensive than the others, it has the advantage of forming a layer of any desired thickness; furthermore, the layer is of uniform thickness and adheres more tightly to the iron. Because of its resistance to corrosion the galvanized product is used as a roofing material and in gutters and cornices.

Galvanized iron has the advantage over tin plate (sheet iron coated with tin) of resisting corrosion longer after the surface is broken and the iron exposed. The zinc being more active than the iron will corrode first, thus protecting the iron, while in the case of tin plate, once the surface is broken, the iron corrodes first since it is more active than tin.

Important alloys of zinc are *brass* (Cu, Zn), *bearing metal* (Zn, Cu, Sn, Sb), and *German silver* (Cu, Zn, Ni).

Compounds of zinc. *Zinc oxide*, ZnO, is the most extensively used of the compounds of zinc. It is a white powder at ordinary temperatures which changes to a yellow color on heating. When cooled it again becomes white. The oxide is obtained by burning zinc in air, by heating the basic carbonate, or by roasting of the sulfide. Principal use of the compound is in the rubber industry where it is used as a filler, particularly in automobile tires. It is also used as a body for interior paints. As a body in paints it possesses the advantage over white lead of not darkening on exposure to an atmosphere containing hydrogen sulfide. Its covering power, however, is inferior to white lead and it is used primarily for interior paints. Because of its mildly alkaline and antiseptic properties, the oxide also finds some use in the preparation of ointments and medicinally as an antiseptic powder.

Zinc hydroxide, $Zn(OH)_2$, is formed as a white precipitate when sodium or potassium hydroxide is added to a solution of a zinc salt, *e.g.*

$$Zn^{++} + 2\ OH^- \longrightarrow Zn(OH)_2 \downarrow$$

The hydroxide is amphoteric and dissolves in both acids and bases. In the above reaction, an excess of sodium hydroxide redissolves the precipitated hydroxide with the formation of zincate ions:

$$Zn(OH)_2 + 2\ OH^- \longrightarrow ZnO_2^{--} + 2\ H_2O$$

The hydroxide is also soluble in ammonium hydroxide because of the formation of an ammonia complex:

$$Zn(OH)_2 + 4\ NH_3 \longrightarrow Zn(NH_3)_4^{++} + 2\ OH^-$$

Zinc sulfide, ZnS, is a white metallic sulfide and is precipitated in neutral or alkaline solution with hydrogen sulfide:

$$Zn^{++} + H_2S + 2\ OH^- \longrightarrow ZnS \downarrow + 2\ H_2O$$

Zinc sulfide is an ingredient of *lithopone*, a mixture of barium sulfate and zinc sulfide, used as a paint body and produced by the reaction:

$$BaS + ZnSO_4 \longrightarrow BaSO_4 \downarrow + ZnS \downarrow$$

Zinc chloride, $ZnCl_2$, hydrolyzes readily in water to give an acid solution. The salt is highly poisonous and because of its antiseptic action is used as a wood preservative. It finds limited use as a cleaner for metals before soldering and mixed with zinc oxide produces a certain type of cement.

Zinc sulfate heptahydrate, $ZnSO_4 \cdot 7\ H_2O$, commonly called *white vitriol*, is prepared by the action of sulfuric acid on the oxide or carbonate of zinc. It is used extensively in the preparation of lithopone.

CADMIUM

Occurrence and metallurgy. Because of its close similarity to zinc, cadmium is a constituent of zinc ores. The proportion of cadmium is usually about one part in 200. The mineral CdS, called *greenockite*, is also known although it is relatively unimportant as a source of cadmium metal. Cadmium is obtained as a by-product in the smelting of zinc ores. After the roasting of zinc sulfide ore, both the cadmium and zinc are present as oxides. The oxide of cadmium is more easily reduced than zinc oxide, and the metal itself is more volatile than zinc; hence the greater portion of the cadmium metal is found in the first portion of the distillate. By fractional distillation, the cadmium may be recovered in a high degree of purity.

The amount of cadmium metal produced annually is dependent upon the amount of zinc produced. In 1944 the United States produced 3,834,409 kilograms of the metal out of an estimated world production of seven million kilograms. Its average price in the same year was 95 cents a pound.

Properties and uses. Cadmium is a white metal more malleable than zinc. It is very similar to zinc in chemical properties, appearing just below zinc in the activity series. Its compounds, like those of zinc, are all divalent. The addition of a strong base to a solution of a soluble salt produces a white precipitate of cadmium hydroxide. Unlike zinc, the hydroxide is not amphoteric, as it will not dissolve in an excess of the base. However, the hydroxide is soluble in ammonium hydroxide because, like zinc, cadmium ion forms a complex with ammonia, $Cd(NH_3)_4^{++}$.

The metal is becoming of increasing economic importance. Its principal use at present is in the manufacture of low melting alloys used for fuses and automatic fire sprinklers, and in the production of bearing metal. It offers considerable promise as a plating material in place of zinc and tin. When alloyed with copper, a product of durability, hardness, and tensile strength is produced which may be used for telegraphic and power transmission lines. An alloy of the metal is used in watch and clock hairsprings; other alloys with gold and silver are used in making jewelry. Rods of metallic cadmium found use in atomic energy piles because the metal is a good neutron absorber (p. 426).

Compounds of cadmium. *Cadmium sulfide*, a yellow salt, is precipitated from solutions of cadmium salts by hydrogen sulfide. It is less soluble in acid than zinc sulfide and a separation of the two metals may be effected with hydrogen sulfide if the hydronium ion concentration of the solution is carefully regulated. This is the basis for the separation of cadmium and zinc ions in qualitative analysis. Cadmium sulfide is used as a yellow pigment in the manufacture of paints.

Finely divided *cadmium oxide*, CdO, in air is very toxic to breathe. An incendiary bomb containing an alloy of magnesium and cadmium was invented and manufactured in World War II. As the incendiary burns, highly toxic CdO smoke is produced. Since toxic chemicals were not used in this war, the bombs remained for some time as a secret new weapon.

Cadmium sulfate hydrate, $3\ CdSO_4 \cdot 8\ H_2O$, and metallic cadmium are used in the manufacture of standard electrical cells for scientific work.

MERCURY

Mercury was probably known in very early times although it seems likely that its discovery came after silver, gold, copper, tin, and lead were known. Mercury played an important role in the early work of the alchemists as it was regarded by many as one of the elements of which all matter is composed. Mercury was given the name quicksilver because of its liquid character and its silver-white appearance. The metal was diligently studied and efforts were made to fix it (solidify it) as it was believed by many that it would be changed to gold in the process. Mercury was not recognized as a true metal or its identity as an element established until the middle of the eighteenth century. Its Latin name, *hydrargyrum*, meaning liquid silver, is the source of the symbol Hg.

Occurrence. Mercury is sometimes found in the native condition dispersed as small globules in rock masses, but by far the largest source of the metal is the mineral *cinnabar*, HgS. In 1937, Italy led the world in production of mercury with 3,208 metric tons, followed by Spain with 978 tons, and the United States with 569 tons. Most of the metal produced in the United States comes from California and Oregon. The average price of the metal is about $2.00 per pound.

Metallurgy. The metallurgy of mercury is quite simple. The ore containing the sulfide is heated or roasted in small furnaces or retorts. Since the oxide of mercury is unstable toward heat, if formed in the roasting process, it quickly decomposes and metallic mercury is obtained directly, according to the equation:

$$HgS + O_2 \longrightarrow Hg + SO_2$$

Because of its volatile nature, the mercury is distilled from the impurities present and is collected in iron flasks. The metal may be further purified by filtering through chamois skin or by allowing the mercury to drop slowly through dilute nitric acid which oxidizes impurities more easily than the metal. Redistillation provides still another means of purification. It is stored in iron flasks of a capacity of 76 pounds of mercury.

Properties. Mercury is a silver-white metal and possesses the unique property of being a liquid at ordinary temperatures, the only common metal possessing this property. Its melting point is $-39°$; boiling point, $357°$; and its density, 13.6. It appears near the bottom of the activity series and is thus a very inactive metal; it is one of the "noble" metals. It is not affected by oxygen of the air at ordinary temperatures but if heated to about $300°$ slowly combines with oxygen to form mercuric oxide. It does not dissolve in the nonoxidizing acids but dissolves readily in nitric acid to form either mercurous or mercuric nitrate, depending upon whether or not mercury is present in excess.

$$3 \text{ Hg} + 8 \text{ HNO}_3 \longrightarrow 3 \text{ Hg(NO}_3)_2 + 2 \text{ NO} + 4 \text{ H}_2\text{O} \text{ (excess HNO}_3\text{)}$$
$$6 \text{ Hg} + 8 \text{ HNO}_3 \longrightarrow 3 \text{ Hg}_2(\text{NO}_3)_2 + 2 \text{ NO} + 4 \text{ H}_2\text{O} \text{ (excess Hg)}$$

Mercury vapor and its salts are poisonous although the free metal may be taken internally under certain conditions. Because of its relatively low boiling point and hence volatile nature, free mercury should never be allowed to stand in an open container in the laboratory. Evidence shows that inhalation of its vapors is distinctly injurious.

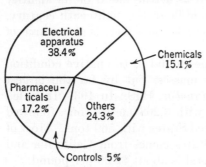

Fig. 134. Uses of mercury.

The metal alloys readily with most of the metals (except iron and platinum) to form *amalgams;* any alloy of mercury is so termed.

Uses of mercury. The principal use of mercury is in the preparation of its salts, many of which have important medicinal uses. Because of its convenient wide range between the freezing and boiling points and its uniform expansion with rise in temperature, it finds extensive use in the manufacture of thermometers. Its high density, 13.6, makes it useful as a liquid in barometers. Some mercury is used in the preparation of dental amalgams of gold and silver for filling teeth. Its thermal properties are such that some modern boilers use mercury instead of water and attain higher heat efficiency. The distribution of uses of the metal is shown in Figure 134.

Compounds of mercury. Mercury forms two series of compounds, *mercurous* compounds in which the valence of mercury is one, and *mercuric* compounds in which the valence of the metal is two. The most important of the mercurous compounds is the chloride, Hg_2Cl_2, commonly called *calomel*, which is used medicinally as a liver stimulant and cathartic. It may be prepared by the reduction of mercuric chloride with metallic mercury:

$$\text{HgCl}_2 + \text{Hg} \longrightarrow \text{Hg}_2\text{Cl}_2 \downarrow$$

The reverse of this reaction may take place on exposure of the mercurous chloride to light resulting in the formation of the more soluble and highly poisonous mercuric chloride; hence calomel should be stored in darkened bottles. Mercurous chloride is insoluble; therefore, it is not readily absorbed by the body when given internally.

Mercurous nitrate, $Hg_2(NO_3)_2$, is prepared from nitric acid and excess mercury and is one of the few soluble mercurous salts.

Mercuric chloride, $HgCl_2$, commonly called *corrosive sublimate,* is a white crystalline salt soluble in water. It may be prepared by direct combination of the elements mercury and chlorine or by heating a mixture of sodium chloride and mercuric sulfate:

$$HgSO_4 + 2\ NaCl \longrightarrow HgCl_2 + Na_2SO_4$$

The product is removed by sublimation. The chloride is very poisonous and is widely used in dilute solutions (about 1 per cent) as a germicide. If taken internally its action on the kidneys is destructive and causes death. The albumen combines with the mercuric ions to form an insoluble white solid. The action of Hg^{++} on the protein albumen is like the action of heat on the white of an egg.

Mercuric ions are readily reduced by stannous ions, *e.g.,* the addition of stannous chloride to a solution containing mercuric ions results in the formation of metallic mercury or mercurous chloride depending upon the relative amounts of reactants:

$$Hg^{++} + Sn^{++} \longrightarrow Hg \downarrow + Sn^{++++} \text{ (excess } SnCl_2)$$
$$2\ Hg^{++} + SnCl_2 \longrightarrow Hg_2Cl_2 \downarrow + Sn^{++++} \text{ (excess } Hg^{++})$$

These reactions are used as a basis for qualitative tests for the presence of mercuric ions or stannous ions.

Mercuric iodide, HgI_2, exists in two allotropic forms:

$$HgI_2 \underset{\text{red}}{\overset{126°}{\rightleftharpoons}} HgI_2 \atop \text{yellow}$$

The yellow variety may be cooled to room temperature without change in color; however, slight friction produced by rubbing or scratching causes it to change over rapidly to the red form.

The treatment of mercury with nitric acid and alcohol yields *mercuric fulminate,* $Hg(CNO)_2$, a highly unstable and explosive compound. It is used in percussion caps as a detonator to initiate the explosion of TNT or gunpowder.

Mercuric thiocyanate, $Hg(CNS)_2$, may be prepared from a soluble mercury salt and a thiocyanate. It burns with a copious ash which is often referred to as "Pharaoh's serpents."

No hydroxides of mercury are known. The addition of sodium or potassium hydroxide to a solution containing mercurous or mercuric ions precipitates *mercurous oxide* and *mercuric oxide* respectively. The latter compound exists in both a red and a yellow form. The red compound is usually obtained by heating mercuric nitrate. Mercuric oxide is of historical significance since Priestley's work with it led to the discovery of the element oxygen.

The addition of ammonium hydroxide to a solution of mercuric chloride results in the formation of a white precipitate of an amino compound, $HgNH_2Cl$:

$$HgCl_2 + 2 NH_3 \longrightarrow HgNH_2Cl \downarrow + NH_4Cl$$

An amino group, NH_2, has been substituted for one of the chlorine atoms in mercuric chloride. The action of ammonium hydroxide on mercurous chloride is somewhat similar; in addition to the above products, metallic mercury in a very finely divided condition is obtained:

$$Hg_2Cl_2 + 2 NH_3 \longrightarrow Hg \downarrow + HgNH_2Cl \downarrow + NH_4Cl$$

In the latter reaction the finely divided mercury produces a black precipitate, and the reaction is often used as a confirmatory test for the presence of mercurous ions.

EXERCISES

1. List the formulas and mineral names for the more important ores of Zn, Cd, Hg.
2. Point out similarities and differences between members of this subgroup.
3. How could you distinguish chemically between the three metals, Zn, Cd, Hg?
4. Describe the manufacture of "galvanized" iron. What are its advantages and its disadvantages?
5. What do you understand by the terms: calomel, amalgam, lithopone, sherardizing, spelter?
6. What properties of mercury make it useful in the manufacture of thermometers?
7. By means of a single reagent, how could you distinguish between: Zn and Hg? Zn^{++} and Cd^{++}? $Zn(OH)_2$ and $Cd(OH)_2$? Cd^{++} and Hg^{++}? $ZnCl_2$ and Hg_2Cl_2? $HgCl_2$ and Hg_2Cl_2?
8. Mercury is sold in iron cylinders called flasks, which hold about $2\frac{2}{3}$ liters of liquid mercury. What is the approximate weight of this mercury in kilograms? in pounds?
9. Suggest a method for preparing: $ZnCl_2$ from Zn; $CdCl_2$ from $CdSO_4$; $HgSO_4$ from Hg; Hg_2Cl_2 from $HgCl_2$; $HgCl_2$ from Hg.
10. List several of the commercially important alloys of zinc; of cadmium; of mercury.

REFERENCE

H. R. Hanley, "The Story of Zinc, Part 1," *J. Chem. Ed.* **10**, 600 (1933).

XXXV

Group III Elements: Aluminum and Boron

$$_5\text{B}^{10.8}\ \begin{smallmatrix}1\\2\\3\end{smallmatrix}\ \begin{smallmatrix}1\\1\\1\end{smallmatrix} \qquad _{13}\text{Al}^{27}\ \begin{smallmatrix}1\\2\\8\\3\end{smallmatrix}\ \begin{smallmatrix}1\\1\\1\\1\end{smallmatrix}$$

Element	Symbol	Sp. Gr.	Melting Point	Boiling Point	Valence
Boron	B	2.45	2300	2550	3
Aluminum	Al	2.70	660	1800	3

The five elements boron, aluminum, gallium, indium, and thalium appear in Group III*A* of the periodic table. Group III*B* includes scandium and yttrium plus the two rare-earth series, *i.e.*, the lanthanide and actinide series (chap. IV).

Aluminum and boron are present in the earth's crust in very appreciable quantities. The remaining elements are very rare, and extraction of them from earth rocks is very costly. All of the elements in this group are similar to aluminum in many respects. All exhibit a valence of three. Boron, the first element of the group, is distinctly nonmetallic in properties. Aluminum is amphoteric, while the remainder exhibit metallic characteristics.

ALUMINUM

Although the element itself was isolated only a little more than a hundred years ago, compounds of aluminum have been known and used for centuries. The Romans used the word *alum* to describe any astringent substance, and it seems likely that the compound of aluminum which we know as alum today was included in this group.

Because of the activity of aluminum and the stability of its compounds, efforts to liberate the element were unsuccessful until 1827 when Wöhler succeeded in producing it by the reduction of aluminum chloride with metallic potassium:

$$\text{AlCl}_3 + 3\text{ K} \longrightarrow \text{Al} + 3\text{ KCl}$$

However, the cost of the method prohibited its production in any quantity, and for many years the metal was only a curiosity. It was recognized that the element would be extremely useful if it could be produced economically, and many attempts were made to develop cheaper processes of manufacture. The substitution of metallic sodium for the potassium reduced the cost from $160 to $10 per pound. By developing electrolytic methods for the preparation of sodium, the cost of aluminum dropped to $4 a pound. The cost of producing aluminum by reduction with sodium thus ran parallel to the cost of producing sodium, a figure which remained too high for commercial purposes. Efforts to produce the metal electrolytically from water solutions in a manner similar to that for many other metals failed; a coating of aluminum oxide was produced almost immediately which stopped the passage of the current. Likewise the use of carbon as a reducing agent was not successful, as aluminum carbide was produced instead of the free metal. The problem was finally solved in 1886 by an American, Charles Martin Hall, while working as a student at Oberlin College. He found that electrolysis of aluminum oxide could be effected in a molten bath of *cryolite*, Na_3AlF_6. As this process was industrialized the price of aluminum quickly dropped to about thirty cents a pound.

Occurrence. Aluminum is the most abundant of the metals and stands third in abundance among the chemical elements, the percentage in the earth's crust being 7.4. It does not occur in the free state because of its activity, but its compounds are spread widely over the earth's surface. It is a constituent of most siliceous soils and rocks such as *clay*, $2 H_2O \cdot Al_2O_3 \cdot 2 SiO_2$; *feldspar*, $KAlSi_3O_8$ or $NaAlSi_3O_8$, and *mica*, $KH_2Al_3(SiO_4)_3$ or $NaH_2Al_3(SiO_4)_3$. The ore of aluminum is *bauxite*, $Al_2O_3 \cdot 2 H_2O$, large deposits of which are found in France, British and Dutch Guiana, and in the states of Arkansas and Alabama. Bauxite is the only ore of aluminum at present because of the difficulties of extracting the metal from other naturally occurring compounds. Crystalline oxides of aluminum are found in nature, such as *corundum* and *emery*. *Cryolite*, Na_3AlF_6, a double fluoride salt, is found in Greenland and is important as a solvent in the electrolytic production of metallic aluminum.

Metallurgy. The process for the preparation of aluminum today is essentially the same as that developed by Hall in 1886. Purified dehydrated bauxite is dissolved in molten cryolite. The cryolite acts as a solvent for the bauxite much the same as water acts as a solvent for ordinary salt. The bauxite-cryolite mixture when melted is a good conductor of the electric current, and electrolysis results in the decomposition of the Al_2O_3 to form metallic aluminum and oxygen. The electrolysis is carried out in carbon-lined vats which act as cathodes. The anodes are carbon rods (Fig. 135) which dip into the electrolyte. At the beginning of the process, the carbon anodes are brought near the bottom of the carbon-lined vat to produce an arc to melt the cryolite. Electrolysis of the Al_2O_3 then begins with aluminum ions moving toward the sides and bottom of the vat, and the oxygen ions moving toward the carbon anodes. At the cathode, aluminum ions are discharged and metallic liquid aluminum settles to the bottom of the vat where it may be drawn off. Oxygen, which is produced at the anodes, rapidly oxidizes the latter. About 0.6 pound of carbon is used for every pound of aluminum produced; hence the carbon electrodes must be frequently replaced. The resistance to the

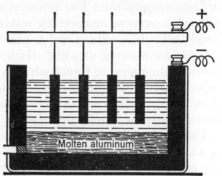

Fig. 135. Preparation of aluminum by electrolysis (Hall process).

passage of the current produces enough heat to keep the cryolite bath in a molten condition. The aluminum metal thus produced is above 99 per cent pure, which is adequate for most purposes. Principal costs of the above method are the electric energy required and the purification of the bauxite before electrolysis. The process is not successful unless the bauxite ore is carefully purified; it is particularly important to remove the iron oxide which is nearly always present. This purification is accomplished in the following manner: (1) The ore is ground and treated with sodium hydroxide under pressure to convert the aluminum oxide to aluminate:

$$Al_2O_3 + 2\,NaOH \longrightarrow 2\,NaAlO_2 + H_2O$$

The oxide of iron is not amphoteric and hence is insoluble in the alkali and may be filtered off. (2) The solution of sodium aluminate is diluted with water and heated to hydrolyze the salt and precipitate aluminum hydroxide:

$$NaAlO_2 + 2\,H_2O \longrightarrow Al(OH)_3 \downarrow + NaOH$$

(3) The hydroxide is filtered off and ignited to the oxide, which may then be dissolved in the cryolite bath. The caustic soda is recovered.

Properties of aluminum. Aluminum, with a specific gravity of 2.7, is the lightest of the common metals with the exception of magnesium. At ordinary temperatures aluminum is soft, malleable, and ductile but when heated above 150° becomes quite brittle. The melting point is 660° and the boiling point about 1800°. Its tensile strength is high and it is a good conductor of heat and electricity. Although the metal is high in the activity series, it is quite resistant to corrosion because of the formation of a protective layer of oxide on the surface. At high temperatures, however, the metal burns vigorously. The aluminum sheeting of airplanes can completely burn after being ignited at high temperature. The action of aluminum with water is similar to that with oxygen; momentary reaction takes place to form the oxide which coats the surface and prevents further action, thus making it suitable for cooking utensils. Hydrochloric and sulfuric acids readily dissolve aluminum to form hydrogen, but nitric acid attacks the metal only slightly. Aluminum dissolves in sodium or potassium hydroxides with the formation of an aluminate salt and hydrogen, a behavior characteristic of amphoteric metals.

Uses. Aluminum combines the properties of lightness, durability, and strength — characteristics which make it suitable for a wide variety of uses. Its use in the manufacture of cooking utensils is familiar to everyone. The metal finds extensive use as a structural material in the manufacture of automobiles, airplanes, watercraft, streetcars, and railway coaches. In wire and cables it is used for the transmission of electric power. For wires of equal cross section copper is a better conductor than aluminum, but on a pound for pound basis aluminum is the better conductor. Aluminum foil is used as a wrapping for soaps, food products, and tobacco. Aluminum powder is a constituent of "silver" paint and is used also in the reduction of certain metal oxides (see thermite process). Much aluminum metal is used in the manufacture of alloys, since these alloys possess greater tensile strength and are more easily machined than the pure metal. Among the more important alloys of aluminum are *duralumin* (Al with small amounts of Cu, Mg, and Mn) and *magnalium* (Al with a small amount of Mg), both of which are used in the construction of crankcases for automobiles and other automotive parts.

The thermite process. If aluminum powder is mixed with certain powdered metallic oxides and the mixture ignited, aluminum takes away the oxygen from the metallic oxide and leaves the metal in the free state. At the same time a great quantity of heat and light energy is released. Advantage is taken of this affinity of aluminum for oxygen in the mixture called *thermite*, developed by Goldschmidt. Thermite is a mixture of iron oxide and aluminum both in granular form. When the mixture is ignited by means of magnesium ribbon, a very vigorous reaction takes place:

$$Fe_2O_3 + 2 Al \longrightarrow Al_2O_3 + 2 Fe + 184,400 \text{ calories}$$

The heat energy produced in the reaction raises the temperature of the mixture to approximately 3000°, which is sufficient to melt both the aluminum oxide and the iron. The thermite mixture is convenient as a ready source of liquid iron for welding broken rails or steel shafts by placing it in a magnesia crucible as shown in Figure 136, directly above the object to be welded. The molten iron produced in the reaction is allowed to flow over the broken part and weld the pieces together.

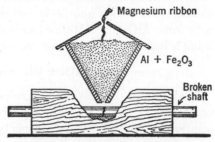

Fig. 136. Thermite welding.

Certain metal oxides which are difficult to reduce by other methods may be reduced in a manner analogous to the above. Manganese and chromium may be prepared from their oxides in this way.

Aluminum oxide. Aluminum oxide is found in nature in several forms. Bauxite is the principal source of the metal. *Corundum* and *emery*, naturally occurring crystalline forms of the oxide, find extensive use as abrasives in grinding and polishing. An artificial product called *alundum* is produced by fusing bauxite in an electric furnace. The latter is very inactive and resistant to corrosion of acids; it is used as a refractory and as a filtering medium for corrosive liquids.

Certain transparent crystalline forms of the oxide are prized gems. *Sapphire* is aluminum oxide containing small amounts of iron oxide and titanium oxide, while the *ruby* contains a small amount of chromium oxide. Synthetic rubies and sapphires are now produced by mixing aluminum oxide with the proper ingredients to give the desired color and passing the mixture through an oxyhydrogen flame. The fused material is cut and polished. These synthetic gems possess the exact composition of the natural product. Apparently the only way to differentiate between the natural and synthetic varieties is by a microscopic examination which reveals a characteristic dispersion of tiny gas bubbles in the natural product. The synthetic gem industry has grown extensively in recent years and at the present time about six million carats of these gems are produced annually. Principal application of the artificial products is for jewels in watches and certain electrical measuring devices.

Aluminum hydroxide. Aluminum hydroxide, $Al(OH)_3$, is formed as a white flocculent precipitate when ammonium hydroxide is added to the solution of an aluminum salt. The hydroxide is amphoteric as it dissolves in both strong bases and acids, *e.g.*:

$$Al(OH)_3 + 3 H^+ \longrightarrow Al^{+++} + 3 H_2O$$
$$Al(OH)_3 + 3 OH^- \longrightarrow AlO_3^{---} + 3 H_2O$$

In the first reaction, aluminum acts as a metal and the hydroxide is neutralized by the acid to produce Al^{+++}. In the latter reaction, the aluminum acts as a nonmetal and dissolves in the base to form aluminate ions, AlO_3^{---}. Meta-aluminate ions, AlO_2^-, may be formed by using a lesser amount of base, according to the reaction

$$Al(OH)_3 + OH^- \longrightarrow AlO_2^- + 2 H_2O$$

If aluminum hydroxide is precipitated in a solution containing an organic dye, the hydroxide adsorbs the color and removes it from solution. This adsorptive property of aluminum hydroxide is used advantageously in the dye industry. Certain fabrics and materials will not adsorb a dye directly and the addition of a *mordant* is necessary — something which will fix the dye to the cloth. Aluminum hydroxide acts in this capacity if precipitated within the fibers of the cloth.

Aluminum hydroxide also finds use, because of its adsorptive capacity for suspended matter, in the purification of water.

Aluminum salts. In general, aluminum salts are highly hydrolyzed in water solutions; in fact many of the salts do not exist at all in aqueous solution. *Aluminum sulfide*, which can be prepared by direct combination of the metal with sulfur, is completely decomposed when added to water. *Aluminum carbonate* likewise hydrolyzes and is not stable in aqueous solution. *Hydrated aluminum chloride*, $AlCl_3 \cdot 6 H_2O$, is crystallized from solutions of aluminum in hydrochloric acid. The anhydrous salt cannot be prepared from the above hydrate by heating as hydrolysis takes place, with the formation of a basic salt and the evolution of hydrogen chloride. Aluminum chloride finds extensive use as a reagent in certain organic chemical syntheses and as a catalyst in the cracking of petroleum.

Aluminum sulfate, the cheapest of the soluble salts of aluminum, is prepared by the action of sulfuric acid on clay or bauxite. The salt crystallizes as the hydrate, $Al_2(SO_4)_3 \cdot 16 H_2O$, from its solutions. It is used in the dyeing industry as a mordant, in sizing of paper, in the purification of water, and in the manufacture of other aluminum compounds.

Alums. If equimolecular quantities of potassium sulfate and aluminum sulfate are dissolved in water and the solution allowed to evaporate, crystals of $K_2SO_4 \cdot Al_2(SO_4)_3 \cdot 24\ H_2O$, which is called ordinary alum or *potash alum*, are deposited. The term *alum*, however, does not necessarily refer to a specific substance but is applied to all double sulfate salts which have the general formula:

$$M_2'SO_4 \cdot M_2'''(SO_4)_3 \cdot 24\ H_2O$$

where M' may be Na^+, K^+, NH_4^+, and M''' may be Fe^{+++}, Cr^{+++}, Al^{+++}. Examples are $(NH_4)_2SO_4 \cdot Cr_2(SO_4)_3 \cdot 24\ H_2O$, *ammonium chrome alum;* $K_2SO_4 \cdot Fe_2(SO_4)_3 \cdot 24\ H_2O$, *potassium ferric alum.* Frequently the formula of alums is contracted to the form $M'M'''$ $(SO_4)_2 \cdot 12\ H_2O$, *e.g.,* $KAl(SO_4)_2 \cdot 12\ H_2O$, etc. Alums usually produce octahedral crystals and are said to be isomorphous as they crystallize in the same crystal system. In aqueous solution the double salt behaves as two single salts, a monovalent sulfate and a trivalent sulfate, giving ions of all the constituents. Alums are used in water purification as they hydrolyze with the formation of aluminum hydroxide, which adsorbs and carries down suspended matter in a precipitated form. Potash alum is a constituent of certain baking powders; the addition of water to the baking powder brings about hydrolysis of the aluminum sulfate to form hydronium ions which then act on the bicarbonate in the mixture to release carbon dioxide.

Double and complex salts. Alums are good examples of double salts — two salts that may separately exist but tend to unite and crystallize as a new compound with its own specific properties. $KCl \cdot MgCl_2 \cdot 6\ H_2O$, naturally occurring carnallite, is a further example. Double salts in solution yield both metal ions, which is the principal difference between *double salts* and *complex salts* that yield mainly one metal ion. $K_4Fe(CN)_6$ which may be written $4\ KCN \cdot Fe(CN)_2$ is an example of a complex salt. In solution it exists mainly as potassium ions and ferrocyanide ions, $Fe(CN)_6^{----}$; ferrous ions are not detected by qualitative analytical tests.

Whether a given compound formed by union of two salts is a double salt or complex salt is dependent, then, on its manner and degree of ionization. The ionization of potassium silver cyanide might be shown:

$$K^+ + 2\ CN^- + Ag^+ \rightleftharpoons KAg(CN)_2 \rightleftharpoons K^+ + Ag(CN)_2^-$$

This salt is considered a complex salt as the above equilibrium is apparently far to the right. However, silver may be electrodeposited from a water solution of this salt, which indicates the presence of some free Ag^+ ions. As the low concentration of Ag^+ ions is depleted by electrodeposition, the equilibrium as written shifts to the left and more Ag^+ ions are formed to be electrodeposited.

Ceramics. Clay is a product of the weathering of complex silicates, particularly feldspar, $KAlSi_3O_8$, or $NaAlSi_3O_8$, which is the most abundant of all minerals of the earth's crust. Although rock silicates are in general quite insoluble, ground waters, being dilute solutions of carbonic acid, have in geological time chemically altered them. Feldspar is progressively altered to the mineral *mica* and thence to *kaolin* according to the chemical changes:

$$3 \, KAlSi_3O_8 + H_2CO_3 \longrightarrow \underset{mica}{KH_2Al_3(SiO_4)_3} + 6 \, SiO_2 + K_2CO_3$$

$$2 \, KH_2Al_3(SiO_4)_3 + H_2CO_3 + 3 \, H_2O \longrightarrow \underset{kaolin}{3 \, H_4Al_2Si_2O_9} + K_2CO_3$$

The potassium carbonate is dissolved by water and the clay may be carried in colloidal suspension in streams and finally deposited in beds. Ordinary clays are quite impure — usually containing considerable quantities of iron. Kaolin, also called white clay or china clay, is a clay of high purity. When clay is mixed with water, a very plastic mass is formed which may be molded into any desired shape. This property of clay is the basis for the *ceramic* industries which produce bricks, tile, pottery, stoneware, and porcelain. After the molding and drying of the clay, the product is baked. Most of the residual molecular water is lost, leaving a very hard, resistant, highly porous product. If the porosity is undesirable, the product may be glazed. In glazing, a very thin film of fused matter is deposited on the surface. A cheap glaze can be produced by throwing salt on the object while it is still hot; a thin liquid coating of sodium aluminum silicate forms which becomes compact and impervious when cooled. Bricks and tiles are made from the cheaper and impure forms of clay, while china and porcelain are produced from kaolin.

Lapis lazuli, a naturally occurring silicate of the composition $NaAlSiO_4 \cdot Na_2S \cdot S$, is a valuable gem. An artificial product called *ultramarine* is made by heating a mixture of kaolin, sodium sulfate, carbon, and sulfur. The color which is due to colloidally dispersed sulfur may be varied by using different proportions of sulfur and by changing the conditions of manufacture. The synthetic product in many respects is superior to the natural product.

BORON

Boron appears with aluminum in Group III of the periodic table. Although it is similar to aluminum in many of its chemical properties, in some respects the element is more like silicon in Group IV. Boron exhibits a characteristic valence of 3, but it is much more nonmetallic in character than aluminum and as such its acid-forming properties are more pronounced.

Boron is a relatively rare element (about 0.001 per cent of the earth's crust). It does not occur in the free state but its compounds are found in many areas. *Boric acid*, H_3BO_3, occurs naturally in certain spring waters. *Borax*, $Na_2B_4O_7 \cdot 10\ H_2O$, is found in certain dry lake areas of California. The most abundant of boron compounds is *colemanite*, $Ca_2B_6O_{11} \cdot 5\ H_2O$, deposits of which are found in California and Nevada.

Borax is probably the most important compound of boron; large amounts are used in water softeners and washing powders; smaller amounts are used in making certain kinds of glass, and in forming glazes or enamels for both metal and pottery. Borax in a molten condition will dissolve many metallic oxides with the formation of a glass of a characteristic color. This is the basis for borax bead tests for such metals as cobalt, nickel, manganese, chromium, and iron, as well as the use of borax for cleaning metallic surfaces which are coated with oxide deposits. Borax is readily produced from colemanite by treatment of the former with sodium carbonate solution, filtering off the insoluble calcium carbonate and crystallizing the borax from the solution.

Boric acid, because of its weakly acidic character and its mild antiseptic action is used as an eyewash. It is sparingly soluble in cold water and is precipitated on the addition of an acid to a solution of borax.

A borate may readily be tested for by the addition of sulfuric acid and ethyl alcohol. A volatile compound, *ethyl borate*, $(C_2H_5)_3BO_3$, is produced, which, when ignited, burns with a characteristic green-colored flame.

OTHER ELEMENTS OF GROUP III A

Gallium, indium, thallium. At the time that Mendeléeff devised his periodic table in 1870, a blank space appeared just below aluminum. This led to his predictions of the properties of an element called "eka-aluminum" — predictions which turned out to be remarkably accurate. Four years later the element now known as gallium was discovered with the aid of the spectroscope. Subsequently, the elements indium and thallium were discovered also with the aid of the spectroscope. These three elements may be considered as constituting the *B* division of Group III.

Small amounts of gallium and indium are associated with ores of zinc. Commercial zinc metal may contain as much as two or three ounces of these metals per ton. Aluminum ores, likewise, as might be expected, contain small amounts of these metals. Thallium is somewhat more abundant than the other two — small quantities of it may be obtained from flue dusts which result from the roasting of iron, zinc, copper, or lead sulfides. Small amounts may also be recovered in the refining of cadmium.

Thallium is a metal of about the density and appearance of lead; its melting temperature of 303° C. is near that of lead, 327° C. Thallium gives a green spectral line. It forms trivalent salts which are very poisonous. $Tl_2(SO_4)_3$ may be used as an ant or rat poison.

Thallium has the unexpected property of forming monovalent compounds; TlOH is a strong, water-soluble base resembling the alkali hydroxides.

ELEMENTS OF GROUP IIIB

Group IIIB includes the elements scandium and yttrium and the two rare-earth series of elements. All of the elements in the B series, of course, are of the transitional type, that is, the atoms have incompleted inner shells of electrons. Scandium has the configuration 2, 8, 9, 2 (third shell incomplete) and yttrium has a similar configuration, 2, 8, 18, 9, 2 (again the next to outer shell is incomplete). Between lanthanum and hafnium is a space for elements of atomic numbers 57 to 71. These fifteen elements, collectively called the *rare earths*, must fit into this single space in the periodic chart. A consideration of the atomic structures of these rare earth elements will explain this apparent anomaly.

Lanthanum, of atomic number 57, is the first member of the rare-earth group. It has the following electronic structure:

$$_{57}La^{134} \quad 2 \quad 8 \quad 18 \quad 18 \quad 9 \quad 2$$

Through lanthanum there has been no tendency for elements to present themselves with more than eighteen electrons in the fourth orbit — the capacity of which is thirty-two electrons. Suddenly then, a group of elements of atomic numbers 58–71 is encountered in which the added electrons enter orbit four and progressively fill it from eighteen to thirty-two electrons. Meanwhile, the outer orbits remain essentially unchanged. Thus, these rare-earth elements have almost exactly the same chemical properties, and, accordingly, belong in this one position in the periodic table. The entire list of these elements is shown below the periodic chart (p. 61). The principal source of the rare earths is *monazite sand*, which is a complex mixture of phosphates of these elements. It is an alluvial deposit found principally along the seacoasts of Brazil and India.

Cerium is the only rare earth having even a little practical use. An alloy of cerium and iron, when scraped by a rough, hard, object, produces hot sparks and may be used in laboratory burners or cigarette lighters. Cerium oxide is occasionally used as a catalyst. Since cerium exhibits a valence of four as well as three, cerium compounds are used in oxidation-reduction reactions in analytical chemistry.

It is now believed that actinium is the first member of a second rare-earth series which at the present time would include elements of atomic numbers 89–98. The elements of this latter series are radioactive and are considered with the general subject of radioactivity in chapter XXXI.

EXERCISES

1. Although aluminum is more abundant in the earth's crust than iron, why is it more expensive?
2. Describe briefly the metallurgy of aluminum.
3. What do you understand by the terms: alum; thermite; clay; mordant; bauxite; ceramics?
4. Write equations to show the amphoteric nature of $Al(OH)_3$.
5. Differentiate clearly between a double salt and a complex salt.
6. Why is aluminum hydroxide rather than aluminum sulfide precipitated when hydrogen sulfide is added to an alkaline solution of an aluminum salt?
7. In the purification of bauxite, what is the basis for the separation of iron and aluminum?
8. A one gram sample of impure bauxite when analyzed gave 0.510 g. of aluminum oxide. What was the per cent of aluminum in the bauxite?   Ans. 27.
9. What quantities of ammonium sulfate and ferric sulfate would be needed to produce 100 g. of ammonium ferric alum?
10. Draw electronic configurations for the compounds BH_3 and NH_3. By what mechanism might these two compounds combine to form a third compound?
11. Give reasons for the inability to prepare pure aluminum either by reduction of its oxide with coke, or by electrolysis of aqueous $AlCl_3$ solution.
12. Fumes from electrolytic aluminum-producing pots are channeled through rotoclones to remove solid particles and thence through scrubber spray towers to remove gases. Complete the following table, which shows the success of the process in removing fluorine compounds.

ROTOCLONE			SCRUBBER			
F Intake ppm.[1]	F Discharge ppm.	% Removal	F Intake ppm.	F Discharge ppm.	% Removal	Over-all Efficiency
113	91.4		91.4	7.87		
78.6	63.2		63.2	3.65		

[1] ppm. = parts per million

13. An aluminum plant produces 144,000,000 lb. of aluminum per year. The purchasing agent has at hand the following facts: For each pound of aluminum produced, 0.65 lb. of carbonaceous anode is used and 1.93 lb. of Al_2O_3. Weight of electrolytic material lost as production progresses is reported as so many per cent of the aluminum made: cryolite 1.5 per cent; AlF_3 3 per cent; CaF_2 0.15 per cent. What weights of these five most important materials must the purchasing agent plan to procure each year?

14. Write balanced equations for (a) the preparation of ethyl borate from boric acid and ethyl alcohol in the presence of concentrated sulfuric acid as a dehydrating agent, and (b) the combustion of ethyl borate.

15. Write formulas for: an alum containing gallium instead of aluminum; thallium nitrate; indium sulfide.

16. Write formulas for the sulfates of scandium, yttrium, and the rare-earth metals.

REFERENCES

J. D. Edwards, *et al.*, *The Aluminum Industry*, McGraw-Hill.

Otto Redlich, *et al.*, "Extraction of Alumina from Clay," *Ind. & Eng. Chem.* **38,** 1181 (1946).

Michael A. Striecher, "Dissolution of Aluminum in Sodium Hydroxide Solutions," *ibid.* **41,** 818 (1949)

E. D. Verink, Jr., and R. H. Brown, "Aluminum Alloys," *ibid.* **41,** 2095 (1949).

H. N. Holmes, "The Story of Aluminum," *J. Chem. Ed.* **7,** 233 (1930).

Ronald B. Spacht, "The Corrosion Resistance of Aluminum and Its Alloys," *ibid.* **23,** 253 (1946).

Anon. "Aluminum from Clay," *ibid.* **25,** 159 (1948).

Arthur A. W. Vernon, "Treatment of Aluminum for Corrosion Prevention," *ibid.* **26,** 147 (1949).

XXXVI

Group IV Metals: Tin and Lead

$$_{50}Sn^{118.7} \quad \begin{smallmatrix} | & | & | & | & | \\ 2 & 8 & 18 & 18 & 4 \\ | & | & | & | & | \end{smallmatrix} \qquad _{82}Pb^{207.2} \quad \begin{smallmatrix} | & | & | & | & | & | \\ 2 & 8 & 18 & 32 & 18 & 4 \\ | & | & | & | & | & | \end{smallmatrix}$$

ELEMENT	SYMBOL	SP. GR.	MELTING POINT	BOILING POINT	VALENCE
Germanium	Ge	3.5	1250	. . . .	4
Tin	Sn	7.3	232	2260	2, 4
Lead	Pb	11.4	328	1620	2, 4

Tin and lead are members of Group IV–A along with carbon, silicon, and germanium. Carbon and silicon have been previously discussed, and germanium is relatively rare and unimportant.

TIN

There is some evidence to indicate that tin and lead were regarded as identical metals by early writers. Although lead and copper vessels are common in Roman and Greek relics, comparatively little tin has been found.

The metal does not occur in the free state; hence the ancients must have obtained it from its ores, probably by heating the oxide mineral in a wood fire.

Occurrence. The only ore of tin of importance is the oxide, SnO_2, which is called *cassiterite*. At one time England led in the production of tin, but at the present time most of the ore is mined in British Malaya, Bolivia, and the Dutch East Indies. The United States in prewar times imported about 88,000 tons of tin per year, which is slightly more than 40 per cent of the world's production of that metal. In addition, the United States recovered about 27,000 tons of scrap tin per year.

Metallurgy. The fact that the metallurgy of tin is relatively simple undoubtedly accounts for its use in early times; the method of smelting by simply heating in a wood fire was probably discovered by accident. After the ore is crushed and ground, it is roasted to oxidize sulfides of iron and copper. The ore is next placed in a reverberatory furnace and reduced with coke:

$$SnO_2 + 2\,C \longrightarrow Sn + 2\,CO$$

The liquid tin is collected and cast into blocks. It is refined by heating the blocks to a temperature which melts the tin and leaves most impurities as solid matter. The tin may also be refined by electrolysis, by making impure tin the anode and pure tin sheet the cathode in a cell in which sulfuric and fluosilicic acids are used as the electrolyte.

Properties. Tin is a silver-white metal of moderate hardness, and its melting point of 232° is quite low. It exists in at least two allotropic forms:

$$\underset{gray}{Sn} \overset{18°}{\rightleftharpoons} \underset{white}{Sn}$$

White tin is distinctly crystalline, and if the metal is bent back and forth, it produces a creaking noise called "tin cry" due to the crystals slipping over one another. The gray variety is formed from the white form if the latter is subjected to low temperatures over a long period of time. When the change is once started, it progresses rapidly with a change in appearance from white metallic to a grayish powder. Tin buttons on coats of Russian soldiers have been known to crumble to a gray powder in winter. The action is termed "tin disease" or "tin pest."

The metal appears just above hydrogen in the activity series. It does not corrode or tarnish in the air, and dilute acids act on the metal only slowly. Hydrochloric and sulfuric acids act slowly on the metal to produce stannous salts:

$$Sn + 2\,H^+ \longrightarrow Sn^{++} + H_2$$

Concentrated nitric acid acts vigorously on the metal to form meta-stannic acid:

$$Sn + 4\,HNO_3 \longrightarrow H_2SnO_3 \downarrow + 4\,NO_2 + H_2O$$

Uses. One of the principal uses of tin is in the production of tin plate. In the process, sheet iron which has been cleaned of oxide coating by "pickling" in acid, is dipped into molten tin and a thin layer of tin is coated onto the iron surface. The tin acts as a protective coating for the iron, which is the more active metal. If the surface of tin plate is scratched so that the iron is exposed, corrosion takes place rapidly probably because of an electric couple set up between the two metals. Most of the tin plate is used in the manufacture of cans for storage of foods. Utensils of various kinds are also made from tin plate. Tin pipes are used for conveying distilled water, and tin foil is a common wrapping material. Considerable tin is used in the production of alloys: *bronze* (Cu, Sn); *pewter* (Cu, Pb, Sb, Sn); *solder* (Pb, Sn); and *type metal* (Pb, Sn, Sb). The distribution of tin used in the United States for various commercial products is approximately as shown in Figure 137.

Tin is a comparatively expensive metal; its price fluctuates around 60 cents per pound. A "tin can" is really an iron can with a very thin coating of protective tin on the surface. Similarly a "tinsmith" works with iron

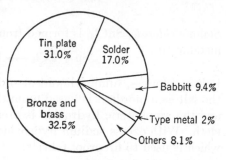

Fig. 137. Uses of tin.

sheeting, which may have a coating of tin, zinc, or other metals. Much zinc, aluminum, or lead foil now is substituted for the more expensive tin foil.

Compounds of tin. Tin forms two series of compounds, *stannous* and *stannic*. The higher valence form, stannic, behaves more as a nonmental than the stannous form; hence stannic salts are much less common than stannous. Both stannous and stannic hydroxides are amphoteric, being soluble in acid and base; the addition of sodium hydroxide to the hydroxides of tin produces stannites and stannates respectively:

$$H_2SnO_2 + 2\ OH^- \longrightarrow SnO_2^{--} + 2\ H_2O$$

$$H_4SnO_4 + 2\ OH^- \longrightarrow SnO_3^{--} + 3\ H_2O$$

Stannous chloride, $SnCl_2$, is produced from hydrochloric acid and the metal:

$$Sn + 2\ HCl \longrightarrow SnCl_2 + H_2$$

The salt tends to hydrolyze and although it is particularly subject to oxidation, this may be prevented by the addition of metallic tin to the salt solution. Stannous chloride is an important laboratory reducing agent used in qualitative and quantitative analysis procedures. The salt also finds commercial application as a mordant in dyeing and in "weighting" silk. Black *stannous sulfide*, SnS, is precipitated from solutions containing stannous ions, Sn^{++}, by the action of H_2S. The sulfide is soluble in ammonium or sodium polysulfides, which enables its separation from many other metallic sulfides in qualitative analysis:

$$SnS + (NH_4)_2S_2 \longrightarrow 2\,NH_4^+ + SnS_3^{--}$$
$$\text{ammonium thiostannate}$$

$$SnS + Na_2S_2 \longrightarrow 2\,Na^+ + SnS_3^{--}$$
$$\text{sodium thiostannate}$$

Stannic chloride, $SnCl_4$, is formed from the action of excess chlorine on metallic tin:

$$Sn + 2\,Cl_2 \longrightarrow SnCl_4$$

It is a colorless, fuming liquid at ordinary temperatures. The use of the salt as a mordant is based upon the fact that it hydrolyzes readily and the amphoteric hydroxide is precipitated within the fibers of the cloth. With excess sodium hydroxide, the salt forms *sodium stannate*, which is used to fireproof fabrics:

$$SnCl_4 + 6\,NaOH \longrightarrow Na_2SnO_3 + 4\,NaCl + 3\,H_2O$$

Stannic sulfide, SnS_2, is precipitated as a yellow solid from solutions of stannic salts or stannates by the action of hydrogen sulfide. It is soluble in both ammonium and sodium polysulfide solutions to form the thiostannate ion, SnS_3^{--}.

LEAD

Lead appears to have been one of the earliest known metals. Lead statues and objects have been found in Egyptian tombs, and the element is mentioned several times in the Old Testament. Uses of the metal in early times included water pipes, backing for glass mirrors, coffins, weights, net sinkers, and arrow tips.

Occurrence. Various estimates place the percentage of lead in the earth's crust at about 0.0005 per cent, which is much smaller than the percentage of such elements as zirconium, cerium, and vanadium, which we usually think of as being rare elements. There has been marked concentration of the limited natural occurrence of lead by percolating earth water and it occurs chiefly as the sulfide, *galena*. *Cerussite*, $PbCO_3$, and *anglesite*, $PbSO_4$, are less common ores but nevertheless are found in sufficient quantities to warrant mining operations.

Lead ores are widely distributed over the earth's surface, the metal being produced on all of the five continents. In North America, principal deposits are in the United States in Missouri, Kansas, Oklahoma, Arizona, and Idaho. In Europe, Spain is one of the principal sources. Australia is the largest producer in the British Empire.

Metallurgy. Lead ores are crushed and usually concentrated by gravity and flotation processes. The concentrate is then subjected to a partial roasting process in which part of the lead sulfide is changed to lead oxide and part to lead sulfate:

$$2\,PbS + 3\,O_2 \longrightarrow 2\,PbO + 2\,SO_2$$
$$PbS + 2\,O_2 \longrightarrow PbSO_4$$

The product of the roasting operation is mixed with limestone to act as a flux to remove siliceous impurities and coke to act as a reducing agent on the oxides present. The mixture is smelted in a small blast furnace. Although the reactions are somewhat complicated, the principal ones may be represented by the equations:

$$2\,PbO + C \longrightarrow 2\,Pb + CO_2$$
$$PbS + 2\,PbO \longrightarrow 3\,Pb + SO_2$$
$$PbSO_4 + PbS \longrightarrow 2\,Pb + 2\,SO_2$$

The product of the smelting is crude lead or lead bullion which contains small amounts of gold, silver, copper, and other metals. The metal may be partially refined by heating and stirring in the presence of air which oxidizes copper, arsenic, and antimony. The resulting oxides float on the surface of the metal and may be removed by skimming. To further purify the lead and to remove valuable metals, two methods are employed: (1) Betts' process and (2) Parkes process (see p. 455).

In the former process crude lead is made an anode in an electrolytic cell in which a sheet of pure lead is used as the cathode in an electrolyte of *fluosilicic acid*, H_2SiF_6. The process is similar to the refining of copper; lead dissolves from the anode and is plated out on the pure cathode. Gold, silver, and copper form anode mud, while other metallic ions remain in solution.

Properties. Lead is one of the most dense of the common metals with a specific gravity of 11.3. It is soft and malleable but has little tensile strength. A freshly cut surface has a bright metallic appearance but on standing becomes coated with a thin coherent layer of oxide and a basic carbonate. Because of a protective covering on its surface, the metal is relatively inactive and resistant to corrosion.

In the activity series it appears above hydrogen, but the action of acids on it is very slow. With hydrochloric and sulfuric acids a coating of lead chloride or lead sulfate quickly covers the surface, thus preventing further action. It is readily soluble in hot nitric acid, with the formation of the nitrate salt and oxides of nitrogen:

$$3\,Pb + 8\,HNO_3 \longrightarrow 3\,Pb(NO_3)_2 + 2\,NO + 4\,H_2O$$
$$\text{or} \qquad 3\,Pb + 8\,H^+ + 2\,NO_3^- \longrightarrow 3\,Pb^{++} + 2\,NO + 4\,H_2O$$

The metal slowly reacts with water which contains air, forming a loose deposit of lead hydroxide:

$$2\ Pb + 2\ H_2O + O_2 \longrightarrow 2\ Pb(OH)_2$$

Because of this action lead pipes should not be used for carrying drinking water since lead compounds are highly poisonous.

Finely divided lead burns in air with the formation of the oxide, PbO, and unites with oxygen at lower temperatures to form Pb_3O_4, a red oxide.

Uses. Because of its relative inactivity and the ease with which it may be worked, lead is used extensively in the manufacture of a wide variety of articles. One of its principal uses is in the manufacture of plates for storage batteries. Sheet lead is used extensively in lining sinks and vats, and for conduits for corrosive chemicals. Other uses include lead shot, cable coverings, lead foil, alloys, lead pipes, and production of white lead for paints. The use of lead in the United States is shown in Figure 138. Principal alloys are pewter, solder, type metal, and bearing metal.

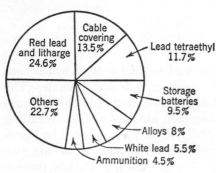

Fig. 138. Uses of lead.

Compounds of lead. Several oxides of lead are known, the more important ones being the *monoxide*, PbO; *red lead*, Pb_3O_4; and *lead dioxide*, PbO_2. Lead monoxide is a by-product of the refining of lead in which the crude metal is heated in contact with the air to oxidize other metals which may be present. During this process a considerable amount of lead is oxidized. The oxide is yellow in color and is known commercially as *litharge*. It finds use in the rubber industry, in the manufacture of optical glass, and mixed with glycerin as a plumber's cement. Pb_3O_4 may be obtained from lead or litharge by heating at temperatures below 500°. Nitric acid decomposes the oxide with the formation of lead dioxide:

$$Pb_3O_4 + 4\ HNO_3 \longrightarrow PbO_2 + 2\ Pb(NO_3)_2 + 2\ H_2O$$

PbO_2 is used as a pigment in paints, in storage battery plates, and in the manufacture of flint glass. Lead dioxide may also be prepared by the oxidation of litharge with a hypochlorite.

Lead resembles tin in that it forms series of divalent and tetravalent compounds. If sodium hydroxide is added to a soluble lead salt solution, white *plumbous hydroxide*, $Pb(OH)_2$, is precipitated:

$$Pb^{++} + 2\,OH^- \longrightarrow Pb(OH_2\downarrow$$

The hydroxide is amphoteric since an excess of alkali dissolves the precipitate forming plumbite ion, PbO_2^{--}:

$$Pb(OH)_2 + 2\,OH^- \longrightarrow PbO_2^{--} + 2\,H_2O$$

Although $Pb(OH)_4$ is not known, salts of the compound exist; for example, Pb_3O_4 or Pb_2PbO_4 may be considered a salt of H_4PbO_4, and *calcium plumbate*, Ca_2PbO_4, is well known. Lead with a valence of four does not produce metallic ions but is present in the plumbate radical, PbO_4^{----}.

Lead forms many salts, only a few of which will be considered here. *Lead nitrate* and *lead acetate* are both soluble salts and may be formed from litharge and nitric or acetic acid. The latter salt has a sweet taste and is sometimes called "sugar of lead" and like all soluble lead salts is highly poisonous. Lead chloride is precipitated when chloride ion is added to a solution containing lead ions:

$$Pb^{++} + 2\,Cl^- \longrightarrow PbCl_2\downarrow$$

The compound, however, is soluble in hot water, which enables its separation from mercurous and silver chlorides which are insoluble in both cold and hot water. Other halide salts of lead, *lead bromide* and *lead iodide*, are also insoluble. *Lead sulfide*, a black salt, is precipitated when H_2S is passed into alkaline or slightly acid solutions containing lead ions:

$$Pb^{++} + H_2S \longrightarrow PbS\downarrow + 2\,H^+$$

It is readily soluble in dilute nitric acid:

$$3\,PbS + 8\,HNO_3 \longrightarrow 3\,Pb(NO_3)_2 + 2\,NO + 4\,H_2O + 3\,S$$
$$\text{or} \quad 3\,PbS + 8\,H^+ + 2\,NO_3^- \longrightarrow 3\,Pb^{++} + 2\,NO + 4\,H_2O + 3\,S$$

Lead chromate, $PbCrO_4$, is precipitated as a yellow salt by the addition of a soluble chromate to a solution of lead ions:

$$Pb^{++} + CrO_4^{--} \longrightarrow PbCrO_4\downarrow$$

The reaction is frequently used as a test for the presence of lead ions. Commercially the chromate salt finds use as a pigment in paints. *Lead tetraethyl* is used in the manufacture of antiknock motor fuels. It is prepared by the reaction of ethyl bromide and a sodium-lead alloy according to the equation:

$$4\,C_2H_5Br + Na_4Pb \longrightarrow Pb(C_2H_5)_4 + 4\,NaBr$$

The manufacture of white lead. *Basic lead carbonate,* $(PbCO_3)_2Pb(OH)_2$, commonly called *white lead,* is an important compound of lead. It is one of the chief constituents of paints. The old

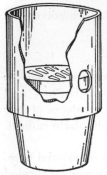

Dutch process for its manufacture is still widely used despite the economic impracticability of the method (Fig. 139). Metallic lead is cast into thin perforated discs called "buckles" to expose as large a surface as possible. These buckles are placed in earthenware jars above acetic acid solution. A layer of these jars is covered with spent tanbark, on which is placed another tier of jars. A room is thus filled with these pots and closed for a period of three or four months except for a certain amount of ventilation. The heat produced from the fermentation of the tanbark vaporizes the acetic acid which attacks the lead buckles. Carbon dioxide from the fermentation enters into the reaction, and the lead buckles are slowly changed into the basic carbonate. The reactions are probably complex, but the essential changes taking place may be represented by the equations:

Fig. 139. A clay pot used in the manufacture of white lead by the old Dutch process.

$$2\ Pb + 2\ HC_2H_3O_2 + O_2 \longrightarrow 2\ Pb(OH)C_2H_3O_2$$
$$3\ Pb(OH)C_2H_3O_2 + 2\ H_2CO_3 \longrightarrow (PbCO_3)_2Pb(OH)_2\downarrow + 3\ HC_2H_3O_2 + H_2O$$

Acetic acid is regenerated in the process and its action on the lead plates is therefore continuous. The swollen lead buckles are removed and ground to a fine powder under water. The unchanged lead settles rapidly to the bottom and is thus separated from the basic carbonate. The principal objection to the method from an economic standpoint is the long period of time necessary for the completion of the process with the attendant freezing of invested capital. However, white lead produced by the Dutch process is still preferred by many painters because of a certain physical structure of the product.

White lead of the same composition as Dutch white lead may be produced by other methods. In the Carter process, molten lead is atomized in a stream of air or superheated steam. The finely divided metal is rotated in wooden cylinders with acetic acid and carbon dioxide. Formation of the basic carbonate takes place relatively fast, the entire operation being completed in about fifteen days.

An electrolytic method is also used for the manufacture of the basic carbonate. Metallic lead is made the anode in a cell with an iron cathode, and an electrolyte containing sodium acetate and sodium carbonate. Lead dissolves and forms Pb^{++} at the anode. Precipitation of white lead follows:

$$3 Pb^{++} + 4 Na_2CO_3 + 2 H_2O \longrightarrow (PbCO_3)_2Pb(OH)_2 \downarrow + 2 NaHCO_3 + 6 Na^+$$

Annual production of white lead in the United States is about 85,000 tons.

Paints. Ordinary paints contain three essential ingredients: (1) a "vehicle," which is essentially a quick-drying oil; (2) a "body," or opaque substance of high covering power; and (3) a "pigment," if a color other than white is desired. Linseed oil is used as the vehicle or carrier of the body of the paint, which is usually white lead. The oil oxidizes in the air to form a hard, tough film which adheres to the surface of wood or other material and protects it. Linseed oil is usually boiled with lead and manganese oxides which act as catalysts and hasten the time of drying. White lead is the most common of the substances used for paint bodies because of its high covering power. The main objection to its use is the darkening action by hydrogen sulfide which produces black lead sulfide. Titanium oxide is now largely replacing white lead as a body material in paints.

Interior paints contain lithopone or zinc white as a body since these substances are not darkened by hydrogen sulfide. If a colored paint is desired, a pigment is added to the above ingredients. Common pigments are red lead, lead chromate, Prussian blue, iron oxide, chromium oxide, and carbon. In addition, a filler is frequently added to prevent the body from being spread too thin.

GROUP IV*B* ELEMENTS
TITANIUM, ZIRCONIUM, HAFNIUM, AND THORIUM

ELEMENT	SYMBOL	SP. GR.	MELTING POINT	BOILING POINT	VALENCE
Titanium	Ti	4.5	1800	3000	3, 4
Zirconium	Zr	6.4	1700	2900	4
Hafnium	Hf	12.1	1700	3200	4
Thorium	Th	11.2	1845	3000	4

The first three are transitional elements of Group IV*B*. Although thorium is a member of the actinide series in Group III*B*, it is usually included in a discussion of the properties of titanium, zirconium, and hafnium because of its close similarity in properties. The chemical properties of these elements resemble those of silicon but become increasingly more metallic until thorium definitely acts as a metal. The predominant valence is 4 and, much as silica, SiO_2, occurs naturally, the oxides of these elements occur in small amounts with formulas and mineral names being, respectively: TiO_2, *rutile;* ZrO_2, *zirconia;* HfO_2, *hafnia;* ThO_2, *thoria.* Titanium is more abundant than usually realized, constituting about 0.4 per cent of the earth's crust. Along with rutile, the mineral *ilmenite,* $FeTiO_3$, is fairly common. Zirconium and titanium ores are mined from diverse rock concentrations of their minerals. One large plant is effecting gravity and electromagnetic concentration of them from Florida heavy beach sands. There is very little hafnium and it is so intimately associated with zirconium that it is rarely separated therefrom; the chemistry and solubilities of their compounds are very similar. ThO_2, *thoria,* is concentrated from some black coastal sands of South America by gravity means since its density is quite high.

Titanium and zirconium metals may be prepared by reduction of their oxides with aluminum powder or by heating their chlorides with magnesium metal. Titanium and zirconium metals when pure are particularly resistant to corrosion and have high melting points. Ferrotitanium alloy is used in the steel industry as titanium removes nitrogen from iron. A ferrozirconium alloy, by virtue of the affinity of zirconium for oxygen and sulfur is used in attaining a purer fine-grained steel.

Pure TiO_2 is a particularly white substance which is taking the place of "white lead" in many paints. Smoke may be produced by emitting $TiCl_4$ liquid into moist air:

$$TiCl_4 + 2\,H_2O \longrightarrow TiO_2 + 4\,HCl$$

Finely divided TiO_2 in a fog of HCl constitutes the smoke. Zirconia has a high melting point and low electrical conductivity and is used as a refractory or for electrical insulators. Thoria mixed with a little ceria and heated to a high temperature exhibits the bright white light of Welsbach gas mantles.

EXERCISES

1. Point out similarities and differences between carbon, silicon, tin, and lead.
2. Describe the production of tin from cassiterite.
3. Discuss the relative advantages and disadvantages of "tin plate" and "galvanized iron."
4. Outline briefly the methods generally employed in recovering metallic lead from galena ores.
5. Describe the preparation of "white lead."
6. Write equations to show that both tin and lead may exhibit nonmetallic characteristics.

7. Give formulas and names of three compounds containing the elements lead, arsenic, and oxygen.

8. Show by equations how tin and lead differ in their reactions with concentrated nitric acid. On the basis of these reactions how could you easily differentiate between samples of tin and lead?

9. What tests would you apply in the laboratory to differentiate between PbO_2 and SnO_2? $PbCl_2$ and $SnCl_2$? $Pb(OH)_2$ and $Sn(OH)_2$? Pb^{++} and Sn^{++}?

10. Stannous chloride reduces ferric chloride according to the equation:

$$2\,FeCl_3 + SnCl_2 \longrightarrow 2\,FeCl_2 + SnCl_4$$

A 1 g. sample of iron ore is treated with hydrochloric acid to convert all the iron into $FeCl_3$. If 0.747 g. of $SnCl_2$ is required to reduce the iron obtained as $FeCl_3$, what is the per cent of iron in the sample?

11. Approximately how many pounds of As_2O_3 are used in making 1 ton of $Pb_3(AsO_4)_2$?

12. By use of a diagram account for the difference in melting points of different Pb-Sn solders. What is a eutectic?

REFERENCES

C. W. Cuno, "The Romance of Lead in Missouri," *Ind. and Eng. Chem.* **23,** 108 (1931).

G. O. Hiers and C. H. Rose, "Lead in Building and Construction," *ibid.* **27,** 1133 (1935).

O. C. Ralston and F. J. Cservenyak, "Potential Uses of Titanium Metal," *ibid.* **42,** 214 (1950).

Robert J. Nekervis, "Tin and Its Alloys," *ibid.* **43,** 2272 (1951).

W. B. Blumenthal, "Zirconium Compounds in Water Repellents for Fabrics," *ibid.* **42,** 640 (1950).

———, "Some Features of Zirconium Industry," *J. Chem. Ed.* **26,** 472 (1949).

Christopher C. Vogel, "The Manufacture of 'Ethyl' Antiknock Compound," *ibid.* **24,** 55 (1948).

C. L. Mantell, *Tin,* Reinhold.

Helena M. Meyer, "Titanium," 1220–1232, U. S. Dept. of Interior, *Minerals Yearbook* (1949).

XXXVII

Chromium, Manganese, and Related Metals

$$_{24}Cr^{52} \begin{smallmatrix} | & | & | & | \\ 2 & 8 & 13 & 1 \\ | & | & | & | \end{smallmatrix} \qquad _{25}Mn^{54.9} \begin{smallmatrix} | & | & | & | \\ 2 & 8 & 13 & 2 \\ | & | & | & | \end{smallmatrix}$$

ELEMENT	SYMBOL	SP. GR.	MELTING POINT	BOILING POINT	VALENCE
Chromium	Cr	7.1	1615	2200	2, 3, 6
Manganese	Mn	7.2	1260	1900	2, 3, 4, 6, 7

Although in different groups in the periodic table (Cr in Group VI and Mn in Group VII) chromium and manganese nevertheless behave similarly in many respects. Both exhibit several valences, acting as metallic elements in lower states of valence and as nonmetallic elements in higher valence states. Both chromium and manganese are widely used in alloys, particularly in alloy steels.

CHROMIUM

Occurrence and preparation. The principal ore of chromium is $Fe(CrO_2)_2$, called *chromite* or *chrome iron ore*. About one-half of the world's supply comes from Rhodesia; smaller amounts come from Russia, India, Greece, and Turkey. Very small deposits of the ore have been found in Maryland, Oregon, and Pennsylvania. The United States annually consumes about 300,000 tons of the element, nearly all of which is imported.

The pure metal is most readily obtained by the reduction of chromic oxide with metallic aluminum (Goldschmidt process, p. 476):

$$Cr_2O_3 + 2\,Al \longrightarrow 2\,Cr + Al_2O_3$$

Ferrochrome, an alloy of iron and chromium used in the production of steel alloys, is readily prepared from chromite and carbon in an electric furnace according to the reaction:

$$Fe(CrO_2)_2 + 4\,C \longrightarrow Fe + 2\,Cr + 4\,CO$$

Properties and uses. Chromium is a very hard, silvery white metal, very resistant to corrosion. It dissolves slowly in hydrochloric acid with the liberation of hydrogen. In nitric acid, chromium assumes a so-called passive state, a property also shown by iron and nickel. When these metals are placed in nitric acid a momentary reaction may take place but the action soon stops. The reasons for this behavior are not very well understood. Several theories have been advanced, one such theory assumes the formation of an allotropic form of the element which is insoluble in nitric acid; another assumes the formation of an insoluble oxide film on the surface of the metal which stops further action. It is claimed by others that mechanical or electrical strains may be set up in the metal. In any case the passivity can usually be removed by scratching the surface of the metal.

Alloyed with iron, chromium produces steels possessing properties of high tensile strength, toughness, hardness, and resistance to corrosion. *Stainless steel* contains 12 to 14 per cent chromium. Chromium steels are valuable in making cutting tools because of the hardness of the alloy. Other uses include armor plate, safes, and vaults. It has been found that engraved plates coated with a thin layer of chromium last twice as long as case hardened steel plates.

Chromium is popular as a plating for automobile parts such as radiators, for tableware, and for fixtures used for a variety of purposes. Such plated articles are resistant to corrosion and possess a bright, lasting luster.

Other alloys of chromium include *nichrome* (Ni, Cr, Fe) used as electrical resistance wire, and *stellite* (Cr, W, Co) used for cutting tools.

Compounds of chromium. The name of the element chromium is derived from the Greek word *chroma*, meaning color, since the compounds of the element are colored. Chromium exhibits three valences, 2, 3, 6, and forms three series of compounds. A few typical compounds will be discussed.

Chromous and chromic compounds. Of these the chromic compounds are the most stable and most important. Chromous salts may be prepared by reduction of chromic salts with a reducing agent such as Zn in the presence of an acid. Chromous ion is readily oxidized in the air to chromic ion, hence chromous compounds are very good reducing agents.

If NaOH is added to a solution containing Cr^{+++} ions, green gelatinous $Cr(OH)_3$ is precipitated. The hydroxide is amphoteric and will dissolve in an acid to form a chromic salt, *e.g.*

$$Cr(OH)_3 + 3\,H^+ \longrightarrow Cr^{+++} + 3\,H_2O$$

or dissolve in an excess of alkali to form a chromite:

$$Cr(OH)_3 + 3\,OH^- \longrightarrow CrO_3^{---} + 3\,H_2O$$

Chromic oxide, Cr_2O_3, may be produced by heating the hydroxide or by heating the metal in air at an elevated temperature. This compound, green in color, is used as a paint pigment and for coloring certain ceramic products.

Chromic sulfate, $Cr_2(SO_4)_3$, used in the tanning of leather may be produced from chromic hydroxide and sulfuric acid.

Beautiful reddish violet crystals of *chrome alum*, $K_2SO_4 \cdot Cr_2(SO_4)_3 \cdot 24\,H_2O$, may be obtained by crystallizing a solution containing equimolecular quantities of potassium and chromium sulfates.

Chromates and dichromates. Oxidation of chromites in an alkaline solution with sodium peroxide or other oxidizing agents results in the formation of chromates, *e.g.*

$$2\,CrO_3^{---} + 3\,Na_2O_2 + 4\,H_2O \longrightarrow 2\,CrO_4^{--} + 8\,OH^- + 6\,Na^+$$

The valence of the element changes from 3 to 6 in this oxidation and the color changes from green to a bright yellow. The chromium atom now appears in the chromate acid radical, thereby exhibiting its nonmetallic or acidic character in the higher state of oxidation.

Chromates are usually prepared from chromite ore by fusion with an alkali carbonate and an oxidizing agent, *e.g.*

$$2\,Fe(CrO_2)_2 + 4\,K_2CO_3 + 7\,KNO_3 \longrightarrow Fe_2O_3 \downarrow + 4\,K_2CrO_4 + 4\,CO_2 + 7\,KNO_2$$

Extraction of the fused mass with water yields a solution of K_2CrO_4, which is separated from the insoluble iron oxide by filtration.

Chromates are salts of *chromic acid*, H_2CrO_4. The anhydride of the acid, CrO_3, is readily obtained as a red crystalline compound by treatment of a chromate with concentrated sulfuric acid:

$$K_2CrO_4 + H_2SO_4 \longrightarrow K_2SO_4 + H_2O + CrO_3$$

In the presence of a dilute acid, chromates are converted to **dichromates** containing the orange red dichromate ion, $Cr_2O_7^{--}$, *e.g.*

$$2\,K_2CrO_4 + H_2SO_4 \longrightarrow K_2Cr_2O_7 + K_2SO_4 + H_2O$$

The addition of an alkali to a dichromate results in the re-formation of a chromate. This behavior is due to the equilibrium existing in solution between chromate and dichromate ions:

$$2\,CrO_4^{--} + 2\,H^+ \rightleftharpoons Cr_2O_7^{--} + H_2O$$

It is evident that the addition of H^+ ions (acid) will favor the reaction to the right while addition of OH^- ions (base) will shift the equilibrium to the left.

Both chromates and dichromates are effective oxidizing agents. Reduction products include chromic ions. In the tanning of leather a dichromate is reduced to a chromic salt which undergoes hydrolysis and precipitates $Cr(OH)_3$ within the leather, thereby preventing its decay. A mixture of a dichromate with concentrated sulfuric acid is used in cleaning laboratory glassware. $PbCrO_4$ and $BaCrO_4$ are used as yellow paint pigments. Basic lead chromate, $PbO \cdot PbCrO_4$, called *chrome red* is also used as a paint pigment.

MANGANESE

Manganese is found in nature principally as the ore MnO_2, called *pyrolusite*. It is a soft, black mineral which usually contains impurities of iron oxide, lime, and silica. Although small deposits of the ore have been found in the United States, this country produces only a small percentage of that consumed annually. Russia produces about half of the world's supply; smaller amounts are produced in Africa, India, and Brazil. Approximately 700,000 tons of the metal are consumed annually in this country, nearly all of which is imported. There is little demand for the pure metal. If manganese dioxide is heated with carbon, reduction takes place but the product contains carbon. The pure metal may be obtained by reduction of the dioxide with powdered aluminum (Goldschmidt process).

Properties and uses. The pure metal resembles iron in many properties. It has a somewhat reddish color, and is relatively soft. Like iron the addition of even a small percentage of carbon gives a very hard and brittle product. If the metal is heated to redness, reaction with steam takes place readily with the formation of hydrogen. In the activity series the element appears between aluminum and zinc; hence, manganese dissolves readily in acids.

About 90 per cent of the manganese consumed in this country is used in the manufacture of steel. In small percentages its presence aids in the removal of sulfur and oxygen; in larger amounts (10 to 12 per cent) the manganese alloys with the iron to produce a product which is very hard and tough, but which is more readily forged and machined than steels which are free of the element. Manganese steel is particularly well adapted to the construction of steel rails and parts of machinery which are subject to extreme wear. For the purpose of producing manganese steels, two alloys of iron and manganese are employed, *spiegeleisen* containing 10 to 20 per cent manganese and *ferromanganese* which contains 70 to 80 per cent manganese. Both are produced by the reduction of ores containing both manganese and iron oxides with carbon. *Manganese bronze* (Cu, Mn, Zn, Sn), an alloy particularly resistant to the action of sea water, is used in the production of ships' propellers. Another alloy, *magnanin* (Cu, Ni, Mn), is used as electrical resistance wire.

Compounds. Manganese exhibits valences of 2, 3, 4, 6, 7 and forms five series of compounds. A few typical compounds will be discussed.

Manganous compounds. The addition of an alkali to a solution containing manganous ions, Mn^{++}, precipitates white $Mn(OH)_2$. The hydroxide rapidly oxidizes in the air to brown $MnO(OH)_2$ or $MnO_2 \cdot H_2O$. The more important manganous compounds are the sulfate and chloride. The latter is readily prepared from MnO_2 and HCl (see p. 197). Pink MnS is precipitated from neutral or alkaline solutions containing Mn^{++} ions. In general, manganous compounds are fairly stable in the air.

Manganic compounds. The hydroxide and several manganic salts are known but they are unstable and are easily reduced to manganous compounds.

Tetravalent compounds. Of these, manganese dioxide is by far the most important. This compound which occurs in nature is insoluble in the nonreducing acids; in alkalies it does not dissolve readily but when fused with certain metallic oxides, forms *manganites* (*e.g.*, $CaMnO_3$), salts of the hypothetical acid, H_2MnO_3.

Manganates. When a manganous compound or MnO_2 is fused with an alkali hydroxide or carbonate in the presence of an oxidizing agent such as chlorate or nitrate, a greenish colored *manganate* salt is formed:

$$3\,MnO_2 + 2\,K_2CO_3 + 2\,KNO_3 \longrightarrow 3\,K_2MnO_4 + 2\,CO_2 + 2\,NO$$

This reaction is frequently employed as a qualitative test for the presence of manganese; the appearance of the green color indicates the presence of the element. The manganates are stable only in alkaline solution; when water or acid is added, oxidation and reduction take place with the formation of MnO_2 and a permanganate. This behavior serves as a means of preparing permanganates:

$$3\,K_2MnO_4 + 2\,H_2O \longrightarrow 2\,KMnO_4 + MnO_2 + 4\,KOH$$

Permanganates. *Permanganic* acid, $HMnO_4$, may be prepared from a manganous salt or manganese dioxide by reaction with HNO_3 and PbO_2:

$$2\,Mn^{++} + 6\,H^+ + 5\,PbO_2 \longrightarrow 5\,Pb^{++} + 2\,HMnO_4 + 2\,H_2O$$

The permanganates are purple in color and the above reaction is frequently employed as a qualitative test for manganese.

The most important of the permanganates is $KMnO_4$, prepared as explained in the previous section. It is used widely as an oxidizing agent. In acid solution it is reduced by Fe^{++}, $C_2O_4^{--}$, SO_2, and C_2H_5OH to Mn^{++}. Since the MnO_4^- ion is purple in color and the Mn^{++} ion practically colorless, the endpoint of the reaction is readily evident by the disappearance of color. In neutral or alkaline solution, the permanganates are reduced to MnO_2. $KMnO_4$ is used also as a disinfectant and as a medicinal.

Technetium and rhenium are elements appearing with manganese in Group VII. Both are very rare, and have no commercial uses at present. Rhenium compounds analogous to manganese compounds have been prepared. Technetium is so rare that little information about the element or its compounds is available in chemical literature at the present time.

RELATED METALS

$$_{42}\text{Mo}^{95.95} \quad {}^{2\ 8\ 18\ 13}_{} \qquad _{74}\text{W}^{183.9} \quad {}^{2\ 8\ 18\ 32\ 12\ 2}_{} \qquad _{92}\text{U}^{238.1} \quad {}^{2\ 8\ 18\ 32\ 18\ 13}_{}$$

ELEMENT	SYMBOL	SP. GR.	MELTING POINT	BOILING POINT	VALENCE
Molybdenum	Mo	10.2	2620	3700	2, 3, 4, 6
Tungsten	W	19.3	3370	5900	2, 4, 5, 6
Uranium	U	18.5	<1850	3500	3, 4, 6

Molybdenum, tungsten, and uranium. In properties these elements closely resemble chromium. Like chromium they exhibit a variable valence and form several series of compounds. Examples of a few similar compounds are $CaCrO_4$, calcium chromate; $CaMoO_4$, calcium molybdate; $CaWO_4$, calcium tungstate; $CaUO_4$, calcium uranate; $Na_2Cr_2O_7$, sodium dichromate; $Na_2U_2O_7$, sodium diuranate; $K_2SO_4 \cdot Cr_2(SO_4)_3 \cdot 24\ H_2O$, potassium chrome alum; $K_2SO_4 \cdot U_2(SO_4)_3 \cdot 24\ H_2O$, potassium uranium alum.

Like chromium, the principal use of these metals is in the elemental state. Molybdenum and tungsten form important alloys with steel.

The principal source of molybdenum is *molybdenite*, MoS_2, deposits of which are found in Colorado. It is a soft, shiny mineral which looks very much like graphite. The sulfide may be roasted to yield the oxide, which can then be reduced with carbon to produce metallic molybdenum. $PbMoO_4$, *wulfenite*, is mined in New Mexico and Norway.

Most of the molybdenum extracted from the above minerals is alloyed with iron to form *ferromolybdenum*, which is used in the production of special alloy steels. A steel containing molybdenum is quite heat resistant and may be used in making high-speed tools.

Tungsten is also an important element for alloy steels, particularly for armor plate and steels which are to be subjected to high temperatures. Tungsten steel may be heated to high temperatures without losing its "temper." Tungsten also finds use in various electrical devices, as filaments in incandescent lamps and radio tubes, as contact points in spark plugs, etc. The principal minerals of tungsten are *scheelite*, $CaWO_4$, and *wolframite*, $FeWO_4 \cdot MnWO_4$. The latter mineral gets its name from the German for tungsten, *wolfram;* the symbol for tungsten is also derived from this name.

Tungsten is a very hard metal and possesses the highest melting point of all the elements except carbon. It is very resistant to corrosion and to the action of chemicals.

Uranium has gained special attention recently as a source of material used in the production of atomic bombs (see p. 423). The radioactive properties of uranium are discussed in chapter XXXI. The principal sources of uranium are *pitchblende*, U_3O_8, and *carnotite*, $K_2O \cdot 2 UO_3 \cdot V_2O_5 \cdot 3 H_2O$. These minerals are found in the Belgian Congo and near Great Bear Lake in Canada. Small quantities of carnotite are mined in Colorado and Utah. All deposits of uranium minerals are now under the control of an international committee.

EXERCISES

1. Show similarities of chromium and manganese by listing formulas of analogous compounds of the two elements.
2. Complete and balance the equations:
   - (a) $FeSO_4 + KMnO_4 + H_2SO_4 \longrightarrow Fe_2(SO_4)_3 + K_2SO_4 +$
   - (b) $FeSO_4 + K_2Cr_2O_7 + H_2SO_4 \longrightarrow Fe_2(SO_4)_3 + K_2SO_4 +$
   - (c) $MnO_2 + HCl \longrightarrow$
   - (d) $Cr_2O_3 + Al \longrightarrow$
   - (e) $CrO_4^{--} + H^+ \longrightarrow$
   - (f) $K_2Cr_2O_7 + HBr \longrightarrow CrBr_3 +$
3. Outline a method by which you could prepare each of the following:
   - (a) $Mn(NO_3)_2$ from MnO_2
   - (b) K_2MnO_4 from MnO_2
   - (c) $CrCl_3$ from $K_2Cr_2O_7$
   - (d) $HMnO_4$ from $Mn(NO_3)_2$
   - (e) $K_2Cr_2O_7$ from K_2CrO_4
   - (f) $MnCl_2$ from $KMnO_4$
4. What desirable properties are possessed by chromium and manganese alloy steels?

5. A standard solution of $KMnO_4$ is often used in determining the amount of iron in a sample. Any iron in a sample is first converted to the ferrous state, after which the resulting solution may be titrated in acid solution with the standard $KMnO_4$ solution. The reaction is

$$5 \text{ Fe}^{++} + KMnO_4 + 8 \text{ H}^+ \longrightarrow K^+ + Mn^{++} + 5 \text{ Fe}^{+++} + 4 H_2O$$

The equivalent weight of an oxidizing agent (in this case $KMnO_4$) or reducing agent (in this case Fe^{++}) is determined by the number of electrons transferred per mole of substance. Since manganese changes from $+7$ to $+2$ in valence, 5 electrons are gained per mole of $KMnO_4$ and its equivalent weight is 158 (mol. wt.) divided by 5, or 31.6. A normal solution of $KMnO_4$ would contain 31.6 g. of that salt per liter of solution. Only one electron is lost per mole of Fe^{++}. Hence the equivalent weight of Fe^{++} is its atomic or ionic weight, *i.e.*, 55.8.

Suppose 50 ml. of a solution containing Fe^{++} is found to react with 100 ml. of 0.1 N $KMnO_4$ solution. (*a*) What is the normality of the Fe^{++} solution? (*b*) What weight of Fe^{++} would be contained in the solution? (*c*) If this amount of Fe^{++} were obtained from a 1 g. sample of iron ore, what would be the percentage iron in the sample? Ans. (*a*) 0.2, (*c*) 55.8.

6. (Work ex. 5 before attempting this one.) A standard solution of $K_2Cr_2O_7$ is also frequently used in determining Fe^{++} in a sample by titration in acid solution. The equation for the reaction is

$$6 \text{ Fe}^{++} + K_2Cr_2O_7 + 14 \text{ H}^+ \longrightarrow 2 K^+ + 2 \text{ Cr}^{+++} + 6 \text{ Fe}^{+++} + 7 H_2O$$

The molecular weight of $K_2Cr_2O_7$ is 294.2. (*a*) What is the equivalent weight of $K_2Cr_2O_7$? (*b*) A 1 g. sample of iron ore is treated to obtain iron as Fe^{++}. 25 ml. of 0.1 N $K_2Cr_2O_7$ solution is used to titrate the iron. What is the percentage iron in the sample? Ans. (*b*) 13.95.

7. Sodium oxalate ($Na_2C_2O_4$, mol. wt. 134) may be used to standardize a solution of $KMnO_4$. The reaction is

$$5 \text{ Na}_2C_2O_4 + 2 KMnO_4 + 16 \text{ H}^+ \longrightarrow$$
$$10 \text{ Na}^+ + 2 K^+ + 2 Mn^{++} + 10 CO_2 + 8 H_2O$$

If 50 ml. of $KMnO_4$ solution is used to titrate 0.335 g. of pure $Na_2C_2O_4$, what is the normality of the permanganate solution? Ans. 0.1.

8. How would you differentiate chemically between Mn and Cr? Mn^{++} and Cr^{+++}? MnO_4^- and $Cr_2O_7^{--}$? MnO_2 and Cr_2O_3?

9. Name the compounds and give the valence of Cr or Mn in $Cr_2(SO_4)_3$; H_2CrO_4; $CrCl_2$; MnS; $KMnO_4$; Na_2MnO_4.

10. An ore contains 1.2 per cent tungsten as water-insoluble $CaWO_4$ in a water-insoluble siliceous rock. It is gravity concentrated to an 8 per cent tungsten-containing concentrate — no chemical change involved. The ground concentrate is now heat treated in a furnace with Na_2CO_3. Write an equation showing the reaction of calcium tungstate with soda. The resulting sodium tungstate may be water leached from the insoluble silicate and calcium carbonate. Write an equation to show what happens when calcium chloride is added to the sodium tungstate. What percentage of tungsten is in the precipitate? Write equations showing what would happen to any $PbMoO_4$ that might be present in the ore during the above processing.

REFERENCES

W. M. Latimer and J. H. Hildebrand, *Reference Book of Inorganic Chemistry,* Macmillan.

L. M. Williams, "Manganese," *Ind. and Eng. Chem.* **32,** 1168 (1940).

H. W. Davis, "Molybdenum," U. S. Dept. of Interior, *Minerals Yearbook* (1949), 785–791.

—— "Tungsten," *ibid.* 1233–1247.

J. J. Katz and E. Rabinowitch, *The Chemistry of Uranium,* McGraw-Hill, 1951.

U. S. Atomic Energy Commission and U. S. Geol. Survey, *Prospecting for Uranium,* U. S. Government Printing Office, 1949.

XXXVIII

Metals of Group VIII *B*

$$_{26}\text{Fe}^{55.85} \quad {}^{2\ 8\ 14\ 2} \qquad _{27}\text{Co}^{58.94} \quad {}^{2\ 8\ 15\ 2} \qquad _{28}\text{Ni}^{58.69} \quad {}^{2\ 8\ 16\ 2}$$

$$_{44}\text{Ru}^{101.7} \quad {}^{2\ 8\ 18\ 15\ 1} \qquad _{45}\text{Rh}^{102.9} \quad {}^{2\ 8\ 18\ 16\ 1} \qquad _{46}\text{Pd}^{106.7} \quad {}^{2\ 8\ 18\ 17\ 1}$$

$$_{76}\text{Os}^{190.2} \quad {}^{2\ 8\ 18\ 32\ 14\ 2} \qquad _{77}\text{Ir}^{193.1} \quad {}^{2\ 8\ 18\ 32\ 15\ 2} \qquad _{78}\text{Pt}^{195.2} \quad {}^{2\ 8\ 18\ 32\ 16\ 2}$$

METAL	SYMBOL	SP. GR.	MELTING POINT	BOILING POINT	VALENCE
Iron	Fe	7.86	1535	3000	2, 3
Cobalt	Co	8.9	1480	2900	2, 3
Nickel	Ni	8.9	1450	2900	2, 3
Ruthenium	Ru	12.2	2450	>2700	2, 3, 4, 6, 7
Rhodium	Rh	12.5	1950	>2500	2, 4
Palladium	Pd	12.0	1555	2200	2, 4
Osmium	Os	22.5	2700	>5300	2, 3, 4, 8
Iridium	Ir	22.4	2350	>4800	3, 4
Platinum	Pt	21.5	1750	4300	2, 3, 4, 6

Group VIII*B* contains three triads of elements as listed above. These triads appear at the middle of long periods of elements in the periodic table and are members of transition series of elements. The elements of any given triad have many similar properties, but there are marked differences between the properties of the triads, particularly between the first triad and the other two. Iron, cobalt, and nickel are much more active than members of the other two triads; these elements are also much more abundant in the earth's crust. Metals of the second and third triads have many properties in common and are usually grouped together and called the "platinum metals."

IRON AND STEEL

Without question iron is the most important and useful of the metals. The period in which we now live is often designated as the age of iron and steel, and it has been said that we probably could get along without all the other metals better than we could do without iron. Evidence indicates that iron was known in prehistoric times although it seems likely that copper and bronze were known and used prior to its discovery. Ores of the metal are easily reduced with carbon, and its discovery probably came about by accidentally heating the ore in a wood fire.

The importance of iron as a commercial product depends upon the fact that the properties of the metal may be made to vary by the addition of small amounts of alloying elements, and, equally important, the properties vary with the heat treatment of the metal. Less than one per cent of carbon added to iron changes the relatively soft metal into a hard, strong product. As a matter of fact, the pure metal has little industrial importance; it is much too soft and weak for most purposes. However, the addition of small amounts of foreign substances so completely alters the original properties of the iron that it becomes adaptable to a wide variety of uses. Principal products of iron are cast iron, wrought iron, and steel.

Occurrence. Iron stands fourth in abundance among the chemical elements present in the earth's crust (see p. 16). Studies of earth density and of the rate of travel of vibrations through it indicate that the center of the earth is probably composed chiefly of iron, in which case iron would be the most abundant of the chemical elements of the whole earth. The element is rarely found in the free state except in meteorites, which are largely iron with a small percentage of nickel. Compounds of iron are widely distributed and are constituents of many rocks and soils.

Ferrous iron compounds are greenish, whereas ferric compounds are yellow to brown or red. An esthetic chemist gazing at the magnificent coloring of the Grand Canyon of the Colorado might speculate that this would be a drab-colored world without iron compounds. Compounds of the other abundant elements are largely colorless. Even the natural and sometimes artificial pink of cheeks and lips is due to iron compounds. Rocks or soils with a reddish color usually contain relatively large amounts of iron. Iron is present in the hemoglobin of the blood. Concentrations of naturally occurring iron oxides are ores which are used for the production of iron and its products. Among these are *hematite*, Fe_2O_3, and *magnetite*, Fe_3O_4, a mineral having magnetic properties and commonly called *lodestone*.

Eighty per cent of the ore mined in the United States comes from the Mesabi Range in the Lake Superior region of Minnesota. Most of the ore from this region is obtained by the open-pit mining method; huge steam shovels scoop it up from the surface. Other iron-producing areas of the United States are Alabama and Michigan.

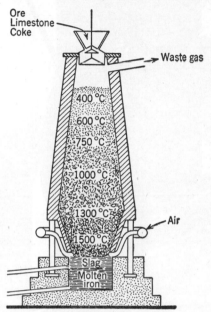

Iron pyrites, FeS₂, often called "fool's gold" because of its yellow, flaky appearance, is another abundant naturally occurring compound of iron but is not much used for commercial extraction because of the greater ease of obtaining iron from other minerals. In England the principal ore of iron is *siderite*, $FeCO_3$.

Metallurgy. Iron may be obtained from its oxide ores by reduction with carbon. This operation is carried out in a huge cylindrical furnace called a *blast furnace*, a cross section of which is shown diagrammatically in Figure 140. These furnaces vary in height from 75 to 100 feet and are 20 to 25 feet in diameter near the base. They

Fig. 140. Blast furnace for the manufacture of pig iron.

are constructed from heavy steel plates and lined with firebrick. Ore, limestone, and coke are introduced at the top of the furnace through a series of hoppers, which are manipulated so that gases produced by the reactions are not lost. The operation of a blast furnace is continuous, and at intervals the iron is tapped and run off. The usual impurity present in iron ore is silica, so limestone is added as a flux to form a slag which may be drawn off. In the event that the impurity in the ore is of a basic nature, such as carbonates of calcium or magnesium, then silica is added as a flux to form the slag. The coke serves as a fuel to melt the iron and as a reducing agent to convert the oxide ore to metal. Near the bottom of the furnace a hot blast of air is introduced through *tuyères* to burn the coke. An average charge for a furnace at 15 minute intervals is: ore, 9 tons; limestone, 3 tons; coke, 5 tons. In addition about 12 tons of air are necessary to burn the coke in this charge. Air combines with the carbon and forms carbon dioxide

$$C + O_2 \longrightarrow CO_2$$

Fig. 141. Blast furnace and stoves for heating air.

which then passes upward through the hot carbon above and is reduced
to carbon monoxide

$$CO_2 + C \longrightarrow 2\,CO$$

The carbon monoxide ascends toward the upper part of the furnace
and reduces the ore in successive stages, first to magnetic oxide of iron,
then ferrous oxide, and finally iron, according to the equations:

$$3\,Fe_2O_3 + CO \longrightarrow 2\,Fe_3O_4 + CO_2$$
$$Fe_3O_4 + CO \longrightarrow 3\,FeO + CO_2$$
$$FeO + CO \longrightarrow Fe + CO_2$$

Slag formation occurs near the central portion of the furnace according
to the reactions:

$$CaCO_3 \longrightarrow CaO + CO_2$$
$$CaO + SiO_2 \longrightarrow CaSiO_3$$

Molten iron and slag collect in the *crucible* at the bottom of the furnace
where they may be drawn off from time to time. The temperatures
in the various parts of the furnace are shown in the diagram. The
iron which is tapped from the furnace is an impure variety called *pig
iron*. It contains a considerable amount of dissolved carbon as well
as sulfur and phosphorus as impurities. A large blast furnace produces
approximately 600 tons of pig iron every 24 hours. In addition to the
slag a third product of the blast furnace is a mixture of gases which is
sometimes called *blast furnace gas* or *producer gas*. Besides carbon
dioxide and nitrogen (from the air) the furnace gas contains considerable carbon monoxide and some hydrogen, both of which are combustible. The mixture therefore has fuel value and much is employed in
preheating air in giant stoves for use in the blast furnace. The preheated air enters the blast furnace at a high temperature and combustion of the coke ensues rapidly, thus producing a higher temperature
than if cold air were used. Blast furnace gas is removed near the top
of the furnace. The products of the furnace with the approximate
composition of each are shown in Table 36. Slag is used for road ballast
and in the manufacture of certain types of cement.

Due to the impurities present in pig iron, the product cannot be
welded or forged and possesses little tensile strength. If pig iron is
melted with scrap iron, *cast iron* is produced which is useful for objects
that are not subject to sudden jarring or shock such as radiators,
parts for stoves, and certain types of heavy machinery. Cast iron is
comparatively easily melted and expands when cooled and thus fills
every part of the mold into which it is poured. Two varieties of cast
iron are defined depending upon the rate at which the molten metal is

cooled. *Gray cast iron* is produced by cooling the metal slowly, in which case the carbon present in the iron separates as graphite. If the metal is suddenly quenched by plunging into water or oil, *white cast iron* is formed in which the carbon remains combined with the iron as the chemical compound *cementite*, a carbide of iron of the composition Fe_3C.

TABLE 36

PRODUCTS OF THE BLAST FURNACE AND THEIR
COMPOSITION

Pig Iron		Gases		Slag
Fe	93–95 %	CO	25 %	Chiefly $CaSiO_3$
C	3–5 %	CO_2	13 %	Some $FeSiO_3$
Si	1 %	N_2	57 %	$Ca_3(PO_4)_2$
S	less than 1 %	H_2	3 %	$MgSiO_3$
P	0.1–0.3 %			

The location of blast furnaces for the production of pig iron depends to a great extent upon the accessibility of the three principal raw materials used in the furnace, namely, ore, coal (from which coke is obtained), and limestone. Principal iron and steel producing localities in the United States are Pittsburgh, Birmingham, Ala., and the Chicago district. Pittsburgh is admirably located for steel production because of its proximity to the limestone and coal deposits in Pennsylvania. The ore is transported by ship from the Lake Superior ore region to Buffalo where it is shipped overland the relatively short distance to Pittsburgh. Similarly, steel mills in the Chicago district are conveniently located near coal deposits, and water transportation through the Great Lakes brings the ore directly to the furnaces on Lake Michigan.

Steel. The manufacture of steel consists essentially in the purification of pig iron, which, as has been pointed out, contains a rather high percentage of carbon in addition to smaller amounts of silicon, phosphorus, and sulfur. Since the latter three impurities are objectionable, it is desirable to remove as much of them as is possible. However, a certain amount of carbon is desirable as the properties of iron are considerably modified by even small percentages. Steel is a product which is nearly pure iron containing relatively small and varying amounts of carbon. The more common types of steel and their uses are shown below:

Type	Carbon Content	Uses
Low carbon steel	less than 0.3%	rivets, wire, and nails
Medium carbon steel	0.3 to 0.8%	railroad rails and axles
High carbon, or tool steel	0.8 to 2%	tools, springs, and files

In recent years small amounts of many other metals have been added to steel to impart certain characteristic properties. The addition of manganese produces a very tough steel; molybdenum and chromium yield a steel which is resistant to corrosion; tungsten forms an alloy which retains its temper when heated.

The removal of the impurities from pig iron is effected by oxidation, and the process depends upon the fact that the *impurities in the iron are more easily oxidized than the iron itself.* There are two principal processes for the conversion of pig iron to steel: (1) the Bessemer process and (2) the open hearth process. Each will be discussed briefly.

Bessemer process. This process was invented by an American, Kelly, in 1852 and modified and improved a few years later by Bessemer, an Englishman. The Bessemer converter is a pear-shaped furnace of about 15 tons capacity and mounted on trunions which allows it to be tilted to any desired angle. A cross sectional diagram of the furnace is shown in Figure 142. The furnaces are lined with either magnesia or silica brick depending upon the impurities present in the pig iron to be treated. Pig iron containing relatively large percentages of phosphorus and sulfur must be treated in a magnesium oxide brick-lined furnace, since the lining acts as a flux to combine with these two elements to form slag. Most of the converters in the United States are silica-lined since they use pig iron produced from ores of low phosphorus and sulfur content. The bottom of the furnace is perforated with a number of small holes through which air may be blown into the converter.

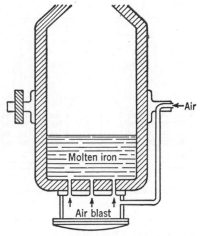

Fig. 142. Bessemer converter for the manufacture of steel.

The converter is charged with about 15 tons of molten pig iron while in a nearly horizontal position. The air blast is then turned on and the converter is tilted to a vertical position. The blast of air passing through the molten iron oxidizes the impurities present; the carbon is nearly completely removed as carbon monoxide and carbon dioxide, and the oxides of sulfur and phosphorus form a slag with the basic lining of the converter. A good deal of heat is produced from the oxidation of carbon, and as a result a dazzling shower of sparks is emitted from the mouth of the converter. A single "blow" requires only fifteen to twenty minutes after which the steel produced is poured into ingot molds. Enough carbon is added to the mold to bring the carbon content of the steel up to the desired percentage. The advantage of the process lies in the rapidity with which steel may be produced; its disadvantage is a lack of uniformity of the finished product as the reactions take place so rapidly that careful control is not possible.

Basic open hearth process. Most of the steel in the United States is produced by this process. The basic open hearth furnace consists of a shallow crucible lined with calcite and magnesia. Below the

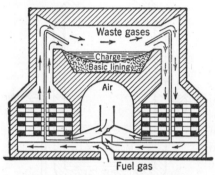

Fig. 143. Open hearth furnace.

crucible is a checkerwork of brick so arranged that the heat from the spent gases is used to preheat the entering gases (Fig. 143). Fuel for the furnace is either producer gas from the blast furnace or oil in the form of a spray. The fuel gas and oxygen are passed over the hot brick checkerwork and allowed to come together just above the crucible of the furnace. Combustion takes place rapidly because the gases have been preheated to a high temperature. The spent gases pass through the checkerwork on the other side of the furnace where their heat is imparted to the brickwork. Every few minutes the direction of the gases is reversed so that the incoming gases are always preheated to a high temperature, the spent gases meantime passing over the checkerwork which has been cooled by the incoming gases.

The capacity of an open hearth furnace varies between 50 and 150 tons. The furnace is charged with molten pig iron, limestone to act as a flux, and scrap which acts as an oxidizing agent to oxidize the carbon and other impurities. The slag floats on top of the molten iron and prevents its rapid oxidation by incoming air used to burn the fuel gas. Carbon is slowly oxidized and converted to carbon dioxide. From eight to twelve hours are required for the oxidation and hence very careful control of the product is possible. When the carbon content has been reduced to the required percentage and the sulfur and phosphorus have been removed, the iron is tapped and run into ingot molds from which the ingots are finally removed, taken to the rolling mill, and processed. If an alloy steel is wanted, the above process is followed except just before tapping a certain amount of the alloying element is added to the furnace. Sulfur and phosphorus are particularly objectionable in steel as they give a brittle product. Hence, these latter elements must be reduced to a small percentage.

Wrought iron. The purest form of commercial iron is *wrought iron*, which is produced in a *puddling* furnace (Fig. 144), arranged in such a way that the heat is reflected onto the surface of the metal from the low roof. The bottom of the furnace is covered with a layer of ore which acts as an oxidizing agent. The furnace is charged with pig iron and some limestone is added as a flux. Carbon and sulfur are oxidized and lost by volatilization while the other elements are oxidized and combine with the lime to form a slag. As the impurities are removed, the melting point of the iron gradually rises and the mass becomes plastic or semifluid. In order to increase the rate of oxidation the mass is stirred or

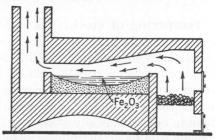

Fig. 144. A puddling furnace for the preparation of wrought iron.

"puddled" with long iron rods called "rabbles." As the mass becomes less fluid, it is removed on the rabbles in balls weighing about one hundred pounds each. These plastic balls of iron are subjected to squeezing or rolling to remove most of the slag. Not all of the slag is removed, however, as examination shows the product to consist of long fibers of iron separated by thin sheets of slag. Wrought iron is very tough and strong and is used in the manufacture of such articles as horseshoes, chains, and other products, where these properties are desired. Wrought iron, about 99.8 per cent iron, is more expensive than steel because of the labor of producing it. In recent years it has been largely replaced by low carbon steels which have similar properties and are produced much less expensively.

Crucible steel. Very high grades of steel such as are used in watch-springs, razor blades, files, etc., are usually prepared by heating small batches of wrought iron or better grades of open hearth steel in small crucibles. An electric furnace allows a very careful control of temperature. Carbon and alloying elements may be added in required amounts. Such high grade steels are called "crucible steels."

Allotropic forms of iron. The properties of steel may be modified greatly by conditioning the crystalline form of the iron. At ordinary temperatures a body-centered cubic lattice form of iron exists which is comparatively soft and magnetic and in which carbon is insoluble — it is termed *alpha* iron. When alpha iron is heated above 900°, an allotropic modification known as *gamma* iron forms as a face-centered cubic lattice. Gamma iron is very hard and nonmagnetic and possesses the important property of forming a solid solution with carbon. At 1400° a further allotrope is formed called *delta* iron. The properties of the latter are not well known. The equilibrium relations between the three allotropes may be shown in the following manner:

$$\text{Alpha} \underset{}{\overset{900°}{\rightleftharpoons}} \text{Gamma} \underset{}{\overset{1400°}{\rightleftharpoons}} \text{Delta}$$

Tempering of steel. If a steel at a temperature above 900° is quickly cooled by "quenching" in water or oil, the gamma iron with its hardness and carbon solubility does not have time to alter to alpha iron with its properties of softness and carbon insolubility. At room temperatures the unstable gamma iron would require centuries to transform completely to the alpha form. Gamma iron is much too hard to be mechanically worked or fashioned. A steel containing some gamma iron for strength may be heated to some temperature between 200° and 600° for a time to enable more or less *tempering* of its hardness — to enable a desired amount of gamma to convert to alpha iron according to the particular strength and hardness qualities wanted in the product. During this reheating, cooling stresses are also removed.

In the higher carbon steels, a very hard compound of iron and carbon called cementite, Fe_3C, appears to be formed. Crystals of cementite which may be viewed through a microscope have marked effects on the properties of the steel. Heat treatment will cause some of the cementite to decompose to iron and graphite flakes, resulting in a softer product. The size of crystals formed is also important in determining properties — a steel of minute crystals or grains has more strength than a coarse-grained product. Grain size is somewhat regulated by heat treatment and also by mechanical pounding or pulling of the metal. In general a mechanically worked product has smaller grain size and greater tensile strength.

Case hardening. A low carbon steel makes a good structural beam; it has toughness, strength, and yet enough bend to it that it does not readily break. However, a low carbon steel being relatively soft is easily surface marred. An industrial process consists in heating a low carbon steel in a carbon or carbon-compound (usually cyanide) bath, in which event some carbon dissolves into the outer $\frac{1}{16}$ inch or so of the iron to yield a high carbon, hard, wear-resisting surface. This process is called *case hardening*.

Properties of pure iron. Pure iron is a soft, silver-white metal with a melting point of 1535°. The metal is fairly high in the activity series and is thus classed as one of the more active metals. It does not react with cold water but decomposes steam to form hydrogen. It readily displaces hydrogen from hydrochloric and sulfuric acids. When placed in concentrated nitric acid the metal assumes a *passive* condition, which, according to one explanation, is due to the formation of an adherent oxide film. If the surface is scratched, the metal acts in a normal manner. The metal is magnetic, which makes it useful in the construction of motors, generators, and other electrical devices.

Corrosion. Iron exposed to the action of moist air rusts rapidly with the formation of a loose, crumbly deposit of the oxide. The oxide does not adhere to the surface of the metal as does aluminum oxide and certain other metal oxides, but instead peels off thus exposing a fresh surface of iron to the action of the air. As a result, a piece of iron will rust away completely in a relatively short time unless steps are taken to prevent the corrosion. The mechanism of rusting is rather obscure, but it has been established that the rust is a hydrated oxide of iron and is formed by the action of both oxygen and moisture, and is markedly enhanced by the presence of minute amounts of carbon dioxide.

Corrosion of iron is inhibited by coating it with numerous substances. It may be covered with paint, an aluminum powder gilt, with tin, or with organic tarry substances. Galvanizing or sherardizing iron with zinc has been discussed (p. 466). Alloying iron with metals such as nickel or chromium yields a less corrosive steel.

Compounds of iron. Iron forms two series of compounds, *ferrous*, in which the valence of iron is two, and *ferric* compounds, in which the valence is three. Solutions of these compounds produce ferrous, Fe^{++}, and ferric, Fe^{+++}, ions respectively. Ferric compounds are the more stable as, in general, ferrous compounds may be oxidized to the higher state of valence quite easily, often by the oxygen of the air.

The addition of a soluble hydroxide to a solution containing ferrous ions results in the formation of a pale green precipitate of *ferrous hydroxide*. The compound is easily oxidized by oxygen of the air and soon after precipitation, unless oxygen is excluded, oxidation to *ferric hydroxide* occurs. Ferric hydroxide is precipitated as a brownish-red solid by the addition of a soluble base to a solution containing ferric ions. Neither ferrous nor ferric hydroxides are amphoteric and are thus insoluble in an excess of base.

Iron compounds with alkali cyanides form two series of complex salts — *ferrocyanides* which produce $Fe(CN)_6^{----}$ ions in solution and *ferricyanides* which produce $Fe(CN)_6^{---}$ ions. *Potassium ferrocyanide*, $K_4Fe(CN)_6$, is produced by heating together organic matter, potassium carbonate, and scrap iron. The salt is obtained as yellow crystals by evaporation of the solution obtained in leaching the above mixture. *Potassium ferricyanide* may be obtained as dark red crystals by oxidizing potassium ferrocyanide with chlorine. These two compounds are important in testing for the presence of ferrous and ferric ions. Ferric ions react with ferrocyanides to form a characteristic blue precipitate of *ferric ferrocyanide*, called *Prussian blue*, e.g.

$$4\ \overset{\text{III}}{\text{Fe}^{+++}} + 3\ \overset{\text{II}}{\text{Fe}(\text{CN})_6}^{----} \longrightarrow \overset{\text{III}}{\text{Fe}_4}[\overset{\text{II}}{\text{Fe}}(\text{CN})_6]_3 \downarrow$$

Ferrous ions react with ferricyanide ions to form *ferrous ferricyanide*, a blue insoluble compound which is called *Turnbull's blue*, e.g.

$$3\ \overset{\text{II}}{\text{Fe}^{++}} + 2\ \overset{\text{III}}{\text{Fe}(\text{CN})_6}^{---} \longrightarrow \overset{\text{II}}{\text{Fe}_3}[\overset{\text{III}}{\text{Fe}}(\text{CN})_6]_2 \downarrow$$

The two colors are nearly identical blues in the above cases; nevertheless, the presence of ferrous and ferric ions may be detected in a sample even in the presence of each other. The formation of the blue precipitate by the addition of a ferrocyanide to a solution must mean the presence of ferric ions and the formation of the blue precipitate by the addition of a ferricyanide must mean that ferrous ions are present. Of course, the formation of the blue precipitate with both ferro- and ferricyanide would mean that both ferrous and ferric ions were present in the sample.

If iron is dissolved in dilute sulfuric acid and the solution evaporated to dryness, light green crystals of the heptahydrate of ferrous sulfate, $FeSO_4 \cdot 7\ H_2O$, sometimes called *green vitriol* or *copperas*, are obtained. This salt is one of the more widely used salts of iron and much is obtained by the evaporation of "pickling" solutions, which are by-products of the cleaning of iron by dipping it into sulfuric acid before galvanization. The compound is important as a disinfectant and weed killer and is also used in the purification of water and as a reducing agent in the laboratory. If equimolecular quantities of ferrous sulfate and ammonium sulfate are dissolved in water and the solution allowed to evaporate, bluish-green crystals of *Mohr's salt*, $FeSO_4 \cdot (NH_4)_2SO_4 \cdot 6\ H_2O$, are obtained. This compound is ordinarily employed in quantitative procedures as a reducing agent as it is more stable than green vitriol.

Blueprints. Blueprint paper is made by dipping paper into a solution of ferric ammonium citrate and potassium ferricyanide. When such paper is covered with tracing cloth or tracing paper on which the lines of a drawing are recorded in black ink, and exposed to sunlight, the ferric salt will be reduced to a ferrous salt where the light comes in contact with the paper. On wetting the blueprint paper the ferrous salt reacts with the ferricyanide to form Turnbull's blue. The latter compound will form everywhere on the paper except directly under the black lines of the drawing. On washing the paper, the ferricyanide and ferric salt remaining are removed and the drawing appears as white lines on a blue background.

COBALT AND NICKEL

The largest source of nickel and cobalt ores is a deposit in the Sudbury district of Ontario, Canada. The minerals are largely sulfides and arsenides of cobalt and nickel associated with some copper, silver, and iron sulfides. Because of the mixed nature of the ore deposit, the metallurgy of obtaining the metals is quite complex. Rock masses containing 2 to 3 per cent of nickel silicate have been found in southern Oregon and northwest Washington. Research is now being carried out to develop an economical method of extracting the nickel.

Both cobalt and nickel depend for their major uses on the property of the elements of resisting corrosion. The metals may be plated electrolytically over iron to give a cobalt or nickel plate or may be alloyed with other metals to give corrosion-resisting products. Nickel alloys are used in coinage, in electrical resistance wire (nichrome), and in a noncorrosive *monel metal*, which is 72 per cent nickel, 26.5 per cent copper, and 1.5 per cent iron. A very hard, noncorrosive alloy called *stellite* contains cobalt, chromium, and tungsten.

Like iron, cobalt and nickel form two series of compounds with characteristic valences of 2 and 3. The divalent compounds are the more stable and more important. Cobalt salts in hydrated form or in solution are usually pink or blue; nickel salts are usually green. A dilute solution of $CoCl_2 \cdot 6 H_2O$, light pink in color, may be used as an invisible ink. After drying, heat will bring out a visible blue color due to the dehydration of the salt. Cobalt oxide may be incorporated into glass or glazes to give a beautiful blue color. Both cobalt and nickel may be detected by a borax bead test; cobalt gives a dark blue, nickel a brown color.

THE PLATINUM METALS

Platinum and the platinumlike elements, ruthenium, rhodium, palladium, osmium, and iridium, are somewhat like gold and silver in that they do not displace hydrogen from mineral acids; they occur in the free state as nuggets or specks in alluvial or quartz rock, have relatively high densities, and may be fashioned into polished objects which are resistant to tarnishing. As transition elements below iron, cobalt, and nickel in Group VIII, they resemble the latter in electronic structure, general catalytic activity, and tendency to form complex compounds.

Predominant valences for the elements are two and four. *Platinous chloride*, $PtCl_2$, *platinic chloride*, $PtCl_4$, *palladous chloride*, $PdCl_2$, and *palladic chloride*, $PdCl_4$, are well known compounds. The tendency of the elements to form complex compounds is evidenced in *potassium chloroplatinate*, K_2PtCl_6, and *potassium chloro-osmiate*, K_2OsCl_6. When platinum is dissolved in aqua regia, *chloroplatinic acid*, H_2PtCl_6, is formed.

Ruthenium and osmium have the unusual property of exhibiting a valence of eight in the compounds OsO_4 and RuO_4. The latter are produced when the finely divided metals are heated in oxygen. OsO_4 melts at 40° C. and boils at 130° C.; its vapor is poisonous, irritating to the eyes, and has the odor of bromine.

Although rhodium and iridium resemble platinum in many chemical properties, they also are like cobalt, which is above them in the periodic table. Like cobalt, they exhibit a valence of three in numerous complex compounds, as for example: $K_3Co(NO_2)_6$, $K_3Rh(NO_2)_6$, and $K_3Ir(NO_2)_6$.

Platinum is placer mined from alluvial gravel in the Ural Mountains and concentrated from the rock material with which it is associated by virtue of its high specific gravity (21.5). Only osmium and iridium have higher densities than platinum. Small amounts of platinum are associated with gold in Colombia, South Africa, and the western United States. Other platinum metals are found associated with or alloyed with platinum. Platinum and palladium are by-products in the purification of nickel from certain Canadian ores.

Platinum is used in jewelry, in dentistry, and in the making of laboratory crucibles and articles which may have to withstand corrosion or high temperature. It has a specific use in finely divided form, as a catalyst, usually mixed with a carrier such as asbestos fibers. Because it has about the same coefficient of expansion as glass, it may be sealed through glass for the conduction of electricity. The other platinum metals are used as substitutes for platinum or may be alloyed with it. Rhodium and iridium increase the hardness of platinum or of gold, and, thus, increase their wearing qualities. A platinum-rhodium alloy is commonly used as a thermocouple. Platinum varies in price (about $90 per ounce in 1952), whereas gold is stabilized by governmental regulation at $35 per ounce.

EXERCISES

1. With reference to the manufacture of pig iron in the blast furnace give:
   (a) Raw materials, relative amounts, and functions of each.
   (b) Products of the blast furnace.
   (c) Equations for reactions taking place in the furnace.
2. What property of iron makes it such a valuable substance to man?
3. Contrast the differences in composition and properties of (a) pig iron, (b) Bessemer steel, (c) open-hearth steel, (d) wrought iron.
4. Name eight elements that are sometimes alloyed with iron in an alloy steel.
5. Write equations for the preparation of a household bluing from ferric oxide, common acids, and potassium ferrocyanide.
6. Name four elements other than Fe that may be found in pig iron.
7. What are "transition" groups? List similarities of the elements: cobalt, nickel, and iron.
8. How could you differentiate between the three metals: iron, cobalt, and nickel?
9. List the formulas and mineral names of important ores of iron.
10. Describe the changes taking place during the tempering of steel.
11. Describe exactly how you would test a sample for the presence of both ferrous and ferric salts.
12. A hematite ore analyzes 28 per cent iron. What weight of Fe_2O_3 is present per ton of ore? What weight of coke is needed per ton of iron ore? Assume that the coke is 60 per cent efficient in the chemical change

$$Fe_2O_3 + 3\ C \longrightarrow$$

13. Mention the chemical nature of the coating given to iron in *three* of the following processes: galvanizing; parkerizing; sherardizing; case hardening; making Russia iron (treating with steam).
14. (a) A green glaze may be given pottery by heating nickel carbonate with sodium silicate. Write the equation. (b) Cobalt oxide reacts with borax to form blue cobalt metaborate and sodium metaborate. Write the equation.
15. Complete the equations:

$$Cl_2 + Pt \longrightarrow \qquad H_2PtCl_6 + KNO_3 \longrightarrow$$
$$PtCl_4 + HCl \longrightarrow \qquad PdCl_2 + Zn \longrightarrow$$

REFERENCES

H. M. Boylston, *An Introduction to the Metallurgy of Iron and Steel*, Wiley.

E. F. Burchard, "Sources of Ores of the Ferro-Alloy Metals," *J. Chem. Ed.* **10,** 359 (1933).

S. Horwood Tucker, "Catalytic Hydrogenation Using Raney Nickel," *ibid.* **27,** 489 (1950).

Charles M. Parker, "Panorama of Steel," *ibid.* **28,** 236 (1951).

Wilson L. Orr and Henry A. Stafford, "Theory of Corrosion for Engineers," *ibid.* **27,** 202 (1950).

F. N. Speller, *Corrosion: Causes and Prevention*, McGraw-Hill.

E. E. Thum (ed.), *Book of Stainless Steels*, American Society for Metals.

C. P. Larrabee and S. C. Snyder, "Iron, Mild Steels, and Low Alloy Steels," *Ind. & Eng. Chem.* **41,** 2122 (1949).

M. H. Brown and W. B. DeLong, "Stainless Steels and Other Ferrous Alloys," *ibid.* **41,** 2139 (1949).

XXXIX

Introduction to Organic Chemistry I

Among the contributions of chemical science to modern living is knowledge of or preparation of such substances as gasoline, vitamins, hormones, plastics, explosives, fats, proteins, carbohydrates, perfumes, medicinals, alcohols, and wood products. The element carbon is common in the molecular composition of all these compounds or mixtures. As a matter of fact, all plant and animal tissues are largely composed of carbon compounds and water plus a small mineral content. Somewhere in the neighborhood of 300,000 carbon compounds are known. Many of them have been synthesized; some have been obtained only from natural sources. The reason must be clear why a separate branch of chemistry is needed to systematize and classify our knowledge of such a large number of compounds. The study of the compounds of carbon is called *organic chemistry*.

Most of the compounds thus far considered in this book have been classified as acids, bases, salts, and oxides of metals or nonmetals — substances which are derived from minerals in the earth's crust. Frequently these are referred to as inorganic compounds and their chemistry as *inorganic chemistry*. Organic chemistry and inorganic chemistry constitute the two major divisions of the general subject.

The multiplicity of carbon compounds is explained in the exceptional ability of carbon atoms to combine with one another to form long continuous chainlike structures containing many carbon atoms. Rarely in inorganic compounds does the number of like atoms in a molecule exceed five, but organic molecules containing a dozen or more carbon atoms are common. Carbon, with four electrons in its valence orbit, forms compounds by sharing its electrons with atoms of other elements or *with itself*. Two given carbon atoms may share one, two, or three pairs of electrons between themselves to give rise to three fundamental classes of compounds. To further augment the number of carbon compounds, different arrangements of the same atoms within a molecule produce different compounds. Although the number of organic compounds currently known seems very large, we can say with certainty that the field is still in its infancy; the number of possible organic substances is exceedingly great.

Historically many of the materials listed above as examples of organic compounds were believed to be products of living organisms — hence organic. Following much laboratory experimentation, however, chemists were able to demonstrate that certain products, which had been considered previously as the results of vital or living processes, could be produced in the laboratory. One of the classical examples of this type of work was Wöhler's synthesis of urea. In the year 1828, Wöhler, a German chemist, produced urea, a decomposition product of proteins, by heating ammonium cyanate, a compound of inorganic origin:

$$NH_4CNO \longrightarrow CO(NH_2)_2$$

This was the beginning of a new era in the synthesis of carbon compounds, which hitherto had been deemed impossible of preparation in the laboratory. The vital force idea was discarded and today rapid strides are being made in the preparation of sugars, vitamins, and related compounds. Every day new compounds are produced in the laboratory of the synthetic organic chemist, and many of these compounds have an important bearing on our everyday life.

When you studied the conductivities of aqueous solutions of acids, bases, and salts, you noted that, as a group, they were relatively good conductors of the electric current. In marked contrast to this is the fact that aqueous solutions of alcohol, sugar, glycerol, and the like are very poor conductors. This would be interpreted as suggesting little or no ionization in the case of organic compounds. In keeping with the arguments above, ionic inorganic reactions proceed almost instantaneously, but organic reactions frequently require, even under the most favorable conditions, considerable time before they approach completion.

Some sources of organic compounds. Reference to Table 37 will show sources of some of the more familiar organic substances.

Of the substances listed, some, such as benzene, phenol, wood alcohol, acetic acid, are pure compounds; others, such as fats, proteins, coal tar, petroleum, are complex mixtures. Starch and cellulose molecules are of a high degree of complexity, the structures of which have not been fully determined.

Petroleum is an extremely valuable raw material of nature. From it are obtained such important commodities as gasoline, kerosene, fuel oils, lubricating oils, paraffin, and wax. To what extent the petroleum

TABLE 37

SOURCES OF ORGANIC SUBSTANCES

Source	Organic Compound or Mixture
Animals	fats, proteins
Plants	starch, cellulose
Coal (destructive distillation)	coal tar, benzene, phenol, naphthalene
Wood (destructive distillation)	wood alcohol, acetone, acetic acid
Petroleum (fractional distillation)	cleaner's naphtha, gasoline, kerosene, mineral oil, vaseline
Fermentation processes	ethyl alcohol, acetone, butyl alcohol
Laboratory synthesis	almost unlimited numbers and types of compounds

industry plays a part in our national economy is evident from the fact that annually the United States markets more than $2\frac{1}{2}$ billion dollars worth of petroleum products.

A vast variety of products are obtained from coal tar from the destructive distillation of coal. Benzene, toluene, phenol, naphthalene, and many others are the starting materials in the preparation of a great number of dyes, perfumes, medicinals, plastics, and explosives. The value of coal tar products annually exceeds one-half billion dollars.

The importance of the synthetic organic chemical industries cannot be overemphasized. The organic chemist has been able in many instances to duplicate natural products in his laboratory and, probably more important, has produced substances never found in nature. In many cases synthetic products are superior to natural products, and we can accurately say that man has improved over nature.

Perhaps no other field of chemistry has such a direct bearing on our everyday lives. More than 50 per cent of our trained graduate chemists are "organic" chemists engaged in the research and production of the hundreds of substances which were unknown two or three generations ago. With the exception of a few basic inorganic substances such as iron and steel, sulfuric acid, caustic soda, and soda ash, the tonnage of organic substances produced by chemical industry far exceeds that of inorganic products.

HYDROCARBONS

Compounds composed of the elements carbon and hydrogen only are termed *hydrocarbons*. They are among the simplest of organic compounds and will be considered first. Although hundreds of hydrocarbons are known, we shall limit our discussion to a few of the simpler ones. For convenience we may group the hydrocarbons into series, four of which will be considered: *alkane, alkene, alkyne,* and *benzene* series. The first few members of each series are shown in Table 38. In the general formula for each series n is equal to the number of carbon atoms in the molecule.

TABLE 38

SOME COMMON HYDROCARBONS

ALKANE C_nH_{2n+2}		ALKENE C_nH_{2n}		ALKYNE C_nH_{2n-2}		BENZENE C_nH_{2n-6}	
Methane	CH_4					Benzene	C_6H_6
Ethane	C_2H_6	Ethene	C_2H_4	Ethyne	C_2H_2	Toluene	C_7H_8
Propane	C_3H_8	Propene	C_3H_6	Propyne	C_3H_4	Xylene	C_8H_{10}
Butane	C_4H_{10}	Butene	C_4H_8	Butyne	C_4H_6		
Pentane	C_5H_{12}						
Hexane	C_6H_{14}						
Heptane	C_7H_{16}						
Octane	C_8H_{18}	Octene	C_8H_{16}	Octyne	C_8H_{14}		

Each of the above series is called a *homologous series,* since any member of each group differs from the preceding or following member by one carbon atom and two hydrogen atoms (CH_2). For example, butane, C_4H_{10}, in the alkane series differs from propane, C_3H_8, immediately preceding it by CH_2, and also differs from pentane, C_5H_{12}, the member following by the same amount (CH_2). In any given series the members possess similar chemical properties and the physical properties show a gradual change in progressing from the compounds of few carbon atoms to those containing a large number. Compounds of the first three series are often referred to as *chain* compounds, since the carbon atoms are arranged one after another as in a chain; members of the benzene series are referred to as *ring* compounds as the carbon atoms are joined together as a closed system or ring.

Structural formulas. The inorganic chemist uses molecular formulas, *e.g.,* H_2SO_4, H_2O, $NaCl$, to show the composition of compounds; but molecular formulas are inadequate in representing organic compounds, since different arrangements of atoms in the molecule give rise to different compounds (this property is termed isomerism, and will be discussed in more detail later). For example, the molecular formula C_2H_6O may represent either ethyl alcohol or dimethyl ether. It is necessary then to show *how* the atoms are joined together in the molecule — in other words the arrangement of the atoms in the molecule — in order to get a complete picture of the substance. Friedrich Kekulé, about a century ago, instituted the use of *structural* or *graphic* formulas to clarify the molecular structure of organic compounds. Kekulé's contributions brought order out of chaos and enabled the organic chemist to make great strides in the synthesis of organic substances on the basis of this so-called "picture chemistry."

The basis for structural formulas is the valence number four of the carbon atom. The carbon atom with four electrons in its outer shell neither gives up nor takes up electrons but rather shares these electrons with other atoms of carbon or with atoms of other elements; thus the compounds of carbon are covalent and nonionic. A structural formula shows how these electrons are shared with other atoms; for example, methane, CH_4, may be represented:

$$\begin{array}{c} H \\ \cdot\cdot \\ H:C:H \\ \cdot\cdot \\ H \end{array}$$

Four electrons from the carbon atom and four electrons from the hydrogen atoms are mutually shared; the formula shows four pairs of shared electrons. Each pair of electrons represents a covalence of one. In writing structural formulas, a pair of electrons is usually replaced with a dash to indicate a single bond of valence; thus methane would be shown as

$$\begin{array}{c} H \\ | \\ H-C-H \\ | \\ H \end{array}$$

Carbon atoms may share a pair or more of electrons between themselves, thus ethane, C_2H_6, would be shown

$$\begin{array}{ccc} H \ H & & H \ H \\ \cdot\cdot \ \cdot\cdot & & | \ \ | \\ H:C:C:H & \text{or} & H-C-C-H \\ \cdot\cdot \ \cdot\cdot & & | \ \ | \\ H \ H & & H \ H \end{array}$$

and propane, C_3H_8

$$\begin{array}{c} H \ \ H \ \ H \\ | \ \ \ | \ \ \ | \\ H-C-C-C-H \\ | \ \ \ | \ \ \ | \\ H \ \ H \ \ H \end{array}$$

Where there can be no question of the arrangement of the atoms in a compound, a condensed structural formula may be used; for example, the above hydrocarbons might be represented as CH_4; CH_3-CH_3; $CH_3-CH_2-CH_3$.

The alkane series of hydrocarbons. This series is sometimes referred to as the *methane* series, after the first member, or the *paraffin* series, the term paraffin meaning inactive. The general formula of the series is C_nH_{2n+2}, where n is an integral number, 1, 2, 3, 4, etc. The first four members of the series are gases at ordinary temperatures; members containing from five to fifteen carbon atoms are liquid, while the higher members of the series are solids. Thus it is evident that a gradual increase in the boiling points of these compounds takes place as the number of carbon atoms in the molecule increases.

Methane is the principal constituent of natural gas. It is formed also during the decay of organic matter under water in marshes and swamps in the absence of air; thus is derived its common name of *marsh gas*. In coal mines where it is known as *fire damp*, it is the principal cause of explosions. It may be produced in the laboratory by fusing together sodium acetate and sodium hydroxide:

$$NaC_2H_3O_2 + NaOH \longrightarrow Na_2CO_3 + CH_4 \uparrow$$

Chemical properties of the paraffins. As the name paraffin implies, these hydrocarbons are characterized by their inactivity and show little tendency to react with other substances. However, strong oxidizing agents may react with these compounds; for example, if methane and chlorine gases are mixed and allowed to stand in the sunlight, chlorine atoms are substituted successively for the hydrogen atoms in the molecule according to the following equations:

$$CH_4 + Cl_2 \longrightarrow CH_3Cl \text{ (methyl chloride)} + HCl$$
$$CH_3Cl + Cl_2 \longrightarrow CH_2Cl_2 \text{ (methylene chloride)} + HCl$$
$$CH_2Cl_2 + Cl_2 \longrightarrow CHCl_3 \text{ (chloroform)} + HCl$$
$$CHCl_3 + Cl_2 \longrightarrow CCl_4 \text{ (carbon tetrachloride)} + HCl$$

Chloroform is used as a general anesthetic in surgery and carbon tetrachloride for solvent and cleaning purposes. Other members of the alkane series react similarly with chlorine and the other halogens.

All hydrocarbons are combustible and, if complete burning is allowed to take place, carbon dioxide and water are formed as oxidation products, *e.g.:*

$$CH_4 + 2 O_2 \longrightarrow CO_2 + 2 H_2O$$
$$C_3H_8 + 5 O_2 \longrightarrow 3 CO_2 + 4 H_2O$$
$$2 C_8H_{18} + 25 O_2 \longrightarrow 16 CO_2 + 18 H_2O$$

Incomplete combustion results in the formation of some carbon monoxide or free carbon:

$$2 C_8H_{18} + 23 O_2 \longrightarrow 13 CO_2 + 2 CO + C + 18 H_2O$$

All internal combustion engines produce some carbon monoxide.

Petroleum. This black oily liquid for which nations may even go to war is the principal source of the paraffin hydrocarbons. Petroleum is a mixture of gaseous, liquid, and solid hydrocarbons, most of which belong to the methane series. The United States is the world's largest producer, annually producing more than a billion barrels.

Courtesy The Lummus Company

Fig. 145. Hundred-octane aviation gasoline plant.

The hydrocarbons contained in petroleum are separated by means of fractional distillation (p. 188), a process which takes advantage of a difference in the boiling points of the compounds. When petroleum is heated, those constituents with the lowest boiling points distil over first, followed by the higher boiling components. By changing the receivers of the distillate at intervals, several fractions are obtained. By repeated fractional distillation of these fractions, the hydrocarbons may be separated in relatively pure form. Principal products of the refining of petroleum are shown in Table 39.

One of the most important products of the refining of petroleum is gasoline, and because of its great demand for use in motor cars and airplanes, efforts have been made to increase the yield of this important fuel. It is evident from Table 39 that gasoline is a mixture of the

TABLE 39

PRINCIPAL PRODUCTS OF THE REFINING OF PETROLEUM

Hydrocarbons	Products	Boiling Point Range	Uses
CH_4 C_2H_6 C_3H_8 C_4H_{10}	natural gas	$-160°$ to $0°$	fuel gas for heat and power
C_5H_{12} C_6H_{14}	petroleum ether or ligroin	$35°$ to $70°$	solvent for fats and oils
C_7H_{16} C_8H_{18}	gasoline	$70°$ to $150°$	motor fuel, solvent
C_9H_{20} to $C_{14}H_{30}$	kerosene fuel oil	$150°$ to $250°$	fuel, illuminating oil
$C_{15}H_{32}$ to $C_{20}H_{42}$	middle fraction or cracking oil, lubricating oil	$250°$ and up	lubrication; cracked to gasoline
Above $C_{20}H_{42}$	vaseline paraffin tar residue petroleum coke		medicinal candles road surfacing fuel

lower hydrocarbons, having an average of seven or eight carbon atoms. By subjecting petroleum fractions to high heat and pressure it is possible to break down fuel oils and higher boiling fractions which contain higher hydrocarbons into gasoline and lower hydrocarbons. This process is referred to as *cracking* petroleum. The following equation is typical of the cracking operation:

$$C_{14}H_{30} \longrightarrow C_8H_{18} + C_5H_{12} + C$$

By means of the cracking process, it is possible to utilize less desirable petroleum distillation fractions and to greatly increase the yield of gasoline.

Isomers. If we study the graphic formulas for butane and higher hydrocarbons of the methane series, we may note that it is possible to arrange the atoms in the molecule in more than one way, thus giving rise to two or more different arrangements for the same formula. For example we may write butane, C_4H_{10}, graphically as

$$\begin{array}{ccccc} & H & H & H & H \\ & | & | & | & | \\ H- & C- & C- & C- & C- H \\ & | & | & | & | \\ & H & H & H & H \end{array}$$

in which the carbon atoms are arranged in a continuous chain. In no case in this formula are more than two carbon atoms attached to any single carbon atom. However, it is possible to write a formula for butane as

$$
\begin{array}{c}
\text{H} \quad \text{H} \quad \text{H} \\
| \quad\ | \quad\ | \\
\text{H--C--C--C--H} \\
| \quad\ | \quad\ | \\
\text{H} \quad | \quad \text{H} \\
\text{H--C--H} \\
| \\
\text{H}
\end{array}
$$

in which three carbon atoms are attached to a single carbon atom. The result is a branched chain compound. Both of these butanes are known and have been prepared; the latter is termed *isobutane* to differentiate it from the continuous chain butane which is called *normal* butane. Such compounds with the same molecular formula but with a different arrangement of the constituent atoms in the molecule are called *isomers*, and the name applied to this phenomenon is *isomerism*. Careful study of the formulas for butane will show that these two arrangements are the only ones possible which will satisfy all valence requirements. As the number of carbon atoms increases, the number of isomers also increases. A study of the formulas for pentane will reveal the following three possible isomers (hydrogen atoms are not shown):

$$
\begin{array}{ccc}
| \quad | \quad | \quad | \quad | & \qquad | \quad | \quad | \quad | & \qquad | \\
\text{--C--C--C--C--C--} & \qquad \text{--C--C--C--C--} & \qquad \text{--C--} \\
| \quad | \quad | \quad | \quad | & \qquad | \quad | \quad | \quad | & \qquad | \quad | \quad | \\
& \qquad\qquad\ \ \text{--C--} & \qquad \text{--C--C--C--} \\
& \qquad\qquad\ \ \ | & \qquad | \quad | \quad | \\
& & \qquad\qquad \text{--C--} \\
& & \qquad\qquad\ \ |
\end{array}
$$

The student should find it interesting to draw structural formulas for the possible isomers of hexane, C_6H_{14}, and heptane, C_7H_{16}.

The alkene series of hydrocarbons. This series has the general formula, C_nH_{2n}, and is sometimes referred to as the *olefin* series or the *ethylene* series after ethylene, the first member. Names for the members of the alkene series are derived from names of compounds of the alkane series with the same number of carbon atoms, by changing the *ane* ending to *ene*; thus C_4H_8 is *butene* from butane, C_4H_{10}, etc.

Members of the series are characterized by containing one carbon to carbon linkage which involves the sharing of two electron pairs, thus:

$$
\begin{array}{cc}
\qquad\qquad\quad \text{H} \qquad\qquad \text{H} \\
\text{H:C::C:H} \qquad \text{H:C:C::C:C:H} \\
\ \ \text{H} \quad \text{H} \qquad\quad\ \text{H} \ \text{H} \quad \text{H} \ \text{H}
\end{array}
$$

Ethene, C_2H_4, commonly called ethylene, is the simplest member of the series; it may be prepared by the dehydration of ethyl alcohol with concentrated sulfuric acid at a temperature of about 160°

$$C_2H_5OH \xrightarrow[\text{heat}]{H_2SO_4} C_2H_4 + H_2O$$

or may be obtained as a product of the cracking of petroleum.

Ethylene gas is now used as an anesthetic either alone or mixed with ether. Less nausea and discomfort seem to be its principal advantages over ether. It is also employed in hastening the ripening of citrus fruits where it causes the development of a uniform orange or yellow color. In addition, ethylene is used as a starting material in the preparation of many organic compounds, among which is mustard gas, employed for military purposes.

Unsaturation. When we write the structural or graphic formula for ethene, we employ the usual method of putting down the carbon atoms in a chain and dividing the four hydrogen atoms equally between the two carbon atoms:

$$\begin{array}{c} H-C=C-H \\ |\quad| \\ H\ \ H \end{array}$$

In order to satisfy valence requirements of carbon, we may put an additional bond between the carbon atoms making two bonds or a double bond. The double bond obviously stands for two pairs of shared electrons. That we are justified in so representing the formula for ethene becomes clear when we consider the chemical properties of the compound. Ethene has the property of adding two hydrogen atoms to form ethane, and we might represent the change as

$$\begin{array}{c} H-C=C-H + H_2 \longrightarrow \begin{array}{c} H\ \ H \\ |\quad| \\ H-C-C-H \\ |\quad| \\ H\ \ H \end{array} \end{array}$$

Other elements may also add to the compound; for example, ethene readily absorbs bromine to form ethylene dibromide, $C_2H_4Br_2$:

$$\begin{array}{c} H-C=C-H + Br_2 \longrightarrow \begin{array}{c} Br\ Br \\ |\quad| \\ H-C-C-H \\ |\quad| \\ H\ \ H \end{array} \end{array}$$

Because it has the capacity to add atoms, ethylene is said to be *unsaturated*. All members of the alkene series contain double bonds between a pair of carbon atoms and thus are unsaturated.

The alkyne series of hydrocarbons. Members of this series have the general formula C_nH_{2n-2}. The names are derived from the hydrocarbons of the methane series by replacing the *ane* ending of the latter with *yne*, thus C_3H_4 is propyne, from propane, C_3H_8, etc. Members of this series possess a higher degree of unsaturation than the alkene series. Ethyne, more commonly called *acetylene*, is written with a triple bond:

$$H : C ::: C : H \quad \text{or} \quad H—C{\equiv}C—H$$

This triple bond denotes a sharing of three electron pairs between two carbon atoms. Another example is butyne, C_4H_6

$$H—\overset{\displaystyle H}{\underset{\displaystyle H}{C}}—\overset{\displaystyle H}{\underset{\displaystyle H}{C}}—C{\equiv}C—H$$

These compounds as would be expected add more bromine or hydrogen than do corresponding members of the alkene series:

$$H—C{\equiv}C—H + 2\,Br_2 \longrightarrow H—\overset{\displaystyle Br}{\underset{\displaystyle Br}{C}}—\overset{\displaystyle Br}{\underset{\displaystyle Br}{C}}—H$$
tetrabromoethane

Acetylene is readily produced by the action of water on calcium carbide:

$$CaC_2 + 2\,H_2O \longrightarrow Ca(OH)_2 + C_2H_2$$

The gas has a high heat of combustion, a property which is taken advantage of in the acetylene-oxygen torch for welding purposes. Acetylene also finds use as a starting material in the preparation of *neoprene*, an artificial rubber.

Polymerization. Like molecules of many organic substances may be made to combine to form complex molecules with new properties. This phenomenon is known as *polymerization*, and the product may be termed a *polymer*. Thus the formation of benzene, C_6H_6, from a condensation of three molecules of C_2H_2, might be termed polymerization, and benzene could be considered to be a polymer of acetylene. Synthetic rubbers appear to be polymers of simple hydrocarbons.

The benzene series of hydrocarbons. The general formula for members of this series is C_nH_{2n-6}. Many of these compounds are obtained from coal tar, a by-product of the destructive distillation of coal. The smaller ratio of hydrogen atoms to carbon atoms in the molecules of these compounds than in any of the preceding series would lead one to the conclusion that they are unsaturated. Although certain reactions show these compounds to possess some degree of unsaturation, nevertheless, they do not add the elements hydrogen and bromine with the facility of members of the alkene and alkyne series.

Kekulé suggested that members of this series possess a ring structure with six carbon atoms joined together; *e.g.*, benzene has a structure which is most frequently represented:

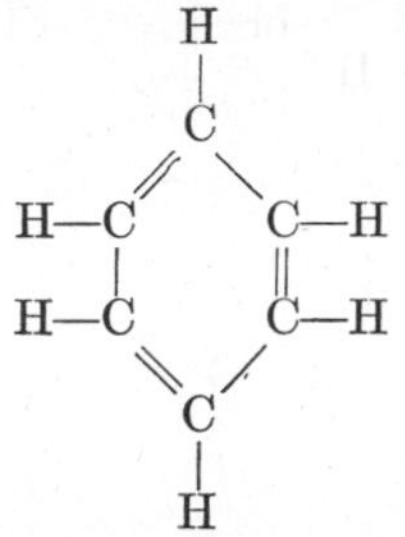

or simply

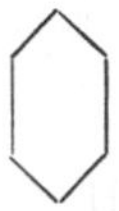

The carbon atoms are arranged in the form of a hexagon with double bonds between alternate carbon atoms and with a hydrogen atom attached to each carbon. The benzene ring structure is usually shown simply as the figure of a hexagon. The reactions of benzene indicate that it possesses a symmetrical structure, *i.e.*, the carbon atoms all bear the same relationship to each other. This hexagon arrangement of carbon atoms seems to be the basic structure of all members of the benzene series of hydrocarbons as well as for their many derivatives. Toluene, the member following benzene, has a CH_3 group substituted for one of the hydrogen atoms and is shown structurally as

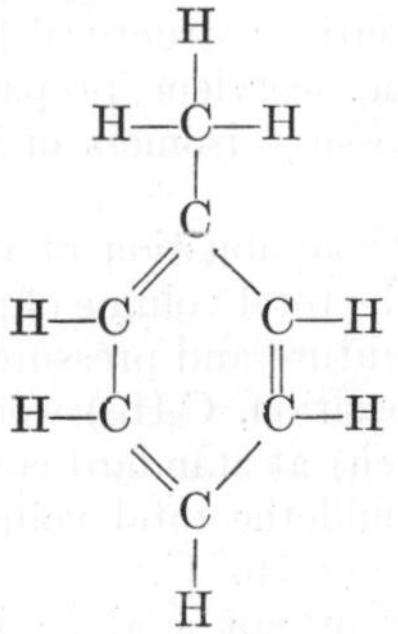

or

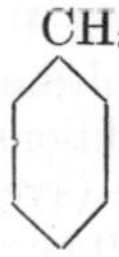

Aliphatic and aromatic hydrocarbons. Hydrocarbons of continuous chain structures are referred to as *aliphatic* hydrocarbons while those possessing a ring structure with alternating double bonds between carbon atoms are termed *aromatic* hydrocarbons. In accordance with these definitions, the first three series of hydrocarbons discussed — alkanes, alkenes, alkynes — would be aliphatic compounds and the last series — benzene — would be classed as aromatic hydrocarbons. Examples of aromatic hydrocarbons of other series might include naphthalene

and anthracene

both of which are obtained as products of coal tar and which serve as starting materials for the preparation of many dyes and medicinals.

EXERCISES

1. What do you understand by the terms: hydrocarbon; homologous series; unsaturated hydrocarbon; polymerization; structural formula; isomers?
2. Draw structural formulas for methane, acetylene, propane, ethylene, benzene.
3. Write structural formulas for all possible isomers of heptane, C_7H_{16}. How many possibilities did you find?
4. Write an equation for the complete combustion of ethane. Compare the volume of reacting substances with the total volume of products, all measured under the same conditions of temperature and pressure.
5. One liter of gasoline (average composition, C_8H_{18}) weighs 798 g. Calculate the volume of air (20 per cent oxygen) at standard conditions necessary for its complete combustion. What would the total volume of products be at standard pressure and a temperature of 546° C.? Ans. 9800 l.; 8000 l.
6. How could you determine whether or not a given hydrocarbon was unsaturated?

REFERENCES

J. B. Conant, *The Chemistry of Organic Compounds*, Macmillan.
H. J. Lucas, *Organic Chemistry*, American Book Company.
E. Wertheim, *Textbook of Organic Chemistry*, Blakiston.
"Boom in Natural Gas," *Life* **32**, 11, 88 (1952).

XL

Introduction to Organic Chemistry II

DERIVATIVES OF THE HYDROCARBONS

The substitution of elements or radicals for one or more of the hydrogen atoms in a hydrocarbon results in the formation of many types of compounds which are referred to as *derivatives* of the hydrocarbons. For example, methyl chloride, CH_3Cl, which is one of the products formed by the treatment of methane with chlorine, may be considered as being derived from the hydrocarbon methane:

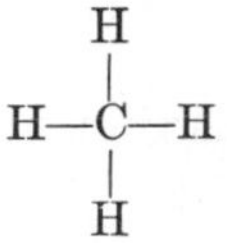

<pre>
      H   H
      | |
  H—C—H   H—C—H
      | |
      H   Cl
   methane   methyl chloride
</pre>

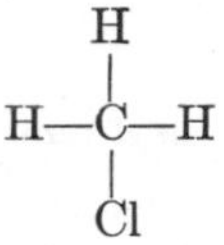

The CH_3 radical is termed *methyl* and derives its name from the parent hydrocarbon methane. Corresponding radicals of other hydrocarbons of the methane series are similarly derived. The general term, *alkyl* radicals, includes all radicals derived from the methane series. The specific name of the radical is obtained by replacing the ending *ane* by *yl*. The composition of the radical will be the same as the parent hydrocarbon except it will contain one less hydrogen atom; thus C_2H_5 is the *ethyl* radical, C_3H_7 the *propyl* radical, etc. Obviously, the valence of alkyl radicals must be 1.

Because of the relative inactivity of the hydrocarbons, their derivatives in most cases cannot be produced directly by substitution of another element or group but are produced from reactions of other types of organic compounds. These derivatives of the hydrocarbons may be classified into groups or types of compounds depending upon the atom or group of atoms substituted for the hydrogen atom. Such groups are called *functional* groups and determine in a large measure the properties of the compound. Compounds with the same func-

533

tional group or groups exhibit very similar chemical properties. In Table 40 are summarized several of the more important types of derivatives with the general formula for compounds of each type.

TABLE 40

ORGANIC DERIVATIVES WITH GENERAL FORMULAS

Type of Compound	General Formula [1]
Alcohol	R—OH
Alkyl halides	R—X (where X = F, Cl, Br, I)
Amine	R—NH$_2$
Ether	R—O—R'
Aldehyde	R—C—H $\overset{\|\|}{O}$
Ketone	R—C—R' $\overset{\|\|}{O}$
Acid	R—C—OH $\overset{\|\|}{O}$
Ester	R—C—O—R' $\overset{\|\|}{O}$

[1] R stands for an alkyl radical; R' is also an alkyl radical which may be the same or different from R.

Similar to the hydrocarbons, a homologous series of each type of compound is possible, for example the following amines constitute such a series: CH_3NH_2, $C_2H_5NH_2$, $C_3H_7NH_2$, $C_nH_{2n+1}NH_2$.

ALCOHOLS

Alcohols have the general formula R—OH and in structure are somewhat similar to metallic hydroxides or bases. However, they show no tendency to form hydroxide ions in solution, and thus those properties which usually we associate with bases, such as bitter taste, soapy feeling, effect on litmus, etc., are not exhibited by the alcohols. Alcohols might also be considered as being derived from water in which one of the hydrogen atoms in the water molecule has been replaced with an alkyl radical. Indeed in many respects alcohols resemble water more in chemical properties than they resemble metallic hydroxides.

While it is theoretically possible to substitute more than one OH group for hydrogen atoms in methane, such a compound is not actually known and it seems likely that compounds in which more than one OH group is attached to the *same* carbon atom are very unstable if indeed they exist at all.

Structurally the oxygen atom present in the hydroxide group of an alcohol is linked to the carbon atom in the alkyl radical by a single pair of shared electrons. The oxygen atom also shares a pair of electrons with the hydrogen atom of the hydroxide group; thus methyl alcohol would be shown:

$$
\begin{array}{c}
\text{H} \\
| \\
\text{H}:\overset{..}{\underset{..}{\text{C}}}:\overset{..}{\underset{..}{\text{O}}}:\text{H} \quad\text{or}\quad \text{H}-\overset{\displaystyle \text{H}}{\underset{\displaystyle \text{H}}{\text{C}}}-\text{O}-\text{H} \\
\text{H}
\end{array}
$$

Isomers become possible in alcohols of more than two carbon atoms; for example, propyl alcohol, C_3H_7OH may be written structurally as

$$
\text{H}-\overset{\text{H}}{\underset{\text{H}}{\text{C}}}-\overset{\text{H}}{\underset{\text{H}}{\text{C}}}-\overset{\text{H}}{\underset{\text{H}}{\text{C}}}-\text{O}-\text{H} \quad\text{or}\quad \text{H}-\overset{\text{H}}{\underset{\text{H}}{\text{C}}}-\overset{\text{H}}{\underset{\text{OH}}{\text{C}}}-\overset{\text{H}}{\underset{\text{H}}{\text{C}}}-\text{H}
$$

The first isomer is called a *primary* alcohol since the OH group is attached to a carbon atom which itself is linked directly to but one carbon atom; the second is called a *secondary* alcohol, since the OH group is attached to a carbon to which are directly linked two other carbon atoms. With the higher alcohols it is possible to have an OH group attached to a carbon atom, to which carbon atom there is direct linkage to three other carbon atoms, in which case the alcohol is termed a *tertiary* alcohol. The structural formulas above for the propyl alcohols are usually written in a semistructural manner, *i.e.*, CH_3—CH_2—CH_2OH for *normal* propyl alcohol, and CH_3—$CHOH$—CH_3 or, better still, $(CH_3)_2CHOH$ for *isopropyl* alcohol.

In naming alcohols, the ending *-ol* is sometimes substituted for the ending *e* of the hydrocarbon from which the alcohol is derived; thus methyl alcohol is *methanol;* ethyl alcohol is *ethanol;* propyl alcohol is *propanol,* etc.

Methyl alcohol. Methyl alcohol or *methanol,* also called wood alcohol, is one of the products of the destructive distillation of wood. Until a few years ago this method provided almost the sole source of methanol; however, recently a catalytic process has been developed in which the following reaction takes place:

$$CO + 2\,H_2 \longrightarrow CH_3OH$$

The gases are passed over zinc oxide or other suitable catalysts at an elevated temperature and under pressure.

Methyl alcohol is a colorless liquid which boils at 67°. It is extremely toxic when taken internally. Large quantities of methanol are employed commercially as a solvent for varnishes, shellacs, and lacquers, which are readily soluble in the alcohol. It is used also as a denaturant for ethyl alcohol, and as a starting material in the preparation of formaldehyde and other chemicals.

Ethyl alcohol. Ethyl alcohol, C_2H_5OH, or *ethanol*, and sometimes referred to as "grain" alcohol, is a colorless liquid and in physical properties is quite similar to methanol. It is much less poisonous than methyl alcohol, although if taken in large amounts may be decidedly harmful. The boiling point of ethanol is 78° which is not very different from that for methanol, 67°. A mixture of the two therefore is not easily separated by distillation.

As an industrial chemical, ethyl alcohol finds extensive application. Like methanol, it is used as a solvent for varnishes and lacquers. Tinctures are alcoholic solutions, of which tincture of iodine is familiar to all. Flavoring extracts, tonics, lotions, and many medicines contain large percentages of alcohol. Ethanol is used as a starting material in the preparation of ethyl acetate, ethylene, ether, and other important chemical compounds. Because of its low freezing point, −117°, alcohol is employed as an antifreeze in automobile radiators. Many other uses of lesser importance for ethyl alcohol might be listed. In the United States alone nearly 200 million gallons are produced annually.

Ethyl alcohol is produced on an industrial scale by the fermentation of glucose and fructose. Glucose or fructose may be obtained by hydrolysis of cane or malt sugar or starch (p. 549). The reaction occurring during the fermentation may be represented by the equation:

$$C_6H_{12}O_6 \longrightarrow 2\,C_2H_5OH + 2\,CO_2$$

The fermentation is catalyzed by certain *enzymes*, which are organic compounds produced from yeast cells. Solutions containing 10 to 15 per cent alcohol are usually produced by these fermentation processes since higher concentrations of alcohol would kill the yeast cells. By fractional distillation of these solutions a concentration of approximately 95 per cent alcohol is readily prepared and in this concentration industrial alcohol is usually marketed.

The concentration of an alcoholic solution is usually expressed in terms of "proof" rather than percentage. A 95 per cent alcohol solution is 190 proof, 100 per cent alcohol is 200 proof, a 45 per cent whisky is 90 proof, etc. Alcohol used for beverages is taxed highly by the federal government; however, alcohol used for industrial purposes other than beverages is tax free. Usually some nonpalatable substance (denaturant) is added to ensure that it not be diverted to beverage manufacture.

Other alcohols. *Ethylene glycol*, $C_2H_4(OH)_2$, because of its relatively high boiling point, 198°, and its noncorrosive action on metals finds use as an antifreeze in automobile radiators. It is produced commercially by means of the following reactions:

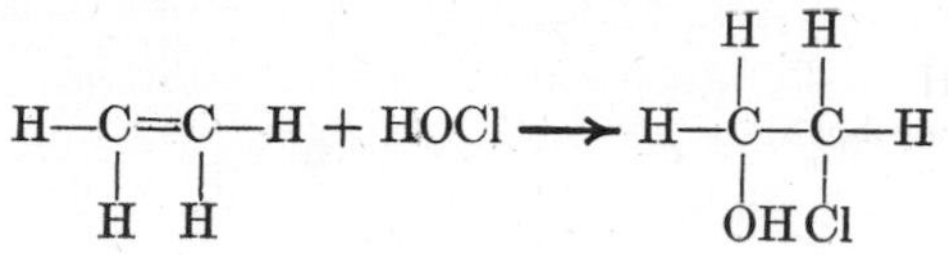

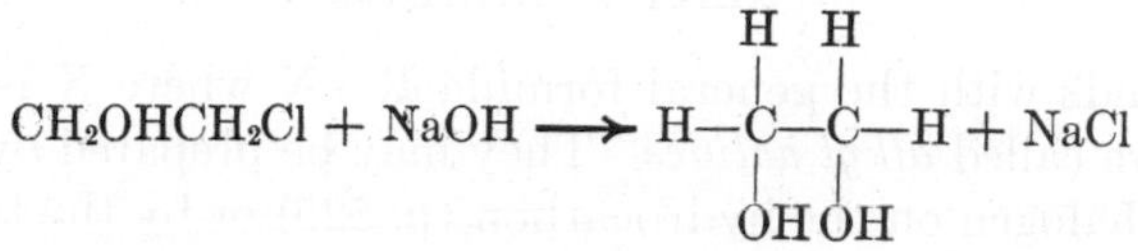

$$H-C=C-H + HOCl \longrightarrow H-\overset{\overset{\displaystyle H}{|}}{\underset{\underset{\displaystyle OH}{|}}{C}}-\overset{\overset{\displaystyle H}{|}}{\underset{\underset{\displaystyle Cl}{|}}{C}}-H$$

$$CH_2OHCH_2Cl + NaOH \longrightarrow H-\overset{\overset{\displaystyle H}{|}}{\underset{\underset{\displaystyle OH}{|}}{C}}-\overset{\overset{\displaystyle H}{|}}{\underset{\underset{\displaystyle OH}{|}}{C}}-H + NaCl$$

Glycerin, $C_3H_5(OH)_3$, is a colorless, viscous liquid with a sweet taste produced as a by-product of soap manufacture. Besides its use in many toilet preparations, it is the starting material in the manufacture of nitroglycerin, a powerful explosive.

Phenol, C_6H_5OH, commonly known as *carbolic acid* is obtained from coal tar. It is highly corrosive and produces severe burns on the skin. It is useful as an antiseptic in killing certain bacteria. Although phenol contains the characteristic group of an alcohol, OH, it behaves chemically as a weak acid and may be neutralized with strong bases to form salts. Phenol is the starting material in the preparation of many important commercial products including resins, picric acid, many dyes, aspirin, and other drugs. Phenol is an example of a derivative of an aromatic or ring structure hydrocarbon.

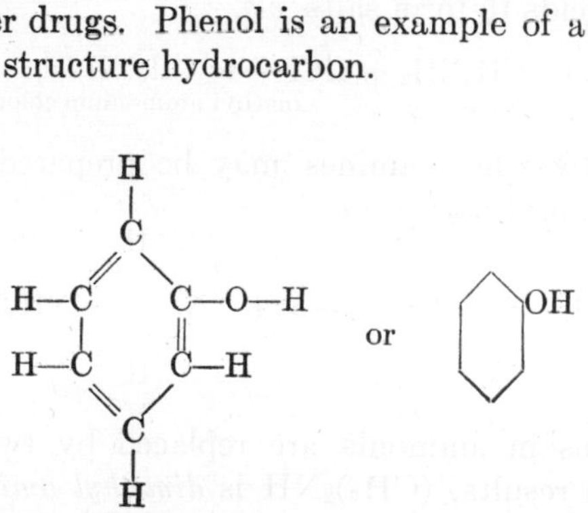

or

phenol

Benzyl alcohol is a typical aromatic alcohol.

benzyl alcohol

ALKYL HALIDES

Compounds with the general formula R—X where X is one of the halogens are called *alkyl halides*. They may be prepared by the action of the free halogen on the hydrocarbon (p. 525) or by the treatment of an alcohol with a hydrohalogen acid, *e.g.*

$$C_2H_5OH + HCl \longrightarrow C_2H_5Cl + H_2O$$

AMINES

Amines may be considered as derivatives of ammonia in which one or more of the hydrogen atoms of the ammonia molecule have been replaced with an organic radical. As a matter of fact, these compounds are very similar in chemical properties to ammonia. The simpler amines are gaseous at ordinary temperatures and have an odor very much like ammonia. Similar to ammonia they show basic properties and react with acids to form salts, *e.g.*

$$CH_3NH_2 + HCl \longrightarrow CH_3NH_3Cl$$
methyl ammonium chloride

One method by which amines may be prepared is the action of ammonia on an alkyl halide, *i.e.*

$$R\!-\!X + 2\,NH_3 \longrightarrow R\!-\!N\!\!\begin{array}{c}H\\\\H\end{array} + NH_4X$$

If two hydrogens in ammonia are replaced by two alkyl groups a *secondary* amine results; $(CH_3)_2NH$ is *dimethyl amine*, $(C_6H_5)_2NH$ is *diphenyl amine*, etc. The substitution of three alkyl groups for the three hydrogen atoms gives a *tertiary* amine; $(C_2H_5)_3N$ is *triethyl amine*, etc.

Aniline,

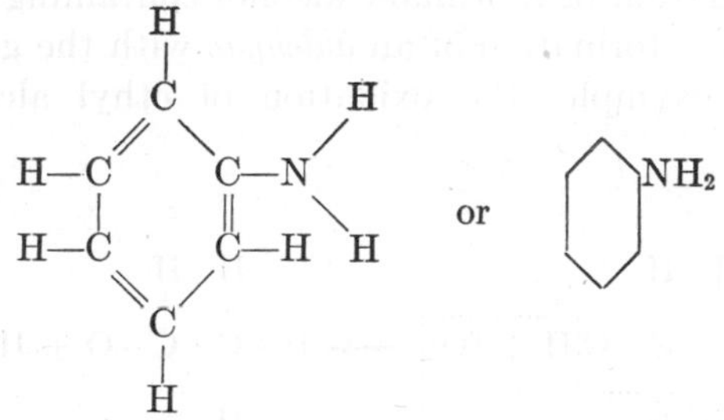

or

is one of the more important aromatic amines. It is a starting material in the preparation of many aniline dyes, medicinals, and drugs.

ETHERS

The general formula for ethers is R—O—R' where R and R' may be the same or different alkyl radicals. Ethers are oxides somewhat analogous to the oxides of inorganic chemistry. They may be considered as being derived from water by the replacement of the two hydrogen atoms in the water molecule with alkyl radicals.

In general ethers are prepared by the dehydration of alcohols with sulfuric acid. If ethyl alcohol is mixed with concentrated sulfuric acid, and the mixture is warmed to 140°, *diethyl ether* and water are formed according to the reaction

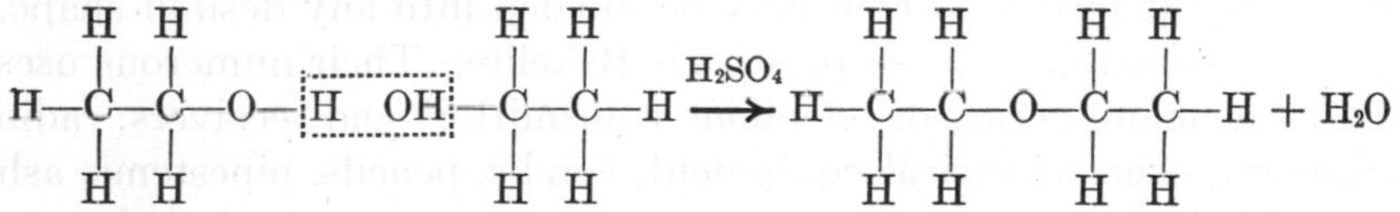

If the above mixture is heated to 160° or above, further dehydration takes place with the formation of ethylene.

Diethyl ether, commonly called *ether*, is used as an anesthetic in surgery. It is a highly inflammable and volatile liquid with a boiling point of 35°. Other uses include its solvent action on waxes, gums, resins, and fats. In the analysis of certain food products for fat content, the fat is extracted with ether.

In naming the ethers, the names of the alkyl radicals present are given followed by the term ether, or if the alkyl radicals are the same, the prefix di- may be employed, *e.g.*, $C_3H_7OC_2H_5$ is propyl ethyl ether; CH_3OCH_3 or $(CH_3)_2O$ is methyl methyl ether, or better, dimethyl ether. The latter compound is isomeric with ethyl alcohol.

ALDEHYDES

The gentle oxidation of a primary alcohol containing the —CH_2OH group results in the formation of an *aldehyde* with the general formula

$$R—C—H.$$
$$\;\;\;\;\|$$
$$\;\;\;\;O$$

For example, the oxidation of ethyl alcohol produces *acetaldehyde:*

$$
\begin{array}{cc}
\;\;H\;\;H & \;\;\;\;\;H\;\;H \\
\;\;|\;\;\;| & \;\;\;\;\;\;|\;\;\;| \\
H—C—C—O\lfloor H + (O) \rfloor & \longrightarrow\;\; H—C—C{=}O + H_2O \\
\;\;|\;\;\;| & \;\;\;\;\;\;| \\
\;\;H\;\lfloor H \rfloor & \;\;\;\;\;\;H
\end{array}
$$

The slow oxidation of methyl alcohol yields *formaldehyde*, HCHO, which is the simplest of the aldehydes. In this case the R of the general formula is a hydrogen atom rather than an alkyl radical.

$$
CH_3OH + (O) \longrightarrow\;\; H—C{=}O + H_2O
$$
$$
\;|
$$
$$
\;H
$$

Formaldehyde is one of the more important of the aldehydes; a 40 per cent solution is commonly marketed under the trade name of *formalin*. It is used as a preservative for museum specimens, and also as a disinfectant and insecticide. One of the principal uses is in the preparation of synthetic resins. If phenol and formaldehyde are heated slowly together in the presence of a catalyst, a resinous product similar to hard rubber is formed, which may be molded into any desired shape. The more common of these plastics is Bakelite. Their numerous uses include the manufacture of telephone transmitters and receivers, radio equipment, other electrical equipment, combs, pencils, pipestems, ash trays, etc.

Furfuraldehyde,

$$
\begin{array}{c}
CH{=}CH \\
|\;\;\;\;\;\;\;\;\diagdown \\
|\;\;\;\;\;\;\;\;\;\;\;O \\
CH{=}C\;\diagup \\
\;\;\;\;\;| \\
\;\;\;\;\;C{=}O \\
\;\;\;\;\;| \\
\;\;\;\;\;H
\end{array}
$$

a product obtained from waste oat hulls, is becoming increasingly important as a solvent and in the preparation of synthetic plastics and resins.

KETONES

If a secondary alcohol containing the —CHOH group is gently oxidized, a *ketone* of the general formula R—C—R′ is obtained. The
$$\underset{\text{O}}{\overset{\|}{}}$$

C=O group is termed the *carbonyl* group and is characteristic of both aldehydes and ketones. The oxidation of isopropyl alcohol yields *dimethyl ketone*, more commonly called *acetone*:

$$
\underset{\text{CH}_3}{\overset{\text{CH}_3}{\diagdown}}\!\!\!\diagup \text{C} \diagup\!\!\!\underset{\text{OH}}{\overset{\text{H}}{}} + (\text{O}) \longrightarrow \text{CH}_3\!\!-\!\!\overset{\overset{\text{O}}{\|}}{\text{C}}\!\!-\!\!\text{CH}_3 + \text{H}_2\text{O}
$$

Acetone is obtained also in the destructive distillation of wood along with methyl alcohol and acetic acid, or it may be prepared by heating calcium acetate:

$$\text{Ca}(\text{C}_2\text{H}_3\text{O}_2)_2 \xrightarrow{\text{heat}} \text{CaCO}_3 \downarrow + \text{CH}_3\text{COCH}_3$$

At the present time much acetone is produced through the fermentation of corn with certain bacteria. Acetone is one of the more important solvents for varnishes and lacquers, and is used in the manufacture of cordite and smokeless powders. Other uses include the preparation of chloroform and as a solvent for compressed acetylene.

ACIDS

Acids contain the —C—OH or *carboxyl* group as the functional
$$\underset{\text{O}}{\overset{\|}{}}$$

group and may be obtained by the oxidation of alcohols and aldehydes. The oxidation of ethyl alcohol yields acetic acid:

$$
\text{H}\!\!-\!\!\underset{\overset{|}{\text{H}}}{\overset{\overset{|}{\text{H}}}{\text{C}}}\!\!-\!\!\underset{\overset{|}{\text{H}}}{\overset{\overset{|}{\text{H}}}{\text{C}}}\!\!-\!\!\text{OH} + 2\,(\text{O}) \longrightarrow \text{H}\!\!-\!\!\underset{\overset{|}{\text{H}}}{\overset{\overset{|}{\text{H}}}{\text{C}}}\!\!-\!\!\overset{\overset{\text{O}}{\|}}{\text{C}}\!\!-\!\!\text{OH} + \text{H}_2\text{O}
$$

It should be pointed out that the product obtained in the oxidation of an alcohol depends upon the stage of oxidation. An aldehyde may be considered as being the first stage of oxidation of an alcohol followed by acids obtained by further oxidation of the aldehyde. Complete oxidation of an alcohol results in the formation of carbon dioxide and water. It is very often difficult to control the oxidation so that only one type of compound is formed.

Acetic acid is a member of the *fatty acid series* having the general formula R—COOH where R may be a hydrogen atom or an alkyl radical. Common acids of this series are:

HCOOH	formic acid
CH_3COOH	acetic acid
C_2H_5COOH	propionic acid
C_3H_7COOH	butyric acid
C_4H_9COOH	valeric acid
$C_{17}H_{35}COOH$	stearic acid

The hydrogen atom in the —COOH group is responsible for acid properties. In water solutions, these acids are weakly ionized, *e.g.*, acetic acid ionizes:

$$H-\overset{\overset{\displaystyle H}{|}}{\underset{\underset{\displaystyle H}{|}}{C}}-\overset{\overset{\displaystyle O}{\|}}{C}-O-H + H_2O \rightleftharpoons \left[H-\overset{\overset{\displaystyle H}{|}}{\underset{\underset{\displaystyle H}{|}}{C}}-\overset{\overset{\displaystyle O}{\|}}{C}=O \right]^{-} + H_3O^{+}$$

The ionizations are strictly analogous to the ionization of an inorganic acid such as hydrochloric acid:

$$ClH + H_2O \rightleftharpoons Cl^{-} + H_3O^{+}$$

The acid radical of the organic acid is the R—COO group and derives its name from the *ic* acid by replacing that ending with *ate*, *i.e.*, CH_3COO is the acetate radical, C_3H_7COO the butyrate radical, HCOO the formate radical, etc. Like the mineral acids, organic acids are neutralized with bases; the acid hydrogen from the —COOH group combines with the OH group of the base to form water:

$$R-COO \!-\! H + Na \, OH \longrightarrow H_2O + \underset{\text{sodium salt}}{R-COONa}$$

If alcohol produced in the fermentation of sugars and fruit juices is allowed to come in contact with bacteria from mother of vinegar, further oxidation of the alcohol takes place with the formation of vinegar which contains about 4 per cent acetic acid. Hard cider will in time yield a vinegar containing acetic acid. Acetic acid has a number of uses: (1) the production of calcium acetate from which acetone may be obtained by heating, (2) manufacture of "white lead" for paints, (3) the preparation of acetic anhydride used in making cellulose acetate, a type of rayon, (4) the manufacture of many dyes, aspirin, and medicinals.

Pure acetic acid is a colorless liquid with a sharp penetrating odor.

At 18° it freezes to a white solid, very similar in appearance to ice; hence it is often called *glacial* acetic acid.

Other organic acids. *Formic acid*, HCOOH, is the simplest acid of the fatty acid series. It is found in certain nettles and is responsible for their sting. Red ants and bees also contain the acid, which is injected when these insects bite or sting. Formic acid may be prepared by the oxidation of methyl alcohol; however, there is very little demand for the acid.

The acids so far described are classed as *monobasic* acids since they contain only one —COOH functional group per molecule. It is possible to have organic molecules containing, two, three, or more —COOH groups. A few of them are described below:

    Tartaric acid,
$$CHOH—COOH$$
$$CHOH—COOH$$

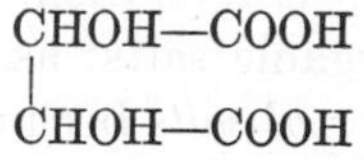

is a *dibasic* acid since it contains two carboxyl groups. It is obtained from grape and other fruit juices.

    Citric acid,
$$CH_2—COOH$$
$$OH—C—COOH$$
$$CH_2—COOH$$

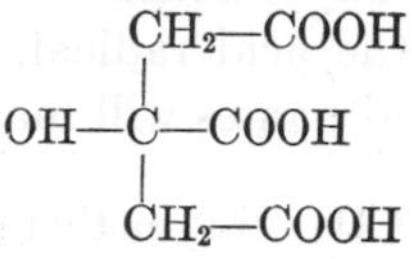

is a *tribasic* acid. It is found in lemons, oranges, and other citrus fruits. It is a solid at ordinary temperatures.

Lactic acid, $CH_3CHOHCOOH$, is found in sour milk as a result of the oxidation of lactose, or milk sugar.

ESTERS

Esters are formed from the reaction of alcohols with acids, the OH group from the alcohol combining with acid hydrogen from the acid to form water, *e.g.*, acetic acid reacts with ethyl alcohol to form *ethyl acetate*

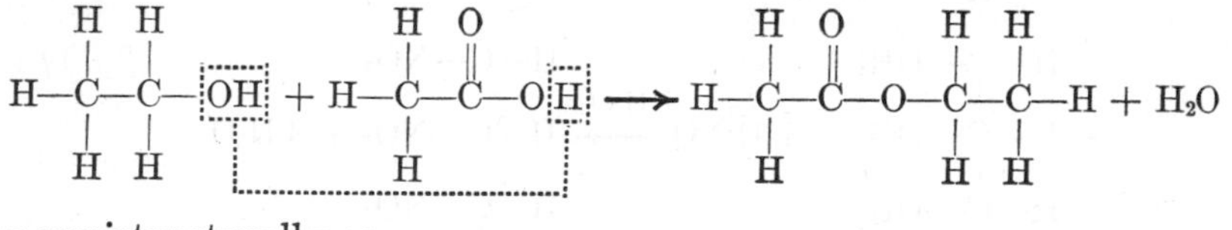

or semistructurally as

$$C_2H_5OH + CH_3COOH \longrightarrow CH_3COOC_2H_5 + H_2O$$
ethyl acetate

The reaction is analogous to the neutralization of an acid with a base in inorganic reactions:

$$Na\underline{OH} + Cl\underline{H} \longrightarrow ClNa + H_2O$$

However, reactions of the latter type are much more rapid than those between alcohols and acids, probably because of the ionization which takes place with inorganic substances. The reaction of an alcohol with an acid is called *esterification*.

The general formula for an ester is R—COO—R′ where R—COO⁻ is the acid radical and R′ is the radical derived from the alcohol from which the ester was prepared. Esters, then, according to their formulas appear to be similar to inorganic salts; as a matter of fact they are sometimes referred to as *ethereal salts* because of their volatile nature. One essential difference between esters and salts is the ionic nature of most salts in contrast to the nonionic character of esters.

In naming an ester, the alkyl radical of the alcohol is named first, followed by the name of the acid radical. The following formulas, written semistructurally, and names will make this clear:

$C_2H_5COO—CH_3$ is methyl propionate
$HCOO—C_2H_5$ is ethyl formate
$C_3H_7COO—C_3H_7$ is propyl butyrate

Many of the esters have a pleasant odor of fruit or flowers and upon this property depends the use of certain esters as perfumes and artificial flavorings. *Amyl acetate*, $CH_3COOC_5H_{11}$, has the odor of bananas and is called "banana oil"; *methyl salicylate*, $C_6H_4OHCOOCH_3$, is "oil of wintergreen"; *ethyl butyrate*, $C_3H_7COOC_2H_5$, has the odor of pineapple.

Esters of inorganic acids may also be prepared, *e.g.*, glycerin reacts with nitric acid in the presence of sulfuric acid:

$$
\begin{array}{ccc}
\text{H} & & \text{H} \\
| & & | \\
\text{H—C—OH} & & \text{H—C—NO}_3 \\
| & & | \\
\text{H—C—OH} + 3\ \text{HNO}_3 \xrightarrow{\text{H}_2\text{SO}_4} & \text{H—C—NO}_3 + 3\ \text{H}_2\text{O} \\
| & & | \\
\text{H—C—OH} & & \text{H—C—NO}_3 \\
| & & | \\
\text{H} & & \text{H} \\
\text{glycerin} & & \text{glyceryl trinitrate}
\end{array}
$$

to form glyceryl trinitrate or *nitroglycerin* as it is commonly called.

Esters, like inorganic salts, may undergo hydrolysis, forming an acid and an alcohol. The process is the opposite of esterification:

$$R—COO—R' + H_2O \longrightarrow R—COOH + R'—OH$$
$$\text{ester} \qquad\qquad\qquad \text{acid} \quad \text{alcohol}$$

FOODS

Foods consist largely of organic compounds and must be considered as an important part of the field of organic chemistry. Foods may be classified into the following groups, of which numbers 1, 2, 3, and 6 are organic compounds:

1. Fats   4. Water and oxygen
2. Carbohydrates   5. Minerals
3. Proteins   6. Vitamins

The functions of food are (1) to produce new body tissue for growth and to replace worn-out tissue, (2) to maintain body temperature, and (3) to produce energy for work and physical activity. While some of the groups of compounds listed above contribute to all three of these functions, we may say in general that proteins are largely responsible for new tissues and building of muscle; carbohydrates and fats through oxidation produce heat and maintain body temperature and furnish energy. Carbohydrates constitute the bulk of a normal diet.

While water and oxygen are frequently not classified as foods, nevertheless both are necessary for the maintenance of life. Minerals are necessary for building the bones and solid structure of the body. Calcium and phosphorus are necessary for bone structure, which is largely calcium phosphate. Iron is a constituent of hemoglobin, the oxygen-carrying portion of the red blood cells. A small amount of iodine is necessary for proper functioning of the thyroid gland. From sodium chloride the body produces hydrochloric acid found in the gastric juice. Although mineral matter in general is needed in only relatively small quantities, these small amounts play a vital role in the life processes.

In addition to the above substances, certain organic compounds called *vitamins* are necessary in small amounts. A lack of any of these vitamins in our diet results in vitamin deficiency diseases such as rickets, pellagra, nervous disorders, and others. Most vitamins are present in the fruits, vegetables, and meats which we eat daily, and if we consume a fairly balanced diet, it is likely that these vital compounds will be obtained in sufficient quantity for maintenance of health in most individuals.

FATS AND OILS

Fats are *glyceryl esters* of the higher molecular weight acids of the continuous chain type. They are obtained from both plants and animals. Usually those fats from animals, *e.g.*, stearin and butterfat, are solid or semisolid, while those derived from plants, *e.g.*, olive oil, cotton seed oil, and corn oil, are liquids and are designated as oils. Oils as applied to organic compounds may be classified into three groups: (1) mineral oils which are derived from petroleum or petroleum products, (2) essential oils which are volatile liquids derived from plants, (3) glyceryl esters. We shall limit our discussion here to fats and oils which are of the latter type.

The principal fats are *stearin, palmitin,* and *olein:*

$$
\begin{array}{lll}
\mathrm{C_{17}H_{35}COO-CH_2} & \mathrm{C_{15}H_{31}COO-CH_2} & \mathrm{C_{17}H_{33}COO-CH_2} \\
\quad\quad\quad\;\; | & \quad\quad\quad\;\; | & \quad\quad\quad\;\; | \\
\mathrm{C_{17}H_{35}COO-CH} & \mathrm{C_{15}H_{31}COO-CH} & \mathrm{C_{17}H_{33}COO-CH} \\
\quad\quad\quad\;\; | & \quad\quad\quad\;\; | & \quad\quad\quad\;\; | \\
\mathrm{C_{17}H_{35}COO-CH_2} & \mathrm{C_{15}H_{31}COO-CH_2} & \mathrm{C_{17}H_{33}COO-CH_2} \\
\quad\quad stearin & \quad\quad palmitin & \quad\quad olein
\end{array}
$$

These esters may be considered as being derived from glycerol and a fatty acid, *e.g.*, stearin from glycerol and stearic acid:

$$
3\,\mathrm{C_{17}H_{35}COO-H} +
\begin{array}{l}
\mathrm{OH-CH_2} \\
\;\; | \\
\mathrm{OH-CH} \\
\;\; | \\
\mathrm{OH-CH_2}
\end{array}
\longrightarrow 3\,\mathrm{H_2O} +
\begin{array}{l}
\mathrm{C_{17}H_{35}COO-CH_2} \\
\quad\quad\quad\;\; | \\
\mathrm{C_{17}H_{35}COO-CH} \\
\quad\quad\quad\;\; | \\
\mathrm{C_{17}H_{35}COO-CH_2}
\end{array}
$$

Stearin and palmitin are saturated esters and are solids at ordinary temperatures; olein is an unsaturated ester with one double bond in each $\mathrm{C_{17}H_{33}}$ chain and is a liquid. The hardness of a fat depends upon the relative amounts of these three esters present. Beef tallow, a hard fat, is about 75 per cent stearin and 25 per cent olein. Lard is softer and is composed of about 60 per cent olein and 40 per cent palmitin; butterfat contains both olein and palmitin and in addition, butyrin, the glyceryl ester of butyric acid.

There is some evidence to indicate that the greater softness of the feminine skin as compared to that of the male is due to a slightly higher glyceryl oleate content.

Liquid fats are frequently hydrogenated to convert them to saturated esters which are solid or semisolid, *e.g.*, the hydrogenation of olein may be represented by the equation:

$$(C_{17}H_{33}COO)_3C_3H_5 + 3\ H_2 \longrightarrow (C_{17}H_{35}COO)_3C_3H_5$$
olein   stearin

Similarly, fish oil, peanut oil, soy bean oil, castor oil, and other unsaturated liquid oils may be hydrogenated to edible solid fats.

Saponification. Soaps are prepared by heating together a fat with sodium or potassium hydroxide solution. Sodium hydroxide produces a hard soap while potassium hydroxide gives a soft soap (liquid). Fats

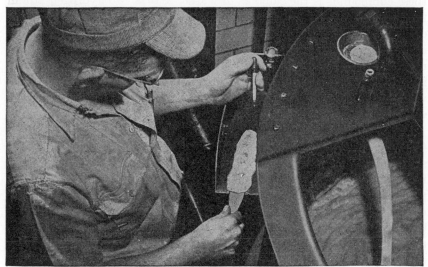

Courtesy Procter & Gamble Co.
Fig. 146. Testing soap in blend tank for alkalinity.

such as tallow, coconut oil, and palm oil are usually employed for soap manufacture. These and similar reactions of an ester with a base are termed *saponification* reactions. The general reaction may be illustrated by the following equation for the preparation of soap from stearin:

$$
\begin{array}{lll}
C_{17}H_{35}COO\!-\!CH_2 & OH\ Na & CH_2OH \\
\quad\quad\quad\quad\ \ \ | & & \ \ | \\
C_{17}H_{35}COO\!-\!CH\ \ + & OH\ Na \longrightarrow 3\ C_{17}H_{35}COONa\ + & CHOH \\
\quad\quad\quad\quad\ \ \ | & & \ \ | \\
C_{17}H_{35}COO\!-\!CH_2 & OH\ Na & CH_2OH \\
\end{array}
$$

sodium stearate

Sodium salts of the higher fatty acids such as sodium stearate, sodium palmitate, and sodium oleate are the principal constituents of ordinary soaps. Glycerin is a by-product of the preparation of soap. It is removed and purified by distillation.

CARBOHYDRATES

Carbohydrates are compounds of carbon, hydrogen, and oxygen, of which sugar, starch, and cellulose are common examples. Those carbohydrates with a sweet taste and which may be used for sweetening purposes are called *sugars*. The term carbohydrate was originally derived from the fact that the proportion of hydrogen to oxygen in these compounds is the same as in water, that is two hydrogen atoms to one oxygen atom, hence, the term hydrate of carbon or carbohydrate. However, these compounds are *not* hydrates; furthermore, all compounds in which the ratio of hydrogen to oxygen is two to one are not carbohydrates nor do all carbohydrates contain these two elements in this proportion. A better definition of a carbohydrate is a compound which is either an alcohol-aldehyde or an alcohol-ketone or a compound which yields either or both of these types of compounds on hydrolysis.

Carbohydrates are conveniently classified as: (1) monosaccharides, (2) disaccharides, and (3) polysaccharides. Disaccharides and polysaccharides yield monosaccharides upon complete hydrolysis. Many monosaccharides, the *hexoses*, have the formula $C_6H_{12}O_6$. Since compounds of this formula may be obtained from most common carbohydrates, we might consider a compound of six carbon atoms as a basic unit in the structure of carbohydrates. Disaccharides contain two monosaccharide units, *e.g.*, sucrose is $C_{12}H_{22}O_{11}$, and polysaccharides contain a greater number of units. We shall consider here only a few of the common members of each of these three groups of carbohydrates.

Monosaccharides. *Glucose* and *fructose* are the more common of this group; their structural formulas are shown below:

$$
\begin{array}{ll}
\text{H} & \\
| & \\
\text{C}=\text{O} & \text{CH}_2\text{OH} \\
| & | \\
\text{CHOH} & \text{C}=\text{O} \\
| & | \\
\text{CHOH} & \text{CHOH} \\
| & | \\
\text{CHOH} & \text{CHOH} \\
| & | \\
\text{CHOH} & \text{CHOH} \\
| & | \\
\text{CH}_2\text{OH} & \text{CH}_2\text{OH} \\
\text{glucose} & \text{fructose}
\end{array}
$$

It is evident that glucose is an alcohol-aldehyde while fructose is an alcohol-ketone. The two compounds are isomers.

Glucose is also called *dextrose*. It is present in many fruit juices and in honey. It may be obtained by the hydrolysis of sucrose, maltose, lactose, and starch. The latter provides the largest source. If starch is heated with dilute hydrochloric acid, hydrolysis takes place as represented by the equation:

$$(C_6H_{10}O_5)_x + x\,H_2O \longrightarrow x\,C_6H_{12}O_6$$

The product which is left as a sirup may be used directly in liquid form or concentrated and crystallized to solid sugar. Glucose is less sweet than cane sugar but is employed for sweetening in pastries and candies, and as a table sirup. Large quantities of glucose are used industrially in the production of ethyl alcohol by fermentation.

Fructose, also called *levulose* or fruit sugar is present in many fruits and is a hydrolysis product of sucrose along with glucose. It is usually prepared by the hydrolysis of *inulin*, a polysaccharide somewhat similar to starch, which is found in dahlia tubers and the Jerusalem artichoke. Other monosaccharides include *mannose* and *galactose*.

Disaccharides. The common disaccharides of the formula, $C_{12}H_{22}O_{11}$ are *sucrose, lactose,* and *maltose.* Of these sucrose is the most common and most familiar. It is obtained in a white crystalline form by the evaporation of juices from the sugar beet or sugar cane and is the common sugar of commerce used for sweetening purposes. Its chemical structure is indicated by the formula:

$$
\begin{array}{ll}
\text{CH}_2\text{OH} & \quad \text{CH} \\
\quad | & \qquad | \\
\text{C--O} & \quad \text{CHOH} \\
\quad | & \qquad | \\
\text{CHOH} & \quad \text{CHOH} \\
\text{O} \quad | & \quad \text{O} \quad | \\
\text{CHOH} & \quad \text{CHOH} \\
\quad | & \qquad | \\
\text{CH} & \quad \text{CH} \\
\quad | & \qquad | \\
\text{CH}_2\text{OH} & \quad \text{CH}_2\text{OH}
\end{array}
$$

It is believed to be a compound formed from glucose and fructose since in the presence of a small amount of hydrochloric acid or of the enzyme, *invertase*, hydrolysis takes place with the formation of one molecule each of glucose and fructose:

$$\underset{\text{sucrose}}{C_{12}H_{22}O_{11}} + H_2O \longrightarrow \underset{\text{glucose}}{C_6H_{12}O_6} + \underset{\text{fructose}}{C_6H_{12}O_6}$$

The term *invert* sugar is used to indicate this equimolecular mixture of glucose and fructose.

Lactose, or milk sugar, is obtained from the milk of mammals. Cow's milk contains about 5 per cent lactose, human milk 8 to 10 per cent. Hydrolysis of lactose produces one molecule each of glucose and galactose:

$$\underset{\text{lactose}}{C_{12}H_{22}O_{11}} + H_2O \longrightarrow \underset{\text{glucose}}{C_6H_{12}O_6} + \underset{\text{galactose}}{C_6H_{12}O_6}$$

Maltose may be produced by the action of the enzyme, *diastase*, on starch. Upon hydrolysis it yields two molecules of glucose:

$$\underset{\text{maltose}}{C_{12}H_{22}O_{11}} + H_2O \longrightarrow 2\ \underset{\text{glucose}}{C_6H_{12}O_6}$$

Starch. Starch is usually represented by the formula $(C_6H_{10}O_5)_x$. The magnitude of x is probably about 20 to 25 so that the molecular weight is large.

Starch is present in nearly all plants. Potatoes contain about 20 per cent; dried rice and corn about 75 and 50 per cent respectively. These substances provide the source of starch for commercial production. It is very insoluble in cold water, but with hot water the granules of starch swell and produce a colloidal solution which if concentrated will set to a gel when cooled. Boiling with hydrochloric acid results in hydrolysis to form glucose.

Cellulose. Cellulose, $(C_6H_{10}O_5)_y$, is a polysaccharide of even higher molecular weight than starch. Although it has the same empirical formula as starch, its properties are very different. It is insoluble in water and organic solvents, is not easily hydrolyzed although boiling for a long time with dilute sulfuric acid gradually results in the formation of glucose.

Cellulose constitutes the principal constituent of all plant fiber. Principal sources are wood and cotton. The latter is practically pure cellulose. Wood fibers in addition contain lignin and resins which bind the material together. In the production of cellulose from wood, the lignin and resin are usually dissolved by means of calcium acid sulfite or a sodium hydroxide and sodium sulfide solution to leave pure cellulose. The manufacture of paper is essentially a process of washing and bleaching the cellulose and pressing it into a compact form in sheets.

Since carbohydrates contain the alcohol group, OH, we might expect them to react with acids to form esters. If cellulose is treated with nitric acid in the presence of concentrated sulfuric acid to act as a dehydrating agent, cellulose nitrates are formed. Intensive nitration results in the production of *guncotton*, a highly explosive compound which is used in the production of smokeless powders, cordite, and as an explosive in torpedoes. Incomplete nitration forms *pyroxylin* which is used in the production of artificial leathers, photographic film, lacquers, and collodion. It is soluble in mixtures of organic solvents. This permits its separation from guncotton, which is insoluble.

Fabric treated with an organic solvent solution of pyroxylin will on evaporation of the solvent have a tough flexible finish that resembles natural leather. *Collodion* is a solution of pyroxylin in a mixture of alcohol and ether. A common lacquer is a solution of pyroxylin in amyl acetate (banana oil). *Celluloid* is produced from cellulose nitrates by forming a plastic mass with camphor; the product may be molded into desired shapes. It is highly inflammable.

Rayon. The principal difference between silk and rayon is in the chemical composition. Silk is a protein while rayon is cellulose or a cellulose derivative. Cotton or cellulose fibers are short, irregular, and dull while those of silk are long, smooth, and bright. In the production of rayon it is mainly a matter of changing the structure of the cotton or wood cellulose fibers. While there are several methods employed for doing this, all methods are the same in principle. In brief, the process consists in dispersing cellulose or cellulose derivative in a liquid in colloidal form which can then be forced through a small orifice or nozzle into a solution which will precipitate the cellulose or its derivative in tiny filaments. These tiny filaments are twisted together to form a larger thread which is then used for weaving purposes. One of the more common methods of producing rayon is by the *viscose* process in which the cellulose is treated with sodium hydroxide and carbon disulfide. A cellulose xanthate solution is formed which is forced through small openings into a bath of sulfuric acid and sodium bisulfate where the cellulose is precipitated in desired fibrous form.

Cellophane. The elastic, transparent, heat resistant, water and oil insoluble material which we call *cellophane* is likewise made from a cellulose xanthate solution by precipitation of the cellulose in film form by ammonium salts.

PROTEINS

Proteins are complex compounds composed of the elements carbon, oxygen, hydrogen, and nitrogen. In addition, the elements phosphorus and sulfur may be present. Proteins are found in plants and are particularly abundant in animals and animal products such as lean meat, cheese, milk, and eggs. Due to their complexity, knowledge of their chemical structure is incomplete, although it has been established that their molecular weights are very large.

Hydrolysis of proteins yields *amino acids* which contain the amine, NH_2, group and the carboxyl, COOH, group. About twenty different amino acids have been obtained from proteins, of which the simplest is amino acetic acid, or *glycine*, CH_2NH_2COOH. Such compounds are amphoteric (may function as either acids or bases), since they contain the basic NH_2 group and the acidic $COOH$ group. These facts have led to the belief that proteins are built up by a combination of amino acids. The basic part of one molecule may combine with the acidic part of another molecule, whose basic part in turn may combine with another acidic group of still another amino acid. Thus a chain containing many molecules of amino acid molecules may be built up; we may illustrate how this combination might take place between glycine molecules:

$$H-N-CH_2-COOH$$

$$H$$

$$H-N-CH_2-CO\,OH \longrightarrow NH_2-CH_2-CO-NH-CH_2-CO-NH-CH_2COOH + 2\,H_2O$$

$$H$$

$$H-N-CH_2-CO\,OH$$

$$H \qquad \text{etc.}$$

When we consider that molecules of many different amino acids may thus combine, we may appreciate the complexity of the actual protein molecules.

VITAMINS

The importance of these vital substances in the diet of man has already been mentioned. Due to the fact that vitamins are present in foods in only minute amounts and because of their complexity, extreme difficulties in their preparation and study in a pure state have been encountered. All are thought to be definite chemical compounds, although the formulas have not been established in all cases. Vitamin studies have progressed rapidly in the last decade and no doubt in the future new vitamins will be found, and in addition we shall know more about the composition and synthesis of those already discovered.

The various vitamins have been designated by letter as well as by name; below are recorded the more common ones with brief statements regarding their sources and functions:

Vitamin A is the general good health vitamin, as it promotes growth and the normal well-being of individuals. It also prevents certain serious eye diseases and helps maintain resistance against infections. This vitamin has been obtained from *carotene*, a compound found in carrots and its composition is thought to be represented by the formula $C_{20}H_{30}$. Vitamin A is found in abundance in dairy products and in green vegetables of all kinds. Other sources are cod-liver oil and hali- but-liver oil.

Vitamin B is now known to be a mixture of several distinct com- pounds. Vitamin B_1 is *thiamine chloride*, $C_{12}H_{17}N_4OSCl$. It is present in yeast and in whole cereals as well as in most vegetables. Other forms of vitamin B are B_2 or *riboflavin*, $C_{17}H_{20}N_4O_6$, and *nicotinic acid*, C_5H_4NCOOH, which helps prevent the disease pellagra.

Vitamin C helps prevent the disease known as scurvy. Its composi- tion has been established as *ascorbic acid*, $C_6H_8O_6$, which is manu- factured and sold commercially. It is present in citrus fruits, particu- larly oranges and lemons, and in cabbage and tomatoes.

Vitamin D, sometimes called the sunshine vitamin, is necessary for normal development of bones, and lack of it in the diet may result in the disease known as rickets. It is essential in the diet of children. Principal sources of the vitamin are milk and cod-liver oil. *Ergosterol*, a fat found in many foods, is converted to vitamin D by the action of ultraviolet rays, hence many foods are now irradiated to increase their vitamin D content. Ergosterol is also present in the skin and exposure to the sun's rays results in the formation of vitamin D — hence the name sunshine vitamin.

Vitamin E is the reproductive vitamin and is said to help prevent sterility in man and animals. Lettuce, meat, and certain vegetable oils are rich sources of this vitamin.

Vitamin G is one of the forms of vitamin B. It promotes a healthy condition of the skin.

Vitamin K aids in prevention of hemorrhage by hastening the clot- ting time of blood. Green vegetables, tomatoes, and eggs are sources.

HORMONES

Hormones are as important to the proper functioning of vital proc- esses as are vitamins. These secretions of the ductless glands of the body are substances of whose chemical nature and composition relatively little is known. They are absorbed directly into the blood stream and carried to various parts of the body. The fact that these secretions are produced in only minute amounts makes their study and analysis difficult. Lack of any one of the hormones results in pro- found effects on the biological processes of the human anatomy.

Adrenalin, the secretion of the adrenal glands, has been prepared in the laboratory and its formula established as $C_9H_{13}NO_3$. It acts as a stimulant for the heart and lungs.

Thyroxin, $C_{15}H_{11}O_4NI_4$, has also been prepared in the laboratory. It is a secretion of the thyroid gland, and a lack of it may result in goiter and impairment of the brain.

Insulin is secreted by the pancreatic gland. The disease, diabetes, appears to be a result of a lack of this hormone. It is obtained from the pancreas of animals for medical administration to humans.

NITRATION AND SULFONATION PRODUCTS OF BENZENE

Nitro compounds. When benzene is heated with a mixture of nitric and sulfuric acids, *nitration* — a process in which an NO_2 (nitro) group is substituted for a hydrogen atom attached to the ring — takes place to form nitrobenzene:

$$\text{benzene}-\text{H} + \text{HO}\!-\!NO_2 \xrightarrow{\ H_2SO_4\ } \text{benzene}-NO_2 + H_2O$$

benzene   nitrobenzene

Further nitration results in the substitution of two or three nitro groups in the benzene nucleus. Reduction of nitro compounds results in the formation of amines, *e.g.,* reduction of nitrobenzene gives aniline, $C_6H_5NH_2$, which is used in the production of dyes and medicinals.

Sulfonic acids. The treatment of aromatic hydrocarbons with hot concentrated sulfuric acid results in *sulfonation* and the formation of sulfonic acids. The reaction of benzene with sulfuric acid results in the formation of benzene sulfonic acid:

$$\text{benzene}-\text{H} + \text{HO}\!-\!SO_3H \longrightarrow \text{benzene}-SO_3H + H_2O$$

benzene   benzene sulfonic acid

Many dyes are produced from sulfonic acids or their derivatives. A typical formula for a dye is that of Congo red:

$$NH_2 \quad\quad\quad\quad NH_2$$
$$\text{—N}=\text{N—}\quad\text{—N}=\text{N—}$$
$$SO_3Na \quad\quad\quad\quad SO_3Na$$

SULFA DRUGS AND PENICILLIN

The remarkable curative power of sulfanilamide came to attention in 1935. Since that time some 5500 compounds allied to sulfanilamide have been described as researchers have tried to attain more potent germ killers with less toxicity to the host. Formulas for a few of them are:

sulfanilamide   sulfapyridine

sulfathiazole

Sulfapyridine and sulfathiazole are examples of *heterocyclic* compounds — compounds which contain some element in addition to carbon in the ring structure.

Penicillin is a specific mold secretion which diffuses from the mold and was found to inhibit bacterial growth near the mold on bacterial test plates. It is specifically effective against gonorrhea and certain other organisms. There are many organisms against which both sulfa drugs and penicillin are effective. Also penicillin will act on some upon which sulfa will not, whereas sulfa is useful for treatment in some cases, such as dysentery, where penicillin seems ineffective.

SYNTHETIC RESINS AND PLASTICS

Natural resins such as pine resins and various tree gums have found considerable use in varnishes. *Shellac* is made from the ground and melted bodies of certain insects that grow on certain trees in India. Modern-day demand has resulted in the construction of large synthetic resin and plastic plants. A synthetic resin is a basic material which may be made by certain chemical changes of a polymerization, condensation, or combination type. The resin may be a plastic or subject to plasticizing. Plastics are classified as *thermosetting*, which once molded and set cannot be remelted, and *thermoplastic* substances, which may be remelted or softened and re-formed a number of times.

If phenol and formaldehyde are compounded under carefully controlled conditions a fairly hard product which may be ground to a powdery resin is obtained. If polymerized to a lesser degree, or with excess phenol, the product may be in itself cast as a plastic. If the powdery resin is heated with a small percentage of some plasticizing agent such as dibutyl phthalate, a plastic product results. Phenolformaldehyde polymerized products are made into plastics with the trade name Bakelite.

The phenolic resins are compounded into molding compositions such as follows:

Material	Per Cent
Resin	40
Hexamethylene tetramine	5
Lime	3
Calcium stearate	1
Mixed waxes	1
Wood fiber	40
Clay	5
Dye	5

Each constituent has a specific function; the wood fiber for filler, the clay for filler and bulk density, the waxes for a product susceptible to better polish, the lime for neutralizing acidity and drying the mix, the hexamethylene tetramine for conversion from thermoplastic to a thermosetting mass, the calcium stearate for prevention of sticking to the mold.

The resin may be dissolved in organic solvents, pigment added if desired, and a coating lacquer is obtained. Other substances which may be used with formaldehyde instead of phenol are urea or melamine.

Since many plants were built during World War II to produce styrene in making buna S synthetic rubber, styrene is currently a comparatively cheap chemical which can be polymerized to give a thermoplastic material of many uses. The composition of styrene is $C_6H_5-CH=CH_2$.

Cellulose nitrate, cellulose acetate, or cellulose propionate may be plasticized by compounding with various agents such as triphenyl phosphate, $(C_6H_5)_3PO_4$.

It is beyond the scope of this book to describe the chemistry of the many plastic materials. Feminine interest in the plastic substance *nylon* suggests a note on the chemistry of its manufacture. If a diamine and a dibasic carbon chain acid are subjected to dehydration, long molecules constituting nylon result:

$$H-O-\overset{O}{\overset{\|}{C}}-(CH_2)_4-\overset{O}{\overset{\|}{C}}-O-H + H-\overset{H}{\overset{|}{N}}-(CH_2)_6-\overset{H}{\overset{|}{N}}-H \longrightarrow$$

adipic acid $\qquad$ a diamine $\qquad$ under controlled conditions

$$H-O-\overset{O}{\overset{\|}{C}}-(CH_2)_4-\overset{O\ H}{\overset{\|\ |}{C-N}}-(CH_2)_6-\overset{H\ O}{\overset{|\ \|}{N-C}}-(CH_2)_4-\overset{O\ H}{\overset{\|\ |}{C-N}}-(CH_2)_6-\overset{H}{\overset{|}{N}}-\text{further similar}$$

linkages

nylon

When nylon is melted, it can be forced through small openings in a disk producing jets which solidify to a thread. When these threads are subjected to cold pulling or stretching, they set to a strong fiber which has marked elastic and durable qualities, usable for hosiery, brush bristles, tennis racket strings, parachutes, tow lines for gliders, etc.

The *alkyd* resins have assumed a controlling position in the surface coating industry. They are made by the esterification and condensation of dibasic acids such as phthalic acid (an oxidation product of the well-known moth repellent naphthalene) with polyhydroxy alcohols such as glycerin. A drying oil such as linseed may be added.

RUBBER AND ELASTOMERS

Natural rubber was first obtained from sap of a species of tree in Brazil. Such trees were selectively planted and grown in the East

Indies and with care a better yield of rubber tree sap (latex) was obtained. The latex when heated with acid yields crude rubber, which in turn may be compounded for desired properties by incorporation of filler materials, antioxidants, and vulcanizing agents such as sulfur. Natural rubber is essentially a high molecular weight hydrocarbon with numerous unsaturated bonds.

With the marked increase in demand for rubber and interruption of supply by war, chemists have developed rubber substitutes which go under the general name of *elastomers*. In many properties, industrially produced elastomers are better than natural rubber; for example, most elastomers are more oil resistant and some are less permeable than rubber. The chemistry of production of a few synthetic rubbers will be briefly described.

Neoprene is produced from acetylene by polymerization to form vinyl acetylene. When this compound is treated with hydrochloric acid, chloroprene is formed.

$$H-C{\equiv}C-CH{=}CH_2 + HCl \longrightarrow H-C{=}C-CH{=}CH_2$$

vinyl acetylene   chloroprene

(with H and Cl substituents on the chloroprene carbons)

When chloroprene is treated with metallic sodium under carefully controlled conditions, carbon-to-carbon linkages are effected between many four-carbon chain units to give neoprene:

$$\begin{array}{ll} H-C{=}C-CH{=}CH_2 & H-C{=}C-CH{=}CH_2 \\ \quad | \quad | & \quad | \\ \quad H \quad Cl & \quad H \\ \quad H \quad Cl \;\; +2\,Na \longrightarrow 2\,NaCl + & \quad H \\ \quad | \quad | & \quad | \\ H-C{=}C-CH{=}CH_2 & H-C{=}C-CH{=}CH_2 \end{array}$$

chloroprene   neoprene

Many molecules like the last one shown polymerize to rubberlike products.

Thiokol is obtained by controlled heating of hydrocarbon dichlorides such as ethylene dichloride, $ClCH_2-CH_2Cl$, with sodium polysulfide, Na_2S_x. The ethylene dichloride can be made from chlorine and ethylene. Ethylene is made by dehydration of ethyl alcohol or by dehydrogenation of ethane.

One of the elastomers manufactured in great bulk has been known as buna S, GR-S, or butadiene-styrene product. Butadiene, $H_2C{=}CH-CH{=}CH_2$, results from dehydrogenating butane.

$$\text{styrene} \quad + \quad \text{butadiene} \quad \xrightarrow[\substack{\text{emulsified in water, cata-}\\ \text{lyst for copolymerization}\\ \text{added—temperature and}\\ \text{time control}}]{} \text{buna S}$$

styrene
1 pound

butadiene
3 pounds

When the desired amount of molecular union has taken place to give a product of desired properties, a stopping agent such as phenyl naphthalene is added and the crude synthetic rubber latex is separated, purified by washing, and compounded for use.

SILICONES

Reference has previously been made to the chemical similarity of carbon and silicon. Recently, many compounds of chainlike structures containing both carbon and silicon have been prepared. They possess the general structure:

$$\cdots -O-\underset{\underset{CH_3}{|}}{\overset{\overset{CH_3}{|}}{Si}}-O-\underset{\underset{CH_3}{|}}{\overset{\overset{CH_3}{|}}{Si}}-\cdots$$

These compounds are known as *silicones* and are remarkable in their stability and resistance to the action of chemicals. The lower molecular weight silicones are oils which are nearly as fluid at low temperatures as at high temperatures. They find application as lubricants in regions of very low temperatures. High molecular weight silicones have properties of elastomers and make suitable rubber substitutes. A puttylike silicone, called "bouncing putty" exhibits nearly perfect elasticity when struck a sharp blow, and may be bounced in the same manner as a rubber ball. Other uses of silicones include moisture and fireproofing agents and insulating coatings for electrical equipment. A silicone finish for textiles makes them water repellent even after laundering or dry cleaning. Silicone polishes for furniture and automobiles last longer than wax and are easier to apply. Because silicone films can be made much thinner than other kinds of insulation, electric motors can now be made much smaller. The chemistry of the silicones is summarized in Figure 147x. It may be noted that cross linking of chains may take place to produce three-dimensional structures of great complexity.

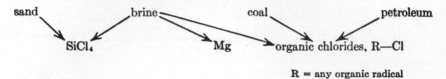

R = any organic radical

$$SiCl_4 + Mg + RCl \longrightarrow MgCl_2 + \text{organo silicone chlorides}$$

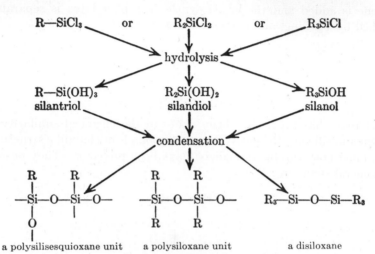

a polysilisesquioxane unit   a polysiloxane unit   a disiloxane

Fig. 147x.   The Chemistry of silicons.

EXERCISES

1. Write structural formulas for ethyl amine, butyl acetate, propionic acid, glyceryl oleate, dibutyl ether, methyl propyl ketone, ethyl iodide, calcium acetate.

2. Write equations for the
   (a) hydrolysis of methyl acetate.
   (b) reaction of ethyl alcohol with butyric acid.
   (c) saponification of glyceryl stearate.
   (d) neutralization of formic acid with calcium hydroxide.
   (e) hydrolysis of starch.
   (f) inversion of sucrose.
   (g) fermentation of glucose.
   (h) combustion of ethyl alcohol in air.
   (i) nitration of benzene.

3. By means of equations, indicate the steps you would take to prepare
   (a) ethylene from ethyl acetate.   (e) nitroglycerin from glyceryl palmitate.
   (b) aniline from benzene.   (f) acetone from acetic acid.
   (c) ethyl amine from ethane.   (g) acetic acid from ethyl alcohol.
   (d) ethyl alcohol from starch.

4. Name and classify the following compounds as to type:

C_3H_7Br; HCOOH; $CH_3COC_4H_9$; C_2H_5CHO; CH_3NH_2; $(C_2H_5)_2O$;
$(C_3H_7COO)_3C_3H_5$; $CH_3COOC_3H_7$; $C_3H_7COOCH_3$; $HCOOCH_3$; CH_3COOH;
C_4H_9OH; $C_6H_{12}O_6$; $C_6H_5COCH_3$; $C_6H_5NH_2$; C_6H_5COOK.

5. Write structural formulas and names of the four butyl alcohols.

6. Indicate the meaning of the terms: functional group; alcohol proof; enzyme; carbohydrate; esterification; saponification; vitamin; elastomer; protein.

REFERENCES

J. B. Conant, *The Chemistry of Organic Compounds*, Macmillan.

B. E. Levine, "The Vitamins," *J. Chem. Ed.* **12,** 357 (1935).

Cornelia T. Snell, "Synthetic Detergents and Surface Activity," *ibid.* **24,** 505 (1947).

H. J. Lucas, *Organic Chemistry*, American Book Company.

H. C. Sherman, *The Chemistry of Food and Nutrition*, Macmillan.

E. Wertheim, *Textbook of Organic Chemistry*, Blakiston.

Roger J. Williams, *Textbook of Biochemistry*, Van Nostrand.

XLI

Chemical Industry and
Chemical Engineering

Chemistry, as a basic science, has applications in many industrial pursuits of man. Accordingly, we make use of such terms as biochemistry, geochemistry, metallurgical chemistry, medicinal chemistry, chemotherapy, agricultural chemistry, food chemistry, etc., pertaining to the application of chemistry to these respective fields. To supply chemicals for all man's diverse enterprises there has grown a "chemical industry." Chemistry in industry is concerned with raw materials, conversion of them to chemical products, their uses, and the techniques involved in their manufacture.

Chemical engineering is concerned with the understanding and application of all those practical processes involved in the handling and production of chemical materials. In the handling of raw materials and the conversion of them to chemical products, the chemical engineer makes use of many "unit operations" and diverse kinds of equipment. Some of these unit operations are of a chemical nature, others are physical. Most chemical industries involve a number of each kind. Some of the more important ones are listed in Table 41.

The fundamental knowledge possessed by the experienced industrial chemist and chemical engineer leads to his service in many varied capacities in industry — with the over-all result that man's health, food, clothing, shelter, and transportation, as well as a growing list of semi-necessities and luxuries, are improved, made more varied, more artistic, and more available through lowered production costs. Chemists and chemical engineers are to be found in every nook and cranny of modern industry. In some units every man, from the president down through the plant superintendent to the departmental foreman, is professionally trained in chemistry or chemical engineering. A great number serve in the research departments of industry.

TABLE 41

PRINCIPAL CHEMICAL ENGINEERING PROCESSES

CHEMICAL UNIT OPERATIONS	PHYSICAL UNIT OPERATIONS
Combustion	Fluid flow
Oxidation	Heat transfer
Neutralization	Proportioning
Silicate formation	Materials handling
Causticization	Gathering
Electrolysis	Storing
Double decomposition	Transporting
Calcination	Conveying
Nitration	Fluid handling
Esterification	Disintegration of material
Reduction	Mixing
Ammonolysis	Heat transfer
Halogenation	Separation
Sulfonation	Leaching, extracting
Hydrogenation	Dissolving
Condensation	Filtering
Polymerization	Crystallizing
Fermentation	Condensing
Pyrolysis	Evaporation
Isomerization	Humidification and dehumidification
Hydrolysis	Absorption
Various organic syntheses	Adsorption
	Catalyzing
	Sampling
	Indicating and recording
	Automatic or manual controls
	Compressing or expanding
	Coagulating

Research activities may be divided into two groups for the purpose of discussion. Experimental research comprises fundamental studies, exploratory work on processes, products, methods, etc., pilot plant development work, full-scale plant experimental work, and product utilization. Research on paper — desk work — comprises correlation of data, process design, economic studies, plant technical service, report and paper preparation, literature search, supervision and direction of research. An individual chemist may specialize in one of these activities or perform a combination of them.

The vital control laboratories, where tests are performed to maintain standards of uniformity, purity, and quality of product, utilize many chemists. The chemists perform the more difficult analyses, design the test procedures, and act in a supervisory capacity. Technicians make the more routine tests.

Dual training in chemistry and law is the basis of the success of patent attorneys serving the process industries. Many chemists serve industry in a consulting capacity. Since many chemists are employed in research, we may ask, "What are the achievements of research?"

Courtesy Spencer Chemical Company

Fig. 147. Pelton wheels and pumps for water scrubbers in ammonia plant.

Some research achievements have been well publicized — the effectiveness of the wonder drug penicillin which is specific and highly effective against certain pathogenic organisms, the large scale production of magnesium and toluene, the establishment of a synthetic rubber industry in a few months, the synthesis of 100 octane gasoline from petroleum, the replacement of the silkworm and the boar brush bristle by the nylon factory, and many more. Less well known are many thousands of improved articles in everyday use.

It is the steady year-to-year improvements that really pay for the research in industry. They go unnoticed but can be seen very clearly by looking back a decade or two. Perhaps one of the more clear cut examples is that of the automobile tire. In 1915, the motorist was fortunate indeed if his tires lasted 5000 miles at less than twenty-five miles per hour, even with the greatest care, including repeated vulcanization. Now tires made from rubber derived from the same trees and cotton of the same quality last 30,000 miles or more at forty-five miles per hour — and the cost per pound of tire is less.

Why is this? Some people say, "That's easy! Antioxidants made all the difference." Others say, "Its accelerators." It is none of these things individually. Research studies by many hundreds of chemists over a period of years have resulted in many thousands of big and little changes; the summation of which is a tire which lasts more than six times as long and costs less. It is doubtful that even a rubber chemist can itemize in a reasonable length of time all the research accomplishments which contributed to this result.

The American Chemical Society, now numbering over 60,000 chemists and chemical engineers, is the largest professional organization in the world. The Society sponsors the publication of *Chemical Abstracts*, which indexes the world's chemical, scientific, and technical publications and patents. The technical library is the proper starting point for chemical research by review of published information or investigational reports on work previously done related to a new project.

An index of the tremendous growth rate of applied chemistry to modern industry is shown in the following facts: In 1863, at the height of the Civil War, the annual production of steel per person was one-half pound. In 1943, it was 1326 pounds per person. A greater tonnage of every mineral commodity has been mined (and most such raw material minerals are chemically converted to useful products) since 1900 than during the combined years of all previous history. During the past twenty-five years industrial research has expanded ten times.

It requires research-acquired chemical knowledge and chemical engineering "know how" to develop and operate plants of chemical industry; three of these industries are summarized in the flow sheet diagrams (Figs. 148–150). Upon examining these flow sheets it is quickly realized that it is a big step from the writing of a few chemical equations or the carrying out of these reactions in the laboratory to large-scale plant production.

REFERENCES

Badger and McCabe, *Elements of Chemical Engineering*, McGraw-Hill.
E. R. Riegel, *Industrial Chemistry*, Reinhold.
R. N. Shreve, *Chemical Process Industries*, McGraw-Hill.

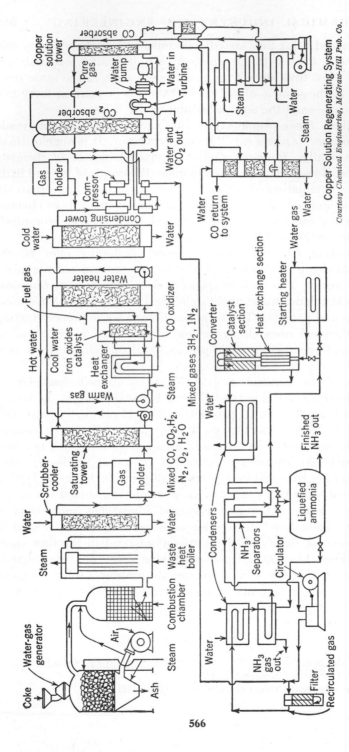

Fig. 148. Ammonia synthesis by the Nitrogen Engineering Corporation process. One ton of liquefied ammonia requires 1.65–1.75 tons of coke, 31,000 gallons of water, 25 tons of coal for steam and power, and 20 man-hours of labor.

Copper Solution Regenerating System

Courtesy Chemical Engineering, McGraw-Hill Pub. Co.

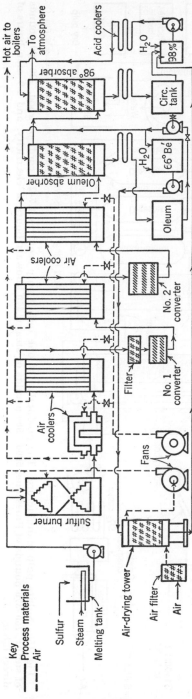

Courtesy Chemical Engineering, McGraw-Hill Pub. Co.

Fig. 149. Manufacture of sulfuric acid by the contact process, with vanadium catalyst. Each ton of 100 per cent acid requires 684 pounds of sulfur, 5000 gallons of water, 25 kilowatt-hours of electricity, and 1.1 man-hours of direct labor. A plant with a capacity of 50 tons of acid per day represents an investment of $230,000.

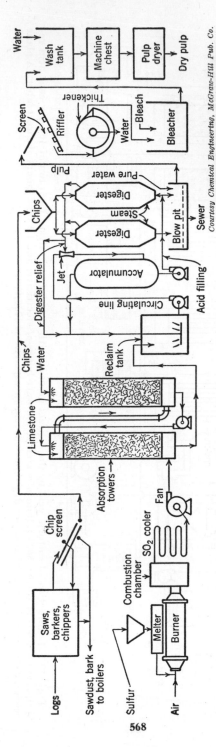

Fig. 150. Sulfite pulp manufacture. The production of one ton of pulp requires 1.7–2.2 cords of wood, 220–300 pounds of sulfur, 260–370 pounds of limestone, 5000–7500 pounds of steam, 410 kilowatt-hours of electricity, and 4.9 man-hours of direct labor.

Appendix

LINEAR

1 meter = 10 decimeters = 100 centimeters = 1000 millimeters
1 meter = 39.37 inches
1 kilometer = 1000 meters = 0.6214 mile
1 inch = 2.54 centimeters
1 micron = .001 millimeter = 1×10^{-3} mm.
1 millimicron = .000001 millimeter = 1×10^{-6} mm.
1 angstrom = 1×10^{-7} millimeter

VOLUME

1 liter = 1000 milliliters = 1000.027 cubic centimeters
1 liter = 1.056 quarts
1 cubic foot = 7.48 gallons = 28.32 liters

WEIGHT

1 gram = weight of 1 milliliter of water at 4°
1 gram = 10 decigrams = 100 centigrams = 1000 milligrams
1 kilogram = 1000 grams = 2.205 pounds avoirdupois
1 pound = 453.6 grams = .4536 kilogram
1 ounce = 28.35 grams
1 metric ton = 1000 kilograms = 2205 pounds
1 long ton = 2240 pounds
1 short ton = 2000 pounds

TEMPERATURE

0° centigrade = freezing point of water = 32° Fahrenheit
100° centigrade = boiling point of water = 212° Fahrenheit
Centigrade temperature = $\frac{5}{9}$ (F − 32)
Fahrenheit temperature = $\frac{9}{5}$ C + 32
0° absolute temperature = −273° centigrade
Absolute temperature = centigrade temperature + 273

ELECTRICAL

1 ampere = strength of current required for the deposition of .001118 gram of silver per second

1 volt = potential necessary to cause a current of 1 ampere to flow through a resistance of 1 ohm

1 ohm = resistance of a column of mercury 106.3 cm. long of uniform cross-section and weighing 14.4521 grams

1 coulomb = 1 ampere second

1 faraday = 96,500 coulombs = quantity of electricity required to deposit electrically 1 gram equivalent of an element

1 joule = 1 volt coulomb

1 watt = 1 ampere volt (unit of power)

1 horsepower = 746 watts

1 kilowatt = 1000 watts

Glossary

absolute temperature: The temperature scale on which the freezing point of pure water is 273° A. and the boiling point is 373° A. at standard pressure. Absolute temperature equals centigrade temperature plus 273.

absolute zero: The temperature, $-273°$ C. or $0°$ A., at which all molecular motion ceases.

acid: A proton donor. A substance which in aqueous solution turns blue litmus red, furnishes hydronium ions, and contains hydrogen which can be replaced by a metal.

acid anhydride: The oxide of a nonmetal which reacts with water to form an acid and no other product.

acid salt: A salt that contains hydrogen replaceable by a metal.

adsorption: The condensation of molecules of a gas or liquid on the surface of a solid.

alcohol: An organic compound containing the OH functional group, *e.g.*, CH_3OH, methyl alcohol, and C_2H_5OH, ethyl alcohol.

aldehyde: An organic compound containing the CHO functional group, *e.g.*, CH_3CHO, acetaldehyde.

alkali: A highly ionized water-soluble metallic hydroxide.

allotropy: The property due to the rearrangement of the atoms or molecules that enables certain elements and compounds to exist in more than one form.

alloy: A solution or mixture of two or more metals.

alpha particle: A helium atom that has lost its two electrons.

alum: A double sulfate salt of the general formula $M'_2SO_4 \cdot M'''_2(SO_4)_3 \cdot 24\ H_2O$, where M' is a monovalent cation such as Na^+, K^+, Li^+, or NH_4^+ and M''' is a trivalent cation such as Fe^{+++}, Cr^{+++}, or Al^{+++}. The above formula is sometimes condensed to $M'M'''(SO_4)_2 \cdot 12\ H_2O$. An example of an alum is $(NH_4)_2SO_4 \cdot Cr_2(SO_4)_3 \cdot 24\ H_2O$ or $NH_4Cr(SO_4)_2 \cdot 12\ H_2O$, ammonium chrome alum.

amalgam: An alloy containing mercury.

amorphous: A term applied to a substance without apparent crystalline structure.

amphoteric substance: One which may act either as an acid or base.

anhydrous substance: One free from water.

anion: A negatively charged ion which moves toward the anode during electrolysis.

anode: The electrode at which oxidation occurs.

atom: The smallest unit of an element that can take part in chemical change.

atomic number: The number of an atom corresponding to the net positive charge on the nucleus.

atomic weight: The relative weight of an atom as compared to the weight of one atom of oxygen, which is taken as 16.0000.

Avogadro's number: 6.02×10^{23}, the number of molecules in a gram-molecule.

base: A proton acceptor; includes metal hydroxides.

basic anhydride: Oxide of a metal.

basic salt: A salt that contains replaceable hydroxyl or oxygen groups.

beta rays: High-speed electrons from a nucleus.

binary compound: A compound of two elements only.

boiling point: The temperature at which the vapor pressure of a liquid is equal to the external pressure.

buffer solution: A solution containing either a weak acid and its salt or a weak base and its salt. Such solutions are resistant to changes in acidity or basicity.

calorie: The quantity of heat necessary to raise the temperature of one gram of water from 15° to 16° centigrade.

carbohydrate: A compound of carbon, hydrogen, and oxygen which is either an alcohol-aldehyde or an alcohol-ketone or a compound which yields either or both on hydrolysis. Usually the proportion of hydrogen to oxygen in the carbohydrate molecule is the same as in water, namely, 2 : 1, *e.g.*, glucose, $C_6H_{12}O_6$, and starch, $(C_6H_{10}O_5)_x$.

catalytic agent: A substance which alters the speed of a chemical reaction but which itself remains unchanged chemically.

cathode: The electrode at which reduction occurs.

cation: A positively charged ion which moves toward the cathode during electrolysis.

centigrade temperature: The temperature scale on which the freezing point of pure water is 0° and the boiling point is 100° at standard pressure.

ceramics: Products manufactured from clay.

colloid: A dispersion of particles consisting of aggregates of molecules.

combining volumes, law of: When gases combine chemically they do so in the ratio of small whole numbers by volume.

combining weight: The weight of an element which will combine with 8 grams of oxygen, or 1.008 g. of hydrogen.

combining weights, law of: To each element may be assigned a number, its combining weight, which in itself or when multiplied by a small whole number expresses the weight of that element that combines with the combining weight of another element.

combustion: A chemical change which produces both heat and light.

compound: A homogeneous substance composed of two or more elements, the proportions of which by weight are fixed and invariable.

concentration: Weight or volume relationship between solute and solvent.

coulomb: Unit quantity of electricity; one ampere flowing for one second.

covalent molecule: One in which the atoms are held together by a sharing of electrons.

cracking of petroleum: A process using pressure and heat in which hydrocarbons of large molecular weight are broken down into hydrocarbons of lower molecular weight.

critical pressure: Pressure necessary to liquefy a gas at its critical temperature.

critical temperature: The temperature above which a gas may not be liquefied irrespective of the pressure.

crystal: A solid in which the component parts (molecules, atoms, or ions) are oriented in a definite pattern or geometric configuration.

cupellation: A process by which gold and silver are separated from lead.

cyclotron: A device for accelerating protons, deuterons, or other charged particles of matter.

decomposition: The process of changing a single substance into two or more simpler substances.

definite proportions, law of: When elements combine, they do so in a fixed and invariable ratio by weight.

deliquescent substance: One capable of absorbing moisture from the air.

density: Mass per unit volume.

depolarizer: A substance which will remove a layer of insulating gas from an electrode.

deuteron: A nucleus of hydrogen of mass two.

dialysis: A process for separating a colloid from a true solution.

diffusion: Intermingling of molecular or ionic particles, one throughout the other.

dipole: A molecule which is electrically unsymmetrical, *i.e.*, the centers of positive and negative charge are not located at the same point within the molecule.

distillation: Vaporization of a substance followed by condensation.

ductility: That property that allows a substance to be drawn into a wire.

Du Long and Petit, rule of: The product of the atomic weight of a solid element and its specific heat is equal to the constant 6.4.

effervescence: Evolution of a gas from solution.

efflorescence: The spontaneous loss of water from a hydrate.

electrode potential: The potential difference in volts between an electrode and a solution of its ions.

electrolysis: A process of bringing about a chemical change through the action of a direct electric current.

electrolyte: A substance which in solution is a conductor of the electric current.

electron: Negative unit charge of electricity of mass $\frac{1}{1845}$ that of hydrogen atom.

electronegative element: One which tends to gain electrons.

electroplating: A process by which a substance is electrolytically deposited.

electropositive element: One which tends to lose electrons.

electrovalent substance: A substance composed of ions.

E.M.F.: Electromotive force; the electric force between two points of different potential.

emulsifying agent: A protective colloid used to stabilize an emulsion of two liquids, *e.g.*, the addition of soap to an oil-water emulsion makes the latter more permanent.

emulsion: A dispersion of one liquid in another, *e.g.*, kerosene in water.

endothermic reaction: A chemical change which absorbs heat energy.

enzyme: An organic compound produced from yeast cells which may act as a catalyst for certain fermentations.

equilibrium (chemical): An apparent state of rest in which two opposing chemical changes are proceeding with exactly the same speed.

equivalent weight: That weight of a substance which contains one gram atom of hydrogen, will combine with one gram atom of hydrogen, or will displace one gram atom of hydrogen; the weight of an element which will combine with eight grams of oxygen.

ester: An organic compound of the general formula $RCOOR'$ produced from the interaction of an organic acid with an alcohol.

eutectic: The lowest melting alloy of two or more given metals.

evaporation: Conversion of a liquid to vapor.

exothermic reaction: A chemical change which evolves heat energy.

Fahrenheit temperature: The temperature scale on which the freezing point of pure water is 32° and the boiling point is 212° at standard pressure.

faraday: Unit quantity of electricity equal to 96,500 coulombs.

Faraday's laws: (1) The quantities of substances produced at the electrodes during electrolysis are directly proportional to the quantity of electricity passing through the solution. (2) The weights of substances formed at the electrodes are directly proportional to their equivalent weights.

filtrate: The liquid which passes through the filter.

fission: Splitting of an atomic nucleus into two parts of approximately the same size.

fixation of nitrogen: A process by which free nitrogen is converted into a useful nitrogen compound.

flux: A substance used to combine with impurities during a smelting process to form a slag.

formula: The proper combination of symbols showing the composition of a compound substance.

fusion: Melting; change of solid to liquid.

gamma rays: High frequency electromagnetic X-rays given off by radioactive substances.

gangue: Worthless rock or mineral matter associated with ores.

gas laws: *Boyle's law.* The volume of a fixed mass of a given gas at constant temperature is inversely proportional to the pressure.

Charles' law. The volume of a fixed mass of a given gas at constant pressure is directly proportional to the absolute temperature.

Dalton's law. The total pressure of a gaseous mixture is the sum of the partial pressures of the component gases.

Graham's law. The rate of diffusion of a gas is inversely proportional to the square root of its density.

gram-atom: The atomic weight of an element expressed in grams.

gram-ion: A mass in grams equal to the sum of the atomic weights of the ion.

gram-molecule: The molecular weight of a substance expressed in grams.

halogen: The term means *salt former* and is applied to the salt-forming family, F, Cl, Br, I.

hard water: Water that reacts with soap to form a precipitate.

heat: A form of energy due to molecular motion.

heat of combustion: The number of calories of heat produced by the complete combustion of a mole of a substance.

heat of formation: The number of calories of heat absorbed or liberated in the formation of a mole of a compound from its constituent elements.

Henry's law: The weight of a gas dissolved in a given weight of liquid at constant temperature is directly proportional to the pressure.

homologous series: A series of compounds whose composition may be represented by a general formula, *e.g.*, methane series of hydrocarbons, C_nH_{2n+2}.

hormone: Organic compound produced as a secretion of a ductless gland. In small amounts these compounds appear to play an important role in many biological processes.

humidity, relative: The ratio of the pressure of water vapor present in the atmosphere to the vapor pressure of water at the same temperature.

hydrate: A compound chemically combined with water, *e.g.*, $Na_2SO_4 \cdot 10 H_2O$.

hydrocarbon: A compound containing only carbon and hydrogen.

hydrolysis: A double decomposition reaction in which water is one of the reactants.

hygroscopic substance: One which takes up moisture.

indicator: A substance which changes color at a definite hydrogen ion concentration.

ion: An atom or group of atoms possessing an electric charge.

isomers: Molecules having the same number and kinds of atoms but which are arranged in different molecular configurations.

isomorphous compounds: Compounds which crystallize in the same geometric configuration.

isotopes: Elements of the same atomic number but different atomic weights.

joule: A volt-coulomb.

ketone: An oxidation product of a secondary alcohol, which has the general formula RCOR'.

kindling temperature: The lowest temperature at which a substance will burst into flame.

Le Châtelier's principle: If a stress is placed upon a system in equilibrium that change takes place which will tend to minimize the effect of the added stress.

legumes: Plants whose roots have nodules containing nitrogen-fixing bacteria.

malleability: The property of a substance that allows it to be rolled or hammered into sheets.

matter: Anything that has mass and occupies space.

melting point: The temperature at which a solid changes to a liquid.

metallurgy: The science of extracting metals from their ores.

molal solution: A solution containing one mole of solute in 1000 grams of solvent.

molar solution: A solution containing one mole of solute in one liter of solution.

mole: A mass in grams numerically equal to the molecular weight of a substance.

molecular weight: The sum of the atomic weights of the atoms that make up the molecule.

molecule: The smallest unit of an element or compound which can exist by itself in the free state.

mordant: A substance used to cause a dye to adhere to cloth more firmly.

neutralization: The reaction of an acid with a base to produce a salt and water.

neutron: A fundamental particle of mass one and no charge.

normal salt: One that contains no replaceable hydroxyl or hydrogen group.

normal solution: A solution which contains one equivalent of solute per liter of solution.

nucleus of an atom: The center of mass of the atom containing protons and neutrons.

ohm: Unit of electrical resistance; the resistance of a column of mercury 106.3 cm. long, weighing 14.4521 grams, and of uniform cross section.

ore: A natural material from which useful elements may be extracted commercially.

osmosis: The diffusion of a solvent through a semipermeable membrane into a more concentrated solution.

oxidation: A process involving the loss of electrons by an atom or group of atoms, or gain in valence.

oxidizing agent: A substance containing an atom or group of atoms that gain electrons; one that loses in valence.

packing effect: The mass loss over and above the summation of atomic particle masses in the formation of atoms.

periodic law: The properties of the elements are periodic functions of their atomic numbers.

permutite: An artificial sodium aluminum silicate, sometimes termed "zeolite," used as a water softener.

pH: A notation for expressing the hydrogen ion concentration of a solution; in other words, the acidity or basicity of a solution.

photosynthesis: A chemical change which utilizes light energy, *e.g.*, the production of plant tissue from CO_2 and water in sunlight.

physical change: A change which does not involve a change in the chemical composition of a substance.

positive ray: Positively charged particle moving away from the cathode in a cathode ray tube.

positron: A subatomic particle of the same mass as the electron but of opposite charge; a positive electron.

precipitate: An insoluble solid which separates from solution.

properties: Qualities or characteristics by which a substance may be identified.

protein: A complex organic compound composed of the elements carbon, hydrogen, oxygen, and nitrogen.

proton: A subatomic particle of mass one carrying a positive charge; a hydrogen ion.

radical: A group of atoms which function as a unit in chemical change.

radioactivity: Spontaneous disintegration of atoms resulting in the emission of alpha particles, electrons, and gamma rays from the nucleus.

Raoult's law: The lowering of the vapor pressure of a solvent by a nonvolatile solute is proportional to the concentration of the solute in the solution.

reaction: A chemical change.

reducing agent: A substance which loses one or more electrons in a chemical change; or gains in valence.

roasting: The heating of a sulfide ore in contact with air.

salt: A compound composed of positive and negative ions (except M—OH compounds).

saponification: The reaction of an ester with a base to form an alcohol and a salt.

saturated solution: One which is in equilibrium with the undissolved solute.

slag: A by-product of smelting produced by the combination of the flux and the impurities in the ore.

sol: Colloidal dispersion of a solid in a liquid.

solute: Dissolved substance.

solution: A homogeneous mixture of two or more substances, the relative proportions of which may be varied within certain limits.

solvent: The dissolving medium or the constituent of a solution present in the larger amount.

specific gravity: The ratio of the weight of a given volume of a substance (solid or liquid) to the weight of an equal volume of water.

specific heat: The quantity of heat in calories necessary to raise the temperature of one gram of a substance one degree centigrade.

standard conditions: $0°$ C. and one atmosphere (760 mm.) pressure.

standard solution: A solution the composition of which is accurately known.

sublimation: Change of solid to vapor or vice versa without appearance of liquid.

substance: Any homogeneous matter.

supersaturated solution: One which contains more solute in solution than a saturated solution would contain at the same temperature and pressure.

surface tension: The force exerted on the molecules in the surface of a liquid by adjoining molecules.

synthesis: The preparation of compounds.

temperature: A measure of heat intensity.

ternary compound: One containing three elements.

theory: A plan or scheme of explaining a set of related facts by means of a set of assumptions; a hypothesis which has been subjected to experimental proof.

thermite: A mixture of iron oxide and aluminum powders used for welding.

transmutation: Conversion of one element to another.

Tyndall effect: A luminous cone of light produced as a result of the scattering of light by particles in suspension.

valence: A number which represents the combining capacity of an atom or radical referred to hydrogen as a standard.

vapor pressure: The partial pressure exerted by a vapor in equilibrium with a liquid or solid.

viscosity: Resistance to flow; opposite of fluidity.

vitamin: A chemical compound which in small amounts appears to be necessary in the diet of man and animals.

volatile: Easily vaporizable; relatively low boiling point.

volt: The potential necessary to drive a current of one ampere through a resistance of one ohm.

watt: A unit of electrical power; a volt ampere.

X-rays: High frequency light waves of short wave length.

Index